ELECTRIC-CIRCUIT THEORY

ELECTRIC-CIRCUIT THEORY

by

F. A. BENSON
D.Eng., Ph.D., A.M.I.E.E.
(*Reader in Electronics at The University of Sheffield*)

and

D. HARRISON
M.Eng., Ph.D., A.M.I.E.E.
(*Senior Lecturer in Electrical Engineering at The University of Sheffield*)

LONDON
EDWARD ARNOLD (PUBLISHERS) LTD

First published 1959

Second Edition 1963

Printed in Great Britain by
Fletcher and Son Ltd. Norwich

CONTENTS

PREFACE

THIS book is based to a large extent on lectures, which the authors have gradually developed during the last ten to twenty years for undergraduate engineers. It is hoped that it will prove of value to other teachers and their students, as it covers almost completely the electric-circuit theory given in the first two post-intermediate years of University engineering courses. It should also be useful to students taking corresponding courses in technical colleges and to those preparing for the examinations of The Institution of Electrical Engineers.

There are few books on electric-circuit theory which deal adequately with both light-current and heavy-current applications. This is regrettable, because the basic material is common, and a comprehensive book on the subject has clearly been a necessity for some time. Electrical-engineering students are expected, nowadays, to deal with quite complex circuits, which need to be resolved and simplified, before the students can understand them and before numerical results can be obtained. A sound knowledge of fundamental circuit theory is therefore essential.

The present book first discusses the fundamentals and then deals with applications to both the light-current and heavy-current branches of electrical engineering over a wide field. A large number of worked examples has been included in the text and carefully-chosen problems, with answers, at the end of each chapter. Great care has been taken to eliminate errors from the worked examples and from the answers to the problems, but it is inevitable that some mistakes will have been made, and any errors brought to notice will be gratefully acknowledged. The authors have included these problems because they are very much in favour of tutorials and the solving of problems as a method of education for engineers. Experience shows that many engineering students find it difficult to apply their theoretical knowledge. They can frequently derive mathematical formulæ but fail hopelessly in using them to obtain solutions to numerical problems.

Many of the problems are new and some have been set as examination questions to undergraduates in the Engineering Departments at the University of Sheffield; these are labelled with the letters [S.U.]. It cannot be claimed that all the other problems are original and, as they have been collected over a long period, it is impossible to acknowledge their sources. The authors have been reminded on many occasions while writing the book, how much they owe to their own teachers and to the many writers who have preceded them in the field. Considerable help has been received from them in preparing the lecture notes which have formed the basis of the text. The many valuable suggestions which have come from students are also acknowledged.

To keep the book to a reasonable size it has been necessary to set a limit to its contents by omitting altogether those topics which could not be explained satisfactorily in the space available, for instance, matrices and transistor circuits. This was preferred to dealing inadequately with a wider range of subjects.

In conformity with modern practice the rationalized M.K.S. system of units has been used where necessary. The inter-relation between the M.K.S. and C.G.S. systems has not been explained because there are already many text-books which cover this subject admirably. In any case, in electric-circuit problems, almost the only units used are the volt, ampere and ohm (with their multiples and sub-multiples) and units such as the henry, derived from them. Thus the problem of the system of units to be employed hardly arises.

Although the authors gave serious consideration to the possibility of arranging the subject matter in the order in which it was likely to be taught, this did not prove to be very practicable, so that both elementary and more advanced work will be found in some chapters. It is suggested that a first reading should include Chapters 1, 2, 3 and 4, that part of Chapter 8 dealing with the elements of transformer theory and the first parts of 12 and 13.

The authors wish to thank the University of Sheffield for permission to use, as problems, some of the questions set in examination papers. The encouragement given by Professor A. L. Cullen, B.Sc. (Eng.), Ph.D., M.I.E.E., throughout the preparation of the manuscript is gratefully acknowledged. Thanks are also due to Messrs. Edward Arnold (Publishers) Ltd. for their help and courtesy in the preparation of the book.

F. A. BENSON
D. HARRISON

Sheffield, 1958

PREFACE TO THE SECOND EDITION

THE opportunity has arisen, during a reprinting of the book, to include a chapter on Transistor Circuits. This has resulted in a new edition, although apart from a few minor modifications and corrections the original text has not changed.

It is a pleasure to acknowledge at this juncture the helpful comments and suggestions which some readers of the First Edition have sent to us.

F. A. BENSON
D. HARRISON

Sheffield, 1962

CHAPTER I

INTRODUCTION

It is assumed that the reader is conversant with the basic concepts of electrical engineering (flux, voltage, current and resistance) and the elements of static electricity. The purpose of this chapter is to present, briefly, some of the definitions of fundamental quantities which will be required later in the book.

Electric power

When current flows through a conductor, power is expended, the amount depending on the magnitude of the current (I) and on the potential difference (V) necessary to send the current round the circuit.

$$\text{Power, in watts} = VI$$

where V is in volts (V) and I in ampères (A).

If the resistance of the conductor is R, in ohms, the power in watts is, by Ohm's Law, also equal to $\frac{V^2}{R}$ or RI^2.

Energy

$$\text{Energy} = \text{Power} \times \text{Time}$$

$$\text{Energy, in joules} = \text{Power, in watts} \times \text{Time, in seconds } (t)$$

$$= VIt = \frac{V^2 t}{R} = RI^2 t.$$

Thus,

$$\text{Energy} = V \times (It)$$

$$= V \times (\text{Quantity of electricity}).$$

The coulomb is the unit of quantity of electricity and is the quantity which passes through a circuit when 1 A flows for 1 sec.

Relationship between electrical and mechanical units of power

The unit of electrical power is the watt.

The unit of mechanical power is the horse-power (h.p.).

1 h.p. = 550 ft lb. of energy/sec.

Now 1 ft = 0·3048 m

and 1 lb = 0·4535 kg

so

$$1 \text{ h.p.} = 550 \times 0{\cdot}3048 \times 0{\cdot}4535 \text{ kg m/sec}$$

$$= 550 \times 0{\cdot}3048 \times 0{\cdot}4535 \times 9{\cdot}81 \text{ newton m/sec}$$

$$= 550 \times 0{\cdot}3048 \times 0{\cdot}4535 \times 9{\cdot}81 \text{ joules/sec}$$

$$= 746 \text{ joules/sec}$$

$$= \underline{746 \text{ watts (W)}}.$$

The practical units of electric power, when dealing with machines, are the kilowatt (kW) $= 10^3$ watts, and the megawatt (MW) $= 10^6$ watts.

The energy consumed when a power of 1 kW is expended for an hour is called the kilowatt-hour (kWh) or sometimes a Board of Trade Unit or Kelvin.

$$1 \text{ kWh} = 1{,}000 \times 3{,}600 \text{ watt seconds (joules)}$$
$$= \underline{36 \times 10^5 \text{ joules.}}$$

Relation between heat energy and electrical energy

The practical unit of heat is the calorie which is the heat required to raise the temperature of 1 gram of water through 1° C.

The relation between the calorie and the joule may be determined in several ways. One is an electrical method where the heat developed by the expenditure of a known amount of electrical energy is measured.

1 calorie may be taken as equivalent to 4·17 joules.* From this relationship the connection between the British Thermal Unit (*i.e.* the heat required to raise the temperature of 1 lb of water through 1° F) and the kWh may be determined.

$$1 \text{ B.Th.U.} = 453{\cdot}5 \times \frac{5}{9} \text{ calories} = \underline{252 \text{ calories}}$$

$$\therefore \quad 1 \text{ kWh} = \frac{36 \times 10^5}{4{\cdot}17 \times 252} \text{ B.Th.U.} = \underline{3{,}426 \text{ B.Th.U.}}$$

EXAMPLE. An electric motor takes 20 A at 240 V when driving a pump raising water at 220 gal/min to a height of 60 ft. Determine the overall efficiency of the set. Assume that 1 gal of water weighs 10 lb.

Solution.

$$\text{Work done/min} = 220 \times 10 \times 60 \text{ ft lb.}$$
$$\therefore \text{ h.p. output} = 220 \times 10 \times 60/33{,}000$$
$$\text{Output in watts} = (220 \times 10 \times 60/33{,}000) \times 746$$
$$\text{Input power} = VI = (240 \times 20) \text{ W}$$
$$\text{Efficiency} = (\text{output/power supplied}) \times 100\%$$
$$= \{(220 \times 10 \times 60 \times 746)/(33{,}000 \times 240 \times 20)\} \times 100\%$$
$$= \underline{62{\cdot}1\%}$$

EXAMPLE. An electric heating vessel takes 5 A at a voltage of 240 V. The vessel holds 2 pints of water. Find the time required to raise the water temperature from 20° C to 100° C. Assume that 90% of the

* Kaye and Laby in *Tables of Physical Constants* give figures varying from 4·169 to 4·19 for different experimenters. It is usually sufficient to use the figure 4·2.

electrical energy is used in heating the water and neglect heat radiation. One gallon of water weighs 10 lb and 1 lb = 453·5 g.

Solution.

$$\text{Mass of water} = 2 \times (10/8) \times 453{\cdot}5 \text{ g}$$

$$\begin{aligned}
\text{Heat gained by water} &= \text{mass} \times \text{specific heat} \times \text{temperature rise} \\
&= 2 \times 1{\cdot}25 \times 453{\cdot}5 \times 1 \times 80 \text{ cal} \\
\text{Heat supplied} &= \{(\text{power} \times \text{time})/4{\cdot}17\} \text{ cal} \\
&= \{5 \times 240 \times \text{time } (t)/4{\cdot}17\} \text{ cal} \\
\text{Heat used for water heating} &= 90 \times 5 \times 240 \times t/(100 \times 4{\cdot}17) \\
\therefore \quad 2 \times 1{\cdot}25 \times 453{\cdot}5 \times 1 \times 80 &= 90 \times 5 \times 240 \times t/(100 \times 4{\cdot}17) \\
\textit{i.e. } t &= 350 \text{ sec} = \underline{5 \text{ min } 50 \text{ sec.}}
\end{aligned}$$

Self-inductance

A current I in a coil generates a flux Φ which threads each turn of the coil itself; so if I varies the flux linking the coil will change. Thus, an e.m.f. e will be induced in the coil equal to $-d(N\Phi)/dt$ where $N\Phi$ is the flux-linkage, N being the number of turns on the coil. With no magnetic material present* the flux will be proportional to I; so $N\Phi = LI$ where L is a ' constant ' for the coil and is called the coefficient of self-inductance. The e.m.f. induced in the coil can therefore also be written as $e = -L\, di/dt$.

The unit of self-inductance (L) is the *henry* and is a measure of the self-inductance of a circuit in which an e.m.f. of 1 V is induced when the current through it varies at the rate of 1 A/sec.

The expression $e = -d(N\Phi)/dt$ represents the mathematical form of the combination of Faraday's Law and Lenz's Law. Faraday carried out many experiments dealing with the e.m.f. induced in a conductor when the magnetic flux linking it changes and he discovered the following law:

If the magnetic flux linking a circuit varies, an e.m.f. is induced with a magnitude proportional to the rate of change of flux.

The direction of this e.m.f. satisfies Lenz's Law which may be stated as follows:

The polarity of the induced e.m.f. is such that the resulting current can produce a flux change opposing the original variation in flux.

EXAMPLE. When the current through a certain coil changes at the rate of 10,000 A/sec the e.m.f. induced in the coil is 100 V. Find the self-inductance (L) of the coil, in henrys (H).

Solution

$$L = 100/10{,}000 = 1/100 \text{ H} = \underline{10 \text{ mH.}}$$

* Within limits, for suitably designed iron-cored coils, L may still be considered as independent of I.

EXAMPLE. Measurements on a certain coil having 1,000 turns show the coil to be linked by 0·05 Wb when a current of 2·5 A is flowing. What is the self-inductance of the coil (L)?

[*Note.* Magnetic flux is measured in units called *webers*, abbreviated Wb.]

Solution

$$L = N\Phi/I = 1{,}000 \times 0{\cdot}05/2{\cdot}5 = \underline{20 \text{ H}}.$$

Energy stored in an inductive coil

The energy stored in an inductive coil can be determined from the work done in establishing the current through the coil. When the current is changing at a rate di/dt the back e.m.f. is $-L\, di/dt$ so the instantaneous power expended is $(-L\, di/dt)\, i$.

Therefore, the energy used in a time dt is

$$(Li\, di/dt)\, dt = Li\, di.$$

If the current rises from zero to a final steady value I the total energy stored $= \int_0^I Li\, di = LI^2/2$. When L is measured in henrys and I in ampères, the energy stored is measured in joules.

Mutual inductance

When two coils are so positioned that magnetic flux lines from one link with the turns of the other, they are *inductively coupled* and *mutual inductance* exists between them. Mutual inductance can be defined as the voltage induced in one coil, when the current in the other is changing at unit rate. Thus, $e_2 = -M\frac{di_1}{dt}$, or, if the current is sinusoidal $\mathbf{E}_2 = -j\omega M\mathbf{I}_1$. M is the coefficient of mutual induction or, simply, the mutual inductance. The unit of M is the *henry*, and the value of M is given by the induced e.m.f. in volts in one coil, when the current in the other is changing at the rate of one ampere per second.

M is determined by the number of turns on the coils, their dimensions and their relative position. Mutual inductance may also be defined in terms of the flux linkage in one coil per unit current in the other. For two circuits, 1 and 2, with mutual inductance, where $e_2 = -M_{12}\frac{di_1}{dt}$ and $e_1 = -M_{21}\frac{di_2}{dt}$, it can easily be shown, from energy considerations, that $M_{12} = M_{21}$.*

* See T. H. Barton, "Mutual Inductance", *Bull. Elect. Eng. Educ.*, No. 10, p. 56 (1953).

Coefficient of coupling

The greatest possible value of mutual inductance that can exist between two coils of self-inductances L_1 and L_2 is $\sqrt{(L_1 L_2)}$ and this is obtained when all the flux from one coil threads all the turns of the other. In practice, M is always less than $\sqrt{(L_1 L_2)}$ and the ratio of M to $\sqrt{(L_1 L_2)}$ is called the *coefficient of coupling*, which is given the symbol k. This has a maximum value of unity and is a dimensionless quantity.

EXAMPLE. Two coils having 1,000 and 100 turns respectively are wound on an iron ring which may be assumed to have a constant permeability of 900 over the working range of current. The cross-sectional area of the ring is 8 cm² and the mean circumference of the iron is 80 cm. Calculate the mutual inductance between the coils.

Solution

The field strength $H = NI/l = 1{,}000I/0{\cdot}8$

The flux density $B = \mu_0 \mu H = 4\pi \times 10^{-7} \times 900 \times 1{,}000I/0{\cdot}8$

Flux $\phi = AB = (8 \times 10^4)\, 4\pi \times 10^{-7} \times 900 \times 1{,}000I/0{\cdot}8$

Linkages formed $= \phi \times 100$

Mutual inductance, M = Linkages/ampère $= 100\,\phi/I$

$\therefore \quad M = \{100 \times 8 \times 10^4 \times 4\pi \times 10^{-7} \times 900 \times 1{,}000/0{\cdot}8\}$ H

i.e. $M = \underline{0{\cdot}113 \text{ H}}.$

EXAMPLE. Two coils have self-inductances of 3 H and 4 H respectively and the mutual inductance between them is 3 H. They are connected in series and a current of 5 A is passed through them. Evaluate the energy of the magnetic field when (*a*) the self and mutual fluxes are in the same direction, (*b*) the self and mutual fluxes are in opposition. [S.U.]

Solution

Self-induced e.m.f. in coil 1 $= -3\, di/dt$ where i is the current.

Mutually-induced e.m.f. in coil 1 due to coil 2 =

$$\pm M\, di/dt = \pm 3\, di/dt$$

Self-induced e.m.f. in coil 2 $= -4\, di/dt$

Mutually-induced e.m.f. in coil 2 due to coil 1

$$= \pm M\, di/dt = \pm 3\, di/dt$$

$\therefore$ Totally induced e.m.f. $= -(3 + 4 \pm 2 \times 3)\, di/dt$

Equivalent self-inductance of whole circuit

$$= 3 + 4 \pm 6 = 13 \text{ or } 1 \text{ H.}$$

Energy when equivalent inductance is 13 H and current is 5 A (fluxes in same direction) $= 13 \times 5^2/2 = \underline{162{\cdot}5 \text{ joules}}.$

Energy when equivalent inductance is 1 H and current is 5 A (fluxes in opposition) $= 1 \times 5^2/2 = \underline{12{\cdot}5 \text{ joules}}.$

EXAMPLE. Two coils having self-inductances of 5 mH and 6 mH respectively are arranged so that the mutual inductance is 4 mH. The coils are connected in parallel across a 40 V d.c. supply so that their magnetic fields aid. Determine the rate of change of current in each coil.

Solution. Let the rate of change of current in coil 1 be di_1/dt and that in coil 2 be di_2/dt.

Then $(5 \times 10^{-3})\, di_1/dt + (4 \times 10^{-3})\, di_2/dt = 40$

and $(6 \times 10^{-3})\, di_2/dt + (4 \times 10^{-3})\, di_1/dt = 40$

so $\underline{di_1/dt = 5{\cdot}71 \times 10^3 \text{ A/sec.}}$

and $\underline{di_2/dt = 2{\cdot}86 \times 10^3 \text{ A/sec.}}$

Capacitance

Consider two conductors between which a voltage V is applied so that charges $+q$ and $-q$ are produced on them. The *capacitance* of the system is defined as the ratio of its charge to its potential, *i.e.* q/V, and is usually denoted by C. If q is expressed in coulombs and V in volts then C is in farads (F). The farad is a large unit; in practice it is more convenient to use the microfarad (μF) which is 10^{-6} farad.

Capacitors in series and in parallel

Consider first a number of capacitors, of individual capacitances $C_1, C_2, C_3 \ldots$, connected in series. The charge on each capacitor is the same. This is so because if one of the plates of the first capacitor acquires a charge $+q$ then the other plate must have a charge $-q$ but since this plate is connected to one plate of the second capacitor, say A, and insulated from everything else, then A must acquire a charge $+q$, and so on. Let $V_1, V_2, V_3 \ldots$ be the voltages across the individual capacitors and V the total applied voltage.

Then $q = CV = C_1V_1 = C_2V_2 = C_3V_3 = \ldots$

where C is the total capacitance of the system.

Now $V = V_1 + V_2 + V_3 + \ldots$

$\therefore\; q/C = q/C_1 + q/C_2 + q/C_3 + \ldots$

i.e. $1/C = 1/C_1 + 1/C_2 + 1/C_3 + \ldots$

Consider now the same capacitors connected in parallel and let the total capacitance of the system be C. In this case each element is subjected to the total applied voltage. Let the charges on the plates of the first capacitor be $+q_1$ and $-q_1$, on the plates of the second $+q_2$ and $-q_2$, etc.

$$\therefore\; q_1 = C_1V,\; q_2 = C_2V,\; q_3 = C_3V, \text{ etc.}$$

The combination has plates with charges $+(q_1 + q_2 + q_3 + \ldots)$ and $-(q_1 + q_2 + q_3 + \ldots)$.

$$\therefore \quad C = (q_1 + q_2 + q_3 + \ldots)/V$$
$$i.e. \quad C = C_1 + C_2 + C_3 + \ldots$$

It will be seen from the above expressions for the total capacitances, and Chapter 2, that $1/C$ behaves like a resistance, so far as combination is concerned.

EXAMPLE. A parallel-plate capacitor is made from two flat plates each having an area of 2 m^2 separated by a sheet of material of thickness 2 mm and having a relative permittivity of 6. Calculate the capacitance of this capacitor neglecting fringing.

Solution. Denote the area of the plates by A and the distance between them by d. The intensity of the field between the plates $E = q/\varepsilon\varepsilon_o A$ where q is the charge, ε_o is the permittivity of free space and is $8{\cdot}855 \times 10^{-12}$ farads/metre and ε is the relative permittivity of the medium.

The voltage between the plates $V = Ed = qd/\varepsilon\varepsilon_o A$

$\therefore$ the capacitance $C = q/V = \varepsilon\varepsilon_o A/d$ farads.

In this case $A = 2$ m^2, $d = 2 \times 10^{-3}$ m and $\varepsilon = 6$,

so that $C = \{6 \times 8{\cdot}855 \times 10^{-12} \times 2/(2 \times 10^{-3})\}$ F

$= \underline{0{\cdot}053\ \mu F}$.

[*Note.* If the capacitance of a capacitor with a certain dielectric is compared with that of a capacitor with a vacuum as dielectric the ratio gives a figure characteristic of the material of the dielectric and is known as its *relative permittivity* or *dielectric constant*. It is a pure number.]

EXAMPLE. A set of six capacitors, having capacitances of 8, 4, 4, 3, 2 and 1 μF respectively, is available. What is the greatest and smallest capacitance that can be obtained from the set?

Solution. The greatest capacitance is obtained when all the capacitors are in parallel and equals $(8 + 4 + 4 + 3 + 2 + 1)$ μF $= \underline{22\ \mu F}$.

The smallest capacitance is obtained when all the capacitors are in series. If this value is C then:

$$1/C = 1/8 + 1/4 + 1/4 + 1/3 + 1/2 + 1/1 = 59/24$$
$$\therefore \quad C = (24/59)\ \mu F = \underline{0{\cdot}4\ \mu F}.$$

Energy stored in a capacitor

Energy is stored in the dielectric between the plates of a capacitor and may be calculated as shown below. Consider a parallel-plate capacitor. The plates attract each other with a force F so that if they are pulled apart a further distance dx work will be expended equal to $F\,dx$ and this must be stored in the extended electric field as potential energy.

Let the voltage across the plates at any instant be v, *i.e.* v is a measure of the work done in moving a unit positive charge from one plate to the other along a line of force against the voltage gradient. If a charge dq is added to the capacitor the work done is $v\,dq$, i.e. $v(C\,dv)$.

Thus, the work done in charging the capacitor from zero voltage to voltage V is:

$$\int_0^V C\,v\,dv = CV^2/2$$

If C is measured in farads and V in volts, the energy stored is measured in joules. This expression for the stored energy should be compared with that obtained above for the energy stored in an inductive coil (or magnetic field).

As an example consider the case of a 4 μF capacitor which is charged to a voltage of 10,000 V. The energy stored is $(4 \times 10^{-6})(10^4)^2/2 =$ 200 joules.

PROBLEMS

1. A room measures 15 × 12 × 10 ft and the air in it has to be maintained at a temperature of 15° C higher than that of the incoming air. The ventilation is such that the air is renewed every 20 min. Obtain the capacity of an electric radiator which is suitable for the purpose. Neglect radiation losses. Assume that the density of air is 0·08 lb/ft³ and that the specific heat of air is 0·25. [*Ans.* 851 W.]

2. An electric crane is required to hoist 1·5 tons 60 ft in 20 sec. The efficiency of the winding gear is 65% and that of the motor 85%. Calculate (*a*) the b.h.p. of the motor and (*b*) the hoisting cost/ton assuming electrical energy costs 1d/kWh. [*Ans.* (*a*) 28·2 h.p. (*b*) 0·092d.]

3. If a copper coil weighing 10·5 lb absorbs 60 W, what will be its temperature after 20 min, if its initial temperature is 16° C? Assume that the power supplied to the coil is kept constant, and that the amount of heat radiated from the coil is negligible. The specific heat of copper may be taken as 0·095. [*Ans.* 54·3° C.]

4. The field coil of a certain machine has 3,000 turns and produces a flux of 0·037 Wb when carrying 2 A. Assuming that the flux is proportional to the current, calculate the self-inductance of the coil. If the field circuit is opened in 0·01 sec, determine the maximum e.m.f. that will be induced, assuming that the current dies away at a uniform rate. What is the energy stored in the magnetic field of the coil?

[*Ans.* 55·5 H, 11,100 V, 111 joules.]

5. The instantaneous current through a 2 H inductor is given by $i = (0{\cdot}04t^2 + 0{\cdot}1)$ A when $0 < t < 10$ sec. Find the instantaneous voltage across the inductor for the specified time interval.

[*Ans.* $0{\cdot}16t$ V.]

6. A glass tube of 3 cm diameter is formed into a ring of 20 cm diameter and is wound uniformly with 1,200 turns of wire. A second coil of 500 turns is wound closely on the first. Determine the mutual inductance between the two windings, if the coupling is perfect.

[*Ans.* 848 μH.]

7. A cylinder of 5 cm diameter and 100 cm long is uniformly wound with 3,000 turns in a single layer. A second layer of 100 turns of much finer wire is wound over the first one near its centre. Calculate the mutual inductance between the two coils. [*Ans.* 740 μH.]

8. Two coils have self-inductance of 3 H and 2 H respectively and the mutual inductance is 2 H. They are connected in series and a current of 4 A is passed through them. Evaluate the energy of the magnetic field when the self and mutual fluxes are (*a*) in the same direction, (*b*) in opposition.

Find, also, the coefficient of coupling. [S.U.]

[*Ans.* (*a*) 72 joules, (*b*) 8 joules, 0·82.]

9. Calculate the capacitance between two spheres in air each 0·2 cm diameter supported on thin insulated rods and placed with their centres 10 cm apart. Assume that the spheres are so far apart that the charge on each of them is equivalent to a charge concentrated at the centre of the sphere. [*Ans.* 0·055 μμF (picofarads).]

10. A parallel-plate capacitor has plates of area 500 cm^2 and separated by a distance of 0·5 cm. The dielectric is composite consisting of a sheet 0·2 cm thick having a relative permittivity of 4 and a sheet 0·3 cm thick having a relative permittivity of 2. If a voltage of 10,000 V is applied to the plates of this capacitor, find the potential gradients in the two dielectrics. [*Ans.* 12,500 V/cm, 25,000 V/cm.]

11. Estimate the capacitance of a cable 3,000 miles long made with an inner conductor of 0·07 in. diameter, the inner surface of the lead sheath which is connected to the return conductor being 0·425 in. diameter. The dielectric is gutta-percha having a relative permittivity of 3·9. [*Ans.* 579 μF.]

12. Three capacitors $C_1 = 1$ μF, $C_2 = 5$ μF and $C_3 = 10$ μF are charged to voltages of 50 V, 100 V and 80 V respectively. They are then connected in parallel with all the positive terminals together. Calculate the voltage across the capacitors when in parallel.

[*Ans.* 84·4 V.]

[*Note.* Readers will be unable to solve problems 9, 10 and 11 using only the information given in this chapter and may have to do some further reading elsewhere before attempting these problems.]

CHAPTER 2

D.C. CIRCUITS

Ohm's Law

Provided the physical conditions of a normal conductor remain the same the potential difference necessary to send a current through the conductor is proportional to the current, *i.e.* potential difference $V \propto$ current I, or

$$V = RI \quad . \quad . \quad . \quad . \quad . \quad . \quad (2.1)$$

where R is a constant of the conductor termed the resistance.

If V is measured in volts and I in ampères then R is in ohms (Ω).

Materials whose conductivity depends not only on the value of the current flowing (or the applied potential difference) but also on its direction, are available and used. For example, silicon carbide possesses a conductivity that varies over a wide range as the current through it is varied, and the well-known junction in a copper-oxide rectifier has a conductivity which is high in one direction of current, low in the reverse direction, and varies with current in either case.

Specific resistance or resistivity

The resistance of a conductor of uniform cross-sectional area A and length l is given by:

$$R = l\rho/A \quad . \quad . \quad . \quad . \quad . \quad . \quad (2.2)$$

where ρ is a characteristic of the material of the conductor and is called the *specific resistance*, or *resistivity*.

If $l = 1$ m and $A = 1$ m^2, then $\rho = R$. Therefore, the specific resistance of a material may be defined as the resistance between opposite faces of a cube of the material of 1 m sides, *i.e.* it is the resistance per metre cube of material. ρ is thus measured in ohms/metre cube, or more simply, in ohm-metre units. The ohm-metre M.K.S. unit is of such an inconvenient size that it is seldom, if ever, used and the ohm-cm and ohm-inch units are usually adopted.

The relationship expressed by equation (2.2) is sometimes called Davy's Law.

EXAMPLE. A d.c. motor situated 1,500 yd from its source of supply takes a current of 200 A. If the voltage drop in the cable is 20 V, find the necessary cross-sectional area of the cable. The specific resistance of the copper conductor is 0·67 microhm/in. cube.

Solution

$$R = V/I = l\rho/A \quad . \quad . \quad . \quad . \quad . \quad . \qquad (2.3)$$

$$\therefore \quad R = 20/200 = (2 \times 1{,}500 \times 36) \times 0{\cdot}67 \times 10^{-6}/A$$

$$\therefore \quad \underline{A = 0{\cdot}724 \text{ sq in.}}$$

The actual value of ρ for a given material depends on the purity of the material and is affected by mechanical processes.

The effect of the internal resistance of a battery

When a battery supplies a current the terminal voltage is not equal to the e.m.f. except in the special case of negligibly-small battery internal resistance. The internal resistance can easily be taken into account, however, as shown below.

In Fig. 2.1, E is the e.m.f. of the battery, r its internal resistance and A and B its terminals. R_l is a load resistor drawing current I.

Then $$I = E/(R_l + r) \quad . \quad . \qquad (2.4)$$

and the terminal voltage of the battery is

$$V = E - Ir$$
$$= \underline{E\{1 - r/(r + R_l)\}} \quad . \qquad (2.5)$$

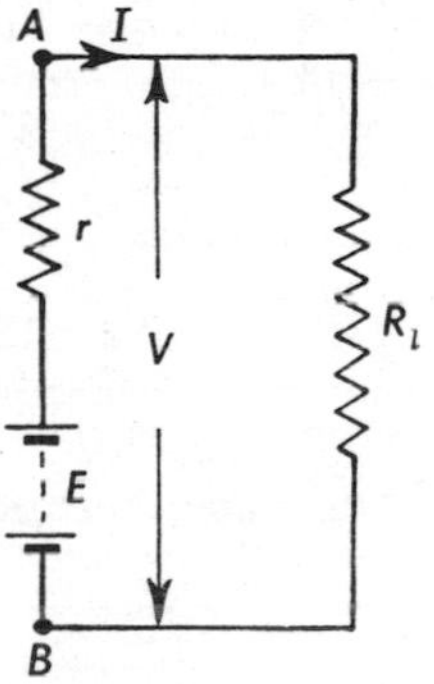

FIG. 2.1

Influence of temperature on resistance

The resistance of all pure metals and of nearly every alloy increases with a rise of temperature. For example, in the case of copper, the resistance at 100° C is about 43% greater than the resistance at 0° C and in this temperature range the resistance-temperature curve is nearly linear.

The specific resistance of a metal at t° C (ρ_t) is given by the following expression:

$$\rho_t = \rho_0(1 + \alpha t + \beta t^2) \quad . \quad . \quad . \quad . \qquad (2.6)$$

where ρ_0 is the specific resistance at 0° C and α and β are constants for a given metal.

The value of β is small so that except when t is high, such as in the case of platinum-resistance thermometers, it is sufficiently accurate to use only the first two terms of the above expression.

Then $$\rho_t = \rho_0(1 + \alpha t) \quad . \quad . \quad . \quad . \quad . \qquad (2.7)$$

and $$R_t = R_0(1 + \alpha t) \quad . \quad . \quad . \quad . \quad . \qquad (2.8)$$

where R_t and R_0 are the resistances corresponding to ρ_t and ρ_0 respectively.

It follows that $$\alpha = (R_t - R_0)/R_0 t \quad . \quad . \quad . \quad . \qquad (2.9)$$

α is called the *temperature coefficient of increase of resistance* and has the units ohms/ohm/° C, or more simply, just /° C.

It is seen from the expression for R_t that a curve of resistance against temperature is a straight line if βt^2 is neglected.

Certain alloys have very small values of α and high values of ρ so they are valuable for constructing precision resistors. Carbon resistors and most thermistors have negative temperature coefficients. Thermistors are commonly made by embedding oxides of nickel, iron, etc. in ceramic binders and have large temperature coefficients; their resistance variation with temperature is less linear than with metals. Thermistors with positive temperature coefficients have been made using material consisting of barium titanate, or barium-strontium titanate, to which small amounts of lanthanum have been added. Suitable ohmic contacts for these thermistors consist of an indium-mercury amalgam which is rubbed on at the desired point.

EXAMPLE. The field current of a motor at 18° C was 1·75 A and after running for five hours at full-load it had fallen to 1·55 A. If the voltage applied to the field was 230 V and the temperature coefficient of the material is 0·00428/° C, calculate the final temperature of the coils.

Solution

At the start of the run the resistance $R_1 = (230/1{\cdot}75)\ \Omega$.
At the end of the run the resistance $R_2 = (230/1{\cdot}55)\ \Omega$.

Now $R_1 = R_0(1 + 18\alpha)$

and $R_2 = R_0(1 + \alpha t)$, where t is the final temperature.

$$\therefore \quad \frac{R_1}{R_2} = \frac{1{\cdot}55}{1{\cdot}75} = \frac{1 + 18\alpha}{1 + \alpha t}$$

But $\alpha = 0{\cdot}00428/°\ C$

so $\underline{t = 50{\cdot}5°\ C.}$

It is evident, therefore, that the increase of resistance is important in electrical machines, because the running temperature of the windings will be considerably greater than the ambient temperature. In fact, the change of resistance with temperature is frequently used to determine the average temperature rise of a machine or transformer winding. Platinum is used for measuring temperatures up to about 1,000° C.

Kirchhoff's Laws

Two laws enunciated by Kirchhoff are valuable for solving problems on networks of conductors. They are:

(1) The sum of the currents arriving at any point in a network is equal to the sum of the currents flowing away from it.

Thus, if four wires are connected to a point P (Fig. 2.2) and carry currents i_1, i_2, i_3 and i_4 in the directions shown, then the total current arriving at $P = i_1$ and the total current leaving is $i_2 + i_3 + i_4$

$$\therefore \quad i_1 = i_2 + i_3 + i_4 \quad . \quad (2.10)$$

(2) In any closed circuit the algebraic sum of the products of the resistance and current taken for each conductor is equal to the algebraic sum of the e.m.f.'s acting round the circuit in the same direction. Consider the mesh ABC of Fig. 2.3 and assume that the currents in the various branches are I_1, I_2 and I_3 as shown.

Applying Kirchhoff's second law and going from A to C to B to A:

$$I_2R_2 - E + I_3R_3 - I_1R_1 = 0 \quad (2.11)$$

This can be deduced by a consideration of the potential differences in mesh ABC as follows:

$E - R_3I_3$ represents the potential of B above C and I_2R_2 is the potential of C below A.

Therefore, $I_2R_2 - (E - I_3R_3)$ is the potential of B below A which is also, of course, I_1R_1.

$$\therefore \quad I_1R_1 = I_2R_2 - E + I_3R_3 \text{ as before.}$$

EXAMPLE. Use Kirchhoff's Laws to find the current in branch CF of the network of Fig. 2.4.

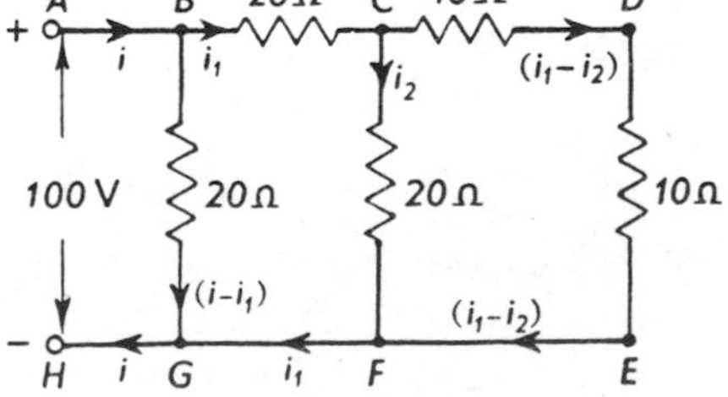

FIG. 2.4

Solution. Let the current in AB be i and that in BC be i_1. Then, applying Kirchhoff's first law at B, the current in BG is $(i - i_1)$. Let the current in CF be i_2, then using Kirchhoff's first law at C, the current in CDE is $(i_1 - i_2)$. Now using the second law,
For loop ACFH,

$$20i_1 + 20i_2 = 100 \quad . \quad . \quad . \quad . \quad (2.12)$$

For loop CDEF,

$$50(i_1 - i_2) - 20i_2 = 0 \quad . \quad . \quad . \quad . \quad (2.13)$$

From these two equations, $i_2 = 2{\cdot}08$ A.

In some networks the solutions of problems are simple because of symmetry; this is illustrated by the following example.

EXAMPLE. Estimate the resistance between points A and B of the cube of Fig. 2.5 which is made up of twelve wires, each of resistance 12 Ω.

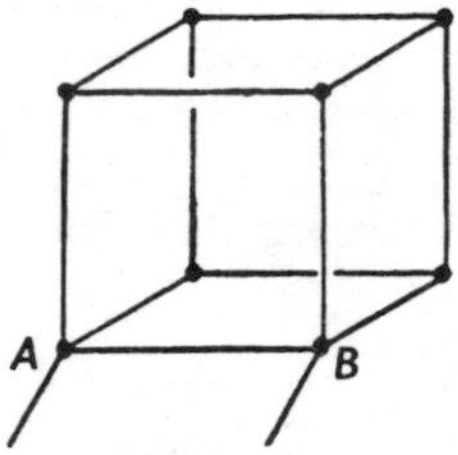

FIG. 2.5

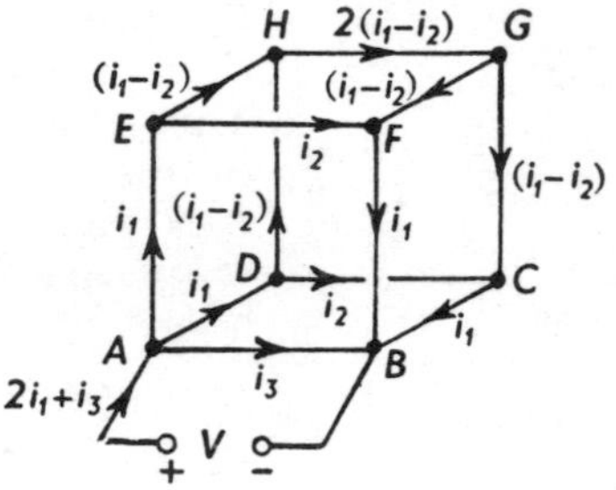

FIG. 2.6

Solution. From considerations of symmetry all the currents may be expressed in terms of three unknowns i_1, i_2 and i_3 as illustrated in Fig. 2.6.

Applying Kirchhoff's second law,
For branch ABCD,

$$12i_3 = 24i_1 + 12i_2 \quad . \quad . \quad . \quad . \quad (2.14)$$

For branch EFGH,

$$12i_2 = 48(i_1 - i_2) \quad . \quad . \quad . \quad . \quad . \quad (2.15)$$

$$\therefore \quad i_2 = 4i_1/5 \text{ and } i_3 = 14i_1/5$$

For the battery circuit and AB,

$$12i_3 = V \quad . \quad . \quad . \quad . \quad . \quad . \quad (2.16)$$

If the effective resistance of the cube between A and B is R, then

$$R(2i_1 + i_3) = V \quad . \quad . \quad . \quad . \quad . \quad (2.17)$$

From the above equations:

$$\underline{R = 7\ \Omega.}$$

In solving problems in the above way, the directions of the assumed currents in the wires are unimportant. If, in any particular branch of the circuit, the current is actually flowing in the opposite direction to that assumed, then the result obtained will simply come out negative.

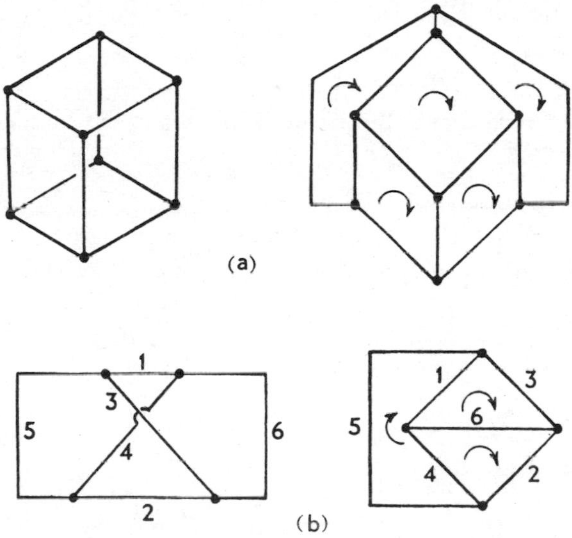

FIG. 2.7

In many problems the networks can be simplified by re-drawing as illustrated by the typical cases of Fig. 2.7.

Resistors in series

Consider n resistors connected in series with a supply of voltage V applied as in Fig. 2.8 (a). It is required to find the equivalent resistance (R) of the circuit.

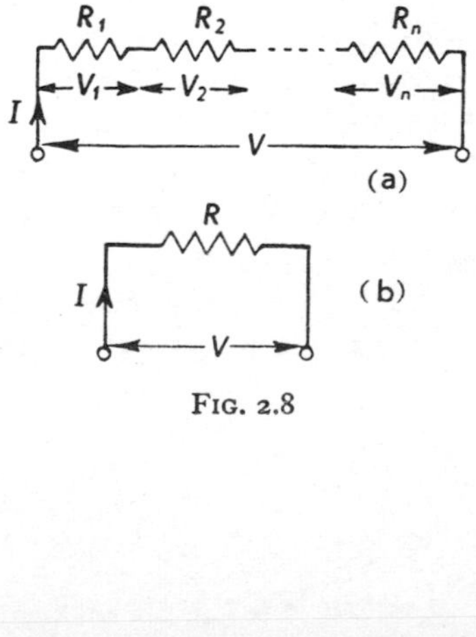

FIG. 2.8

Denote the voltages across the resistors by $V_1, V_2 \ldots V_n$. Applying Ohm's Law to each resistor in turn:

$$V_1 = IR_1,\ V_2 = IR_2, \text{ etc.}$$

$$\therefore\quad V = V_1 + V_2 + \ldots + V_n = I(R_1 + R_2 + \ldots + R_n)$$

But from Fig. 2.8 (*b*),

$$V = RI$$

$$\therefore\quad R = R_1 + R_2 + \ldots + R_n \quad . \quad . \quad . \quad . \quad . \quad . \quad . \quad (2.18)$$

i.e. the total resistance of the circuit is the sum of the resistances connected in series.

Resistors in parallel

In this case $V = I_1R_1 = I_2R_2 = I_3R_3 = \ldots = I_nR_n$

But $\qquad I = I_1 + I_2 + I_3 + \ldots I_n$ (from Kirchhoff's first law)

$$\therefore\quad I = V\left[\frac{1}{R_1} + \frac{1}{R_2} + \frac{1}{R_3} + \ldots + \frac{1}{R_n}\right]$$

But from Fig. 2.9 (*b*), $I = V/R$

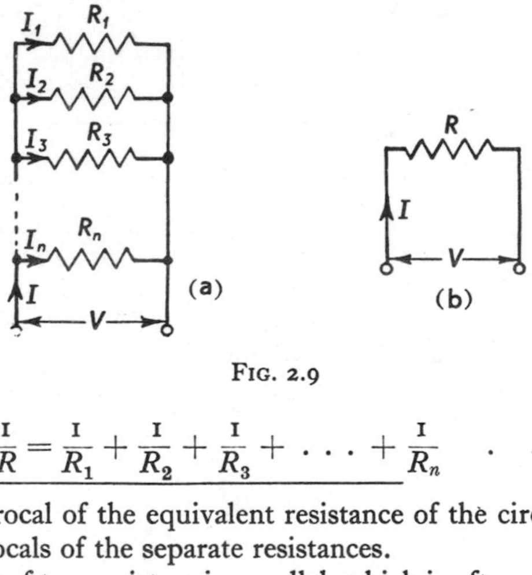

Fig. 2.9

$$\therefore\quad \underline{\frac{1}{R} = \frac{1}{R_1} + \frac{1}{R_2} + \frac{1}{R_3} + \ldots + \frac{1}{R_n}} \quad . \quad . \quad . \quad (2.19)$$

i.e. the reciprocal of the equivalent resistance of the circuit is the sum of the reciprocals of the separate resistances.

In the case of two resistors in parallel, which is often met in practice, the following expressions are useful:

$$R = \frac{1}{\left(\frac{1}{R_1} + \frac{1}{R_2}\right)} = \frac{R_1R_2}{R_1 + R_2} = \frac{\text{product of values}}{\text{sum of values}} \quad . \quad (2.20)$$

$$\text{Also } R = \frac{R_2}{\frac{R_2}{R_1} + 1} = \frac{R_1}{\frac{R_1}{R_2} + 1} = \frac{\text{one value}}{1 + (\text{ratio of values})} \quad . \quad . \quad (2.21)$$

Mixed series and parallel grouping of resistors

EXAMPLE. Calculate the voltage across the parallel branches of the circuit arrangement shown in Fig. 2.10 and the current in the main circuit.

Solution. The parallel combination may be replaced by a single resistor R where

$$\frac{1}{R} = \frac{1}{3} + \frac{1}{9} + \frac{1}{18} = \frac{9}{18}$$

$$\therefore \quad R = 2\ \Omega$$

Current in the main circuit

$$= 100/(1 + 2) = \underline{33{\cdot}33\ \text{A}}$$

Voltage across parallel branches

$$= (100/3) \times 2 = \underline{66{\cdot}67\ \text{V}}$$

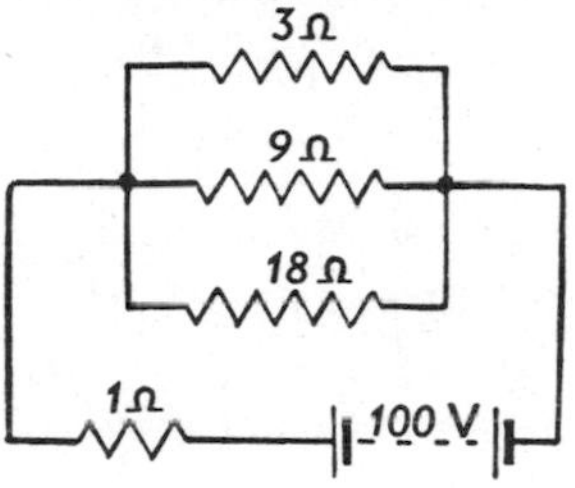

FIG. 2.10

Maxwell's cyclic-current rule

Many network problems are concerned with finding the currents in the various branches when the e.m.f.'s of the voltage sources and the resistor values are specified. So far, in using Kirchhoff's laws, the currents in the branches have actually been considered. It is often convenient, however, to use symbols for the currents round the meshes instead of for the currents in the separate wires. It will soon be evident that the only difference between this method and that previously given is that it substitutes the cyclic-currents idea for the application of Kirchhoff's first law.

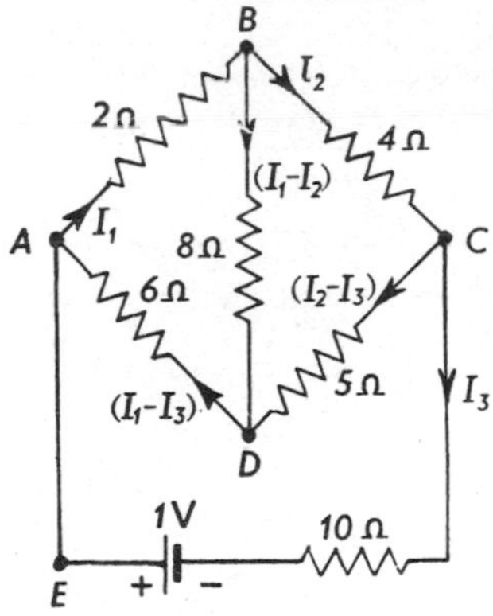

FIG. 2.11

The method will be illustrated and compared with the previous method, using Kirchhoff's two laws, by solving the following example.

EXAMPLE. Evaluate the currents in the various branches of the network shown in Fig. 2.11.

Solution. First Kirchhoff's laws will be employed to solve the problem.

Let a current I_1 flow in AB (Fig. 2.11), a current I_2 in BC and a current I_3 in the battery circuit. Then using Kirchhoff's first law at B, C and D, respectively, the currents in BD, CD and DA can be written down as shown in terms of I_1, I_2 and I_3.

Using Kirchhoff's second law,

From A to B to D to A,

$$2I_1 + 8(I_1 - I_2) + 6(I_1 - I_3) = 0 \quad . \quad . \quad (2.22)$$

From B to C to D to B,

$$4I_2 + 5(I_2 - I_3) - 8(I_1 - I_2) = 0 \quad . \quad . \quad (2.23)$$

From A to D to C to E to A,

$$-6(I_1 - I_3) - 5(I_2 - I_3) + 10I_3 - 1 = 0 \quad . \quad (2.24)$$

From (2.22), (2.23) and (2.24) it is found that

$$I_1 = \underline{0{\cdot}0494 \text{ A}},\ I_2 = \underline{0{\cdot}0445 \text{ A}} \text{ and } I_3 = \underline{0{\cdot}0723 \text{ A}}$$

To use Maxwell's Cyclic-Current Rule and to compare the solution with that above, the figure is re-drawn with mesh currents I_1, I_2 and I_3 as in Fig. 2.12 and Kirchhoff's second law can then be used at once. In a branch such as *AB* it will be evident that the mesh current and the branch current are either the same or one is the negative of the other, depending on the directions chosen. In a branch such as *BD*, however, where the branch is common to two meshes the branch current is the algebraic sum of the mesh currents. Thus, in branch *AB* the current is I_1 from *A* to *B*, in branch *BD* the current is $(I_1 - I_2)$ from *B* to *D* and the current from *D* to *A* is $(I_1 - I_3)$.

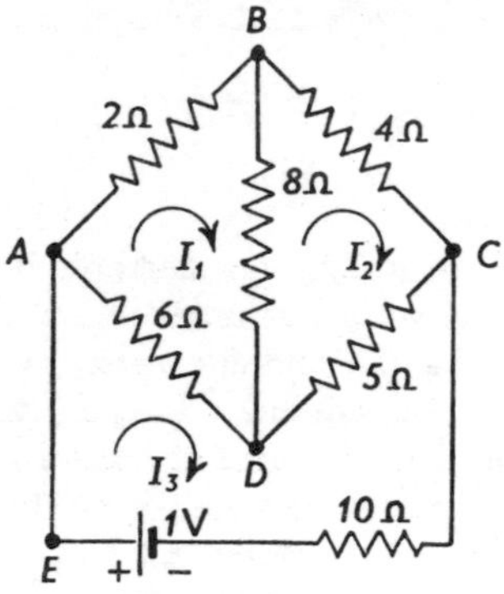

FIG. 2.12

Applying Kirchhoff's second law to the mesh *ABD*, therefore, we have

$$2I_1 + 8(I_1 - I_2) + 6(I_1 - I_3) = 0 \quad . \quad . \quad (2.25)$$

This expression is, of course, identical with equation (2.22) above. In similar ways equations (2.23) and (2.24) can be written down giving I_1, I_2 and I_3.

Simplification of network analysis

It will be evident that, even in relatively simple networks, the methods of solution employing Kirchhoff's laws and Maxwell's rule may be laborious and time consuming. To simplify solutions many theorems have been evolved and some of these will now be presented and their applications illustrated by means of examples.

The Principle of Superposition

In calculating the currents in the branches of a network containing several voltage or current sources, it is often convenient to find the currents in the branches resulting from the presence of one source at a time. This should be repeated for the various sources and finally the individual currents added for each branch to give the actual solution. This is known as the Principle of Superposition.

When applying the principle, omitted e.m.f.'s must be replaced by short-circuits and omitted current sources must be replaced by open-circuits. This is made clear by the two following examples and will be discussed more fully in the next section.

The principle is verified in Chapter 7.

EXAMPLE. Apply the Principle of Superposition to find the currents in the various branches of the network of Fig. 2.13. [S.U.]

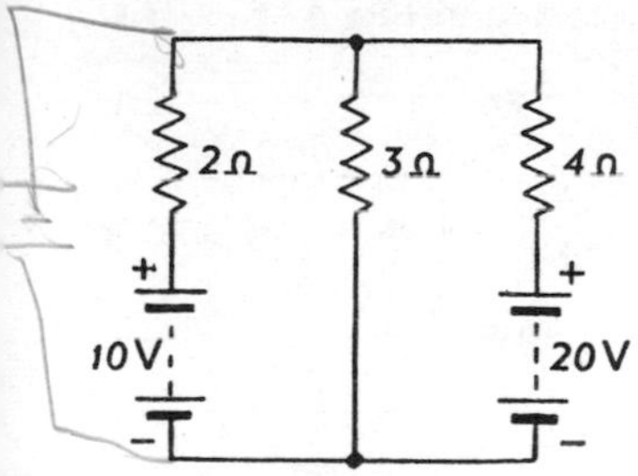

FIG. 2.13

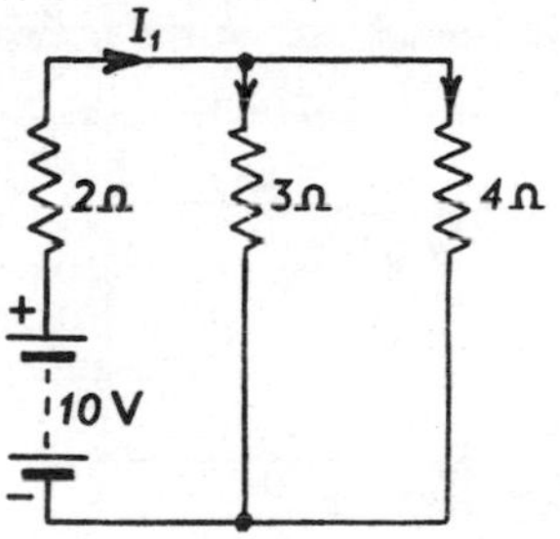

FIG. 2.14

Solution. Consider first that the e.m.f. of 20 V be zero for the time being giving the circuit of Fig. 2.14.

$$\text{Then current } I_1 = \frac{10}{2 + \left(\frac{3 \times 4}{3 + 4}\right)}\text{ A} = 2{\cdot}69\text{ A}$$

$$\text{The current through the 3 }\Omega\text{ resistor} = \frac{4I_1}{(3+4)} = \underline{1{\cdot}54\text{ A}}$$

and the current through the 4 Ω resistor is (2·69 − 1·54) A = $\underline{1{\cdot}15\text{ A.}}$

If now the e.m.f. of 10 V be considered zero the circuit of Fig. 2.15 results.

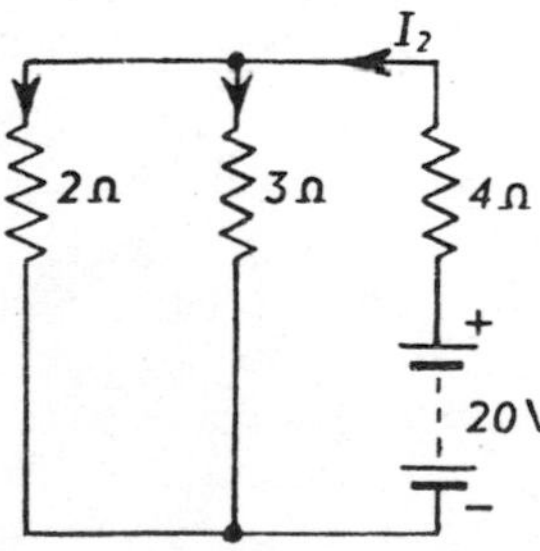

FIG. 2.15

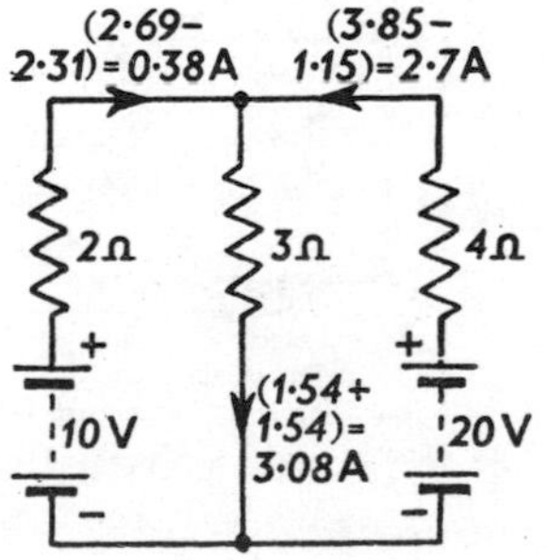

FIG. 2.16

$$\text{Then current } I_2 = \frac{20}{4 + \left(\frac{2 \times 3}{2 + 3}\right)} = \underline{3{\cdot}85 \text{ A}}$$

This divides so that the current through the 3 Ω resistor $= (2 \times I_2)/5$ *i.e.* 1·54 A and the current through the 2 Ω resistor is (3·85 − 1·54) A $=$ <u>2·31 A.</u>

When both e.m.f. sources are present, therefore, the currents are as shown on Fig. 2.16.

EXAMPLE. Apply the Principle of Superposition to find the current in branch *AC* of the network *ABCD* illustrated in Fig. 2.17. [S.U.]

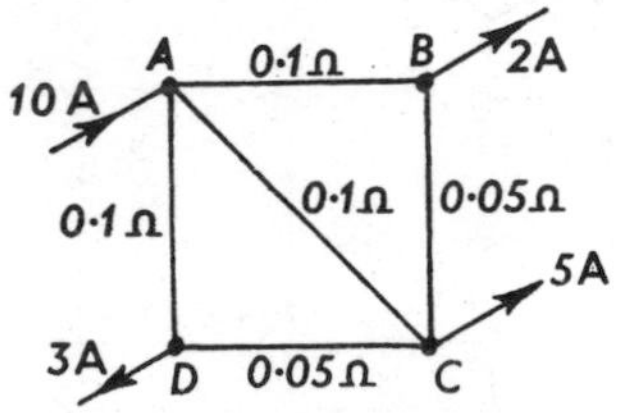

FIG. 2.17

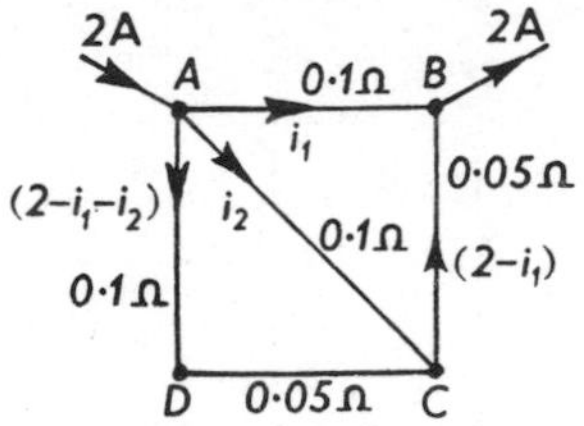

FIG. 2.18

Solution

Consider first the 2 A *load acting alone* (Fig. 2.18).

Let the currents circulate as shown. For loop *ADC* applying Kirchhoff's second law,

$$(2 - i_1 - i_2)0{\cdot}15 = 0{\cdot}1i_2 \quad . \quad . \quad . \quad . \quad (2.26)$$

For loop *ABC*,

$$0{\cdot}1i_1 - (2 - i_1)0{\cdot}05 = 0{\cdot}1i_2 \quad . \quad . \quad . \quad (2.27)$$

From (2.26) and (2.27) $\underline{i_2 = \frac{4}{7} \text{ A}}$ . . . . (2.28)

Consider next the 5 A *load acting alone* (Fig. 2.19).

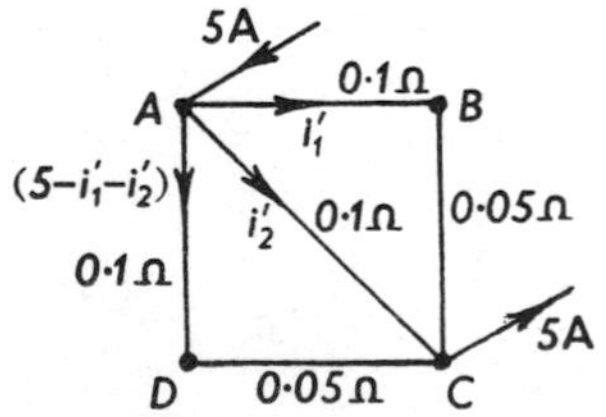

FIG. 2.19

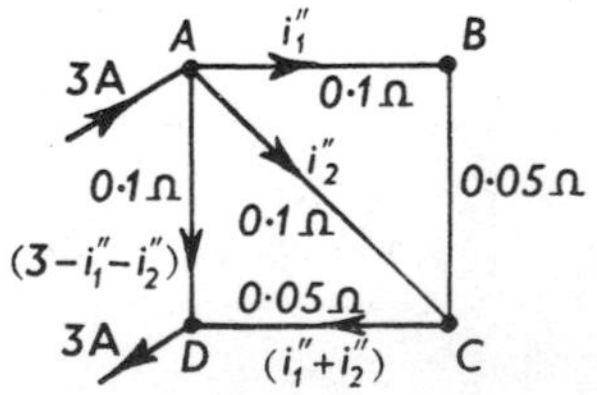

FIG. 2.20

Let the currents circulate as shown.

For loop *ABC*,

$$0{\cdot}15i_1' = 0{\cdot}1i_2' \quad . \quad . \quad . \quad . \quad . \quad (2.29)$$

For loop ADC,

$$0{\cdot}15(5 - i_1' - i_2') = 0{\cdot}1i_2' \quad . \quad . \quad . \quad (2.30)$$

From (2.29) and (2.30) $i_2' = \dfrac{15}{7}$ A . . . . (2.31)

Finally, consider the 3 A *load acting alone* (Fig. 2.20).
Let the currents circulate as shown.

For loop ABC,

$$0{\cdot}15i_1'' = 0{\cdot}1i_2'' \quad . \quad . \quad . \quad . \quad (2.32)$$

For loop ADC,

$$0{\cdot}1(3 - i_1'' - i_2'') = 0{\cdot}1i_2'' + 0{\cdot}05(i_1'' + i_2''). \quad (2.33)$$

From (2.32) and (2.33) $i_2'' = \dfrac{6}{7}$ A . . . . (2.34)

Therefore, using the Principle of Superposition, the total current in branch AC due to all the loads acting simultaneously is $i_2 + i_2' + i_2''$ which from equations (2.28), (2.31) and (2.34) is

$$\left(\frac{4}{7} + \frac{15}{7} + \frac{6}{7}\right) \text{A} = \underline{3{\cdot}57 \text{ A}}.$$

Thévenin's Theorem

The Theorem states that the current flowing through a resistor R_l, connected between any two points A and B in a network, is given by $V/(R_l + R)$. V is the voltage across the two points when R_l is removed and R is the resistance of the network, as seen from points A and B, calculated by assuming that all voltage sources are replaced by resistances equal to their internal resistances.

It will be evident that the Theorem may be stated in the following alternative way:

Any network of circuits having two accessible terminals A and B can be replaced, so far as its external behaviour is concerned, by a single e.m.f. acting in series with a single resistance between A and B. The value to be given to the e.m.f. is that which exists between A and B when the external circuit is disconnected. The value to be given to the resistance is the internal resistance between A and B when all internal sources of e.m.f. are replaced by their internal resistances.

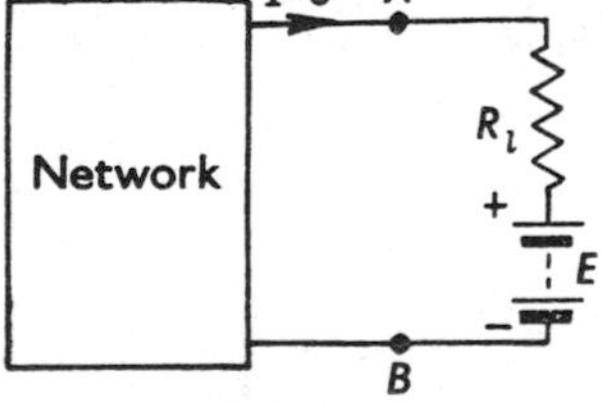

FIG. 2.21

Proof. Fig. 2.21 represents a linear network containing both resistors and e.m.f.'s and having two accessible terminals A and B.

An e.m.f. and a load resistor R_l are connected externally in series across terminals A and B.

Let the e.m.f. be adjusted to a value E so that no current leaves or enters the network. Thus, E is the open-circuit voltage between A and B.

Using the Principle of Superposition the zero current in the external circuit may be regarded as the sum of (*a*) the current resulting from E when all the e.m.f.'s in the network are short-circuited, and (*b*) the current resulting from all the e.m.f.'s in the network when E is short-circuited.

But (*a*) is equal to $E/(R_l + R)$, where R is the resistance of the network as viewed from terminals A and B, when the internal e.m.f.'s are short-circuited. It follows from (*b*), therefore, that the network can be replaced by a single e.m.f. E acting in series with a single resistor, as far as the circuit external to the network is concerned.

Two types of problem arise in practice, one in which a network is supplied with constant voltages, the other where a network is supplied with constant currents. Consider first a constant-voltage supply. In using Thévenin's Theorem a link is removed in the network. In doing this the current supplied to the network is changed so that the voltage applied can only remain constant provided that the internal resistance of the supply is zero.

It follows, similarly, that in the case of a constant-current circuit the internal resistance of the supply must be taken as infinite.

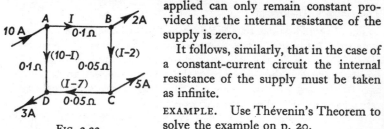

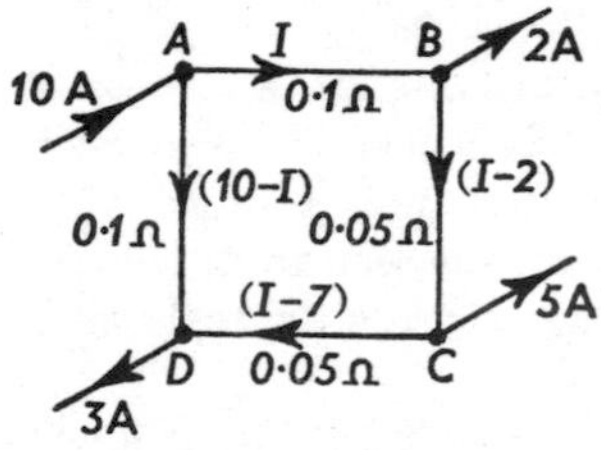

FIG. 2.22

EXAMPLE. Use Thévenin's Theorem to solve the example on p. 20.

[S.U.]

Solution. To use the Theorem, link AC is removed to give the circuit of Fig. 2.22. The voltage V between A and C and the resistance R between A and C are required with AC removed. The Theorem states that the current in AC is then $V/(R_l + R)$ where $R_l = 0{\cdot}1\ \Omega$ is the resistance of the link AC which is removed.

Now $$R = (0{\cdot}15/2)\ \Omega = 0{\cdot}075\ \Omega \quad . \quad . \quad . \quad (2.35)$$

Let the current in $AB = I$; then the currents in the other conductors are given by Kirchhoff's first law and are as shown.

Applying Kirchhoff's second law to loop $ABCDA$:

$$0{\cdot}1I + 0{\cdot}05(I - 2) + 0{\cdot}05(I - 7) = 0{\cdot}1(10 - I) \quad . \quad (2.36)$$

$$\therefore \quad \underline{I = 29/6\ \text{A}}$$

$$\therefore \quad V = 0{\cdot}1I + 0{\cdot}05(I - 2) \quad . \quad . \quad . \quad (2.37)$$
$$= \underline{0{\cdot}625 \text{ volt.}}$$

Current in $AC = 0{\cdot}625/(0{\cdot}1 + 0{\cdot}075) = \underline{3{\cdot}57\ \text{A}}$ . . . (2.38)

and flows from A to C since V, which is the potential of A above C, is positive.

EXAMPLE. For the circuit illustrated in Fig. 2.23 find the current in branch AB using Thévenin's Theorem. [S.U.]

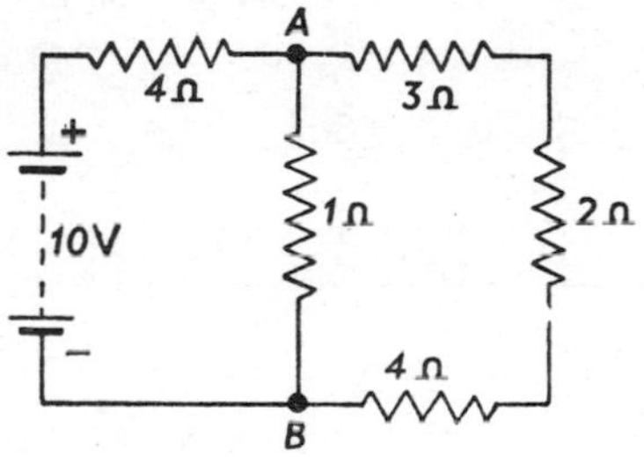

FIG. 2.23

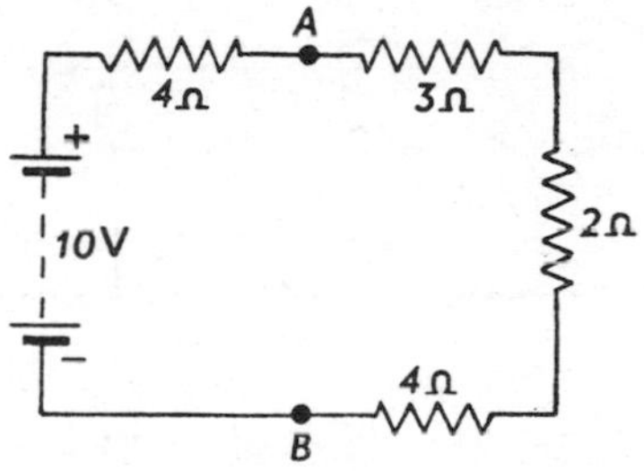

FIG. 2.24

Solution. To use the Theorem link AB is removed to give the circuit of Fig. 2.24.

The resistance R between A and B is then found with the battery short-circuited. The voltage between A and B is also found with link AB removed.

The current in AB is then $V/(R + 1)$ since the resistance of the link AB removed is 1 Ω.

Now $$R = \frac{4 \times (3 + 2 + 4)}{4 + (3 + 2 + 4)} = 36/13\ \Omega.$$

The current in the above circuit (Fig. 2.24) $= 10/(4 + 3 + 2 + 4)$ $= 10/13$ A.

$$\therefore \quad V = (3 + 2 + 4)\ 10/13 = 90/13 \text{ volts,}$$

so current in $$AB = \frac{90/13}{(36/13) + 1} = \underline{1{\cdot}84\ \text{A.}}$$

Repeated use of Thévenin's Theorem

Rogers * has drawn attention to the fact that an electrical network which is, as a whole, so complicated that its solution by the use of mesh equations is unreasonably difficult, or even impracticable, may often be divided into a number of constituent networks each of which is of

* F. E. Rogers, "The Iterated Use of Thévenin's Theorem", *Bull. Elect. Eng. Educ.* No. 4, p. 34 (May 1950). See also F. E. Rogers, *The Theory of Networks in Electrical Communication and other Fields*, pp. 142–4 (Macdonald, 1957).

convenient proportions. To illustrate this he solves the problem which is stated below.

EXAMPLE. By the repeated use of Thévenin's Theorem find the current in branch XY of the circuit of Fig. 2.25.

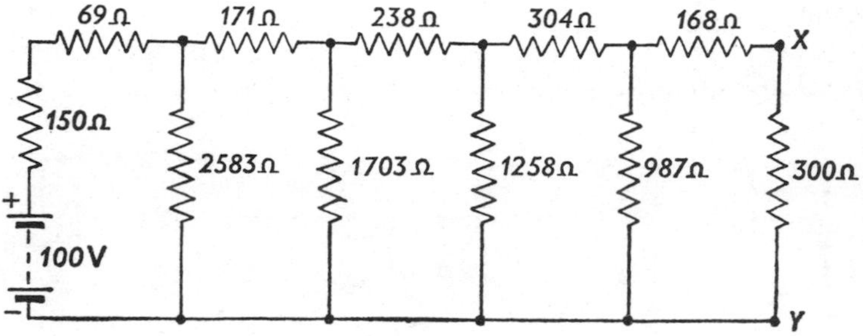

FIG. 2.25

Solution. Thévenin's Theorem shows that the two following arrangements are equivalent:

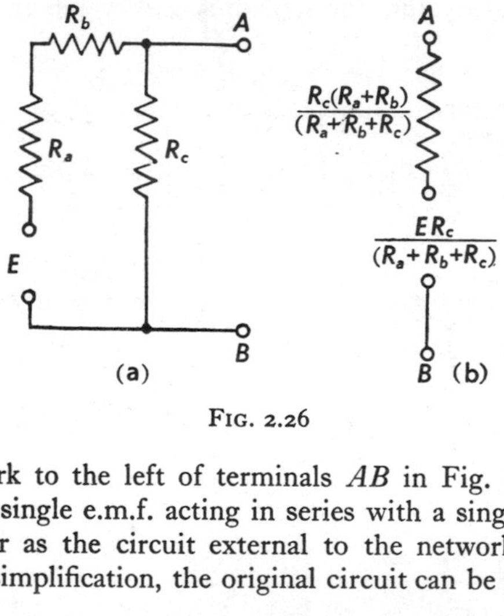

FIG. 2.26

i.e. the network to the left of terminals AB in Fig. 2.26 (*a*) can be replaced by a single e.m.f. acting in series with a single resistor (Fig. 2.26 (*b*)) as far as the circuit external to the network is concerned.

Using this simplification, the original circuit can be reduced to that of Fig. 2.27.

$$R_1 = \frac{2{,}583 \times 219}{2{,}583 + 219} = \frac{2{,}583 \times 219}{2{,}802} = \underline{202\ \Omega}$$

$$E_1 = 100 \times 2{,}583/2{,}802 = \underline{92{\cdot}1\ \text{V}.}$$

Similarly Fig. 2.27 can be reduced to Fig. 2.28.

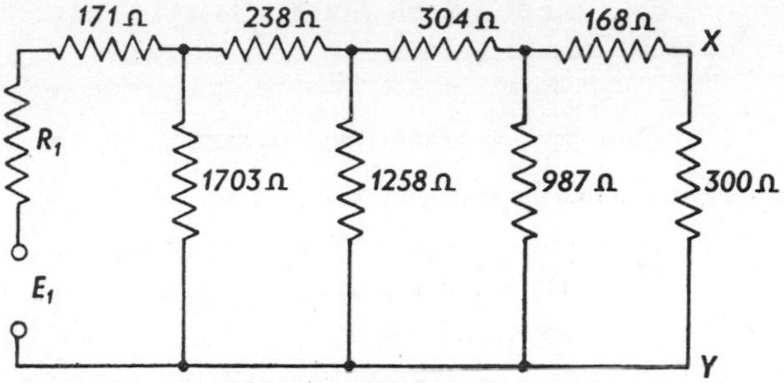

FIG. 2.27

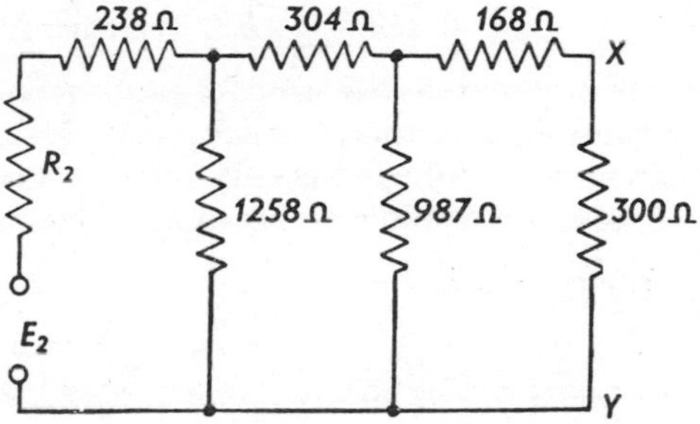

FIG. 2.28

$$R_2 = \frac{1{,}703 \times (202 + 171)}{1{,}703 + (202 + 171)}$$

$$= 1{,}703 \times 373/2{,}076 = \underline{306\ \Omega}$$

$$E_2 = 92{\cdot}1 \times 1{,}703/2{,}076 = \underline{75{\cdot}5\ \text{V}}$$

Similarly Fig. 2.28 can be reduced to Fig. 2.29.

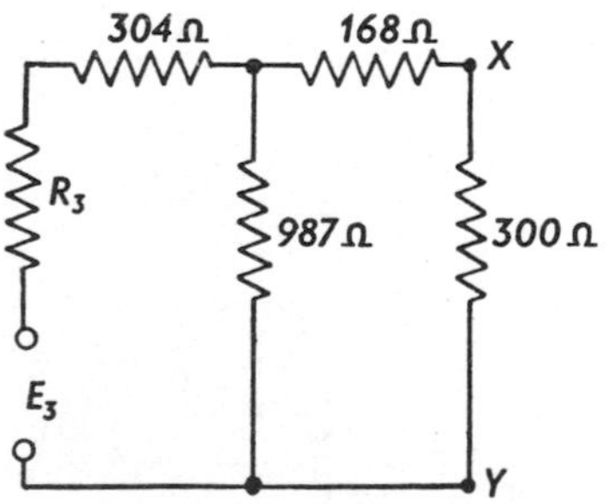

FIG. 2.29

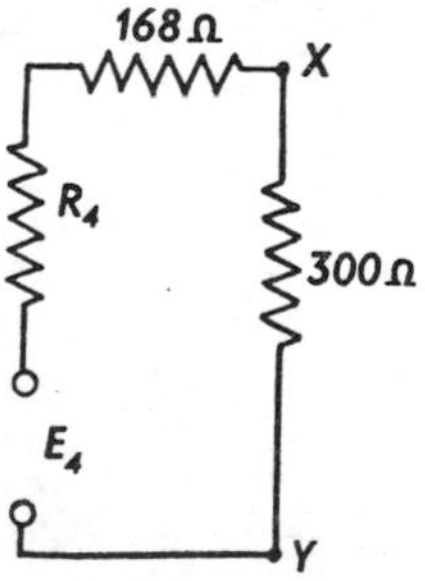

FIG. 2.30

$$R_3 = \frac{1{,}258 \times (306 + 238)}{1{,}258 + (306 + 238)} = \frac{1{,}258 \times 544}{1{,}802}$$

$$= \underline{380\ \Omega}$$

$$E_3 = 75{\cdot}5 \times 1{,}258/1{,}802 = \underline{52{\cdot}7\ \text{V}}$$

Similarly Fig. 2.29 can be reduced to Fig. 2.30.

$$R_4 = \frac{987 \times (304 + 380)}{987 + (304 + 380)} = \frac{987 \times 684}{1{,}671}$$

$$= \underline{403\ \Omega}$$

$$E_4 = 52{\cdot}7 \times 987/1{,}671 = \underline{31{\cdot}1\ \text{V}}$$

The current through the link XY is therefore

$$31{\cdot}1/(403 + 168 + 300)\ \text{A} = \underline{0{\cdot}0357\ \text{A}}$$

The calculation procedure is the same for each equivalent circuit and even if the network had contained many more meshes the solution would have been no more difficult but only longer. The solution using mesh equations, however, would have been formidable in the latter case.

The Reciprocity Theorem

The Reciprocity Theorem states that the current produced in any branch of a linear network, by an e.m.f. in any other branch, equals the current in the other branch which would result if the e.m.f. was transferred to the first branch.

EXAMPLE. Evaluate the currents in the various branches of the network shown in Fig. 2.31 and then utilize the Principle of Superposition and the Reciprocity Theorem together, to find the value of the current in the 1 V battery circuit, when an e.m.f. of 2 V is added in branch BD opposing the flow of the original current in that branch. [S.U.]

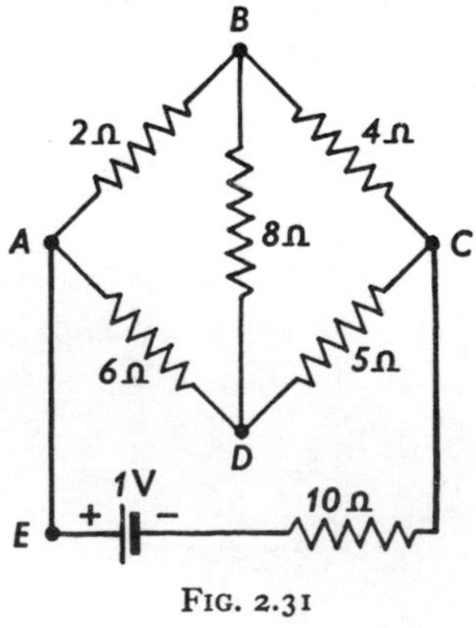

FIG. 2.31

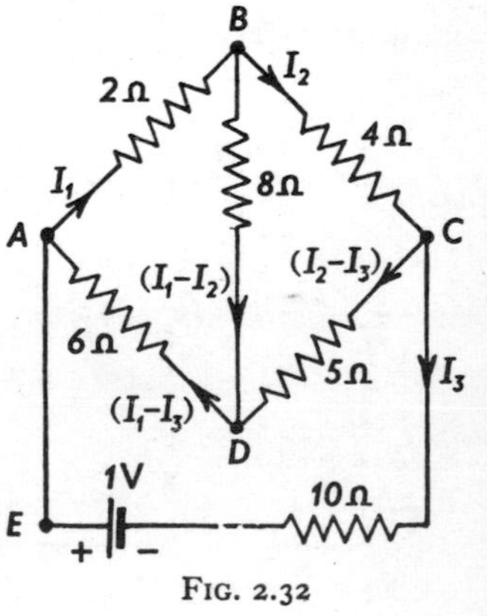

FIG. 2.32

Solution. It has been shown already, using Maxwell's Cyclic-Current Rule that the currents in the various branches of this network are as shown in Fig. 2.32 where

$$I_1 = 0{\cdot}0494 \text{ A}$$
$$I_2 = 0{\cdot}0445 \text{ A}$$
and $$I_3 = 0{\cdot}0723 \text{ A}$$

∴ the current through *BD* is

$$I_1 - I_2 = 0{\cdot}0049 \text{ A from } B \text{ to } D.$$

The new circuit is shown in Fig. 2.33.

Using the Principle of Superposition, the old solution becomes one part of the new required solution, because the current in *CEA* due to the 1 V source is 0·0723 A flowing from *E* to *A*.

Using the Reciprocity Theorem it is seen that if the original e.m.f. of 1 V had been transferred to branch *BD* it would have given rise to a current in *EA* of the same value as that originally in branch *BD*, *i.e.* 0·0049 A.

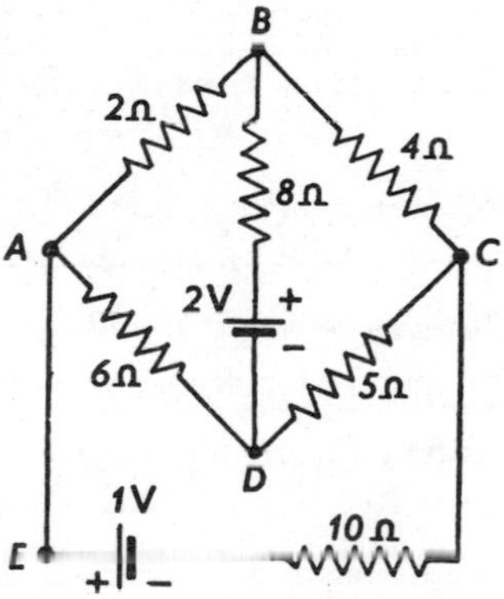

FIG. 2.33

Thus, an e.m.f. of 2 V in branch *BD* gives, by proportion, a current of $-(2 \times 0{\cdot}0049)$ A in *EA*, the minus sign being included because the e.m.f. of 2 V opposes the flow of the original current in *BD*.

∴ the resultant value of the current in *EA* is

$$\{0{\cdot}0723 + (-2 \times 0{\cdot}0049)\} \text{ A}$$
$$= (0{\cdot}0723 - 0{\cdot}0098) \text{ A}$$
$$= \underline{0{\cdot}0625 \text{ A from } E \text{ to } A.}$$

This method of solution is much simpler and shorter than completely re-solving the problem with three new simultaneous equations as would be required if Kirchhoff's laws or Maxwell's Cyclic-Current Rule are used.

Delta–star and star–delta transformations

Certain network problems can be simplified by using a delta–star transformation.

Consider the two networks shown in Fig. 2.34. If they are electrically equivalent, the resistance between any two terminals of the star must be the same as the resistance, viewed from the corresponding terminals of the delta.

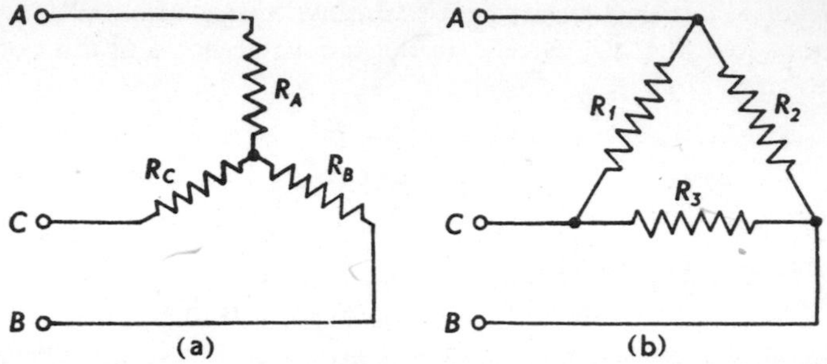

FIG. 2.34

Thus, between terminals A and B,

$$R_A + R_B = R_2(R_1 + R_3)/(R_1 + R_2 + R_3) \quad (2.39)$$

Between terminals A and C,

$$R_A + R_C = R_1(R_2 + R_3)/(R_1 + R_2 + R_3) \quad (2.40)$$

Between terminals B and C,

$$R_B + R_C = R_3(R_1 + R_2)/(R_1 + R_2 + R_3) \quad (2.41)$$

Adding (2.39) and (2.40) and subtracting (2.41) gives,

$$R_A = R_1R_2/(R_1 + R_2 + R_3) \quad (2.42)$$

Similarly,

$$R_B = R_2R_3/(R_1 + R_2 + R_3) \quad (2.43)$$

and

$$R_C = R_1R_3/(R_1 + R_2 + R_3) \quad (2.44)$$

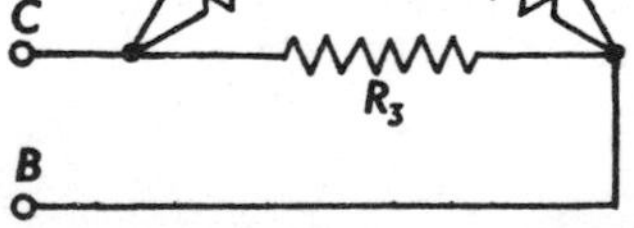

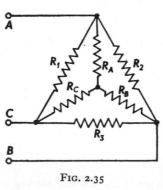

FIG. 2.35

Equations (2.42), (2.43) and (2.44) give the resistances of the equivalent star in terms of the resistances of the delta. These results may easily be remembered by considering Fig. 2.35; for R_A, which lies between R_1 and R_2, is given by the product of these two resistance values divided by the sum of R_1, R_2 and R_3.

If the values of R_1, R_2 and R_3 are required in terms of R_A, R_B and R_C they may be obtained from equations (2.42), (2.43) and (2.44) in the following manner:

$$\frac{1}{R_A} + \frac{1}{R_B} + \frac{1}{R_C} = (R_1 + R_2 + R_3)\left[\frac{1}{R_1R_2} + \frac{1}{R_2R_3} + \frac{1}{R_1R_3}\right] = \frac{(R_1 + R_2 + R_3)^2}{R_1R_2R_3} \quad (2.45)$$

Multiplying (2.45) by (2.42) and (2.43) gives

$$R_A R_B\left[\frac{1}{R_A}+\frac{1}{R_B}+\frac{1}{R_C}\right]=$$
$$\frac{(R_1+R_2+R_3)^2}{R_1R_2R_3}\left(\frac{R_1R_2}{R_1+R_2+R_3}\right)\left(\frac{R_2R_3}{R_1+R_2+R_3}\right)=R_2 \quad (2.46)$$

Thus,

R_2 is given in terms of the resistances of the star R_A, R_B and R_C.

Similarly,

$$R_1 = R_A R_C\left[\frac{1}{R_A}+\frac{1}{R_B}+\frac{1}{R_C}\right] \quad . \quad . \quad . \quad . \quad (2.47)$$

and
$$R_3 = R_B R_C\left[\frac{1}{R_A}+\frac{1}{R_B}+\frac{1}{R_C}\right] \quad . \quad . \quad . \quad . \quad (2.48)$$

The results of equations (2.46), (2.47) and (2.48) are also easily memorized with the help of Fig. 2.35.

An alternative proof of the delta–star transformation has been given by Walsh.* It forms an interesting example in the use of Maxwell's Cyclic-Current Rule and is given below.

If the two networks of Fig. 2.36 are equivalent, the coefficients in the circuit equations for meshes 1, 2 and 3 must correspond identically

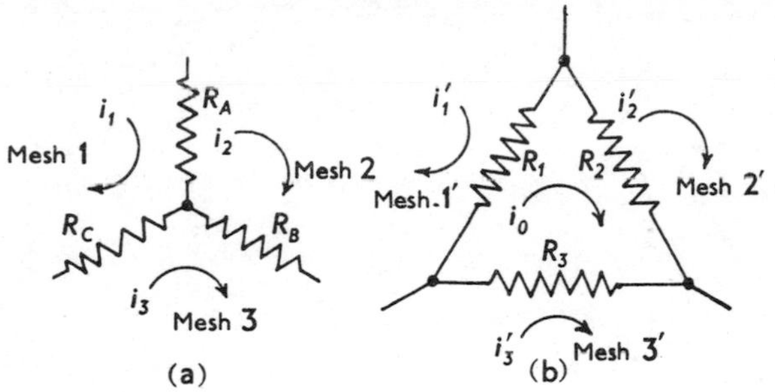

FIG. 2.36

with the coefficients in the circuit equations for meshes 1', 2' and 3' respectively.

Comparing meshes 1 and 1',

In the circuit equation for mesh 1 there are the terms:

$$i_1(R_A+R_C)-i_2R_A-i_3R_C=P, \text{ say} \quad . \quad . \quad (2.49)$$

* T. R. Walsh, "Some Useful Procedures in Circuit and Line Theory", *Bull. Elect. Eng. Educ.*, No. 10, p. 24 (June 1953).

In mesh 1′ there are the terms:

$$i_1'(R_1) - i_0(R_1) = P', \text{ say} \quad . \quad . \quad . \quad (2.50)$$

The circuit equation for the closed-loop mesh in which current i_0 circulates is:

$$i_0(R_1 + R_2 + R_3) - i_1'R_1 - i_2'R_2 - i_3'R_3 = 0 \quad (2.51)$$

so

$$i_0 = (i_1'R_1 + i_2'R_2 + i_3'R_3)/(R_1 + R_2 + R_3) \quad (2.52)$$

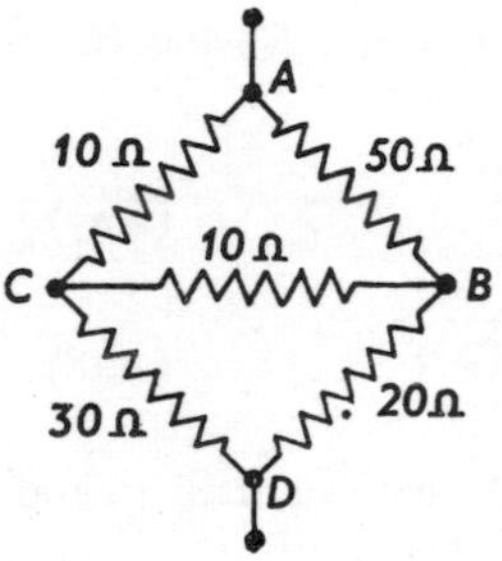

FIG. 2.37

From equations (2.50) and (2.52):

$$P' = \{i_1'(R_1R_2 + R_1R_3) - i_2'R_1R_2 - i_3'R_1R_3\}/(R_1 + R_2 + R_3) \quad . \quad (2.53)$$

But the coefficients of P and P' must be the same, so

$$R_1R_3/(R_1 + R_2 + R_3) = R_C \quad (2.54)$$

and

$$R_1R_2/(R_1 + R_2 + R_3) = R_A \quad (2.55)$$

Similarly, by comparing meshes 2 and 2′ and 3 and 3′, expressions are obtained for R_A and R_B and R_B and R_C.

EXAMPLE. Find the equivalent resistance of the network illustrated in Fig. 2.37 between points A and D by first using a delta–star transformation on mesh ABC.

Solution. Using a delta–star transformation on mesh ABC of the given circuit, the arrangement shown in Fig. 2.38 (a) results

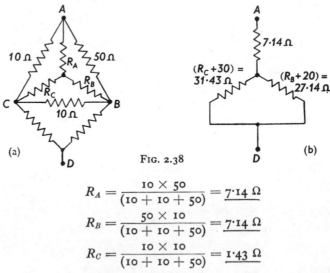

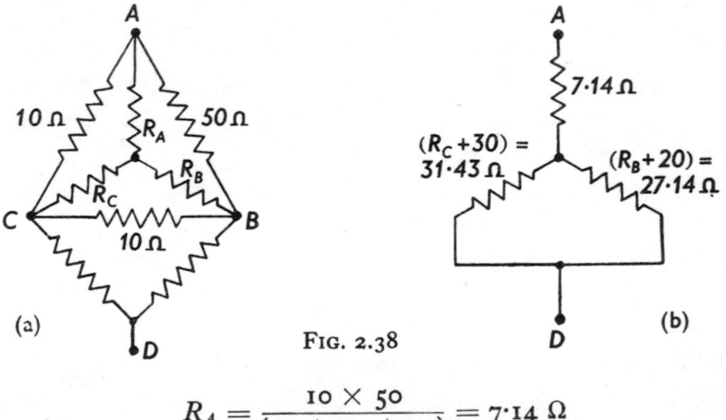

FIG. 2.38

$$R_A = \frac{10 \times 50}{(10 + 10 + 50)} = \underline{7 \cdot 14\ \Omega}$$

$$R_B = \frac{50 \times 10}{(10 + 10 + 50)} = \underline{7 \cdot 14\ \Omega}$$

$$R_C = \frac{10 \times 10}{(10 + 10 + 50)} = \underline{1 \cdot 43\ \Omega}$$

The circuit of Fig. 2.38 (a), therefore, reduces to that of Fig. 2.38 (b).

The equivalent resistance between A and D is:

$$\left(7{\cdot}14 + \frac{31{\cdot}43 \times 27{\cdot}14}{31{\cdot}43 + 27{\cdot}14}\right)\Omega = \underline{21{\cdot}7\ \Omega.}$$

The delta–star transformation is capable of important generalization. Consider n points in a network. These can be connected by resistors in three ways, as shown in Fig. 2.39 for the case of $n = 4$.

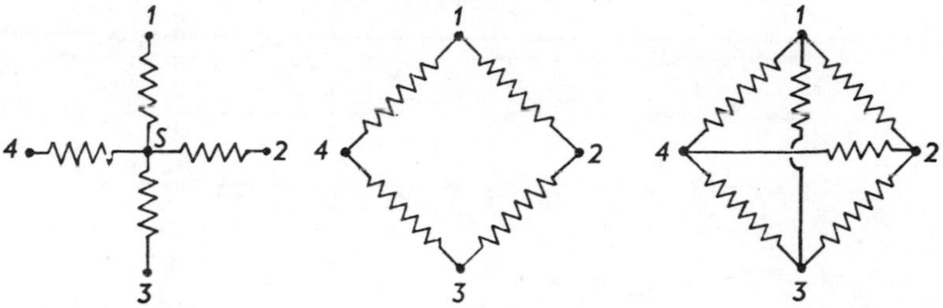

(a) Star-connection (b) Mesh-connection (c) Pair-connection

FIG. 2.39

At (a) the n resistors are connected in star to the star-point S. At (b) the resistors are connected in a closed mesh and at (c) the n points are joined in pairs in all possible ways by $n(n - 1)/2$ resistors.

Rosen * has shown that any star of n lcgs can be replaced by an equivalent pair-connected arrangement of $n(n - 1)/2$ rcsistors. Russell † has given a proof of Rosen's Theorem and stated its converse. He points out that if $n > 3$ a mesh-connected arrangement cannot be replaced by an equivalent star-connected one and although a pair-connected system can sometimes be replaced by a star, the restrictions are severe.

Combined star- and delta-connected loads

If *both* star- and delta-connected loads are present as in Fig. 2.35 the circuit can be analyzed conveniently by first converting the star to a delta in parallel with the existing delta and then combining the corresponding parallel elements to give an equivalent single delta. Alternatively, the Principle of Superposition can be used, first considering the star alone and then the delta and combining the two results.

* A. Rosen, "A New Network Theorem", *J.I.E.E.*, **62**, p. 916 (1924).

† A. Russell, " Star and Pair Connections in Networks ", *Faraday House Journal*, **12**, No. 4, p. 86 (1927).

D.C. Distributors

(a) Distributor fed from one end

Suppose a distributor is fed at one end A (Fig. 2.40). Let currents i_1, i_2, i_3, etc., be taken off at points B_1, B_2, B_3, etc. The resistances of

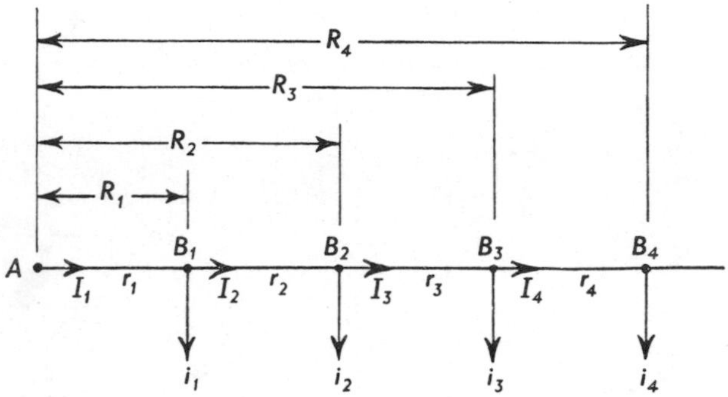

FIG. 2.40

AB_1, AB_2, etc., will be denoted by R_1, R_2, etc. Let the current in AB_1 be I_1, in B_1B_2 be I_2, etc.

The voltage drop to any point along the distributor, say B_3, is

$$\begin{aligned} & I_1R_1 + I_2r_2 + I_3r_3 \\ &= I_1R_1 + I_2(R_2 - R_1) + I_3(R_3 - R_2) \\ &= R_1(I_1 - I_2) + R_2(I_2 - I_3) + R_3I_3 \\ &= R_1i_1 + R_2i_2 + R_3I_3 \quad . \quad . \quad . \quad . \quad . \quad . \quad (2.56) \end{aligned}$$

EXAMPLE. A two-wire distributor 1,000 yd long has the following loads:

Distance from feed (yd)	100	300	500	700	800	1,000
Load (A)	20	30	40	20	40	30

The feed is at 240 V and the end consumer is to receive at 220 V. Evaluate the cross-sectional area of the copper distributor cores. The resistivity of copper is 0·67 microhm/in. cube.

Solution. Let the resistance per yard of each core be $r/2$ so that the resistance per yard of the distributor is r. Using the symbols on Fig. 2.40,

$$R_1 = 100r,\ R_2 = 300r,\ R_3 = 500r,\ \text{etc.}$$

Total voltage drop $= 20\text{ V} = R_1i_1 + R_2i_2 + R_3i_3 + R_4i_4 + R_5i_5 + R_6i_6$ because $I_6 = i_6$ here.

$$\therefore \quad 20 = r[(100 \times 20) + (300 \times 30) + (500 \times 40) + (700 \times 20) + (800 \times 40) + (1{,}000 \times 30)]$$

i.e. $r = (20/107{,}000)\ \Omega.$

But $r/2 = l\rho/A$, therefore $(10/107{,}000) = 36 \times (0{\cdot}67/10^6)/A$ since $l = 36$ in., A is the cross-sectional area of a core in sq. in.

Thus, $A = \underline{0{\cdot}258 \text{ sq. in.}}$

(*b*) Distributor fed at both ends

EXAMPLE. A distributor is fed at both ends at the same voltage and is loaded as shown in Fig. 2.41. Determine the current distribution in the system.

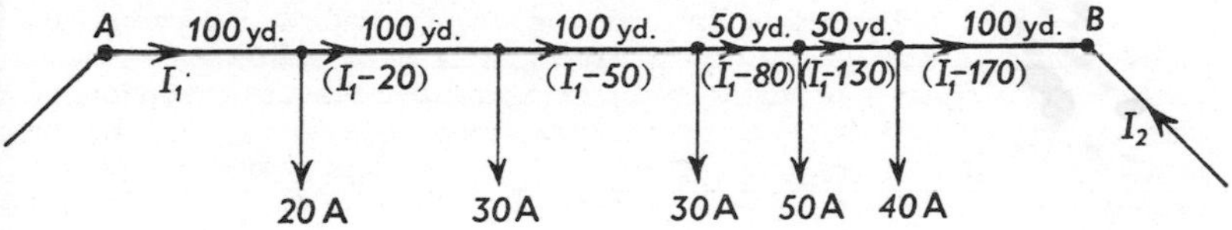

FIG. 2.41

Solution. Let the resistance/yard be r ohms. Suppose the current fed in at A is I_1 ampères and that at B is I_2 ampères. Points A and B are at the same potential so:

$$r\{100\, I_1 + 100(I_1 - 20) + 100(I_1 - 50) + 50(I_1 - 80) + 50(I_1 - 130) + 100(I_1 - 170)\} = 0$$

$$\therefore \quad I_1 = 69 \text{ A}$$

It follows that $I_2 = 170 - I_1 = 101$ A

The current distribution is, therefore, as illustrated in Fig. 2.42.

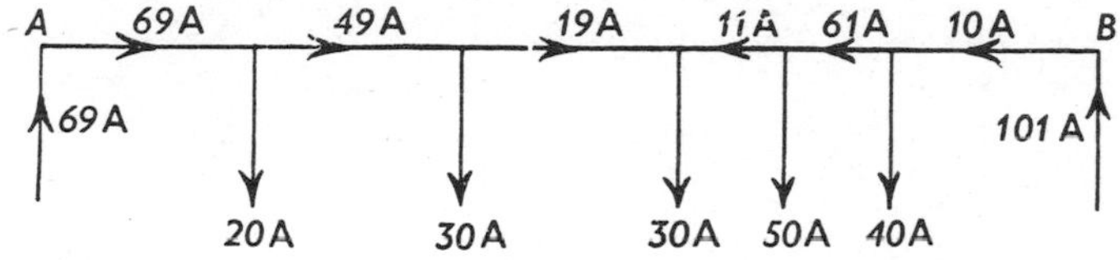

FIG. 2.42

PROBLEMS

1. A, B, C and D are four points in succession at equal distances along a wire. Points A and C and points B and D are also joined by two other similar wires of the same length as the distances between these pairs of points, measured along the original wire. Current enters the network, so formed, at A and leaves at D. Show that one-fifth of it passes along BC. [S.U.]

2. Five points are connected by ten wires, each pair being joined by a wire of the same resistance R. Show that the resistance of the network to current entering at one point and leaving at any other point is $2R/5$.

3. A network is made up of 13 ft of uniform wire, placed to form four equal squares side by side as shown in the diagram. Current enters the

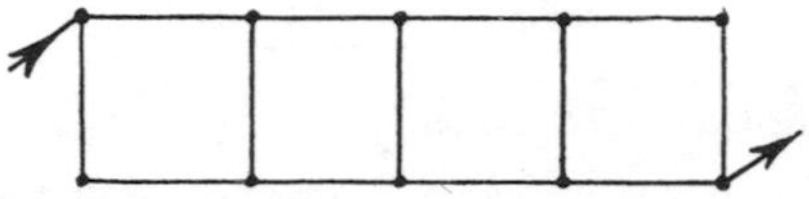

network at one extreme corner and leaves by the diagonally opposite corner. Use Maxwell's Cyclic-Current Rule to show that the total resistance of the network is equal to that of $2\frac{7}{19}$ ft of the wire. [S.U.]

4. A network is formed of uniform wire in the shape of a rectangle of sides $2a$ and $3a$ with parallel wires arranged so as to divide the internal space into six squares of side a, there being good contact at the points of intersection. Prove that if a current enters the framework by one corner and leaves it by the opposite corner, the equivalent resistance of the arrangement is the same as that of a length $121a/69$ of the wire. [S.U.]

5. By first using a delta-star transformation on the mesh $ABCD$ of the circuit shown, prove that the current supplied by the battery is 90/83 A. [S.U.]

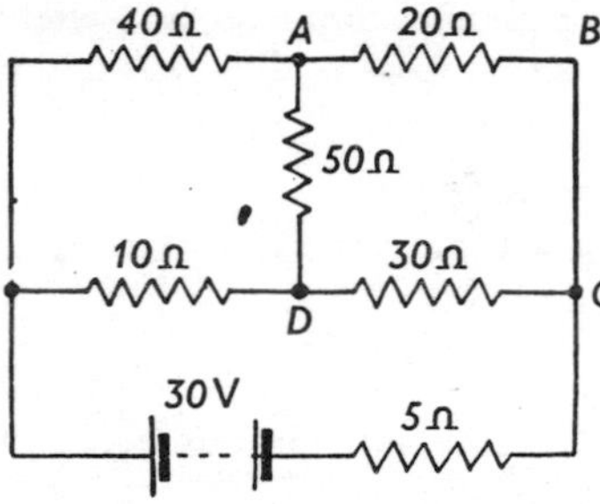

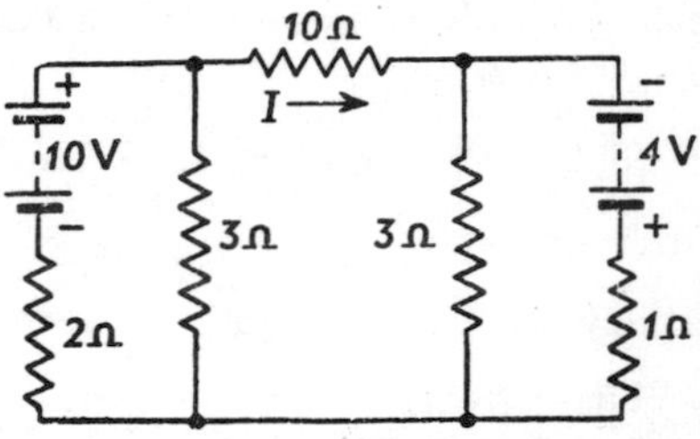

6. Use Thévenin's Theorem to find the current I in the circuit shown. [S.U.] [*Ans.* 0·753 A.]

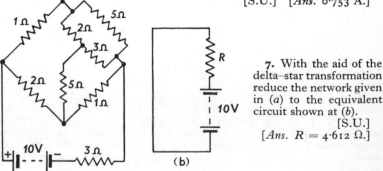

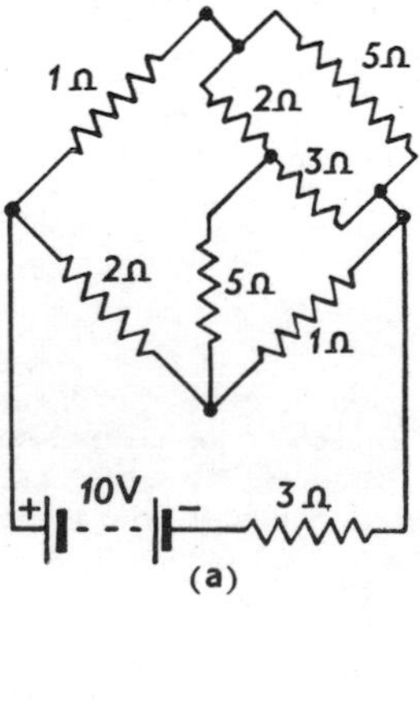

(a)

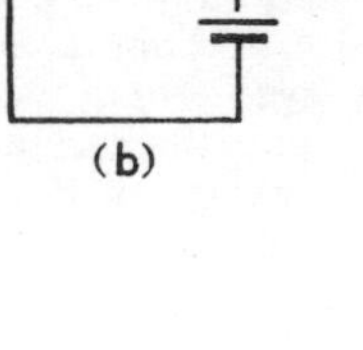

(b)

7. With the aid of the delta–star transformation reduce the network given in (*a*) to the equivalent circuit shown at (*b*). [S.U.] [*Ans.* $R = 4{\cdot}612$ Ω.]

8. In the circuit illustrated the values of the resistors in branches *EB* and *EC* are unknown. The ammeter in branch *EB*, however, reads

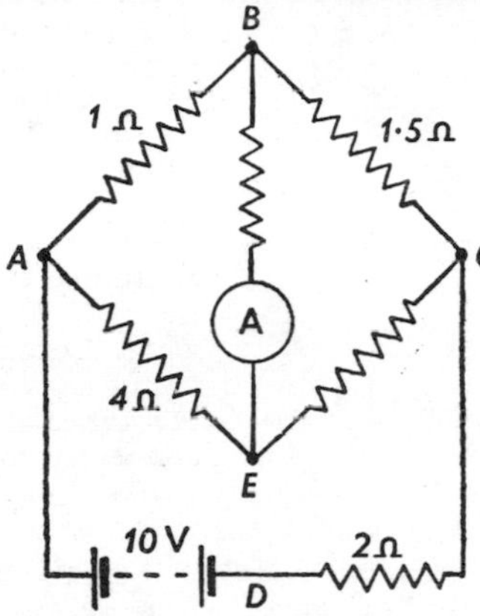

zero. Show that the resistance of branch *EC* is 6 Ω and that the current supplied by the battery is 2·5 A. [S.U.]

9. By the iterated use of Thévenin's Theorem reduce the circuit shown to a single e.m.f. acting in series with a single resistor. Hence, calculate the current in the 10 Ω resistor *XY*. [S.U.]

[*Ans.* 2·16 V, 1,062 Ω, 2·03 mA.]

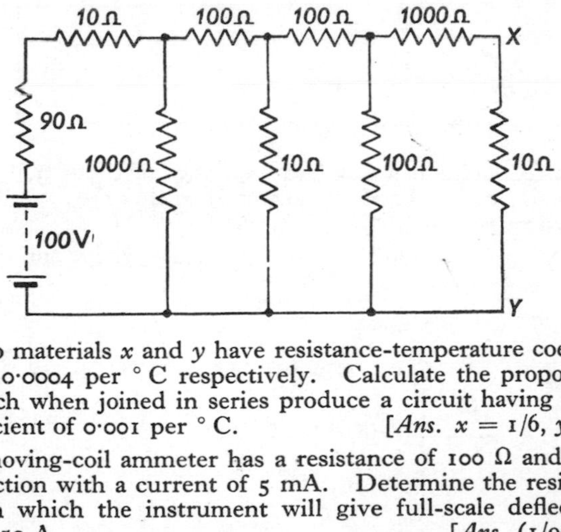

10. Two materials *x* and *y* have resistance-temperature coefficients of 0·004 and 0·0004 per ° C respectively. Calculate the proportions of *x* and *y* which when joined in series produce a circuit having a temperature coefficient of 0·001 per ° C. [*Ans.* $x = 1/6$, $y = 5/6$.]

11. A moving-coil ammeter has a resistance of 100 Ω and gives full-scale deflection with a current of 5 mA. Determine the resistance of a shunt with which the instrument will give full-scale deflection for a current of 50 A. [*Ans.* (1/99·99) Ω.]

12. A milliammeter gives full-scale deflection for a current of 20 mA and has a resistance of 15 Ω. What is the value of the resistor which must be put in series with the instrument if it is to be used as a voltmeter giving 200 V for full-scale deflection? [*Ans.* 9,985 Ω.]

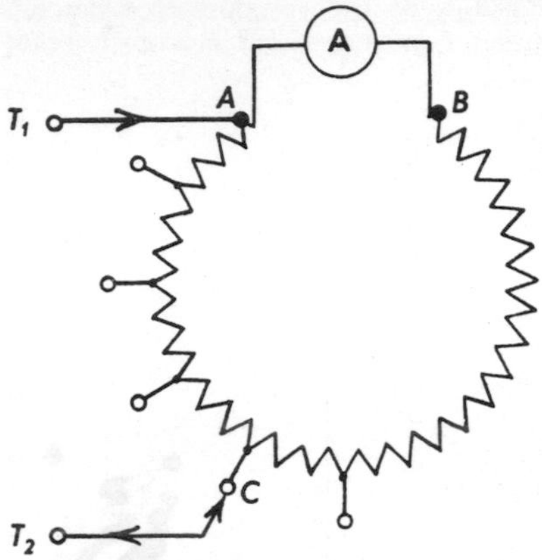

13. The arrangement shown in the diagram represents a Universal shunt. The instrument is connected to points A and B as shown and the outside circuit is connected to A and to variable point C. If the resistance between A and C is $1/n$ of the total resistance of the shunt show that the current through the circuit, when terminal T_2 is connected to C, for a given instrument current, is n times as large as when T_2 is connected to B.

14. The circuit diagram of a Kelvin Double Bridge for measuring very small resistances is illustrated in the figure. R is the resistance

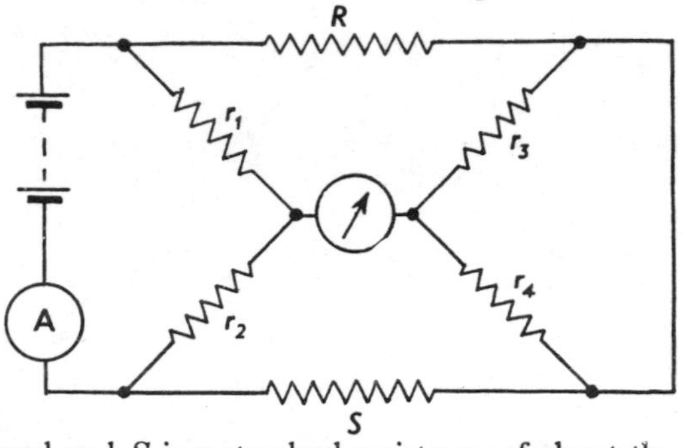

being measured and S is a standard resistance of about the same value. The resistors r_1, r_2, r_3 and r_4 are arranged so that $r_1/r_2 = r_3/r_4$. Prove that, at balance, $R/S = r_1/r_2$.

15. Use Thévenin's Theorem to replace the circuit shown at (*a*) by that of (*b*).

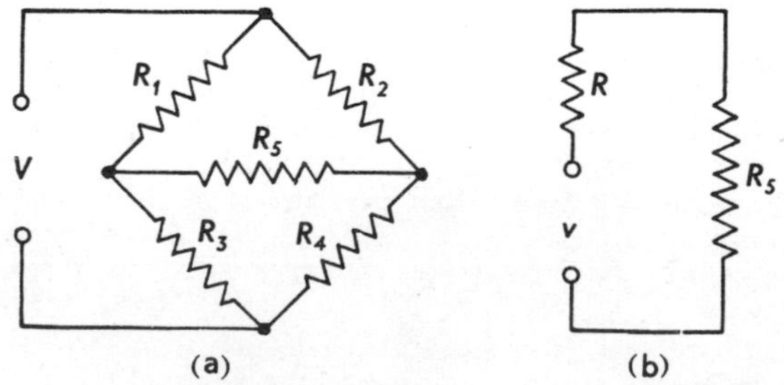

[*Ans.* $R = \{R_1R_3/(R_1 + R_3)\} + \{R_2R_4/(R_2 + R_4)\}$
$v = V\{R_3/(R_1 + R_3) - R_4/(R_2 + R_4)\}$.]

16. The bridge network illustrated balances at 10° C. The ambient temperature rises to 20° C, which brings about a change in P of $-0{\cdot}2\%/°$ C

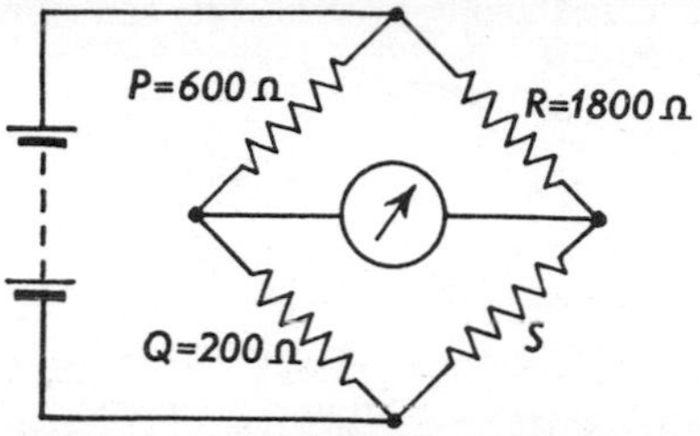

and in Q of $+0{\cdot}15\%/°$ C. The bridge is re-balanced at the new temperature by decreasing R to 1,764 Ω.

Calculate (*a*) the value of S at 10° C,

(*b*) the percentage change in S per ° C rise in temperature.

[*Ans.* (*a*) 600 Ω, (*b*) 0·167%/° C.]

17. An aluminium wire 10 m long and 2 mm diameter is connected in parallel with a copper wire 6 m long. A total current of 2 A is passed through the combination and 1·25 A goes through the aluminium wire. Determine the diameter of the copper wire. The resistivities of copper and aluminium are 1·6 and 2·6 microhms/cm cube, respectively.

[*Ans.* 0·94 mm.]

18. Two tramcars are respectively 2 miles and 5 miles from a 500 V substation which supplies them. The first takes a current of 50 A and the second 30 A. If the resistance of the trolley wire is 0·5 Ω/mile and of the rails 0·02 Ω/mile, evaluate the voltage across each car and the power lost in transmission. [*Ans.* 416·8 V, 370 V, 8,060 W.]

19. A circuit is made up as shown in the diagram. Find I_1, I_2 and I_3.

[S.U.] [*Ans.* $I_1 = 4{\cdot}07$ A, $I_2 = 1{\cdot}215$ A, $I_3 = 1{\cdot}085$ A.]

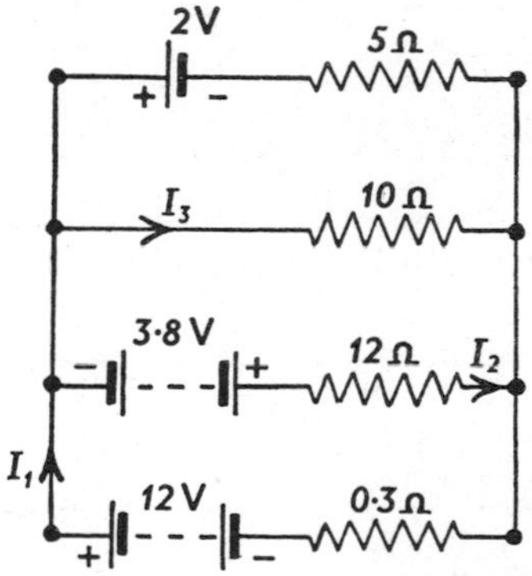

20. The insulation resistance of each of a pair of live mains to earth is determined by using a voltmeter of 80,000 Ω resistance. From the positive main to earth the voltmeter reads 80 V and from the negative main to earth the reading is 30 V. Between both mains the reading is 250 V. What is the resistance of each main to earth?

[*Ans.* 373,333 Ω, 140,000 Ω.]

21. A conductor in the shape of one-half the frustrum of a right-circular cone is illustrated. The parallel end faces have radii of 0·1 and 0·2 in. and the resistivity is $0{\cdot}005\pi$ Ω/in. cube. Prove that the resistance between A and B is 10 Ω.

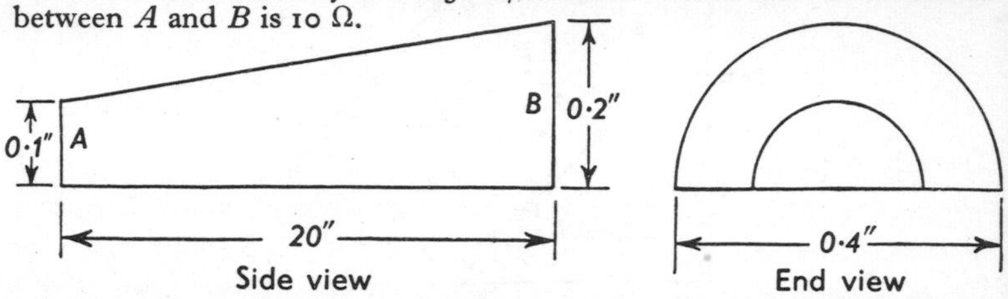

22. Use Thévenin's Theorem to calculate the current I in the circuit shown. [S.U.]

[*Ans.* 53·9 A.]

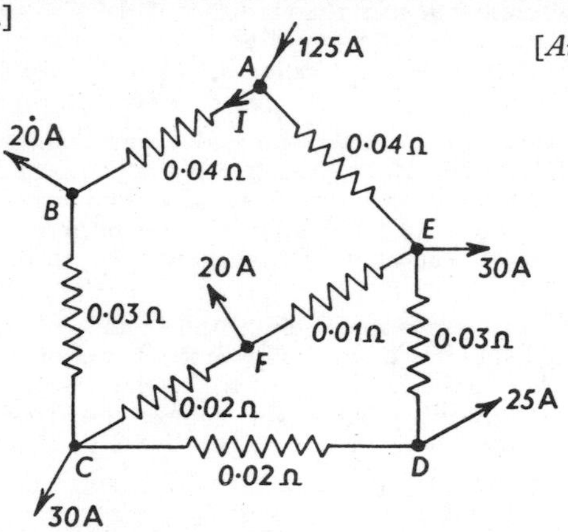

23. A two-wire distributor which is 400 yd long, and which is fed at one end, is loaded as follows:

Distance from feeding point (yd)	100	200	300	350	400
Load (A)	20	30	30	50	40

If the resistance/yard of the distributor is 10^{-4} Ω determine the total voltage drop. [*Ans.* 10·1 V.]

24. A distributor fed at both ends at the same voltage is loaded as shown in the diagram. Calculate the voltage drop from A to C if the resistance/yard is 0·0006 Ω.

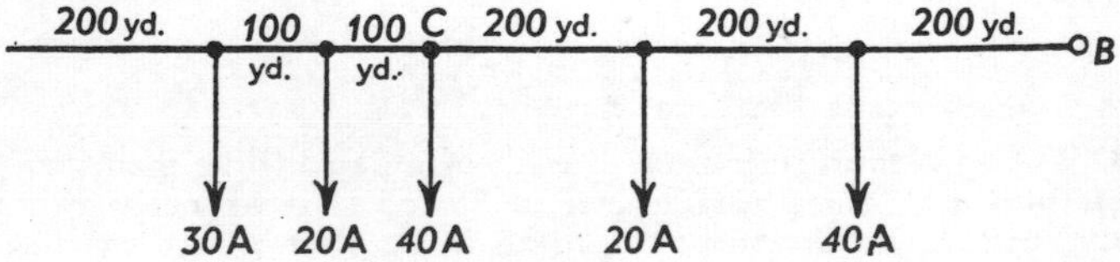

Repeat the problem if B is now supplied at 6 V above A.

[*Ans.* 13·92 V, 11·52 V.]

CHAPTER 3

SINGLE-PHASE A.C. CIRCUITS

Definition of alternating current

An alternating current is one which goes through a complete cycle of changes periodically and has positive and negative values as shown by the examples of Fig. 3.1. The average value of the current over a

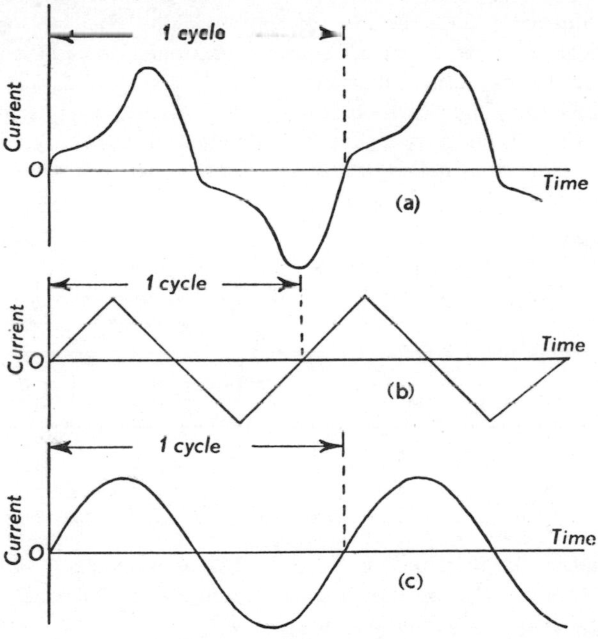

FIG. 3.1

complete cycle is zero. The graphs of Fig. 3.1, which represent the way in which the currents vary with time are called the *wave-shapes*. Normally, students of electrical engineering deal with wave-shapes which deviate little from a sine wave (Fig. 3.1 (*c*)) and often assume them to be perfectly sinusoidal. Frequently, too, the positive part of the wave covers exactly half a cycle and is symmetrical about its centre line (Fig. 3.1 (*c*)), the negative portion of the wave being a true repetition, with reversed sign, of the positive half-wave.

The time for a complete cycle is called the *periodic time* or simply the period (T).

The number of complete cycles per second is called the *frequency* and is usually denoted by the symbol f.

Thus, $f = \frac{1}{T}$ cycles/sec, or $T = \frac{1}{f}$ sec.

In this country the standard frequency is 50 cycles/sec for lighting and power distribution. Electrical engineers have to deal with a wide range of frequencies, however, from almost zero in some cases up to about 10^{11} cycles/sec for certain microwave applications. From now on cycles/sec will be abbreviated to c/s.

The simple alternator

The alternator is a simple rotating machine used to transform mechanical power to electrical power. Its operation is based on the laws of electromagnetic induction.

Consider the single-turn coil of Fig. 3.2 rotating at constant speed ω radians/sec about an axis perpendicular to a uniform magnetic field. The maximum flux linkage, represented by Φ_m, occurs when the coil

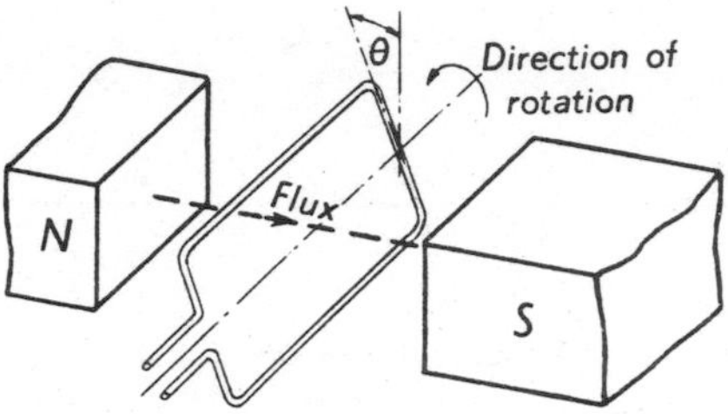

FIG. 3.2

is vertical. The flux linking the coil at an angular displacement θ is $\Phi = \Phi_m \cos \theta$. If time t is measured from the instant when the coil is vertical then $\theta = \omega t$, so $\Phi = \Phi_m \cos \omega t$.

The e.m.f. (e) induced in the coil is given by the Faraday–Lenz Law and equals $(-d\Phi/dt)$

$$\therefore \quad e = \omega\Phi_m \sin \omega t = E_m \sin \omega t \text{ where } E_m = \omega\Phi_m.$$

The induced voltage is therefore sinusoidal. In the alternators used in practice the conductors usually remain stationary in the frame or stator and the poles form the rotating element or rotor. The equations above apply to both cases.

Sinusoidal alternating currents

The sinusoidal waveform is taken as the standard form in electrical engineering. It is simple to deal with mathematically and, as shown in Chapter 10, any continuous periodic function may be represented by a series of sine waves of different frequencies.

Suppose the instantaneous current i varies with time t according to the law

$$i = I \sin \omega t$$

where I is the maximum value of the current and ω is a constant.

Draw a circle of radius OQ which represents to scale the maximum value of current I. Let OQ rotate with constant angular velocity ω radians/sec in an anti-clockwise direction (Fig. 3.3). Time will be

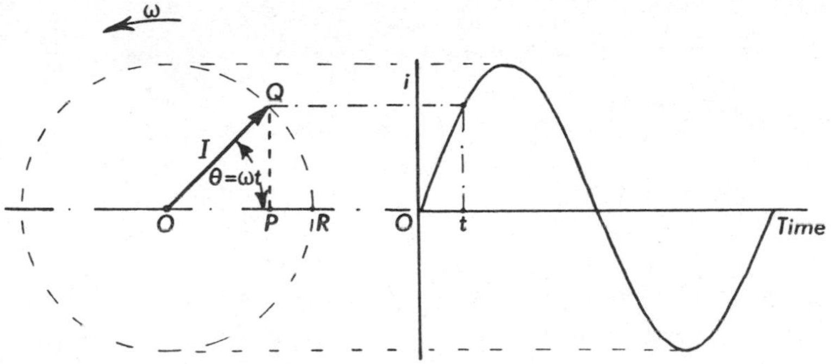

FIG. 3.3

measured from the instant when OQ was in the position OR. At time t the angle which OQ makes with OR is $\theta = \omega t$ radians. It will be seen that $QP = I \sin \omega t$. Thus QP represents the instantaneous current i, so that if values of t be plotted against the corresponding projections of OQ on the vertical, the sinusoidal form of the current will be traced out as illustrated. One revolution of OQ corresponds to one complete cycle of current. Since OQ makes $\omega/2\pi$ revolutions/sec it follows that $f = \omega/2\pi$ c/s, or the constant $\omega = 2\pi f$.

Thus, an alternating current of sinusoidal form is completely determined when the length, speed of rotation and direction at some instant of the corresponding line (or vector as it is called) are known. This vector method of representation gives a simple means of solving alternating-current problems. The remarks made about alternating currents, of course, also apply to alternating voltages or e.m.f.'s of sinusoidal form.

If, instead of measuring time from the instant when Q is at R (Fig. 3.3), it is measured from the point where Q is at R_1 (Fig. 3.4 (a)), then $QP = I \sin \theta = I \sin (\omega t + \phi_1)$. The angle part of this expression $(\omega t + \phi_1)$ is the phase at time t. In fact, the only difference between the two expressions for QP is in the phases. The angle ϕ_1 is this phase difference and is called the *phase angle.* When $t = 0$ in this case $QP = I \sin \phi_1$ and Q is $\phi_1/2\pi$ of a cycle beyond R so that a positive phase difference means a lead in phase.

Similarly, if time is measured from the point where Q is at R_2 (Fig. 3.4 (*b*)), $QP = I \sin (\omega t - \phi_2)$ and the phase angle is now a lagging one when compared with the original one.

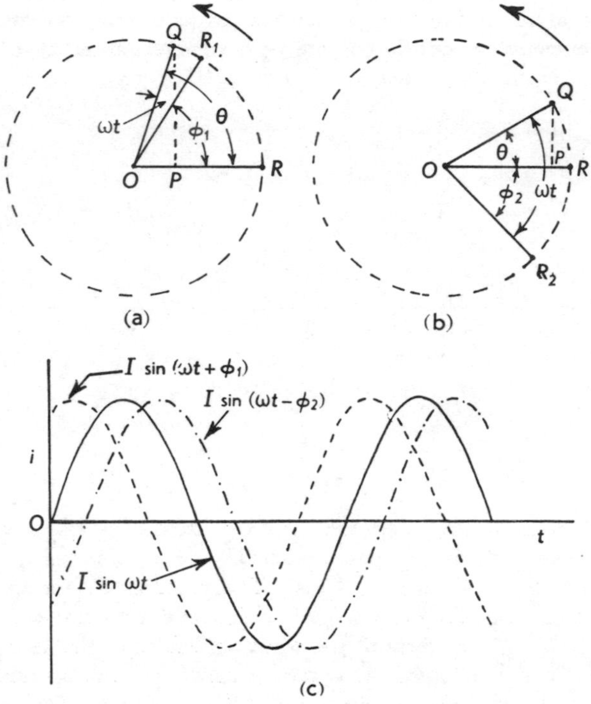

FIG. 3.4

The corresponding waveforms for the three cases are shown in Fig. 3.4 (*c*). The effects of having leading and lagging phase angles can be clearly seen.

If two or more sinusoidal alternating quantities, with identical frequencies, are added together, their resultant is also a sinusoidal quantity, having the same frequency as that of the components. Consider the case of two sinusoidal currents represented by $i_1 = I_1 \sin \omega t$ and $i_2 = I_2 \sin (\omega t - \phi)$.

The sum of these is $i_1 + i_2$

$$= I_1 \sin \omega t + I_2 \sin (\omega t - \phi)$$
$$= (I_1 + I_2 \cos \phi) \sin \omega t - I_2 \sin \phi \cos \omega t$$

Write $a = I_1 + I_2 \cos \phi$ and $b = I_2 \sin \phi$, then

$$i_1 + i_2 = a \sin \omega t - b \cos \omega t$$
$$= \sqrt{a^2 + b^2}\, \{(a/\sqrt{a^2 + b^2}) \sin \omega t - (b/\sqrt{a^2 + b^2}) \cos \omega t\}$$
$$= \sqrt{a^2 + b^2}\, \{\sin \omega t \cos \theta - \cos \omega t \sin \theta\}$$

where $\tan \theta = b/a$.

i.e. $i_1 + i_2 = \sqrt{a^2 + b^2} \sin (\omega t - \theta) = I \sin (\omega t - \theta)$ which shows that the resultant is sinusoidal. The amplitude of the resultant is $I = \sqrt{a^2 + b^2}$

$$= \sqrt{(I_1 + I_2 \cos \phi)^2 + (I_2 \sin \phi)^2} = \sqrt{I_1{}^2 + 2I_1I_2 \cos \phi + I_2{}^2}$$

Vector addition and subtraction

In solving alternating-current problems it is, in many of them, very convenient to employ vectors to represent alternating quantities. The laws of addition and subtraction applying to vectors will be briefly considered. For example, alternating voltages can be represented by vectors and can therefore be added together in the same way as several forces acting at a point. Thus, if only two voltages are to be added the resultant voltage is given by a parallelogram, or triangle, of voltages. For more than two voltages, the resultant voltage is represented by the closing side of a vector polygon. To subtract one voltage $\mathbf{E}_1$, from another $\mathbf{E}_2$, it is necessary to reverse $\mathbf{E}_1$ and then add it to $\mathbf{E}_2$ for $\mathbf{E}_2 - \mathbf{E}_1 = \mathbf{E}_2 + (-\mathbf{E}_1)$. [*Note.* Heavy type is used here to indicate vector quantities. (See Chapter 5.)]

EXAMPLE. An e.m.f. $e_1 = 60 \sin \omega t$ and an e.m.f. $e_2 = 30 \sin (\omega t - \pi/6)$ act together in the same circuit. Find the resultant e.m.f. graphically and by calculation.

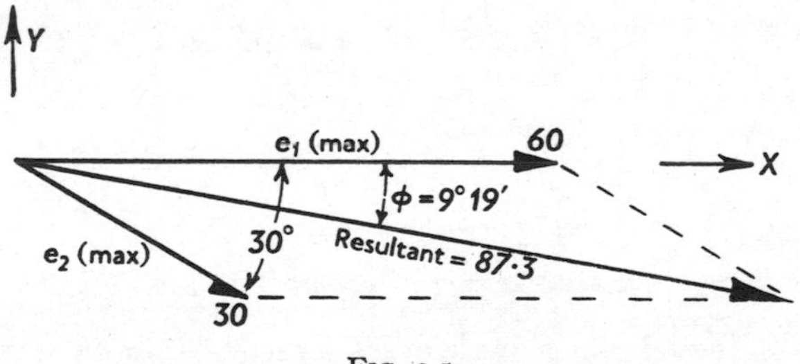

FIG. 3.5

Solution. Fig. 3.5 demonstrates the graphical solution, which is self-explanatory. Resolving the e.m.f.'s in the X and Y directions at right-angles:

$$X = 60 + 30 \cos 30° = 85{\cdot}98$$
$$Y = 0 - 30 \sin 30° = -15$$

The magnitude of the resultant

$$= \sqrt{X^2 + Y^2} = \sqrt{85{\cdot}98^2 + 15^2} = \underline{87{\cdot}3}$$

[Note that this is $\sqrt{60^2 + 2 \times 60 \times 30 \cos(\pi/6) + 30^2}$ as shown previously.]

$$\tan\phi = Y/X = -\ 15/85{\cdot}98 \text{ so } \phi = -\ \underline{9^\circ\ 19'}$$

The resultant e.m.f. is therefore $\underline{87{\cdot}3 \sin(\omega t - 9^\circ\ 19')}$ *

This result could also have been obtained by drawing out the waveforms for e_1 and e_2 as in Fig. 3.3 and adding them together at various values of time, t to plot the resultant curve.

EXAMPLE. The total e.m.f. acting in a circuit is $e_1 = 60 \sin \omega t$. The voltage drop in one part of the circuit is $e_2 = 30 \sin(\omega t - \pi/6)$. Find the voltage drop in the rest of the circuit graphically and by calculation.

Solution. Fig. 3.6 shows the graphical solution, which is self-explanatory.

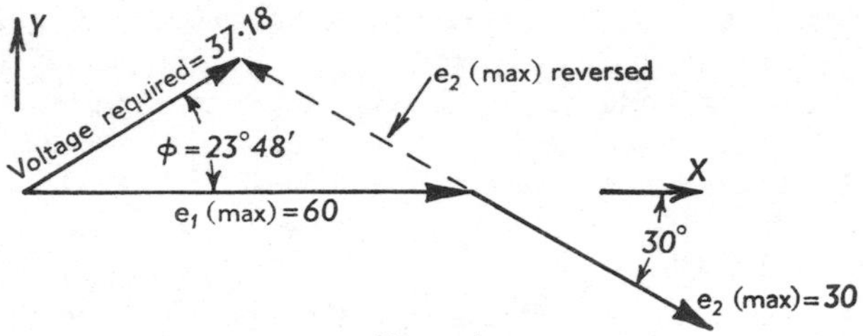

FIG. 3.6

Resolving the e.m.f.'s in the X-and Y directions:

$$X = 60 - 30 \cos 30^\circ = 34{\cdot}02$$
$$Y = 30 \sin 30^\circ = 15$$

The magnitude of the resultant

$$= \sqrt{X^2 + Y^2} = \sqrt{(34{\cdot}02)^2 + (15)^2} = 37{\cdot}18$$
$$\tan\phi = Y/X = 15/34{\cdot}02 \text{ so } \phi = 23^\circ\ 48'$$

Thus, the voltage required is $\underline{37{\cdot}18 \sin(\omega t + 23^\circ\ 48')}$

EXAMPLE. The following four e.m.f.'s act together in the same circuit

$$e_1 = 50 \sin \omega t \qquad e_3 = 20 \sin(\omega t - \pi/6)$$
$$e_2 = 40 \sin(\omega t + \pi/3) \qquad e_4 = 30 \sin(\omega t + 3\pi/4)$$

Find the resultant e.m.f. graphically and by calculation.

* Strictly speaking this should read $87{\cdot}3 \sin(\omega t - 0{\cdot}163)$, the whole angle being expressed in radians. However, the form given is convenient and will be used frequently.

Solution. The graphical solution shown in Fig. 3.7 is self-explanatory.

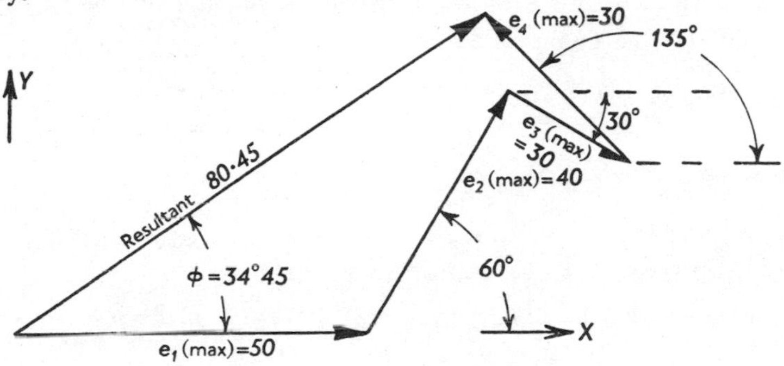

FIG. 3.7

Resolving the e.m.f.'s in the X and Y directions:

$$X = 50 + 40 \cos 60° + 20 \cos 30° - 30 \cos 45° = 66{\cdot}1$$

$$Y = 0 + 40 \sin 60° - 20 \sin 30° + 30 \sin 45° = 45{\cdot}85$$

$$\therefore \quad \text{resultant e.m.f.} = \sqrt{X^2 + Y^2} = \sqrt{(66{\cdot}1)^2 + (45{\cdot}85)^2} = 80{\cdot}45$$

$$\tan \phi = Y/X = 45{\cdot}85/66{\cdot}1, \text{ so } \phi = 34° \, 45'$$

$$\therefore \quad \text{resultant e.m.f.} = 80{\cdot}45 \sin (\omega t + 34° \, 45')$$

EXAMPLE. Using the same four e.m.f.'s as in the previous example calculate and determine graphically the e.m.f. represented by $e_1 - e_4 + e_3 - e_2$.

Solution. The graphical solution is self-explanatory from Fig. 3.8.

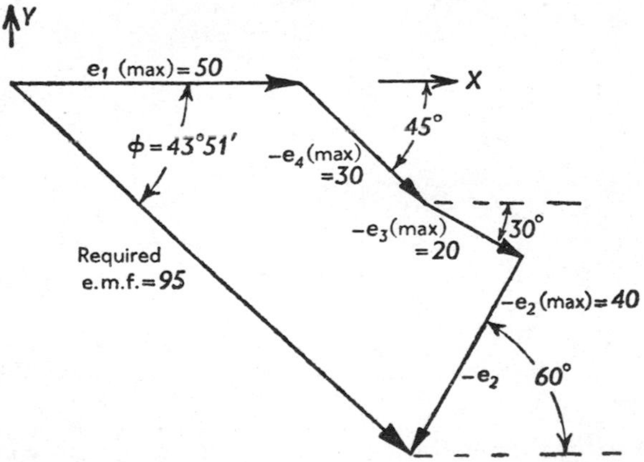

FIG. 3.8

Resolving the e.m.f.'s in the X and Y directions,

$$X = 50 + 20 \cos 30^\circ - 40 \cos 60^\circ + 30 \cos 45^\circ = 68{\cdot}55$$
$$Y = -40 \sin 60^\circ - 20 \sin 30^\circ - 30 \sin 45^\circ = -65{\cdot}85$$

$$\therefore \quad \text{e.m.f. required} = \sqrt{X^2 + Y^2} = \sqrt{(68{\cdot}55)^2 + (65{\cdot}85)^2} = 95$$
$$\tan \phi = Y/X = -65{\cdot}85/68{\cdot}55, \text{ so } \phi = -43^\circ\ 51'$$

Thus, required e.m.f. $= \underline{95 \sin (\omega t - 43^\circ\ 51')}$

Potential difference required to send a sine-wave alternating current through a non-inductive resistor

Let the current be $i = I \sin \omega t$ and the value of the resistance R ohms (Fig. 3.9).

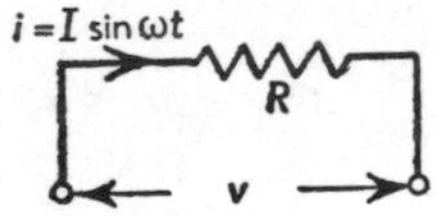

FIG. 3.9

The instantaneous value of the potential difference across $R = v = iR = RI \sin \omega t$ volts.

i.e. $\quad v = V \sin \omega t$ volts

where $\quad V = IR$

Thus, the potential difference v is also of sine-wave form. The current and voltage waves are illustrated in Fig. 3.10. They pass

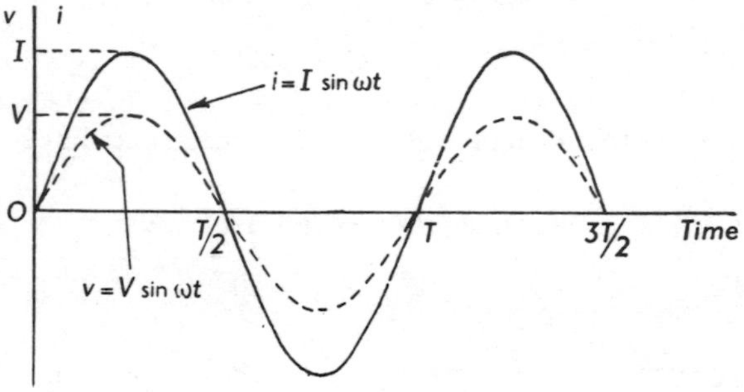

FIG. 3.10

through zero at the same instant and reach their maximum values simultaneously. They are said to be *in phase*, or *co-phasal*. The vector diagram for the arrangement is shown in Fig. 3.11.

FIG. 3.11

Potential difference required to send a sine-wave alternating current through an inductance coil of negligibly-small resistance

Let the self-inductance of the coil be L henrys. When a current of i amps flows in the coil and is varying at a rate di/dt, an e.m.f. of

$-L\,di/dt$ volts is developed and tends to oppose the current variation. If $i = I \sin \omega t$, the e.m.f., $e = -L\,di/dt = -LI\omega \cos \omega t$ volts.

Since the direction of the e.m.f. at any instant is in opposition to the current variation at that instant, then in order to force the current to change according to $I \sin \omega t$, a potential difference must be applied to the coil so as to be exactly equal and opposite to e.

$\therefore$ the applied potential difference $= v = -e = LI\omega \cos \omega t$ volts.

i.e. $v = V \cos \omega t$ volts

where $V = (L\omega)I.$

The quantity $L\omega$ is called the inductive reactance of the coil and is measured in ohms. It is not a constant but varies with frequency.

The current and voltage waves are illustrated in Fig. 3.12.

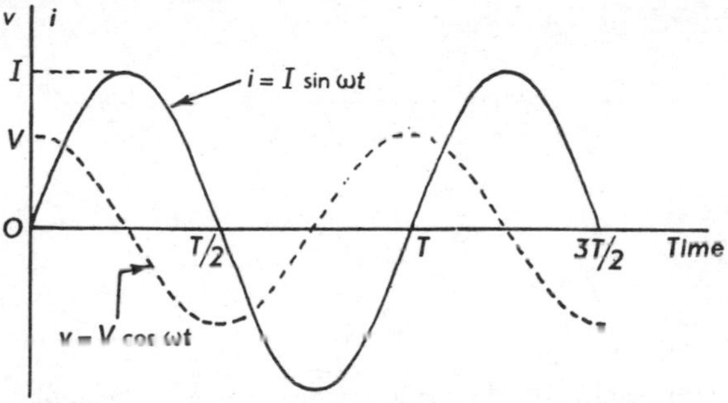

FIG. 3.12

The current attains its maximum positive value 90° later than the applied voltage.

The current is said to *lag* the applied voltage by 90°.

The vector diagram is shown in Fig. 3.13.

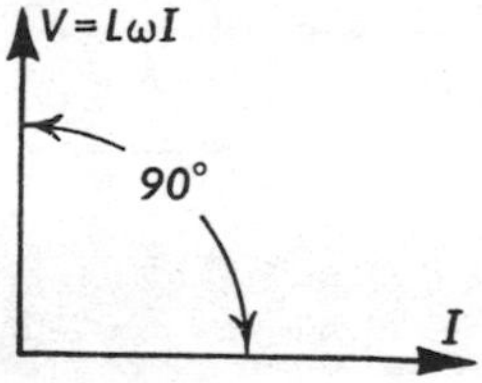

FIG. 3.13

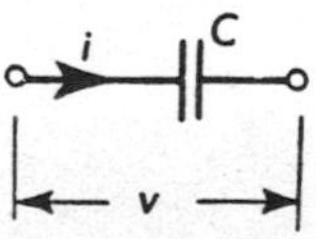

FIG. 3.14

Alternating current through a capacitor due to an applied sinusoidal voltage

Let the applied voltage v of Fig. 3.14 be $-V \cos \omega t$ volts and let the capacitance of the capacitor be C farads. If at time t the quantity of charge on the capacitor is q, then the potential difference across the plates of the capacitor is $v = q/C$

$$\therefore \quad i = dq/dt = C\, dv/dt = CV\omega \sin \omega t \text{ amps}$$

i.e. $\quad i = I \sin \omega t$ amps

where $\quad I = \omega CV$ or $V = I(1/\omega C)$

The quantity $(1/\omega C)$ is termed the capacitive reactance and is measured in ohms. It varies with frequency. The current and voltage waves are illustrated in Fig. 3.15.

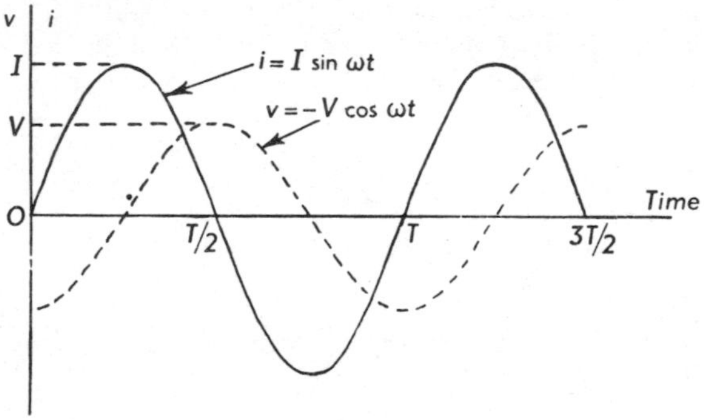

FIG. 3.15

The current reaches its maximum value 90° before the applied voltage, *i.e.* the current *leads* the applied voltage by 90°.

The vector diagram is shown in Fig. 3.16.

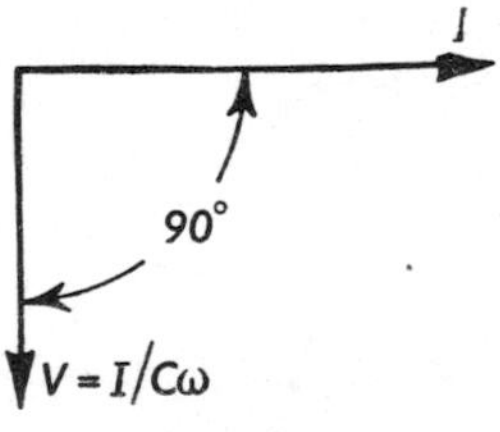

FIG. 3.16

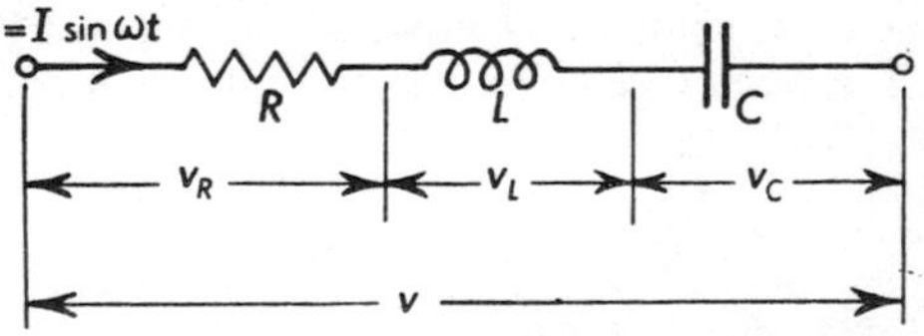

FIG. 3.17

Potential difference required to send a sine-wave alternating current through a resistor, inductor and capacitor in series

Referring to the circuit of Fig. 3.17,

$$v_R = IR \sin \omega t \text{ volts}$$

$$v_L = IL\omega \cos \omega t \text{ volts}$$

$$v_C = (-I/\omega C) \cos \omega t \text{ volts}$$

Now $v = v_R + v_L + v_C = I\left[R \sin \omega t + \left(L\omega - \frac{1}{\omega C}\right) \cos \omega t\right]$ volts

i.e. $$v = I\sqrt{R^2 + \left(L\omega - \frac{1}{\omega C}\right)^2}\left[\frac{R}{\sqrt{R^2 + \left(L\omega - \frac{1}{\omega C}\right)^2}} \sin \omega t + \frac{L\omega - \frac{1}{\omega C}}{\sqrt{R^2 + \left(L\omega - \frac{1}{\omega C}\right)^2}} \cos \omega t\right] \text{ volts}$$

$\therefore \quad v = IZ \sin (\omega t + \phi)$ volts

where $Z = \sqrt{R^2 + \left(L\omega - \frac{1}{\omega C}\right)^2}$ and $\tan \phi = \dfrac{\left(L\omega - \frac{1}{\omega C}\right)}{R}$

Thus, $v = V \sin (\omega t + \phi)$ volts

where $V = ZI$

The quantity Z is termed the impedance of the circuit and is measured in ohms. $\left(L\omega - \frac{1}{\omega C}\right)$ is called the reactance and is denoted by X. It may be inductive, zero or capacitive depending on the relative magnitudes of $L\omega$ and $1/\omega C$.

Thus, if a sinusoidal alternating current flows in a series circuit, the applied voltage is also sinusoidal but is displaced in phase relative to the current by an angle ϕ. If $L\omega > 1/\omega C$, the current lags the applied voltage, whereas if $L\omega < 1/\omega C$ the current leads the applied voltage. When $L\omega = 1/\omega C$ the current and voltage are in phase. This is an important special case and will be considered in detail later.

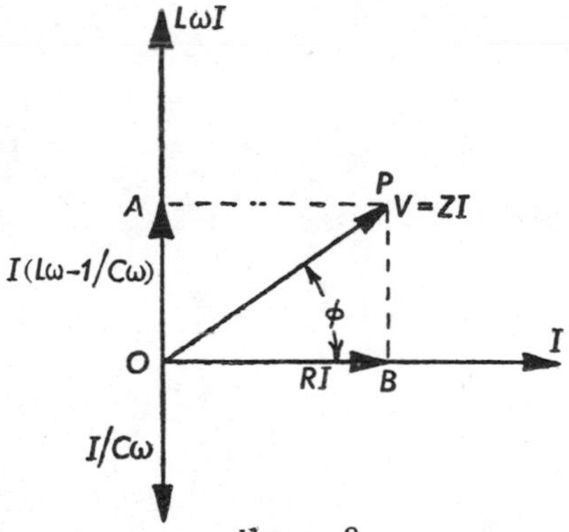

FIG. 3.18

The vector diagram for the series-connected circuit is shown in Fig. 3.18. The current, which is the same for all the elements of the series circuit, is used as a reference and starting point.

From ΔOPB of the vector diagram,

$$OP^2 = OB^2 + PB^2$$

i.e. $$V^2 = I^2\left\{R^2 + \left(L\omega - \frac{1}{\omega C}\right)^2\right\}$$

or $$I = V\Big/\sqrt{R^2 + \left(L\omega - \frac{1}{\omega C}\right)^2}$$

Also $$\tan\phi = PB/OB = (L\omega - 1/\omega C)/R$$

These expressions have already been developed.

Two special cases are illustrated by the vector diagrams of Fig. 3.19;

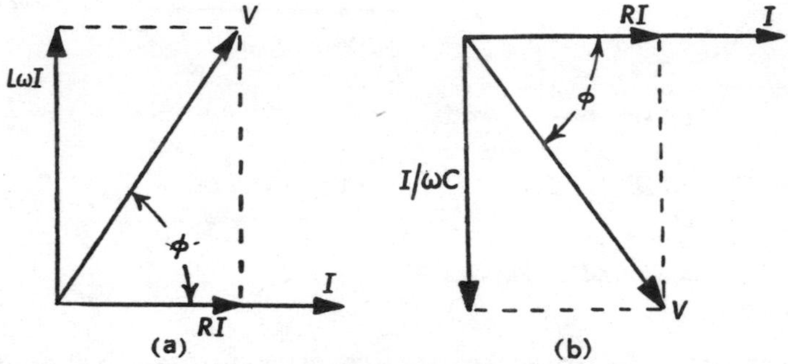

FIG. 3.19

in case (*a*) no capacitance is present, in case (*b*) there is no inductance.

For Fig. 3.19 (*a*), $$V = I\sqrt{R^2 + L^2\omega^2}$$
$$Z = \sqrt{R^2 + L^2\omega^2}$$
$$\tan\phi = L\omega/R$$
I lags V

For Fig. 3.19 (*b*), $$V = I\sqrt{R^2 + \frac{1}{\omega^2C^2}}$$
$$Z = \sqrt{R^2 + \frac{1}{\omega^2C^2}}$$
$$\tan\phi = 1/\omega CR$$
I leads V

EXAMPLE. An a.c. circuit *ABCD* consists of a resistor *AB*, an inductor *BC* and a resistor *CD*, connected in series across a 200 V, 50 c/s supply. The current flowing is 10 A.

The voltages are as follows:

Across *AB* 80 V

Across *BC* 100 V

Across *AC* 145 V

Draw a voltage vector diagram and determine (*a*) the voltage across *BD*, (*b*) the inductance and resistance of the inductor, (*c*) the phase angle between the current flowing and the applied voltage. [S.U.]

Solution. The vector diagram is shown in Fig. 3.20 and is self-explanatory.

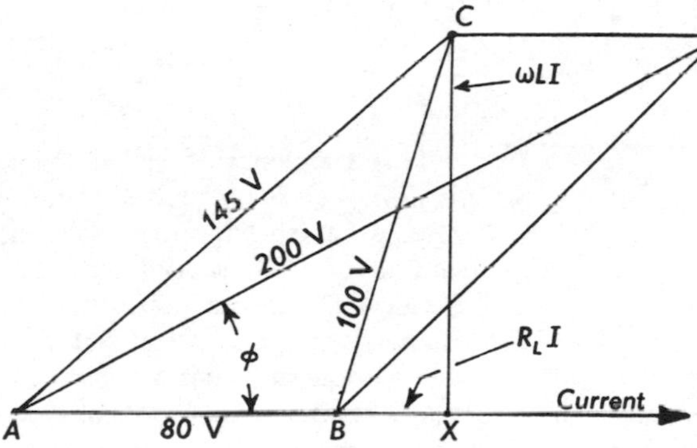

FIG. 3.20

The voltage across $BC = 100$ V $= 10\sqrt{R_L^2 + \omega^2 L^2}$ . . . (3.1)

where R_L and L are the resistance and inductance of the inductor respectively and $\omega = 2\pi \times$ frequency.

The voltage across $AC = 145$ V $= 10\sqrt{(8 + R_L)^2 + \omega^2 L^2}$ (3.2)

since the resistance of AB is evidently 8 Ω.

From (3.1) and (3.2) $R_L = \underline{2{\cdot}89\ \Omega}$ and $L = \underline{0{\cdot}0305\ \text{H}}$.

For the whole circuit,

$$200\ \text{V} = 10\sqrt{(8 + R_L + R_{CD})^2 + \omega^2 L^2} \quad . \quad . \quad (3.3)$$

where R_{CD} is the resistance of element CD.

Putting the values of R_L, L and ω in (3.3) it is found that $R_{CD} = 6{\cdot}7\ \Omega$ and so the voltage across $CD = 67$ V.

Thus, referring to the vector diagram:

$$\cos\phi = \frac{AB + BX + CD}{200} = \frac{80 + 28{\cdot}9 + 67}{200} = \frac{175{\cdot}9}{200}$$

$\underline{\text{so } \phi = 28^\circ\ 25'}$

Also, $BD^2 = CX^2 + (BX + CD)^2 = 18{,}380$

and $\underline{BD = 135{\cdot}6\ \text{V}}$

Series resonance

It has been shown that when $L\omega = 1/\omega C$ in a series LCR circuit the current and the applied voltage are in phase. This can be seen clearly from the vector diagram of Fig. 3.21 for this special case.

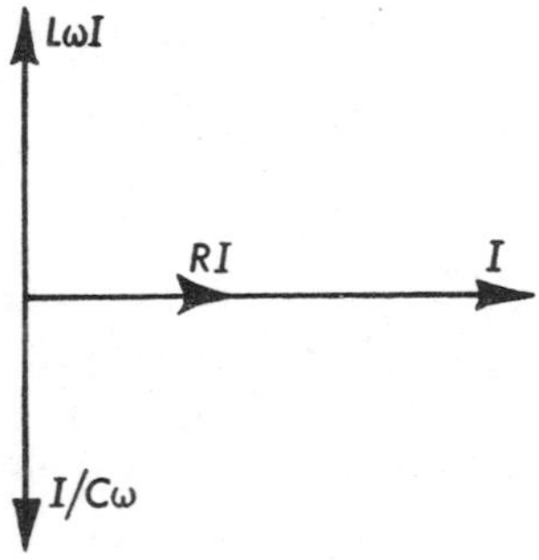

FIG. 3.21

If $$L\omega = 1/\omega C$$
$$\omega = 1/\sqrt{LC}$$
and $$f = 1/2\pi\sqrt{LC}$$

This frequency is called the *resonant frequency* of the circuit. If the applied voltage has this frequency the circuit is said to be in *resonance* with the supply frequency. Under these conditions, the applied voltage is RI and if R is small, the current may attain a very high value for a moderate value of voltage. The maximum values of the voltages across the inductance and capacitance may be many times greater than the maximum value of the applied voltage to the whole series circuit. Series resonance is discussed further in Chapter 14.

EXAMPLE. A circuit consisting of a coil having an inductance of 0·3 H and a resistance of 4 Ω is arranged in series with a capacitor of capacitance 30 μF. Calculate at what frequency resonance will take place and what current will flow if an alternating voltage of 50 V at the resonant frequency is applied to the circuit. Find also the voltage across the capacitor.

Solution. For resonance $f = 1/2\pi\sqrt{LC} =$

$$1/2\pi\sqrt{0{\cdot}3 \times 30 \times 10^{-6}} = \underline{53 \text{ c/s}}$$

At the resonant frequency the current flowing $I = V/R = 50/4 =$ $\underline{12{\cdot}5 \text{ A}}$

The voltage across the capacitor

$$= V_C = I/C\omega = 12{\cdot}5/(30 \times 10^{-6} \times 2\pi \times 53)$$

i.e. $$\underline{V_C = 1{,}251 \text{ V}}$$

Alternating-current circuits in parallel

Consider the particular parallel circuit of Fig. 3.22.

In the case of a series circuit, current is the factor which is common to all elements, but in a parallel circuit, voltage is the common factor. It is convenient therefore to use voltage as a basis of calculation and as the reference in vector diagrams.

For the circuit of Fig. 3.22 let $v = V \sin \omega t$ volts.

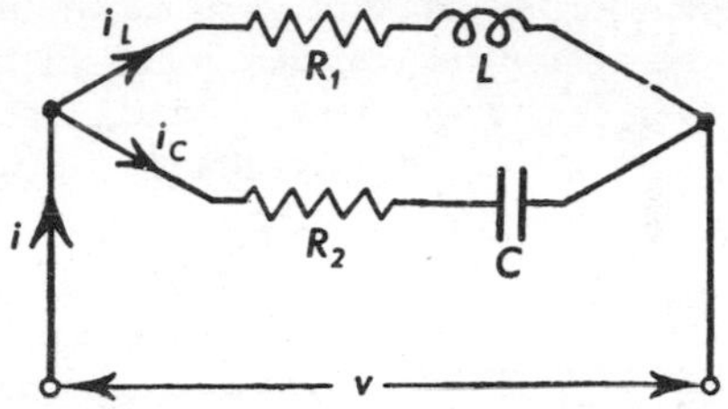

FIG. 3.22

Then regarding each branch separately,

$$i_L = \frac{V}{\sqrt{R_1^2 + \omega^2 L^2}} \sin(\omega t - \phi_1) = \frac{V}{Z_1} \sin(\omega t - \phi_1)$$

where $Z_1 = \sqrt{R_1^2 + \omega^2 L^2}$, $\tan \phi_1 = \dfrac{\omega L}{R_1}$, $\cos \phi_1 = \dfrac{R_1}{Z_1}$, $\sin \phi_1 = \dfrac{\omega L}{Z_1}$

and $$i_C = \frac{V}{\sqrt{R_2^2 + (1/\omega C)^2}} \sin(\omega t + \phi_2) = \frac{V}{Z_2} \sin(\omega t + \phi_2)$$

where $Z_2 = \sqrt{R_2^2 + (1/\omega C)^2}$,

$$\tan \phi_2 = \frac{1}{\omega C R_2},\ \cos \phi_2 = \frac{R_2}{Z_2},\ \sin \phi_2 = (1/\omega C)/Z_2$$

$$\therefore\quad i = i_C + i_L = V\left[\frac{1}{Z_2} \sin(\omega t + \phi_2) + \frac{1}{Z_1} \sin(\omega t - \phi_1)\right] \text{ amps}$$

i.e. $$i = V\left[\left(\frac{\cos \phi_1}{Z_1} + \frac{\cos \phi_2}{Z_2}\right) \sin \omega t - \left(\frac{\sin \phi_1}{Z_1} - \frac{\sin \phi_2}{Z_2}\right) \cos \omega t\right]$$

or $$i = V\left[\left(\frac{R_1}{Z_1^2} + \frac{R_2}{Z_2^2}\right) \sin \omega t - \left(\frac{L\omega}{Z_1^2} - \frac{1/\omega C}{Z_2^2}\right) \cos \omega t\right]$$

$$\therefore\quad i = V[A \sin \omega t - B \cos \omega t]$$

where $$A = \left(\frac{R_1}{Z_1^2} + \frac{R_2}{Z_2^2}\right)$$

and $$B = \left(\frac{L\omega}{Z_1^2} - \frac{1/\omega C}{Z_2^2}\right)$$

Then $$i = V\sqrt{A^2 + B^2}\left[\frac{A \sin \omega t}{\sqrt{A^2 + B^2}} - \frac{B \cos \omega t}{\sqrt{A^2 + B^2}}\right]$$

$$= V\sqrt{A^2 + B^2} \sin(\omega t - \phi) = I \sin(\omega t - \phi)$$

where $$I = V\sqrt{A^2 + B^2}$$

and $$\tan \phi = B/A$$

The vector diagram for the arrangement is shown in Fig. 3.23.

It is seen from this vector diagram that, when R_1 and R_2 are small and $L\omega = 1/\omega C$, then the two currents I_L and I_C are such that the resultant current is small (see Chapter 14).

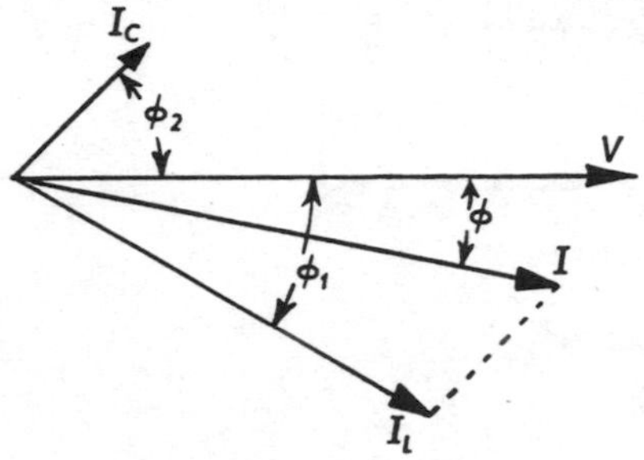

FIG. 3.23

EXAMPLE. Three circuits A, B and C are connected in parallel across a 200 V a.c. supply. Circuit A consists of a bank of lamps taking a current of 10 A. The lamps are non-inductive. Circuit B consists of an inductive resistor taking a current of 20 A which lags the applied voltage by 36° 52′ and C consists of a resistor and capacitor in series taking a current of 10 A which leads the applied voltage by 25° 50′.

Find the current supplied to the whole circuit and the phase-angle difference between it and the applied voltage. Sketch the complete vector diagram for the arrangement.

Solution. The vector diagram, which is self-explanatory, is shown in Fig. 3.24.

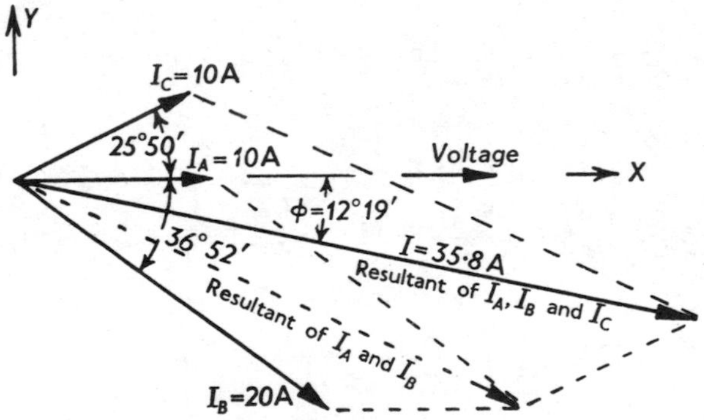

FIG. 3.24

Resolving the three current vectors in the X and Y directions shown gives

$$X = 10 + 10 \cos 25^\circ\, 50' + 20 \cos 36^\circ\, 52' = 35$$
$$Y = 10 \sin 25^\circ\, 50' - 20 \sin 36^\circ\, 52' = -7{\cdot}643$$

$\therefore$ resultant current $I = \sqrt{35^2 + 7{\cdot}643^2} = \underline{35{\cdot}8 \text{ A}}$

and $\tan\phi = Y/X = -7{\cdot}643/35$, so $\phi = \underline{-12^\circ\, 19'}$

EXAMPLE. A coil having a resistance of 1 Ω and a reactance of 1 Ω is shunted by a resistance of 1 Ω. The combination is connected in series with an inductive reactance of 1 Ω. Draw to scale a complete vector diagram for the arrangement and determine the applied voltage necessary to give a current of 1 A in the coil and show that it leads this current by 90°. [S.U.]

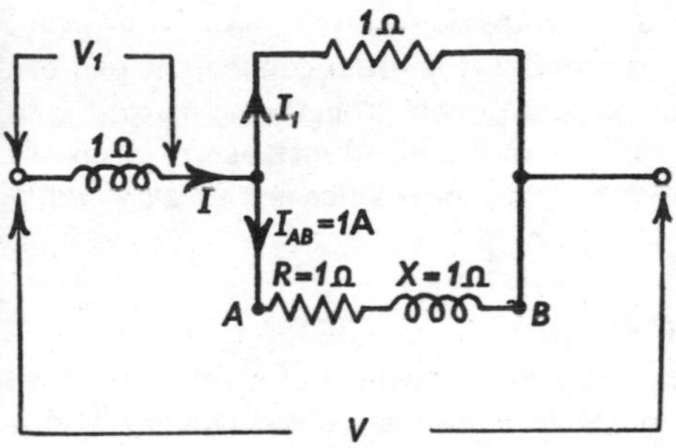

FIG. 3.25

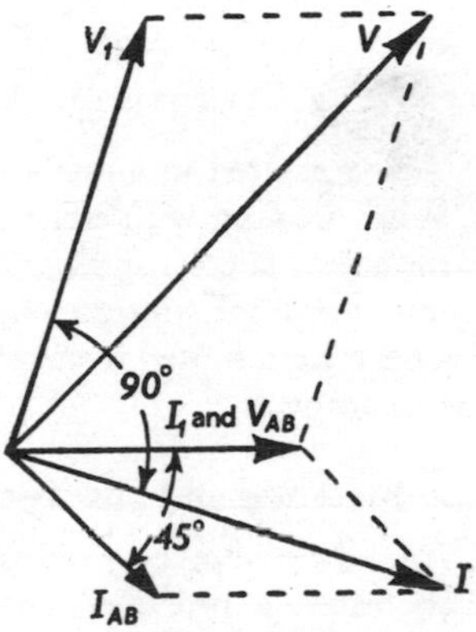

FIG. 3.26

Solution. The voltage across the coil V_{AB} (Fig. 3.25) $= 1\sqrt{1^2 + 1^2} = \sqrt{2}$ volts.

This voltage leads the current I_{AB} by 45°.

Current I_1 is therefore $\sqrt{2}$ A in phase with V_{AB}.

Current I is the vector sum of I_1 and I_{AB} and voltage $V_1 = 1 \times I$. V is the vector sum of V_1 and V_{AB}. The vector diagram is therefore as shown in Fig. 3.26. V is found to be 3 volts and leads I_{AB} by 90°.

Admittance

It was shown in Chapter 2, that if a number of resistors having resistances $R_1, R_2, R_3 \ldots R_n$ are connected in series, the total resistance R of the circuit is the sum of the separate resistances, *i.e.* $R = R_1 + R_2 + R_3 + \ldots + R_n$. If the resistors are replaced by impedors, the total impedance Z is the sum of the separate impedances, *i.e.* $Z = Z_1 + Z_2 + Z_3 + \ldots + Z_n$. In this case the addition has, of course, to be performed *vectorially*.

For resistors in parallel, the reciprocal of the equivalent resistance of the circuit is the sum of the reciprocals of the separate resistances, *i.e.*

$$\frac{1}{R} = \frac{1}{R_1} + \frac{1}{R_2} + \frac{1}{R_3} + \ldots + \frac{1}{R_n}$$

The corresponding impedance equation is:

$$\frac{1}{Z} = \frac{1}{Z_1} + \frac{1}{Z_2} + \frac{1}{Z_3} + \ldots + \frac{1}{Z_n} \text{ (\textit{vector} addition)}$$

The reciprocal of impedance is called *admittance* and is denoted by the symbol Y.

Since Voltage = Current × Impedance

then Current (I) = Admittance (Y) × Voltage (V)

If I is measured in amps and V in volts then Y is measured in *mhos*.

When dealing with circuits in parallel it is often convenient to work with admittances, adding the separate ones together *vectorially* to obtain the total admittance. When the total admittance of a circuit has been determined in this way the total impedance is found by taking the reciprocal.

Conductance and susceptance

Impedance can be resolved into two components at right-angles to each other, a resistive component in phase with the current, and a reactive component (Fig. 3.27 (*a*)). Admittance can be split up into

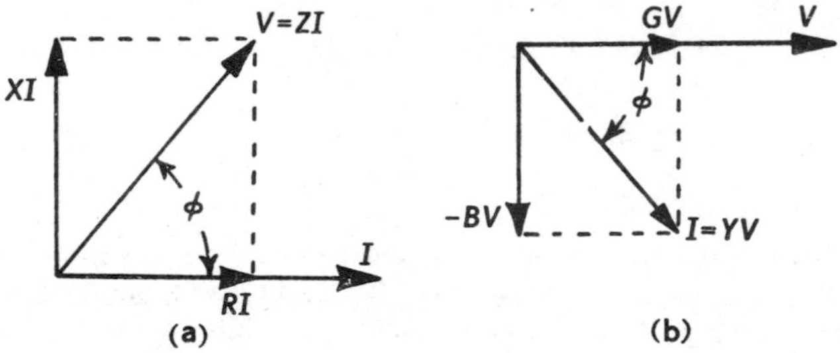

FIG. 3.27

two components in just the same way (Fig. 3.27 (*b*)). The admittance component in phase with the voltage is called the *conductance* and is denoted by the symbol G. The component at right-angles to G is called the *susceptance* which is denoted by the symbol B. Both G and B are measured in mhos.

It follows from Fig. 3.27 that:

$$Y^2 = G^2 + B^2$$

Also:

$$G = Y \cos \phi = (1/Z)(R/Z) = R/Z^2 = R/(R^2 + X^2)$$

$$B = Y \sin \phi = (1/Z)(X/Z) = X/Z^2 = X/(R^2 + X^2)$$

[Note that G is *not* equal to $1/R$ unless $X = 0$, and B is *not* equal to $1/X$ unless $R = 0$.]

EXAMPLE. A coil having an impedance of 25 Ω and a resistance of 15 Ω is connected in parallel with a non-inductive resistance of 10 Ω. Calculate the total admittance, conductance and susceptance. [S.U.]

Solution.

For branch A (Fig. 3.28) the reactance $X = \sqrt{25^2 - 15^2} = 20\ \Omega$

$$G_A = 15/(15^2 + 20^2) = 0{\cdot}024 \text{ mho}$$
$$G_B = 0{\cdot}1 \text{ mho}$$
$$B_A = 20/(15^2 + 20^2) = 0{\cdot}032 \text{ mho}$$
$$B_B = 0.$$

Total conductance $G_T = G_A + G_B = \underline{0{\cdot}124 \text{ mho}}$

Total susceptance $B_T = B_A + B_B = \underline{0{\cdot}032 \text{ mho}}$

Total admittance $Y_T = \sqrt{G_T^2 + B_T^2} = \underline{0{\cdot}128 \text{ mho}}$

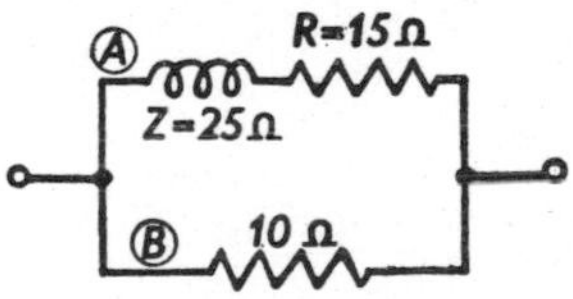

FIG. 3.28

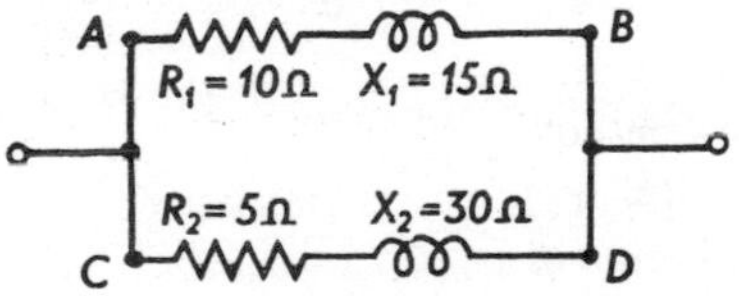

FIG. 3.29

EXAMPLE. For the circuit illustrated in Fig. 3.29 calculate the following particulars: (*a*) the impedance of branch AB, (*b*) the admittance of branch AB, (*c*) the impedance of branch CD, (*d*) the admittance of branch CD, (*e*) the total conductance, (*f*) the total susceptance, (*g*) the resultant impedance.

If a coil with reactance 10 Ω and resistance 55 Ω is placed in series with the circuit, find the equivalent resistance, reactance and impedance of the whole arrangement.

Solution.

Impedance of branch $AB = \sqrt{10^2 + 15^2} = \underline{18{\cdot}03\ \Omega}$

Admittance of branch $AB = 1/18{\cdot}03 = \underline{0{\cdot}0555 \text{ mho}}$

The vector diagram for branch AB is shown in Fig. 3.30 (*a*).

$$\tan\theta_1 = 1{\cdot}5, \text{ so } \theta_1 = 56^\circ\ 18'.$$

Impedance of branch $CD = \sqrt{5^2 + 30^2} = \underline{30{\cdot}41\ \Omega}$

Admittance of branch $CD = 1/30{\cdot}41 = \underline{0{\cdot}0329 \text{ mho}}$

The vector diagram for branch CD is shown in Fig. 3.30 (*b*)

$$\tan\theta_2 = 6, \text{ so } \theta_2 = 80^\circ\ 30'$$

Total conductance $= 0{\cdot}0555 \cos 56^\circ\ 18' + 0{\cdot}0329 \cos 80^\circ\ 30'$
$= \underline{0{\cdot}0362 \text{ mho}}$

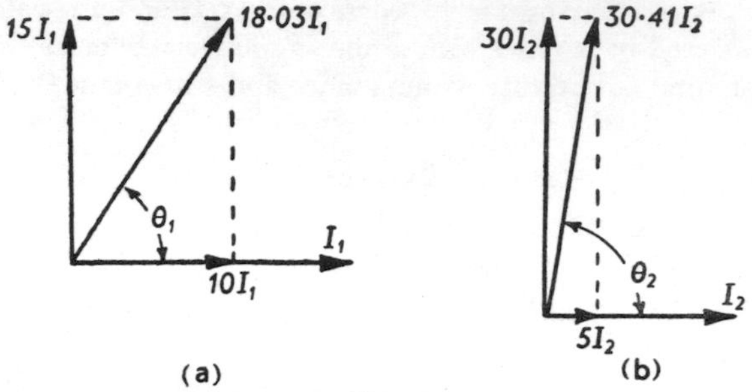

FIG. 3.30

Total susceptance $= 0{\cdot}0555 \sin 56° \, 18' + 0{\cdot}0329 \sin 80° \, 30'$
$= \underline{0{\cdot}0787 \text{ mho}}$

Resultant admittance $= \sqrt{(0{\cdot}0362)^2 + (0{\cdot}0787)^2}$
$= 0{\cdot}0866$ mho

Resultant impedance $= 1/0{\cdot}0866 = 11{\cdot}55 \ \Omega$

The resultant admittance has conductance and susceptance components of 0·0362 mho and 0·0787 mho respectively.

$$\text{Let } \theta = \tan^{-1} (0{\cdot}0787/0{\cdot}0362) = 65° \, 18'$$

The equivalent resistance of the new circuit is therefore $11{\cdot}55 \cos 65° \, 18' + 55 = \underline{59{\cdot}8 \ \Omega}$

The equivalent reactance of the circuit $= 11{\cdot}55 \sin 65° \, 18' + 10 = \underline{20{\cdot}5 \ \Omega}$

Equivalent impedance $= \sqrt{59{\cdot}8^2 + 20{\cdot}5^2} = \underline{63{\cdot}2 \ \Omega}$

Average value of an alternating quantity

The average value of an alternating quantity over one or more complete cycles is zero as is obvious from Fig. 3.1. The average value over half a cycle is, however, not zero and can easily be found knowing the wave-shape.

For example, consider a sinusoidal current of the form

$$i = I \sin \omega t = I \sin \theta$$

$$\text{The half-cycle average value} = \frac{1}{\pi}\int_0^{\pi} I \sin \theta \, d\theta = 2I/\pi$$

$$= (2/\pi) \times \text{maximum value.}$$

Root-mean-square value of an alternating quantity

When a direct current $I_{d.c.}$ amps flows through a resistor of resistance R ohms power is expended equal to $R(I_{d.c.})^2$ watts and the resistor is heated. Similarly, when the current is alternating there is also a heating effect. In fact, either a.c. or d.c. can be used for such purposes as heating a wire or lighting an incandescent-filament lamp. In the case of alternating current the power expended varies from instant to instant and the problem is what value should be assigned to the current which, when squared and multiplied by the resistance, gives the average power expended in the resistor.

Let a sinusoidal current $i = I \sin \theta$ amps flow through a resistor of resistance R ohms.

The power expended at any instant $= Ri^2$ watts

$= RI^2 \sin^2 \theta$ watts

The average power expended during one cycle, P watts

$$= \frac{1}{2\pi}\int_0^{2\pi} RI^2 \sin^2 \theta \, . \, d\theta = \frac{RI^2}{2\pi}\int_0^{2\pi} \frac{(1 - \cos 2\theta)}{2} . \, d\theta = \frac{RI^2}{2}$$

$$= R\left(\frac{I}{\sqrt{2}}\right)^2$$

Thus, the equivalent value of the current which when squared and multiplied by the resistance gives the average power is $I/\sqrt{2}$. It is evident from the way this value has been determined that it is the square root of the average of the square of the current during one cycle, *i.e.* $\sqrt{\frac{1}{T}\int_0^T i^2 \, dt}$ and is, in fact, called *the root mean square value* (*r.m.s. value*), or sometimes *the effective value.*

Thus, for a sine-wave, $I_{\text{r.m.s.}} = (1/\sqrt{2}) \times$ maximum value.

Form factor

The ratio $\dfrac{\text{r.m.s. value}}{\text{half-cycle average value}}$ is called *the form factor.*

For a sine-waveform of current the form factor

$$= (I/\sqrt{2})/(2I/\pi) = 1{\cdot}11$$

EXAMPLE. Find the r.m.s. value of the voltage which increases linearly from 0 to 5 V in 1 sec, drops to zero in negligible time and then repeats the variation. [S.U.]

Solution.

The equation of QP (Fig. 3.31) is:

$$v = 5t$$

$$\therefore \quad \text{r.m.s. value} = \sqrt{\frac{1}{1}\int_0^1 25t^2 \, dt}$$

$$= \underline{2{\cdot}89 \text{ V}}$$

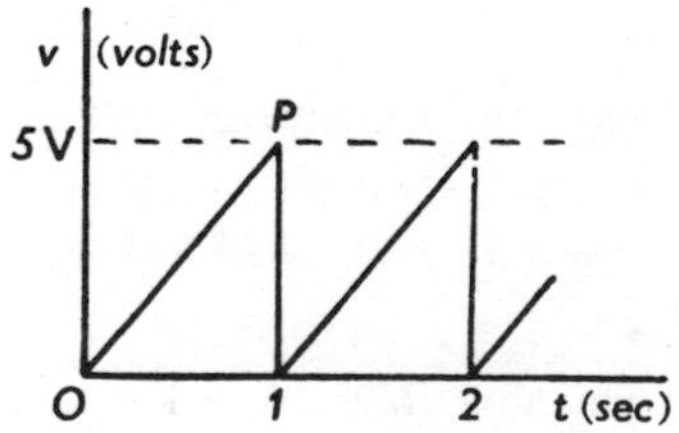

FIG. 3.31

EXAMPLE. Calculate the reading which will be given by a hot-wire voltmeter if it is connected to the terminals of a machine whose voltage waveform is represented by:

$$v = 1{,}000 \sin \omega t + 500 \sin 3\omega t + 250 \sin 5\omega t$$

Solution. The hot-wire voltmeter will read the r.m.s. value of the voltage.

$$\text{R.m.s. value} = \sqrt{\frac{1}{2\pi}\int_0^{2\pi} v^2\, d\theta} \quad \text{where } \theta = \omega t$$

$$= \sqrt{\frac{1}{2\pi}\int_0^{2\pi} [1{,}000^2 \sin^2 \theta + 500^2 \sin^2 3\theta + 250^2 \sin^2 5\theta + 2.1{,}000.500 \sin \theta \sin 3\theta + 2.500.250 \sin 3\theta \sin 5\theta + 2.1{,}000.250 \sin \theta \sin 5\theta]d\theta}$$

$$= \sqrt{\frac{1}{2\pi}\left[\frac{1{,}000^2}{2} + \frac{500^2}{2} + \frac{250^2}{2}\right]2\pi} = \underline{810 \text{ V}}$$

EXAMPLE. The instantaneous values of an alternating current between the angles of 0 and 90° are given in the following table. Find the current which would be shown by the reading of a hot-wire ammeter placed in the circuit. The curve is symmetrical about the axis through 90°, see Fig. 3.32 (a).

Angle (degrees)	0	6	12	18	24	30	36	42
Current (A)	0	9·5	16	20·5	22·5	22·5	21·5	19
Angle (degrees)	48	54	60	66	72	78	84	90
Current (A)	16	14	12·5	12·1	12·5	13·5	14·75	15

Solution. The hot-wire ammeter will read the r.m.s. value of the current. Now the r.m.s. value of an alternating quantity is the square root of the average of the squares. From Fig. 3.32 (*b*) the average value of the squares of the ordinates = 266

$$\therefore \quad \text{r.m.s. value} = \sqrt{266}\ \text{A} = \underline{16{\cdot}3\ \text{A}}$$

Power in alternating-current circuits

Consider first the simple case of a sinusoidal current flowing through a non-inductive resistor of resistance R ohms.

Let $i = I \sin \theta$

Then $v = RI \sin \theta = V \sin \theta$ where $V = RI$

The instantaneous power $= vi = VI \sin^2 \theta$

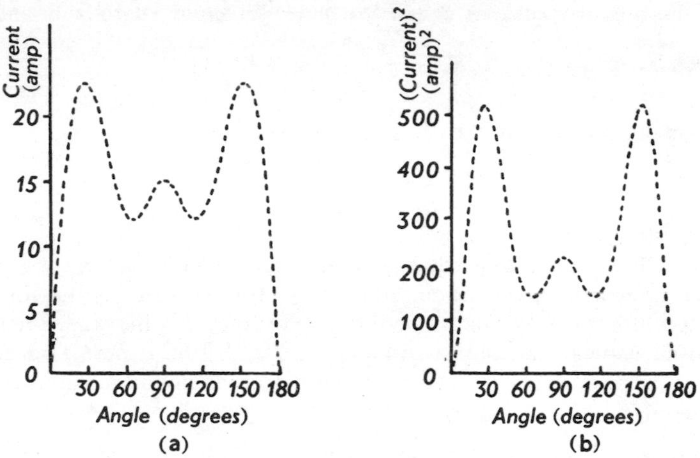

FIG. 3.32

The average power $P = \frac{1}{2\pi}\int_0^{2\pi} VI \sin^2 \theta \, . \, d\theta$

$$= VI/2 = (V/\sqrt{2})(I/\sqrt{2}) = \underline{V_{\text{r.m.s.}} I_{\text{r.m.s.}}}$$

i.e. the mean power is the product of the r.m.s. values of voltage and current.

Now consider the case of a sinusoidal current flowing through a series *LCR* circuit.

Let $i = I \sin \theta$

Then $v = V \sin (\theta + \phi)$ where $V = I\sqrt{R^2 + \left(L\omega - \frac{1}{\omega C}\right)^2}$ and

$\tan \phi = (L\omega - 1/\omega C)/R$

The instantaneous power $= vi = VI \sin \theta \sin (\theta + \phi)$

The average power $P = \frac{1}{2\pi}\int_0^{2\pi} VI \sin \theta \sin (\theta + \phi) \, d\theta$

$$= \frac{1}{2\pi}\int_0^{2\pi} VI[\sin^2 \theta \cos \phi + \sin \theta \cos \theta \sin \phi]d\theta$$

$$= (VI/2) \cos \phi = (V/\sqrt{2})(I/\sqrt{2}) \cos \phi = \underline{V_{\text{r.m.s.}} I_{\text{r.m.s.}}} \cos \phi$$

Thus, the mean power is the product of the r.m.s. values of voltage and current and the cosine of the phase-angle difference between voltage and current. The first example considered above is only a special case of the second when $\cos \phi = 1$.

The quantity $\cos\phi$ is called *the power-factor* of the circuit and is given by $R\Big/\sqrt{R^2 + \left(L\omega - \frac{1}{\omega C}\right)^2}$, *i.e.* R/Z.

$$\begin{aligned}\text{The average power } P &= V_{\text{r.m.s.}}\, I_{\text{r.m.s.}} \cos\phi \\ &= (I_{\text{r.m.s.}}\, Z) I_{\text{r.m.s.}}\, (R/Z) \\ &= R(I_{\text{r.m.s.}})^2\end{aligned}$$

It will be noted that when $\phi = 90°$, such as in a purely capacitive circuit, the mean power absorbed is zero. Readers meeting this subject for the first time will find it interesting to draw out the waveforms of current, voltage and power (product of v and i) for a purely resistive circuit, a purely capacitive circuit and for an LCR circuit having a given value of ϕ.

EXAMPLE. Two coils each take a current of 4 A when connected to a 100 V, 50 c/s supply, and the powers dissipated in them are 240 W and 320 W respectively. Find the current taken, and the power factor, when the coils are connected in series with the 100 V supply. [S.U.]

Solution. For the first coil, the resistance $R_1 = 240/4^2 = 15\ \Omega$ and the impedance $= 100/4 = 25\ \Omega$. Therefore, the reactance $X_1 = \sqrt{25^2 - 15^2} = 20\ \Omega$.

For the second coil, $R_2 = 320/4^2 = 20\ \Omega$, the impedance $= 100/4 = 25\ \Omega$, so the reactance $X_2 = 15\ \Omega$.

When the two coils are connected in series the total resistance is $35\ \Omega$ and the total reactance is $35\ \Omega$.

$$\begin{aligned}\therefore \quad \text{current taken by series combination} &= 100/\sqrt{35^2 + 35^2} \\ &= \underline{2{\cdot}02\ \text{A}}\end{aligned}$$

If the phase-angle difference between the voltage and current is ϕ, $\tan\phi = 35/35 = 1$, so $\phi = 45°$

The power-factor is $\cos\phi = \underline{0{\cdot}707}$

Measurement of power and power factor in single-phase circuits without using a wattmeter

(*a*) The three-voltmeter method

Suppose it is required to measure the power absorbed by an inductive load. A non-inductive resistor of resistance R is connected in series with the load to an alternating voltage supply as shown in Fig. 3.33. The voltages V_1, V_2 and V_3 are measured and an ammeter is included in the circuit.

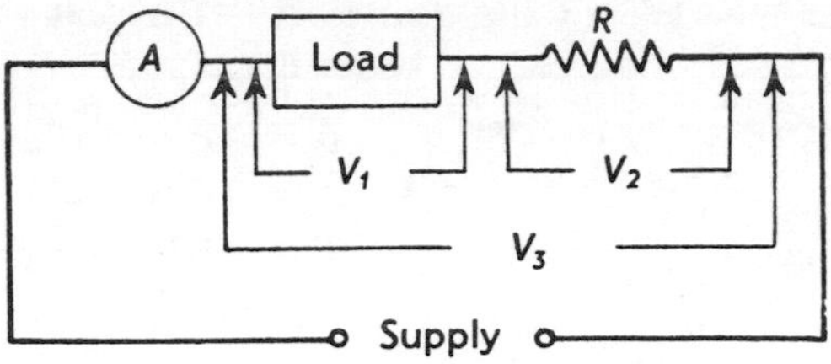

FIG. 3.33

The vector diagram for the arrangement is shown in Fig. 3.34.

The power absorbed in the load is $P = V_1A \cos \phi$. From the vector diagram,

$$\begin{aligned} V_3^2 &= V_1^2 + V_2^2 + 2V_1V_2 \cos \phi \\ &= V_1^2 + V_2^2 + 2V_2P/A \\ \therefore \quad P &= A(V_3^2 - V_1^2 - V_2^2)/2V_2 \\ &= (V_3^2 - V_1^2 - V_2^2)/2R \end{aligned}$$

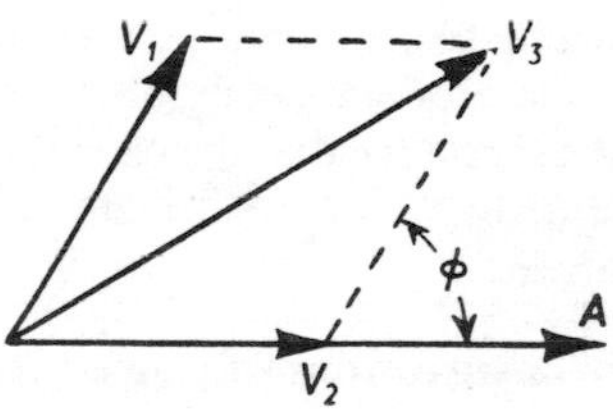

FIG. 3.34

Thus, if R is known the power can be calculated without knowing A.

The power-factor of the load,

$$\cos \phi = (V_3^2 - V_1^2 - V_2^2)/2V_1V_2$$

Thus, the power-factor can be determined without knowing A or R.

To obtain good experimental accuracy R should be chosen so as to make V_1 and V_2 approximately equal.

(*b*) The three-ammeter method

Suppose it is required to measure the power absorbed by an inductive load again. A non-inductive resistor of resistance R is connected in parallel with the load as shown in Fig. 3.35. The currents A_1, A_2 and

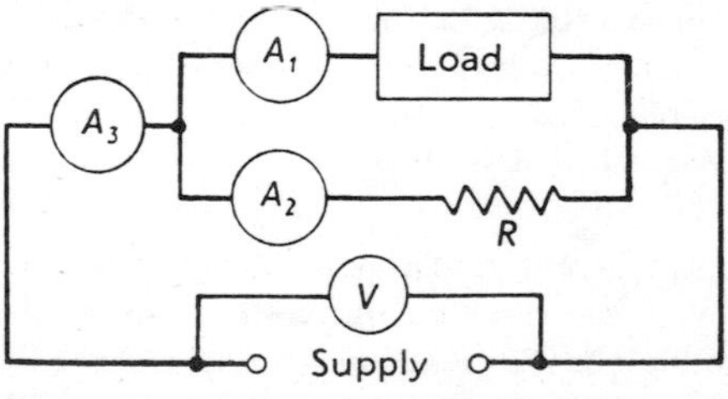

FIG. 3.35

A_3 are recorded and a voltmeter is included in the circuit.

The vector diagram for the arrangement is shown in Fig. 3.36.

The power absorbed in the load is $P = VA_1 \cos \phi$. From the vector diagram,

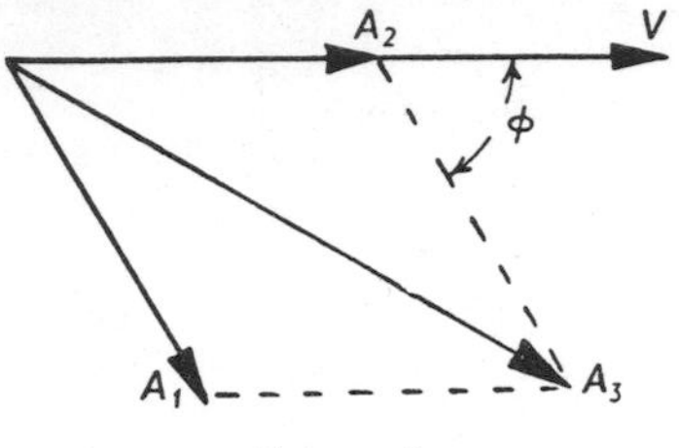

FIG. 3.36

$$A_3^2 = A_1^2 + A_2^2 + 2A_1A_2 \cos \phi$$
$$= A_1^2 + A_2^2 + 2A_2P/V$$
$$\therefore \quad P = V(A_3^2 - A_2^2 - A_1^2)/2A_2$$
$$= R(A_3^2 - A_2^2 - A_1^2)/2$$

The power-factor of the load

$$= (A_3^2 - A_2^2 - A_1^2)/2A_1A_2$$

As in the previous method it is desirable to have A_1 and A_2 of the same order.

In both these methods of measurement instrument losses must be negligible, *i.e.* voltmeters must take negligible current and ammeters must produce negligible voltage drops. Both methods suffer from the disadvantage that the calculations depend on taking the differences of the squares of observed readings. This tends to magnify any experimental errors.

Measurement of power factor using a wattmeter

The simplest method of measuring the power-factor of a circuit is by using a wattmeter in conjunction with an ammeter and a voltmeter. This is because power-factor = watts/(voltage × current). As pointed out by Glynne,* however, this method has the following disadvantages: (*a*) three instruments must be calibrated, (*b*) no indication is given of the sign of the angle (whether leading or lagging) between the current and voltage vectors, (*c*) it is very insensitive to changes of phase-angle in the region of unity power-factor, (*d*) three observations and a calculation are necessary to obtain the result.

Glynne * has shown that a better method for measuring power-factor is to use a wattmeter, capacitor and switch connected as shown in Fig. 3·37.

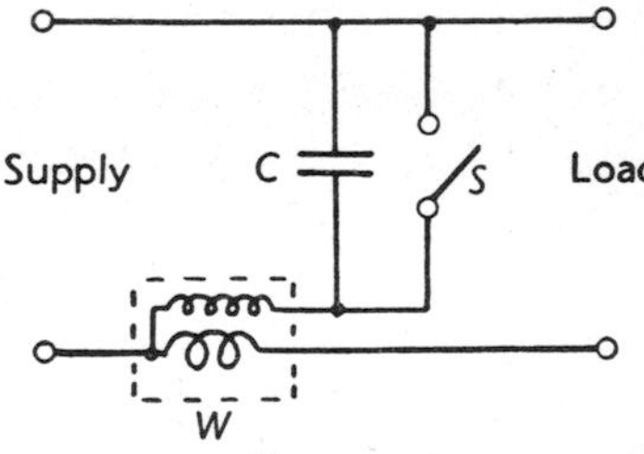

FIG. 3·37

Let the voltage, current and power-factor of the load be V, I and $\cos \phi$ respectively. Assume that the voltage coil of the wattmeter has a resistance R and negligible reactance. Let the readings of the wattmeter with the switch S open and closed be W_2 and W_1 respectively. Then $W_1 = VI \cos \phi$

* A. Glynne, "A New Method of Measuring Power Factor by Wattmeter", *Bull. Elect. Eng. Educ.*, No. 5, p. 42 (November, 1950).

When S is open, the voltage across the wattmeter voltage coil $= RV/\sqrt{R^2 + 1/\omega^2C^2}$, where $\omega = 2\pi \times$ frequency, and the current through the wattmeter current coil is I. The voltage across R is now out of phase with V by an angle $\tan^{-1}(1/\omega CR)$.

$$\therefore \quad W_2 = \frac{VR}{\sqrt{R^2 + 1/\omega^2C^2}} \cdot I \cos\{\phi - \tan^{-1}(1/\omega CR)\}$$

$$\therefore \quad \frac{W_2}{W_1} = \left[\frac{VIR}{\sqrt{R^2 + 1/\omega^2C^2}} \cdot \cos\{\phi - \tan^{-1}(1/\omega CR)\}\right] \Big/ VI\cos\phi$$

$$= R(R + \tan\phi/\omega C)/(R^2 + 1/\omega^2C^2) = a, \text{ say.}$$

If $\quad R = 1/\omega C$ then $\tan\phi = (2a - 1)$

or $\quad \cos\phi = 1/\sqrt{4a^2 - 4a + 2}$

A curve may now be plotted giving phase-angle (or power-factor) in terms of W_2/W_1.

The initial adjustment of $R = 1/\omega C$ is conveniently effected by connecting a resistive load to give an approximately full-scale reading on the wattmeter when S is closed. C is then varied until the wattmeter reading is halved when S is open. To avoid the need for close adjustment of C a small variable resistor may be placed in series with R. This resistor must, however, be short-circuited if the wattmeter is to be employed to measure power as well as power-factor. The absolute accuracy of the meter is of no moment as far as the measurement of power-factor is concerned.

PROBLEMS

1. An inductive coil, in series with a non-inductive resistor, takes a current of 5 A when connected to a 100 V a.c. supply. The voltages across the coil and resistor are 80 V and 30 V respectively. Find the power-factor and power for (*a*) the whole circuit, (*b*) the coil alone.
[*Ans.* (*a*) 0·75, 375 W.,
(*b*) 0·56, 225 W.]

2. When a d.c. voltage of 30 V is applied to a given coil the power consumed is 150 W. When an a.c. voltage of 230 V r.m.s. is applied to the same coil the power consumed is 3,174 W. Show that the reactance of the coil is 8 Ω. [S.U.]

3. Determine the r.m.s. value of a semicircular voltage waveform of maximum value V. [*Ans.* 0·816 V.]

4. Prove that the combined impedance of a resistor of resistance R and a reactor of reactance X in parallel is $RX/\sqrt{R^2 + X^2}$.

5. Find the sum of the following voltages: $40 \sin \omega t$, $20 \sin(\omega t + \pi/6)$, $30 \cos \omega t$, $20 \sin(\omega t - \pi/3)$ and $50 \cos(\omega t + 2\pi/3)$ by representing them vectorially. [*Ans.* $24{\cdot}2 \sin(\omega t - 0{\cdot}096)$.]

6. A piece of equipment consumes 2,000 W when supplied with 110 V and takes a lagging current of 25 A. Determine the equivalent series resistance and reactance of the equipment.

If a capacitor is connected in parallel with the equipment to make the power-factor unity, find its capacitance. The supply frequency is 100 c/s. [S.U.] [*Ans.* 3·2 Ω, 3·02 Ω, 248 μF.]

7. Find the relative heating effects of three current waves of equal maximum value, one rectangular, the second semicircular and the other sinusoidal in waveform. [S.U.] [*Ans.* 1 : 2/3 : 1/2.]

8. Draw a complete vector diagram for the series circuit shown, indicating the various resistance and reactance voltage drops, the voltages

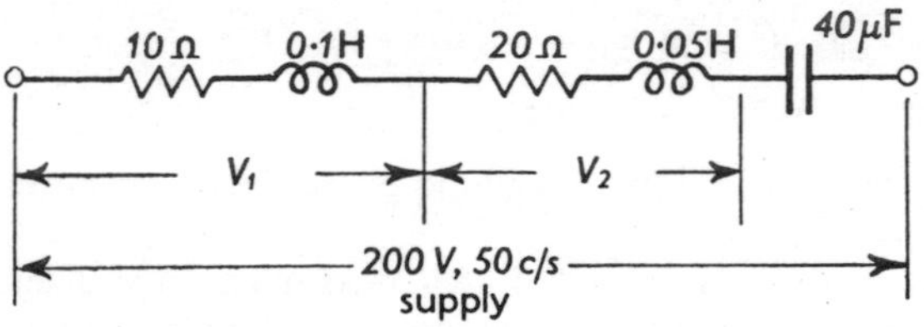

V_1 and V_2, the supply voltage and the current. Find the magnitudes of the voltages V_1 and V_2 and the current. Calculate, also, the power-factor of the circuit. [S.U.] [*Ans.* 149 V, 115 V, 4·53 A, 0·679.]

9. Two coils are connected in parallel across a 200 V, 50 c/s supply. At the supply frequency their impedances are 8 Ω and 10 Ω, respectively, and their resistances are 6 Ω and 4 Ω, respectively.

Find: (*a*) the current in each coil, (*b*) the total current, and (*c*) the total power-factor. [*Ans.* 25 A, 20 A, 43·9 A, 0·609.]

10. A sinusoidal 50 c/s voltage, of 200 V r.m.s., supplies the following three circuits which are in parallel: (*a*) a coil of inductance 0·03 H and resistance 3 Ω, (*b*) a capacitor of 400 μF in series with a resistance of 100 Ω, (*c*) a coil of inductance 0·02 H and resistance 7 Ω in series with a 300 μF capacitor. Find the total current supplied and draw a complete vector diagram. [S.U.] [*Ans.* 29·4 A.]

11. The power absorbed by an inductive load is measured by the three-voltmeter method. The voltage across the load is 210 V, that across the standard resistor 180 V and the supply voltage is 290 V.

Determine the power-factor of the load. [*Ans.* 0·1.]

12. The power absorbed by an inductive load is measured by the three-ammeter method. The current in the main circuit is 6 A while the currents in the standard resistor and the load are 3 A and 4 A respectively. The supply voltage is 200 V.

Determine the power absorbed by the load and its power-factor.

[*Ans.* 366·4 W, 0·458.]

13. Two reactive conductors have each an impedance of 20 Ω. One takes a lagging current of power-factor 0·8 and the other a leading current of power-factor 0·6. Evaluate (*a*) the voltage necessary to send a current of 10 A through the two in series, (*b*) the current taken from the 200 V mains supply when the two are connected in parallel with it. For each case draw a vector diagram showing the relationship of currents and voltages. [*Ans.* (*a*) 282·8 V, (*b*) 14·14 A.]

14. A 100 V, 500 c/s supply is connected across the circuit illustrated at (*a*). Draw the vector diagram for the arrangement.

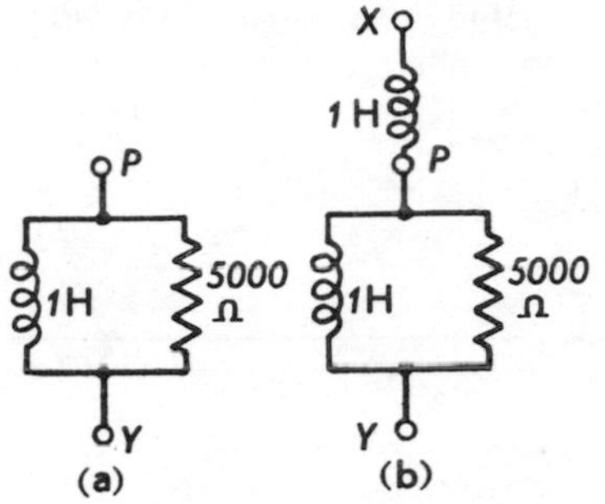

A second coil is now joined in series as in (*b*). By adding suitable vectors to the vector diagram already drawn find the voltage required across the whole circuit XY to maintain 100 V across PY.

[*Ans.* 210 V.]

15. An alternating voltage $v = 10 \sin 100\,\pi t$ is applied across a load which has a lagging phase-angle of 60°. The resulting current in the load has a peak value of 5 A. Write down an expression for the current and draw graphs, to scale, of the voltage and current waveforms. From this, or otherwise, estimate the power taken by the load.

[*Ans.* $5 \sin (100\pi t - 60°)$, 12·5 W.]

16. Two reactive conductors, when traversed by alternating currents of frequency 50 c/s, have the same impedance and also the same power-factor of $1/\sqrt{2}$. The first consists of a capacitor shunted by a non-inductive resistor of 200 Ω. The second consists of an inductive coil. Find the capacitance of the first and the inductance and resistance of the second. [*Ans.* 15·9 μF, 0·318 H, 100 Ω.]

17. Calculate V_1, V_2 and I for the circuit illustrated at resonance.

[*Ans.* 468 V, 461·6 V, 4 A.]

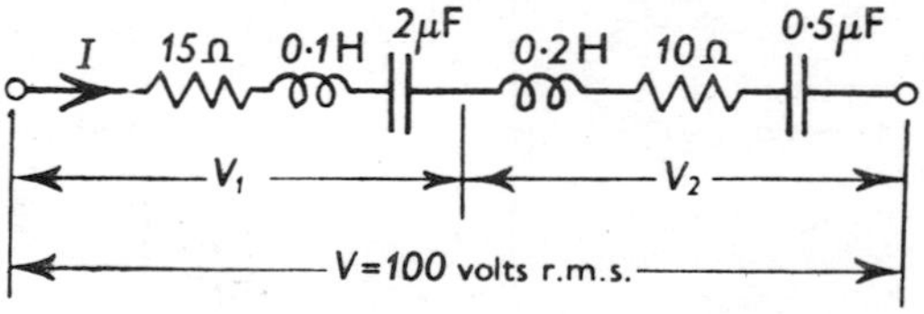

18. A series a.c. circuit connected to 240 V, 50 c/s mains consists of a 1,000 Ω resistor, a 0·2 H inductor and a 2 μF capacitor. Find the current flowing and its phase-angle and state whether it is leading or lagging the applied voltage. Determine, also, the voltage across each component and draw the complete vector diagram for the arrangement.

[*Ans.* 0·131 A, 56° 48′, leading,
V_R = 131 V, V_L = 8·25 V, V_C = 209 V.]

19. A current has the following steady values in ampères for equal intervals of time changing instantaneously from one value to the next: 0, 10, 20, 30, 20, 10, 0, −10, −20, −30, −20, −10, 0, etc. Calculate the r.m.s. value of the current and its form factor.

[*Ans.* 17·8 A, 1·19.]

20. Find the r.m.s. value of the current wave illustrated.

[*Ans.* 6·46 A.]

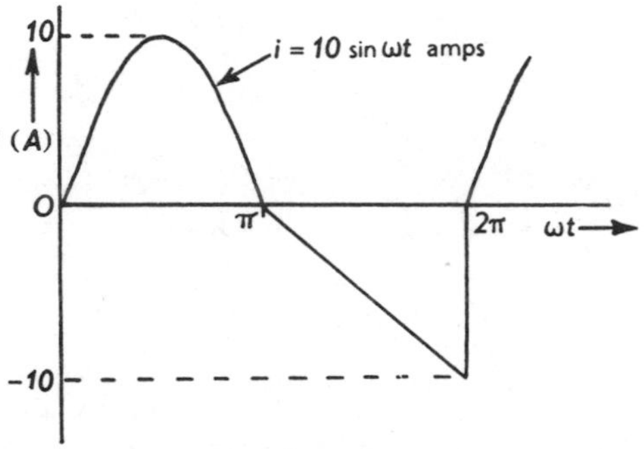

21. A 4 μF capacitor is connected in series with a 400 Ω resistor. This combination is placed in series with two inductors in parallel of inductances 10 H and 5 H respectively. What current will flow through the resistor when a voltage of 100 V r.m.s. at a frequency of 50 c/s is applied to the whole circuit? [*Ans.* 0·212 A.]

22. Inductive loads of 0·8 kW and 1·2 kW at power factors of 0·8 and 0·6 respectively are connected in parallel across a 200 V, 50 c/s supply. Find the total current taken by the combination and determine what value of capacitance connected in parallel with both loads would bring the combined power-factor up to 0·9 lagging.

[*Ans.* 14·87 A at a lagging power-factor of 0·673, 98 μF.]

23. Find the equivalent resistance, reactance and impedance of the whole arrangement illustrated. [*Ans.* 57·6 Ω, 37·2 Ω, 68·56 Ω.]

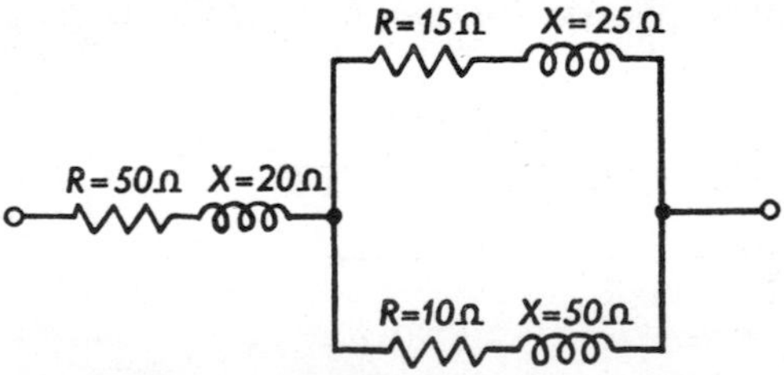

24. Alternating currents of maximum value 100 A have the following waveforms: (*a*) sinusoidal, (*b*) full-wave rectified sinusoidal, (*c*) rectangular, (*d*) triangular. Find the instrument readings in each case when these currents are passed successively through a moving-coil ammeter and a moving-iron ammeter in series.

[*Ans.* (*a*) 0, 70·7 A, (*b*) 63·6 A, 70·7 A, (*c*) 0, 100 A, (*d*) 0, 57·8 A.]

CHAPTER 4

POLYPHASE CIRCUITS

Two-phase systems

A two-phase system is a combination of two single-phase systems the voltages of which differ in phase by 90°. (Fig. 4.1.)

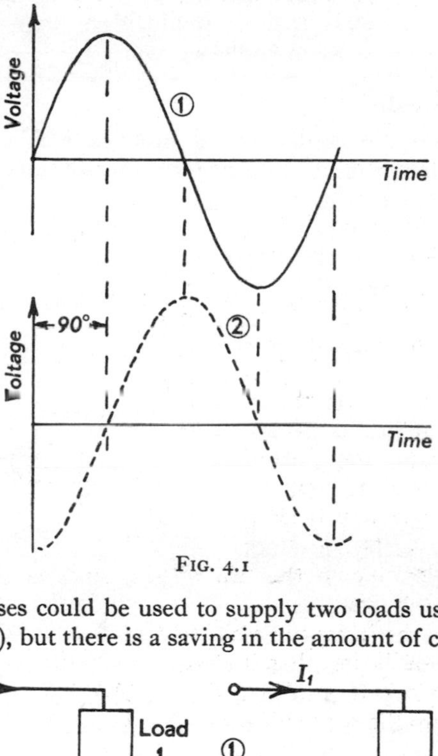

FIG. 4.1

The two phases could be used to supply two loads using four wires as in Fig. 4.2 (*a*), but there is a saving in the amount of copper used for

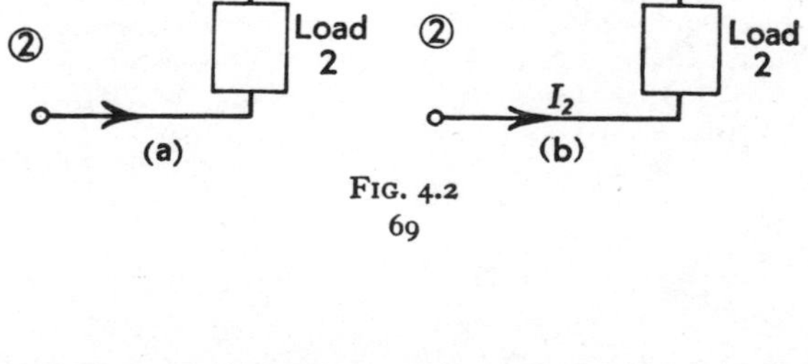

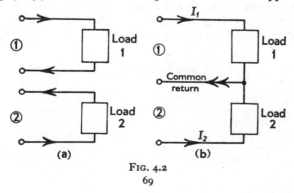

FIG. 4.2

the transmission lines if the two return wires of the four-wire system are combined into one (Fig. 4.2 (*b*)). This is so because the current in the common return wire is the *vector* sum of the two currents in the outgoing wires. If the two loads are identical the currents in the two phases are equal and 90° out of phase. The vector diagram is therefore as shown in Fig. 4.3 and the current in the common return, represented by $OI = \sqrt{2} \times$ the current in each leading-out wire. Thus, the resultant current is less than it would have been if a four-wire system had been used.

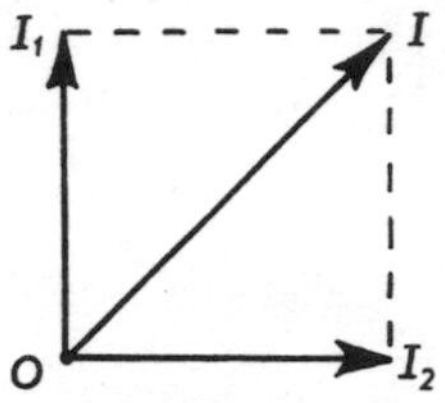

FIG. 4.3

The rotating field

A two-phase system can be used to produce, with stationary coils, a field which rotates in space. Consider two pairs of coils with laminated-iron cores arranged at right-angles to one another, as shown in Fig. 4.4, and connected to the two-phase supply.

At the instant when the current in phase 1 is a maximum the current in phase 2 is zero (see Fig. 4.1). At this time the current in phase 1 will produce a field in the space between the coils of Fig. 4.4 which may be assumed to be vertically downwards (Fig. 4.5 (*a*)). This is the resultant field in the space due to the two phases, since at this instant, no field is produced by phase 2.

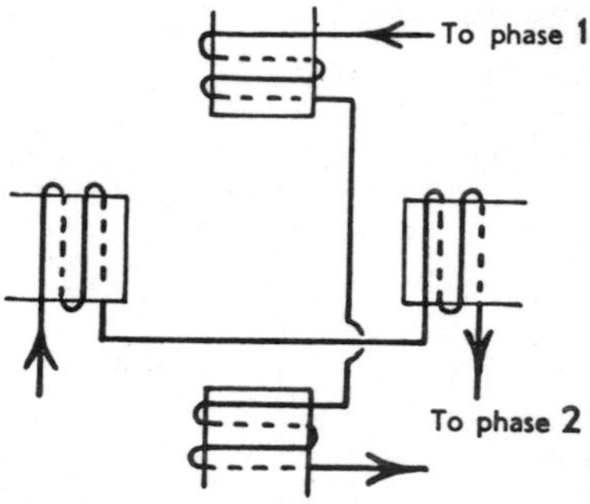

FIG. 4.4

Consider now the instant one-eighth of a cycle later. The current in phase 1 will now be less than it was before and there will be an equal current in phase 2 (refer to Fig. 4.1). Assume the current in phase 2 at this instant produces a field from right to left. The resultant field

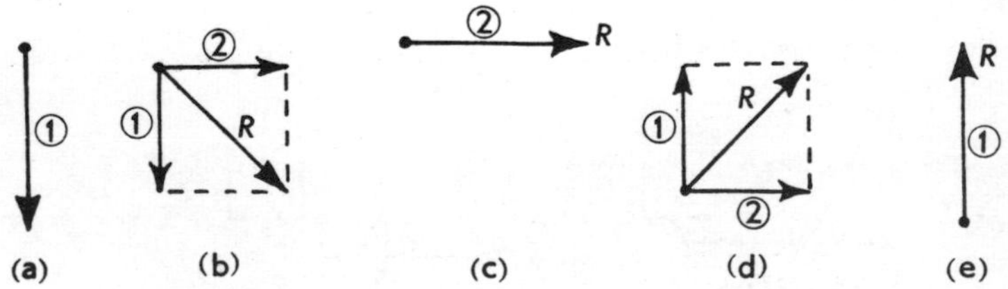

FIG. 4.5

R in the space between the coils is now as shown on Fig. 4.5 (*b*). An eighth of a cycle later still the current in phase 1 is zero and that in phase 2 reaches its maximum value giving the resultant field R of Fig. 4.5 (*c*). After a further eighth cycle the current in phase 1 has reversed and the resultant field is that shown at (*d*) in Fig. 4.5. Finally, after a further eighth cycle the current in phase 1 reaches its maximum value in the reverse direction and the current in phase 2 is zero. The resultant field so produced is that shown in Fig. 4.5 (*e*). Thus, in the half cycle considered the resultant field has rotated through 180° even though the coils have remained stationary. The resultant field is constant in magnitude and rotates at constant speed. These facts can be proved as follows:

Let $\Phi_1 = \Phi \cos \omega t$ represent the flux produced in the space between the coils by the current in phase 1.

Let $\Phi_2 = \Phi \sin \omega t$ represent the flux produced in the space between the coils by the current in phase 2.

The resultant field $= \sqrt{\Phi_1^2 + \Phi_2^2} = \Phi$, a constant.

The angle θ between the resultant field and Φ_1 is given by:

$$\tan \theta = \Phi_2/\Phi_1 = \tan \omega t$$
$$i.e. \quad \theta = \omega t.$$

Thus, the angle between the resultant field and Φ_1 is proportional to time so that the resultant field rotates with a uniform angular velocity ω.

The induction motor relies on a rotating field of this type for its operation although three-phase supplies are generally used instead of two-phase for this purpose. If a rotor constructed in the form of a squirrel cage of copper conductors is placed in the rotating field, e.m.f.'s are induced in the conductors. Thus, as the field rotates, currents flow in the conductors and forces act on the conductors tending to pull them round in the direction of the field.

EXAMPLE. In a two-phase, three-wire system the two phases are unequally loaded. The current in the leading phase is 50 A in phase with its own voltage. The current in the lagging phase is 40 A and lags 25° behind its own voltage.

What is the magnitude of the current in the common return and the phase-angle between it and the 50 A current? [S.U.]

Solution. The vector diagram for the arrangement is shown in Fig. 4.6. The current in the common return wire will be the resultant of the currents 50 A and 40 A.

Resolving the currents in the X and Y directions:

$$X = 50 - 40 \sin 25° = 33{\cdot}096 \text{ A}$$
$$Y = -40 \cos 25° = 36{\cdot}252 \text{ A}$$

The resultant current $= \sqrt{X^2 + Y^2} = \underline{49{\cdot}1 \text{ A}}$

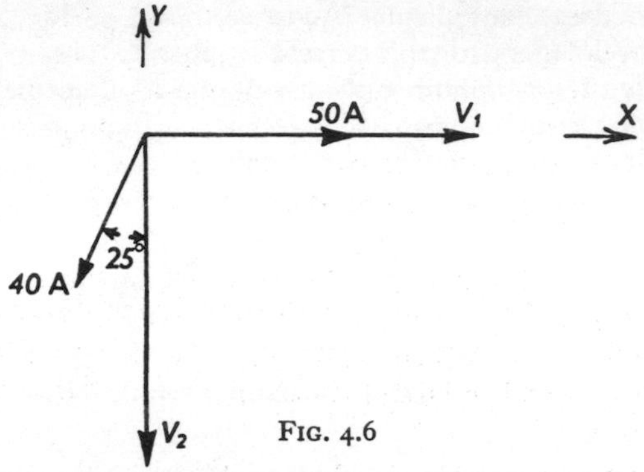

FIG. 4.6

Let the phase-angle between this and the 50 A current be ϕ.

Then $$\tan \phi = Y/X = -1{\cdot}095$$

so $$\underline{\phi = -47^\circ\ 36'}$$

i.e. the current in the common return lags the 50 A current by 47° 36'.

Three-phase systems

A three-phase system is a combination of three single-phase systems of which the voltages differ in phase by 120°. (Fig. 4.7.)

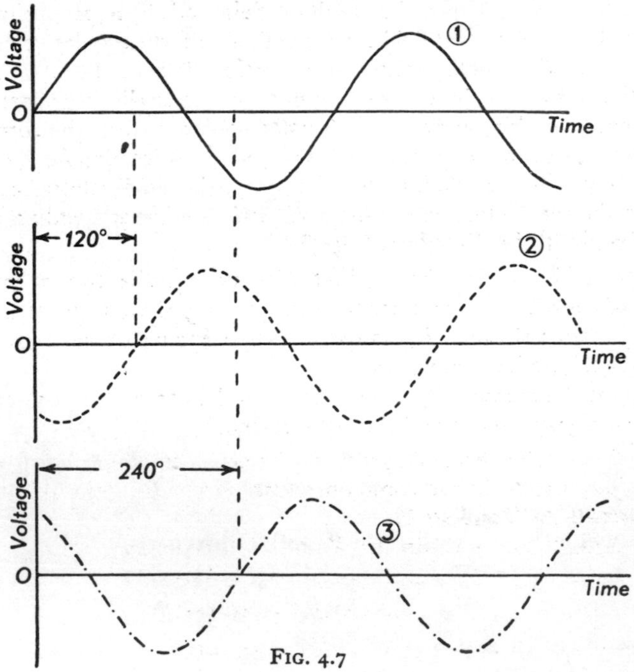

FIG. 4.7

The three phases could be used to supply three loads using six wires, but in practice the return path is usually absent, or is in the form of a single conductor. If the three-phase system and the loads are balanced the algebraic sum of the currents in the three phases is zero and so no return conductor is necessary. This can be seen from current waveforms similar to Fig. 4.7 and can be proved as follows:

Let the current in phase 1 be $i_1 = I \sin \omega t$
then the current in phase 2 is $i_2 = I \sin (\omega t - 120°)$
and the current in phase 3 is $i_3 = I \sin (\omega t - 240°)$

The current through a common return wire would be

$$i_1 + i_2 + i_3 = I\{\sin \omega t + \sin (\omega t - 120°) + \sin (\omega t - 240°)\} = 0$$

Thus, three-phase currents can be transmitted with only three wires, the fourth wire or common return which should be connected to point N being unnecessary (Fig. 4.8). The system shown in Fig. 4.8 is

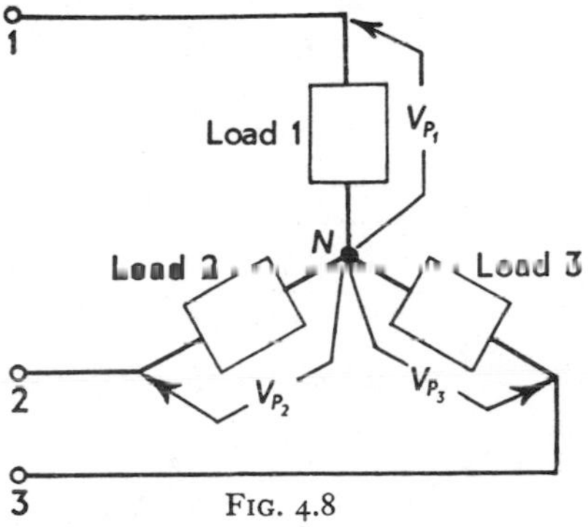

FIG. 4.8

known as the *star connection*. N is called the *neutral point* or *star point*. If there is a voltage V_p between each line and the neutral point, *i.e.* the voltage across a phase, the voltage between any two lines can be found from the vector diagram for the arrangement in the following manner: The three-phase voltages, the V_p's, can be represented by three vectors, equal in length and 120° apart as shown in Fig. 4.9. To find the voltage between lines 2 and 3 it is necessary to subtract V_{p_3} from V_{p_2}. The required voltage is thus the vector sum of V_{p_2} and V_{p_3} reversed, *i.e.* OP. The value of OP is $2OQ$

$$= 2\, V_p \cos 30°$$
$$= \sqrt{3}\, V_p$$

This voltage lags V_{p_2} by 30°. The arrangement is symmetrical, so the voltage between *any* two lines is $\sqrt{3} V_p$. It is evident from Fig. 4.8

that the line current and the phase current are the same for the star connection. For a perfectly balanced system these currents, also shown on the vector diagram of Fig. 4.9, are also 120° apart.

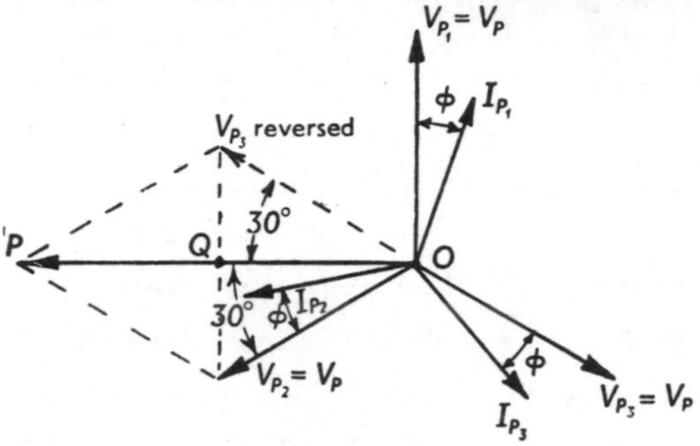

FIG. 4.9

An alternative arrangement to the star connection is *the delta or mesh connection* shown in Fig. 4.10. Here the line voltage is equal to the phase voltage but now the line and phase currents are not the same. To find the relationship between the currents in the lines and those in the

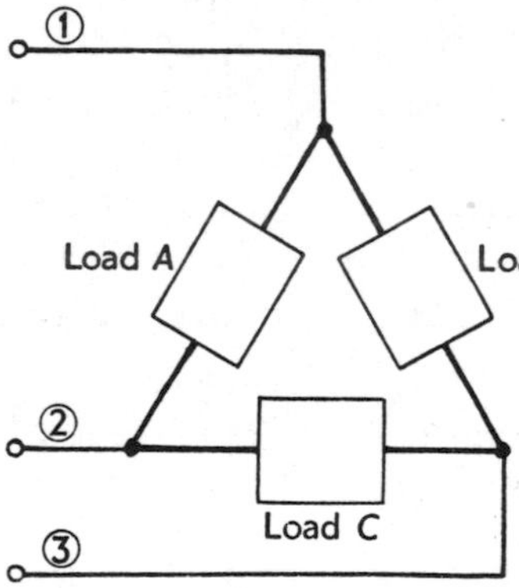

FIG. 4.10

phases it is necessary to draw a vector diagram similar to that of Fig. 4.9. From this it is found that the current in line 1, for example, which is the vector difference between the currents in phases A and B is $\sqrt{3}$ times either of those currents.

Three-phase rotating field

Three-phase currents can be used to produce a rotating field by employing three sets of coils exciting pole pieces placed at 120° to each other. Readers may find it of interest to plot a number of flux vector diagrams, for various instants of time to show that the resultant field rotates, as was done for a two-phase system.

Let the component fluxes due to the three phases be $\Phi \cos \omega t$, $\Phi \cos (\omega t - 120°)$ and $\Phi \cos (\omega t - 240°)$. These fluxes act along axes which are mutually inclined to each other at 120° as shown in Fig. 4.11.

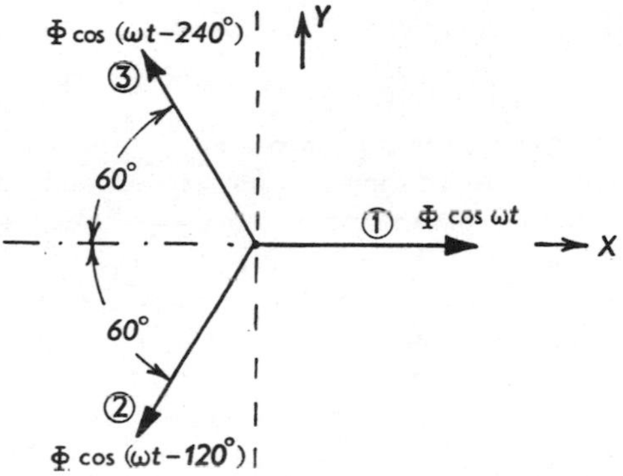

FIG. 4.11

Resolving the vectors in the X and Y directions,

$$X = \Phi \cos \omega t - \Phi \cos (\omega t - 120°) \cos 60° - \Phi \cos (\omega t - 240°) \cos 60°$$

$$= (3/2)\, \Phi \cos \omega t$$

$$Y = \Phi \cos (\omega t - 240°) \sin 60° - \Phi \cos (\omega t - 120°) \sin 60°$$

$$= (-3/2) \Phi \sin \omega t.$$

The resultant flux is $\Phi_R = \sqrt{X^2 + Y^2} = 3\Phi/2$

The angle θ between the resultant flux and X is given by:

$$\tan \theta = Y/X = -\tan \omega t, \text{ so } \theta = -\omega t$$

Thus, the resultant field is constant in magnitude and rotates with a uniform angular velocity. It will be seen that if phases 2 and 3 are interchanged the direction of rotation of the resultant field is reversed. The rotating field is discussed further in Chapter 15 in connection with electrical machines.

Power in polyphase systems

Consider a two-phase three-wire system. Let the instantaneous voltage in phase 1 be $v_1 = V \sin \omega t$ and that in phase 2 be $v_2 = V \sin (\omega t - 90°)$.

If both phases are equally loaded and have the same power-factor, the currents may be represented by $i_1 = I \sin(\omega t - \phi)$, and $i_2 = I \sin(\omega t - 90^\circ - \phi)$. The instantaneous power absorbed

$$= v_1 i_1 + v_2 i_2$$
$$= VI\{\sin \omega t \sin(\omega t - \phi) + \sin(\omega t - 90^\circ) \sin(\omega t - 90^\circ - \phi)\}$$
$$= VI\{2 \cos \phi - \cos(2\omega t - \phi) - \cos(2\omega t - \phi - 180^\circ)\}/2$$
$$= VI \cos \phi = (VI/2)2 \cos \phi = 2V_{\text{r.m.s.}} I_{\text{r.m.s.}} \cos \phi.$$

The total power absorbed is therefore *steady*, without oscillatory components, and equal to twice the mean power absorbed per phase.

In a balanced three-phase system the phase voltages and currents are $v_1 = V \sin \omega t$, $v_2 = V \sin(\omega t - 120^\circ)$, $v_3 = V \sin(\omega t - 240^\circ)$ and $i_1 = I \sin(\omega t - \phi)$, $i_2 = I \sin(\omega t - 120^\circ - \phi)$, $i_3 = I \sin(\omega t - 240^\circ - \phi)$. The total instantaneous power $P = v_1 i_1 + v_2 i_2 + v_3 i_3$. It is easily shown that $P = (3VI \cos \phi)/2 = 3V_p I_p \cos \phi$, where V_p, I_p are the r.m.s. voltage and current per phase. Again the oscillatory components of power cancel so that the power flow is *steady* and equal to three times the mean power per phase.

For a delta connection,

$$V_p = V_l,\ I_p = I_l/\sqrt{3},\ \text{so } P = \sqrt{3} V_l I_l \cos \phi.$$

For a star connection,

$$V_p = V_l/\sqrt{3},\ I_p = I_l,\ \text{so again } P = \sqrt{3} V_l I_l \cos \phi.$$

EXAMPLE. A 100 h.p., three-phase, star-connected motor works on a supply whose line voltage is 2,750 V. The efficiency is 0·9 and the power-factor is 0·85. Calculate the line current.

Solution

$$\text{Input power } P = \frac{\text{Output}}{\text{Efficiency}} = \frac{100 \times 746}{0{\cdot}9} = 82{,}889 \text{ watts.}$$

But $P = \sqrt{3} V_l I_l \cos \phi$

so $I_l = 82{,}889/(\sqrt{3} \times 2{,}750 \times 0{\cdot}85) = \underline{20{\cdot}5\text{ A.}}$

Measurement of power in three-phase circuits

Three-wattmeter method

Power absorbed in a three-phase circuit could be measured by placing one wattmeter in each phase as shown in Fig. 4.12. The total power absorbed would then be the sum of the three readings. The method is not generally used as it requires three instruments, unless the system is balanced, and in the delta-connected arrangement it might

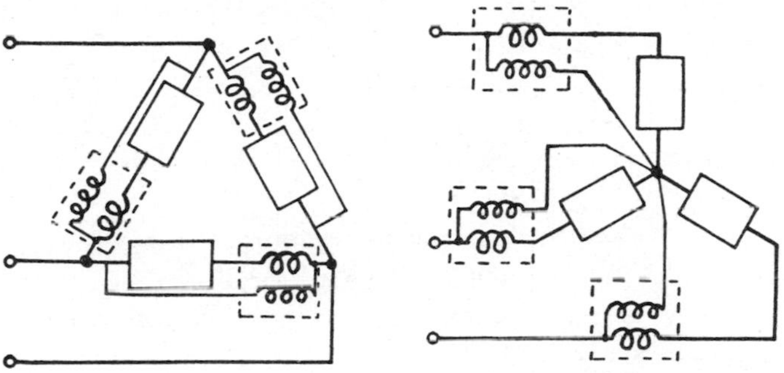

(a) (b)

FIG. 4.12

frequently be difficult to place wattmeter current coils in the actual phases. In the star-connected system, the neutral point may not be available, although an artificial one can be made by connecting three high-value resistors in star to the three lines.

Two-wattmeter method

Power in a three-phase circuit can be measured by using two wattmeters as shown for a star-connected circuit in Fig. 4.13.

Let the instantaneous values of currents and voltages be as shown. All the three currents meet at the neutral point so *whether the system is balanced or not*:

$$i_1 + i_2 + i_3 = 0.$$

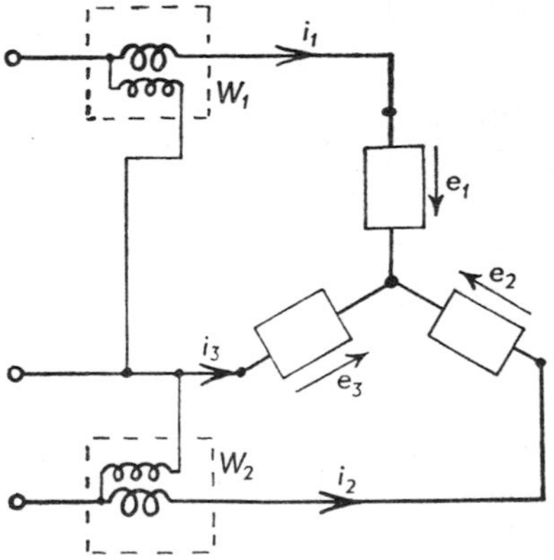

FIG. 4.13

The instantaneous total power $P = e_1i_1 + e_2i_2 + e_3i_3$. Now current i_3, does not flow through either of the wattmeter current coils, so eliminate it.

Then
$$p = e_1i_1 + e_2i_2 + e_3(-i_1 - i_2)$$
$$= i_1(e_1 - e_3) + i_2(e_2 - e_3)$$

Now i_1 is the current through the current coil of W_1 and $(e_1 - e_3)$ is the instantaneous voltage across the voltage coil of W_1. Similarly, i_2 is the current through the current coil of W_2 and $(e_2 - e_3)$ is the instantaneous voltage across the voltage coil of W_2.

$$\therefore\ p = \text{(instantaneous power through } W_1) + \text{(instantaneous power through } W_2)$$

The total average power P = (average power through W_1) + (average power through W_2)

i.e. P = algebraic sum of wattmeter readings.

Consider now the delta-connected system of Fig. 4.14.

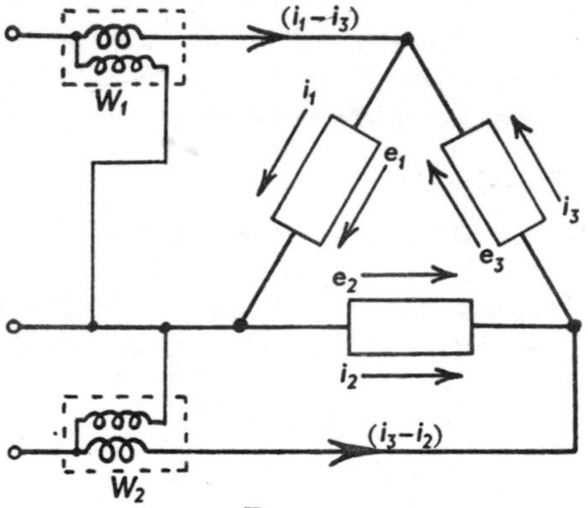

FIG. 4.14

Let the instantaneous values of currents and voltages be as shown. *Whether the system is balanced or not:*

$$e_1 + e_2 + e_3 = 0$$

The instantaneous total power $p = e_1i_1 + e_2i_2 + e_3i_3$. Now voltage, e_3, is not applied to either of the wattmeter voltage coils, so eliminate it.

Then
$$p = e_1i_1 + e_2i_2 + i_3(-e_1 - e_2)$$
$$= e_1(i_1 - i_3) + e_2(i_2 - i_3)$$
$$= e_1(i_1 - i_3) + (-e_2)(i_3 - i_2)$$
= (instantaneous power through W_1) + (instantaneous power through W_2).

Again the total average power $P =$ (average power through W_1) + (average power through W_2)

= algebraic sum of wattmeter readings.

Single-wattmeter method

Power in a *balanced* three-phase circuit can be measured, using only one wattmeter, without breaking the phases. The current coil of the instrument is connected in one line, as illustrated in Fig. 4.15, and the

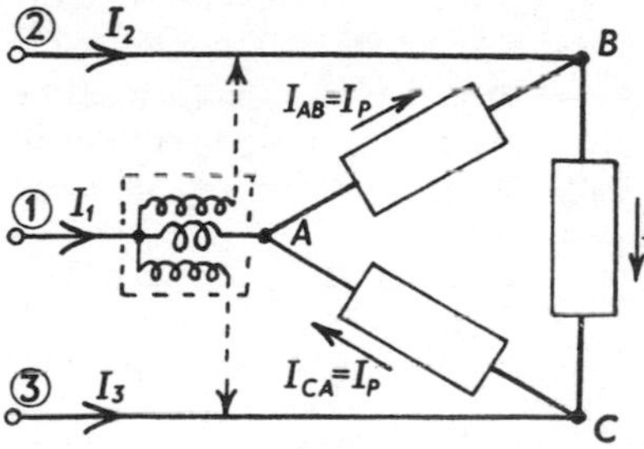

FIG. 4.15

voltage coil is connected alternately between this line and the other two lines. From the two readings on the wattmeter the total power absorbed can be found.

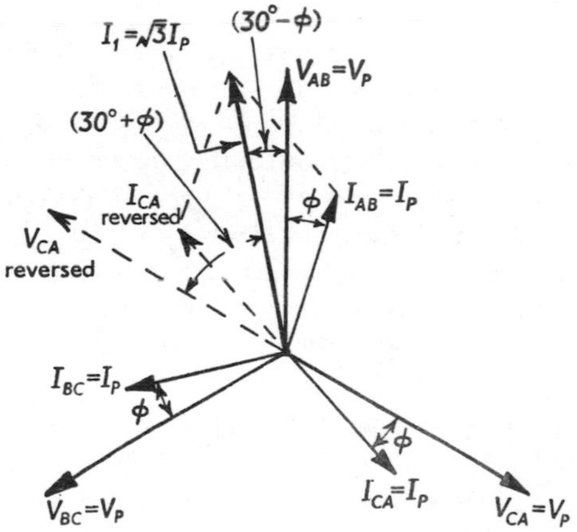

FIG. 4.16

The vector diagram for the arrangement is shown in Fig. 4.16. The current I_1 through the current coil of the wattmeter is the vector difference of I_{AB} and I_{CA}, *i.e.* it is the vector sum of I_{AB} and I_{CA} reversed.

The phase currents are assumed to be lagging behind their respective phase voltages by an angle ϕ.

When the wattmeter voltage coil is connected to **2** the voltage across the coil is V_{AB} and the phase difference between this voltage and the current I_1 through the wattmeter current coil is $(30° - \phi)$.

The wattmeter reading W_a is therefore $V_{AB}I_1 \cos(30° - \phi)$

$$= \sqrt{3}\, V_p I_p \cos(30° - \phi).$$

When the wattmeter voltage coil is connected to **3** the voltage across the coil is V_{CA}. To preserve the true cyclic rotation the voltage coil should have had the end previously at **2** connected to **1** and the end previously at **1** connected to **3**. This, of course, is the reverse of what is done, so the phase relation between the current through the wattmeter current coil and the voltage across its voltage coil is that between I_1 and V_{CA} reversed, *i.e.* $(30° + \phi)$.

The wattmeter reading, now W_b, is therefore $V_{CA}I_1 \cos(30° + \phi)$

$$= \sqrt{3}\, V_p I_p \cos(30° + \phi)$$

$$\therefore \quad W_a + W_b = \sqrt{3}\, V_p I_p \{\cos(30° - \phi) + \cos(30° + \phi)\}$$

$$= 3\, V_p I_p \cos\phi = \text{the total power}$$

It is also found that $W_a - W_b = \sqrt{3}\, V_p I_p \sin\phi$.

$$\therefore \quad \left(\frac{W_a - W_b}{W_a + W_b}\right)\sqrt{3} = \tan\phi.$$

Thus, the phase-angle of the load current and hence the power-factor can also be calculated from the wattmeter readings.

It should be noted that: (*a*) when $\phi = 0$, both wattmeters read the same, (*b*) when $\phi < 60°$, the second wattmeter reading, which is proportional to $\cos(30° + \phi)$, is positive, so the total power is given by the sum of the two wattmeter readings, (*c*) when $\phi = 60°$, the second wattmeter reading is zero, (*d*) when $\phi > 60°$, the second wattmeter reading is negative and so the total power is given by the difference of the wattmeter readings. This corresponds to the case where the power-factor is less than 0·5.

EXAMPLE. A 230 V motor has a full-load output of 10 h.p., the power-factor being 0·8 and the efficiency at full load 0·8. Determine the readings on two wattmeters which are connected to measure the power input.

Solution.

The output = 10 × 746 W = 7,460 W

The input = 7,460/0·8 = 9,325 W

If the readings on the two wattmeters are W_a and W_b,

$$W_a + W_b = 9{,}325 \text{ W} \quad . \quad . \quad . \quad . \quad . \qquad (4.1)$$

The power-factor $\cos\phi = 0{\cdot}8$, so $\tan\phi = 0{\cdot}7499$

$$\therefore \quad 0{\cdot}7499 = \frac{\sqrt{3}(W_a - W_b)}{W_a + W_b} = \frac{\sqrt{3}(W_a - W_b)}{9{,}325}$$

$$\therefore \quad W_a - W_b = 4{,}037 \text{ W} \quad . \quad . \quad . \quad . \qquad (4.2)$$

From (4.1) and (4.2),

$$\underline{W_a = 6{,}681 \text{ W}}$$

and

$$\underline{W_b = 2{,}644 \text{ W}}$$

PROBLEMS

1. Three similar coils, each of resistance 10 Ω and reactance 10 Ω, are connected (*a*) in star, (*b*) in delta, across a 400 V, three-phase supply. Find, in each case, the line current and the sum of the readings of two wattmeters connected to measure the power. [S.U.]

[*Ans.* (*a*) 16·33 A, 8,000 W;
(*b*) 48·97 A, 24,000 W.]

2. Three 20 Ω non-inductive resistors are connected in star across a three-phase supply the line voltage of which is 480 V. Three other equal non-inductive resistors are connected in delta across the same supply, so as to take the same line current. What are the resistance values of these other resistors and what is the current flowing through each of them? [S.U.] [*Ans.* 60 Ω, 8 A.]

3. Two wattmeters measure the total power in a three-phase circuit and are correctly connected. One reads 4,800 W while the other reads backwards. On reversing the latter it reads 400 W. What is the total power absorbed by the circuit and the power-factor? [S.U.]

[*Ans.* 4,400 W, 0·439.]

4. Three coils, each having a resistance of 10 Ω and an inductance of 0·02 H, are connected (*a*) in star, (*b*) in delta, to a three-phase, 50 c/s supply, the line voltage being 500 V. Calculate, for each case, the line current and the total power absorbed.

[*Ans.* (*a*) 24·44 A, 17·93 kW,
(*b*) 73·32 A, 53·89 kW.]

5. A balanced three-phase load has a power-factor of 0·447. Two wattmeters are connected to measure the power input to this load which is known to be 20 kW. Find the readings of the instruments.

[*Ans.* 21·55 kW, −1·55 kW.]

6. A three-phase transformer has its primary windings delta-connected and its secondary star-connected. The primary and secondary line voltages are 6,600 V and 380 V r.m.s., respectively. The maximum flux is 0·02 Wb and the frequency is 50 c/s.

Neglecting losses, determine the number of turns on each primary and secondary winding. [S.U.] [*Ans.* 1,486, 50.]

7. A two-phase, 200 V (per phase), induction motor is to be rewound with a star-connected three-phase winding suitable for a line voltage of 400 V, producing the same air-gap flux. The two-phase winding has 350 turns per phase, the magnetizing current being 6 A. Determine the approximate number of turns per phase required for the three-phase winding, and the magnetizing current. [S.U.] [*Ans.* 405, 3·45 A.]

8. Each of two wattmeters connected to measure the power input to a three-phase circuit reads 10 kW on a balanced load when the power-factor is unity. What does each instrument read when the power-factor falls to (*a*) 0·866 lagging, (*b*) 0·5 lagging, the total three-phase power remaining unaltered? [*Ans.* (*a*) 13·33 kW, 6·67 kW, (*b*) 20 kW, 0.]

9. Each phase of a delta-connected load consists of a 50 Ω resistor in series with a 50 μF capacitor. Determine the line and phase currents, the total power and the kilovolt-amperes when the load is connected to a 440 V, three-phase, 50 c/s supply. Draw a vector diagram to scale showing the voltage and current for each phase and the three line currents.
[*Ans.* 9·46 A, 5·46 A, 4,480 W, 7·24.]

10. A 400 V, three-phase, delta-connected motor is coupled to a d.c. generator which, on full-load, provides a power output of 10 kW. If the efficiencies of the generator and motor are 85% and 90% respectively and the motor power-factor is 0·88, calculate the motor line and phase currents when the generator is on full-load.
[*Ans.* 21·4 A, 12·4 A.]

CHAPTER 5

COMPLEX QUANTITIES

It has been shown in Chapter 3 that sinusoidal alternating quantities can be represented by vectors, with considerable advantage in ease of manipulation. (The representation of a sinusoid by a single rotating vector is not complete, however, and leads to difficulties with multiplication—as will be seen later.) Even so, many common a.c. circuits, particularly those with series and parallel combinations of impedances are rather difficult, if not impossible, to analyze by simple vector methods. This difficulty is resolved by expressing the vectors in algebraic form, so that the relationship between the voltages, currents and impedances appear as equations, which can be solved by algebraic techniques. To do this, *complex* quantities are necessary, and this chapter is concerned with the properties and algebra of such quantities.

Representation of vectors by complex quantities

Simple numbers or magnitudes, positive or negative, may be represented, in one dimension only, as lengths, measured along a straight line from an origin, but the vectors used in electric circuit theory, having direction as well as magnitude, require two dimensions, and are shown as lines on a plane. Thus, in Fig. 5.1 the magnitude of the vector OA is given by its length, and its direction is given by the angle θ between it and the reference axis Ox. Thus the vector may be completely described in terms of its length, or modulus, r and its phase-angle, or argument, θ. Alternatively, it may also be completely described, with reference to the axes Ox, Oy by the co-ordinates of A, $OB = a$ and $BA = b$. This is equivalent to resolving the vector into its two components, one parallel to the x axis and the other parallel to the y axis. The relations between the two methods of description are easily seen by inspection of Fig. 5.1. They are:

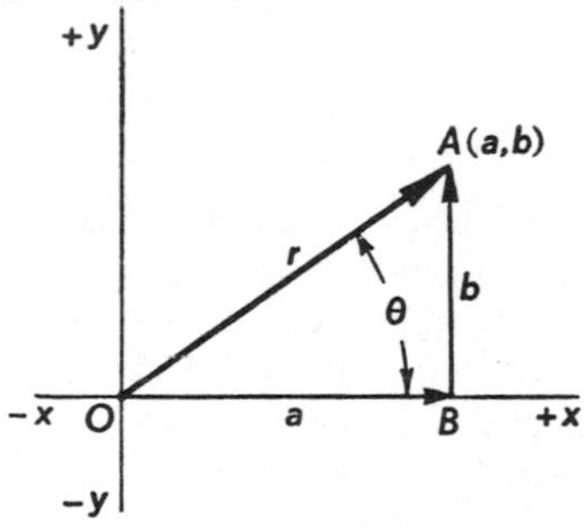

FIG. 5.1

$$r = \sqrt{(a^2 + b^2)};\ \tan\theta = b/a;\ \cos\theta = a/r;\ \sin\theta = b/r.$$

Taking the x axis as the reference direction, the component vector OB can be simply designated a, but it is necessary to use some means of signifying that the component vector BA is perpendicular to the reference axis. This is done by multiplying its scalar length b by the function 'j', so that jb denotes 'a vector of magnitude b perpendicular to the reference axis'. Thus j is an operator, which when used as the multiplier of a vector, turns it through 90° counter-clockwise, without changing its magnitude. Then the original vector can be expressed in algebraic form as the sum of its components $OA = a + jb$.

This in itself is useful as a convenient system of notation, but because the operator j and functions thereof, can be manipulated according to certain rules, it becomes possible to add, subtract, multiply, divide and operate in other ways upon vectors by algebraic routines, without the necessity of graphical constructions.

Since multiplying by j turns a vector lying along the Ox axis through 90°, multiplying by j^2 must turn the vector through 180° counter-clockwise. Thus, in Fig. 5.2, if $OC_1 = c$, $OC_2 = jc$ and $OC_3 = j^2c$. But $OC_3 = -OC_1$, and therefore $j^2 = -1$ and $j = \sqrt{(-1)}$, which is, of course, imaginary. This is only to be expected, because if j *were* expressible as an ordinary number it would mean that a two-dimensional quantity could be expressed in terms of one dimension, which is manifestly untrue. Quantities such as jc or jb are termed *imaginary* and quantities such as $(a + jb)$ are *complex*, a being the *real* component and jb the *imaginary* component.

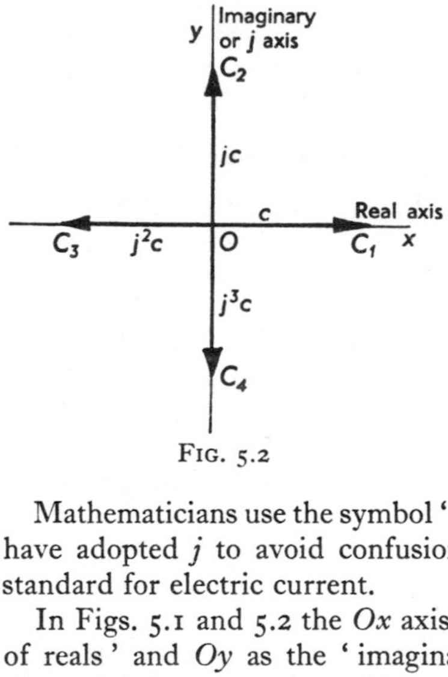

Fig. 5.2

Mathematicians use the symbol 'i' to represent $\sqrt{(-1)}$ but engineers have adopted j to avoid confusion, the symbol i being a recognized standard for electric current.

In Figs. 5.1 and 5.2 the Ox axis is known as the 'real axis' or 'axis of reals' and Oy as the 'imaginary axis' or 'j axis', and the two-dimensional space upon which the vectors are drawn is called the *complex plane*.

The relationships between powers of j are very easy to establish, either algebraically or from Fig. 5.2. For instance, remembering that $j^2 = -1$:

$$1/j = j/j^2 = j/(-1) = -j$$
$$j^3 = j^2j = -j = 1/j$$
$$j^4 = j^2j^2 = (-1).(-1) = +1$$

In Fig. 5.2 OC_4 is obtained by multiplying OC_1 by j^3, but may also be obtained by multiplying OC_1 by $-j$ (or by $1/j$) that is, by turning the vector 90° clockwise instead of 270° counter-clockwise. Multiplying by j^4 turns the vector through 360° so that $j^4 = +1$.

It is easily demonstrated that multiplying by the operator j turns any vector through a right-angle counter-clockwise, whether the original vector lies along one of the reference axes or not. Thus, in Fig. 5.3

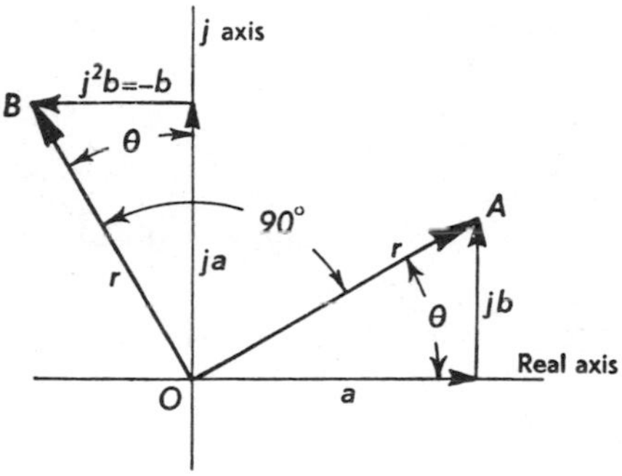

FIG. 5.3

the vector OA, is denoted by $(a + jb)$ and the vector OB, perpendicular to OA, and of the same magnitude, must be denoted by $(-b + ja)$ from the geometry of the diagram. The same result is obtained algebraically as follows:

$$j(a + jb) = ja + j^2b = ja - b = (-b + ja)$$

Symbol conventions

It is desirable, and indeed necessary, to adopt suitable conventions for denoting vector or complex quantities, so that they can be clearly distinguished from scalar quantities. It is now usual in printed texts to use heavy, Clarendon type for vectors and ordinary type for scalars. For example: $\mathbf{R} = a + jb$, but $r = \sqrt{(a^2 + b^2)}$. This convention is impracticable in handwriting and vectors are denoted by a variety of symbols, such as $\dot{R}$, $\underset{.}{R}$, $\bar{R}$, $\underline{R}$ or $[R]$. The symbol preferred naturally depends on the writer, but it is perhaps worth pointing out that dots are easily overlooked. In many cases, however, it is unnecessary to use special symbols to indicate vector quantities, because they are easily distinguished from scalars by the context. Thus, it is evident that R is a vector quantity when it appears in the equation $R = (a + jb)$. In electric-circuit problems, where the vector quantities are voltages, currents, impedances and admittances, it is often quicker to denote these by the ordinary symbols, V, I, Z, Y, indicating the scalar magnitudes or moduli where necessary by $|V|$, $|I|$, $|Z|$, $|Y|$.

Alternative expressions for vectors

As already explained, the vector OA in Fig. 5.1 can be expressed in terms of the Cartesian co-ordinates of A, as $\mathbf{R} = (a + jb)$ or alternatively in terms of the polar co-ordinates, r and θ, the latter being measured counter-clockwise from the real axis. A purely conventional mode of expression is $\mathbf{R} = r\underline{|\theta}$.

The vector OA can also be written as $\mathbf{R} = r(\cos\theta + j\sin\theta)$ since $a = r\cos\theta$, $b = r\sin\theta$. Consider the vector to have constant modulus r, but variable argument θ, that is, to be rotating. Then, differentiating with respect to θ, $d\mathbf{R}/d\theta = r(-\sin\theta + j\cos\theta) = r(j^2\sin\theta + j\cos\theta) = rj(\cos\theta + j\sin\theta) = j\mathbf{R}$.

Another mathematical function exhibits similar properties to this, namely the exponential function,

$$*\exp(mx) = 1 + mx/1! + (mx)^2/2! + \ldots$$
$$d\{\exp(mx)\}/dx = m\{\exp(mx)\}$$

Therefore, if $m = j$ and $x = \theta$,

$$d\{r\exp(j\theta)\}/d\theta = jr\exp(j\theta)$$

Thus it might be suspected that $r\exp(j\theta) = r(\cos\theta + j\sin\theta)$ and the fact that this is true can be shown, either by expanding $\sin\theta$ and $\cos\theta$ as infinite series, or in the following way:

Assume that $\cos\theta + j\sin\theta = A + B\theta + C\theta^2 + D\theta^3 + \ldots$ is true for all values of θ. Then when $\theta = 0$, $A = 1$.

Differentiating with respect to θ, $-\sin\theta + j\cos\theta = 0 + B + 2C\theta + 3D\theta^2 + \ldots$ and putting $\theta = 0$, $B = j$.

Differentiating again, $-\cos\theta - j\sin\theta = 2!C + (3 \cdot 2 \cdot)D\theta + \ldots$ so that putting $\theta = 0$ again $C = -1/2! = j^2/2!$

Continuing this process gives $D = -j/3! = j^3/3!$ and so on, so that

$$\cos\theta + j\sin\theta = 1 + j\theta + (j\theta)^2/2! + (j\theta)^3/3! + \ldots$$
$$= \exp(j\theta)$$

The polar and exponential expressions, $r\underline{|\theta}$, $r(\cos\theta + j\sin\theta)$ and $r\exp(j\theta)$ are most convenient when products and quotients of vectors are required, as will be seen later. The logarithm is obtained most easily from the exponential form, since

$$\dagger \ln\{r(\exp j\theta)\} = \ln(r) + j\theta$$

Addition and subtraction of vectors

Vectors are added by the parallelogram method as shown in Fig. 5.4 so that the vector sum of $OA = (a + jb)$ and $OB = (c + jd)$ is given

* $\exp(mx) \equiv e^{(mx)}$. This form is frequently used for convenience in printing.

† $\ln(x) \equiv \log_e(x)$. This form is frequently used for convenience in printing.

by $OC = \mathbf{R} = (a + c) + j(b + d)$. The modulus of this resultant is therefore $\sqrt{\{(a + c)^2 + (b + d)^2\}}$ and its phase-angle or argument is given by $\tan \phi = (b + d)/(a + c)$.

To subtract vector $\mathbf{R}_2$ from $\mathbf{R}_1$ the negative of the former is added to the latter, giving

$$(a + jb) - (c + jd) = (a + jb) + (-c - jd) = (a - c) + j(b - d).$$

In this case the resultant modulus $= \sqrt{\{(a - c)^2 + (b - d)^2\}}$ and the argument is given by $\tan \phi = (b - d)/(a - c)$.

These results can be extended to any number of vectors and they may be combined in any order, thus $\mathbf{R}_1 + \mathbf{R}_2 + \mathbf{R}_3 - \mathbf{R}_4 = (\mathbf{R}_1 + \mathbf{R}_3) + \mathbf{R}_2 - \mathbf{R}_4 = (\mathbf{R}_1 - \mathbf{R}_4) + (\mathbf{R}_3 + \mathbf{R}_2)$, and so on.

The addition and subtraction of vectors in polar or exponential form is less straightforward, and they must first be expressed in rectangular co-ordinate form.

$$\text{Thus } r_1\underline{|\phi} + r_2\underline{|\theta} = r_1(\cos \phi + j \sin \phi) + r_2(\cos \theta + j \sin \theta)$$
$$= (r_1 \cos \phi + r_2 \cos \theta) + j(r_1 \sin \phi + r_2 \sin \theta)$$

Multiplication of vectors

Multiplying a vector by a scalar quantity merely changes its magnitude but not its argument or phase. Multiplying by j turns a vector through 90° counter-clockwise without changing its magnitude (see Fig. 5.3). The first of these operations can be considered as multiplica-

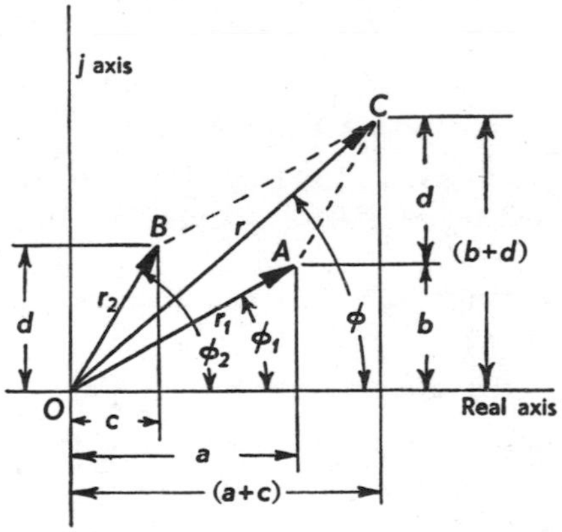

FIG. 5.4

tion by a vector of zero phase-angle, that lying along the real or reference axis. The second is equivalent to multiplication by a vector of unit modulus whose phase-angle is 90°. In general, multiplying one vector by another changes both magnitude and phase-angle. Consider the vectors $OA = \mathbf{R}_1 = (a + jb)$ and $OB = \mathbf{R}_2 = (c + jd)$ in Fig. 5.5. The product is $\mathbf{R} = \mathbf{R}_1\mathbf{R}_2 = \mathbf{R}_1(c + jd) = c\mathbf{R}_1 + jd\mathbf{R}_1$. $\mathbf{R}$ is therefore the vector sum of two components. The first, $c\mathbf{R}_1$ with the same angle as $\mathbf{R}_1$ is $OD = c(a + jb)$. The second is obtained by multiplying

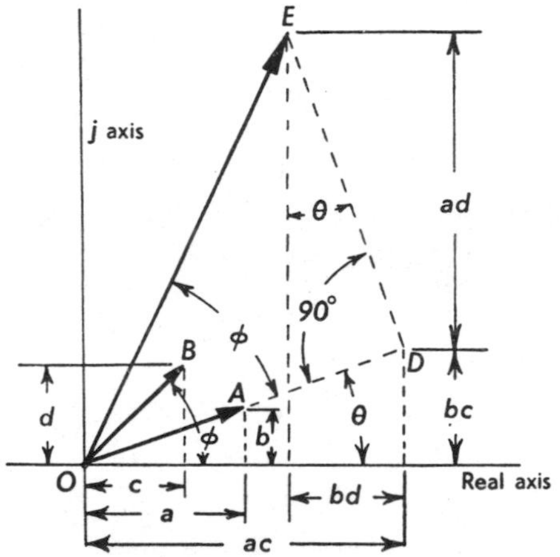

FIG. 5.5

the magnitude of $\mathbf{R}_1$ by d and turning through 90° to take account of the factor j, giving DE, perpendicular to OD. It is clear from the diagram that the real and imaginary components of DE are $-(bd)$ and jad, so that $jd\mathbf{R}_1 = (-bd + jad)$.

Therefore, $\mathbf{R} = (ac + jbc) + (-bd + jad)$

$$= (ac - bd) + j(bc + ad)$$

Since the magnitude $|OD| = cr_1$ and $|DE| = dr_1$, triangles ODE and OFB are similar and angle $AOE = \phi$; angle FOE, the argument of the product vector $= (\theta + \phi)$.

The modulus of the resultant, the length of the vector OE,

$$= \sqrt{\{|OD|^2 + |DE|^2\}} = \sqrt{\{c^2r_1^2 + d^2r_1^2\}} = r_1\sqrt{(c^2 + d^2)} = r_1r_2.$$

= the product of the moduli of the original vectors.

These results are obtained more quickly by applying complex algebra, as follows:

$$\mathbf{R} = \mathbf{R}_1\mathbf{R}_2 = (a + jb)(c + jd) = ac + jbc + jad + j^2bd$$
$$= (ac - bd) + j(bc + ad)$$

The modulus of $\mathbf{R}$ (written $|\mathbf{R}|$) is given by:

$$r = \sqrt{\{(ac - bd)^2 + (bc + ad)^2\}} \text{ which gives}$$
$$r = \sqrt{\{(a^2 + b^2)(c^2 + d^2)\}} = r_1r_2, \text{ as before.}$$

The argument or phase-angle of $\mathbf{R} = \arctan$ * $\{(bc + ad)/(ac - bd)\}$

$$= \arctan \{(b/a + d/c)/(1 - bd/ac)\}$$
$$= \arctan \{(\tan \theta + \tan \phi)/(1 - \tan \theta \tan \phi)\} = (\theta + \phi) \text{ as before.}$$

Alternatively, using the polar forms,

$$\mathbf{R} = \mathbf{R}_1\mathbf{R}_2 = r_1(\cos \theta + j \sin \theta)r_2(\cos \phi + j \sin \phi)$$
$$= r_1 r_2\{(\cos \theta \cos \phi - \sin \theta \sin \phi) + j(\sin \theta \cos \phi + \sin \phi \cos \theta)\}$$
$$= r_1 r_2\{\cos (\theta + \phi) + j \sin (\theta + \phi)\}$$
$$\mathbf{R} = \mathbf{R}_1\mathbf{R}_2 = (r_1 \exp j\theta)(r_2 \exp j\phi)$$
$$= r_1 r_2 \,.\, \exp j(\theta + \phi)$$

Division of vectors

The division of one vector by another is most easily carried out when they are expressed in exponential form, thus,

$$\mathbf{R}_1/\mathbf{R}_2 = (r_1 \exp j\theta)/(r_2 \exp j\phi)$$
$$= (r_1/r_2) \exp j(\theta - \phi)$$

However, it will be instructive to perform the division using the other forms of complex expression, to illustrate the routine.

If $\mathbf{R}_1 = (a + jb)$ and $\mathbf{R}_2 = (c + jd)$,

then $\mathbf{R} = \mathbf{R}_1/\mathbf{R}_2 = (a + jb)/(c + jd)$

To obtain this in the usual form as the sum of real and imaginary components, both numerator and denominator are multiplied by $(c - jd)$, which is the *conjugate* † of $(c + jd)$, giving

$$\mathbf{R} = \{(a + jb)(c - jd)\}/\{(c + jd)(c - jd)\}$$
$$= \{(ac + bd) + j(bc - ad)\}/(c^2 + d^2)$$
$$= (ac + bd)/(c^2 + d^2) + j(bc - ad)/(c^2 + d^2)$$

This process of eliminating the imaginary components from the denominator is known as *rationalization*. If the denominator had been of the form $(c - jd)$ the multiplier would be the conjugate $(c + jd)$, giving the vector quotient as $(a + jb)(c + jd)/(c^2 + d^2)$. Note that the denominator is the square of the modulus of the divisor vector in both cases.†

* $\arctan x \equiv \tan^{-1} x$.

† *Conjugate vectors.* The conjugate of the vector

$$\mathbf{R} = (a + jb) \text{ is } \mathbf{R}^* = (a - jb), \text{ or if}$$
$$\mathbf{R} = r(\cos \theta + j \sin \theta) = r\exp(j\theta)$$
$$\mathbf{R}^* = r(\cos \theta - j \sin \theta) = r\exp(-j\theta).$$

Obviously the conjugate of $(a - jb)$ is $(a + jb)$.
In every case, $\mathbf{RR}^* = (a^2 + b^2) = r^2$.

r, the modulus of the quotient $\mathbf{R}$, is given by:

$$r = |\mathbf{R}_1/\mathbf{R}_2| = \sqrt{\{(ac + bd)^2 + (bc - ad)^2\}}/(c^2 + d^2)$$
$$= \sqrt{\{(a^2 + b^2)(c^2 + d^2)\}}/(c^2 + d^2)$$
$$= \sqrt{(a^2 + b^2)}/\sqrt{(c^2 + d^2)} = |\mathbf{R}_1|/|\mathbf{R}_2| = r_1/r_2$$

which is the quotient of the moduli of the original vectors.

It is left to the reader to show that the phase-angle of the resultant is $(\theta - \phi)$ where $\tan\theta = b/a$, $\tan\phi = d/c$.

Again, for $\mathbf{R} = r_1(\cos\theta + j\sin\theta)/r_2(\cos\phi + j\sin\phi)$ the rationalizing multiplier is $(\cos\phi - j\sin\phi)$, giving

$$\mathbf{R} = (r_1/r_2)(\cos\theta + j\sin\theta)(\cos\phi - j\sin\phi)/(\cos^2\phi + \sin^2\phi)$$
$$= (r_1/r_2)\{\cos(\theta - \phi) + j\sin(\theta - \phi)\}$$

Powers of a vector

It follows from the above that the square of a vector is obtained by squaring the modulus and doubling the phase-angle or argument, or more generally,

$$\mathbf{R}^n = (r\exp j\theta)^n = (r^n)\exp(jn\theta)$$
$$= r^n(\cos n\theta + j\sin n\theta)$$

This holds whether n is positive or negative, integral or fractional.

Equality of vectors

Vectors are equal when they have equal moduli and equal arguments.

Thus if $\mathbf{R}_1 = r_1\underline{|\theta} = (a + jb)$ is equal to

$\mathbf{R}_2 = r_2\underline{|\phi} = (c + jd)$, then

$r_1 = r_2;\ \theta = \phi;\ a = c;\ b = d.$

A well-known example of this occurs in the conditions for balance in an a.c. bridge, which usually appear as a single equality between two complex quantities. This means that there are two distinct equalities or two conditions to be satisfied.

Summary of rules and practical procedures

1. To add or subtract vectors the real and imaginary components are added or subtracted separately. If the vectors are in polar form they must be converted into rectangular Cartesian co-ordinate form before combination.

2. For multiplication and division the most convenient form is the polar or exponential. The modulus of a product is the product of the individual moduli and the argument, the sum of the individual arguments. The modulus of a quotient is the quotient of the moduli and the argument is the difference of the arguments.

3. If addition or subtraction and multiplication or division are required, the rectangular co-ordinate form is usually convenient since both kinds of manipulation can be carried out. However, where it is necessary to perform a large number of multiplications and divisions it is often best to convert from rectangular co-ordinates to the polar form and back again as required. Such problems are found, for instance, in the analysis of closed-loop control systems. Graphical methods * are often used to assist in the conversion, and special slide-rules have also been devised for this purpose.†

EXAMPLE. Evaluate $(6 + j4) + (3 + j3)$ and determine the modulus and argument of the resultant.

Solution.

$$\begin{aligned} \text{Resultant} &= (6 + 3) + j(4 + 3) = \underline{9 + j7} \\ \text{Modulus} &= \sqrt{(9^2 + 7^2)} = \underline{11{\cdot}4} \\ \text{Argument} &= \arctan (7/9) = \text{arc cos } (9/11{\cdot}4) \\ &= \text{arc sin } (7/11{\cdot}4) = \underline{37^\circ\ 53'} \end{aligned}$$

EXAMPLE. Evaluate $\mathbf{R} = (2 + j2)(6 - j3)$.

Solutions.

Method (*a*)

$$\mathbf{R} = 12 + j12 - j6 - j^2 6 = \underline{18 + j6}$$

Method (*b*)

$$\begin{aligned} \mathbf{R} &= 6(1 + j)(2 - j) \\ &= 6(\sqrt{2}\,|\underline{45^\circ})(\sqrt{5}\,|\underline{-26^\circ\ 34'}) = 19\,|\underline{18^\circ\ 26'} \\ &= 19(\cos 18^\circ\ 26' + j \sin 18^\circ\ 26') = 19(0{\cdot}9487 + j0{\cdot}3162) = \underline{18 + j6} \end{aligned}$$

EXAMPLE. Divide $(10 + j7)$ by $(6 + j)$.

Solutions.

Method (*a*)

$$\begin{aligned} \mathbf{R} &= (10 + j7)(6 - j)/(6^2 + 1^2) \\ &= (60 + j42 - j10 + 7)/37 = (67 + j32)/37 \\ &= 1{\cdot}81 - j0{\cdot}865 \end{aligned}$$

$$\begin{aligned} \text{Modulus} &= \sqrt{(3{\cdot}275 + 0{\cdot}75)} = \underline{2{\cdot}0} \\ \text{Argument} &= \arctan (0{\cdot}865/1{\cdot}81) = \underline{25^\circ\ 30'} \end{aligned}$$

Method (*b*)

$$(10 + j7) = \sqrt{(149)}\,|\underline{35^\circ}\quad (6 + j) = \sqrt{(37)}\,|\underline{9^\circ\ 30'}$$

$$\mathbf{R} = \sqrt{(149/37)}\,|\underline{35^\circ - 9^\circ\ 30'} = \underline{2{\cdot}0\,|25^\circ\ 30'}$$

* J. Barbour, "Conversion of Complex to Polar Co-ordinates by Nomogram", *Electrical Energy*, 1, p. 216 (1957).

† See E. Friedlander, "A New Vector Slide Rule", *G.E.C. Journal*, **20**, p. 91 (1953).

PROBLEMS

1. Evaluate $(2 + j5) - (5 - j2) + (1 - j4)$ and express the result in both Cartesian and polar forms.

[*Ans.* $(-2 + j3)$, $3{\cdot}606\angle 123^\circ\, 42'$.]

2. Add together $5\angle 30^\circ$ ($\equiv 5 \cos 30^\circ + j5 \sin 30^\circ$) and $4\angle 45^\circ$ giving the result in polar form. [*Ans.* $8{\cdot}91\angle 36^\circ\, 40'$.]

3. Evaluate $6\angle 15^\circ - 4\angle 40^\circ + 7\angle -60^\circ$.

[*Ans.* $(6{\cdot}23 - j7{\cdot}08) = 9{\cdot}33\angle -48^\circ\, 37'$.]

4. Multiply $50\angle 60^\circ$ by $(7 - j9)$. [*Ans.* $571\angle 8^\circ = 565 + j79{\cdot}4$.]

5. Multiply $(2 + j3)$ by $(5 + j2)$. [*Ans.* $4 + j19$.]

6. Determine the resultant of the product $(10 + j33)(7 + j3)(3 - j2)$ by direct multiplication of the factors as given and also by first converting to polar form.

[*Ans.* $(435 + j841) = 945\angle 62^\circ\, 36'$.]

7. Divide $(4 + j6)$ by $(5 + j2)$

[*Ans.* $(1{\cdot}1 + j0{\cdot}758)$
$= 1{\cdot}34\angle 34^\circ\, 36'$.]

8. Evaluate

$(10 + j33)(4 + j5)(6 - j4)/(7 + j3)$.

[*Ans.* $209\angle 67^\circ\, 45'$.]

9. Determine the modulus and phase-angle of $50(1 + j\omega 3)/\{(1 + j\omega)(1 + j\omega 2)(1 + j\omega 4)\}$ for $\omega = 0{\cdot}1$, $0{\cdot}2$ and $0{\cdot}5$. It is suggested that the moduli and phase-angles of each factor be obtained by the simple graphical construction illustrated in Fig. 5.6, where for $\omega = 0{\cdot}2$ for example $(1 + j\omega 3) = (1 + j0{\cdot}6) = r_1\angle\theta_1$ and for $\omega = 0{\cdot}5$, $(1 + j\omega 4) = (1 + j2) = r_2\angle\theta_2$.

[*Ans.* $47{\cdot}2$, $-23{\cdot}5^\circ$;
$41{\cdot}1$, $-42{\cdot}5^\circ$;
$25{\cdot}5$, $-77{\cdot}5^\circ$.]

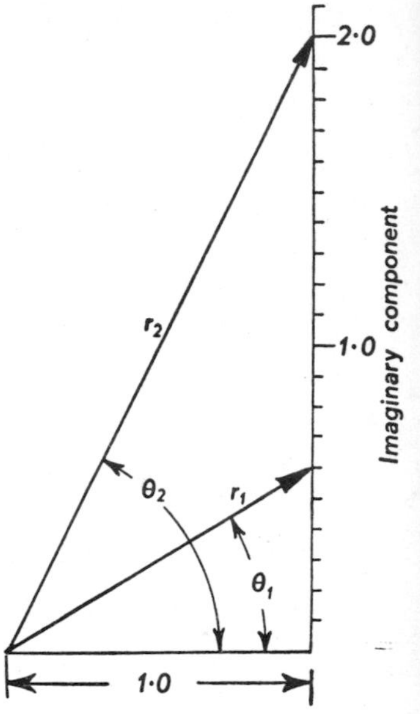

FIG. 5.6

10. If $(a + jb)/(2 + j3) = (5 - j2)/(3 - j4)$ show that $a = 4/25$ and $b = 97/25$.

11. Prove that the condition necessary for the resultant of $\{(a + jb)(a - jd)\}/\{(a + jb) + (a - jd)\}$ to have zero argument is that $a^2 = bd$.

CHAPTER 6

THE USE OF COMPLEX QUANTITIES IN A.C. CIRCUITS

The basic algebra and properties of complex quantities given in Chapter 5 are sufficient for the solution of many a.c. circuit problems. Since sinusoidal alternating quantities can be represented by vectors, and since the latter can be expressed as complex quantities, so can the former. Thus, for a circuit in which the instantaneous current $i = I \sin \omega t$ lags the voltage $v = V \sin (\omega t + \phi)$ by the angle ϕ, the vector diagram is as shown in Fig. 6.1. The voltage vector OB and the current vector OA, expressed in complex form are

$$\mathbf{V} = V\{\cos(\omega t + \phi) + j \sin(\omega t + \phi)\}$$

and

$$\mathbf{I} = I\{\cos \omega t + j \sin \omega t\}.$$

Both these vectors rotate counter-clockwise at a speed ω radians/sec.

Vector impedance

The vector diagram shown in Fig. 6.1, and the above expressions for the voltage and current would apply to a circuit consisting of a resistance

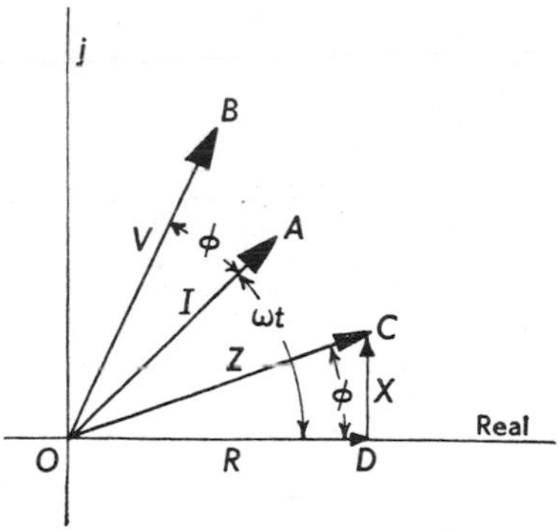

FIG. 6.1

R ohms in series with an inductive reactance X ohms ($X = L\omega$), supplied at frequency $f = (\omega/2\pi)$ c/s. Then, $\tan \phi = X/R$ and the ratio $V/I = Z = \sqrt{(R^2 + X^2)}$.

Thus, to obtain the vector voltage from the vector current the magnitude of the latter must be multiplied by Z and the phase-angle must be advanced by ϕ. This is accomplished, as explained in Chapter 5, by multiplying the current vector by another vector of modulus Z and phase-angle ϕ. This multiplying vector is the 'vector impedance' or, if expressed in complex form, the 'complex impedance', as it may be called to distinguish it from the simple scalar ratio V/I, and is denoted by the symbol $\mathbf{Z}$ and shown in Fig. 6.1 as OC. In complex form,

$$\mathbf{Z} = Z(\cos\phi + j\sin\phi) = Z(R/Z + jX/Z)$$

or $\mathbf{Z} = (R + jX)$, so that the components of OC are $OD = R$ and $DC = X$.

The same result is obtained analytically as follows:

$$\begin{aligned} \mathbf{I} &= I\{\cos\omega t + j\sin\omega t\} \\ \text{and } \mathbf{V} &= V\{\cos(\omega t + \phi) + j\sin(\omega t + \phi)\} \\ &= V\{\cos\phi(\cos\omega t + j\sin\omega t) + j\sin\phi(\cos\omega t + j\sin\omega t)\} \\ &= V\{(\cos\omega t + j\sin\omega t)(\cos\phi + j\sin\phi)\} \\ &= IZ\{(\cos\omega t + j\sin\omega t)(\cos\phi + j\sin\phi)\} \\ &= \mathbf{I}(R + jX) \\ &= \mathbf{IZ} \end{aligned}$$

The impedance vector may also be written in the three forms,

$$\mathbf{Z} = Z(\cos\phi + j\sin\phi) = Z\underline{|\phi} = Z\exp(j\phi).$$

It is important to realize that this vector is different from the vectors representing voltage and current. *The latter rotate but the impedance vector does not.*

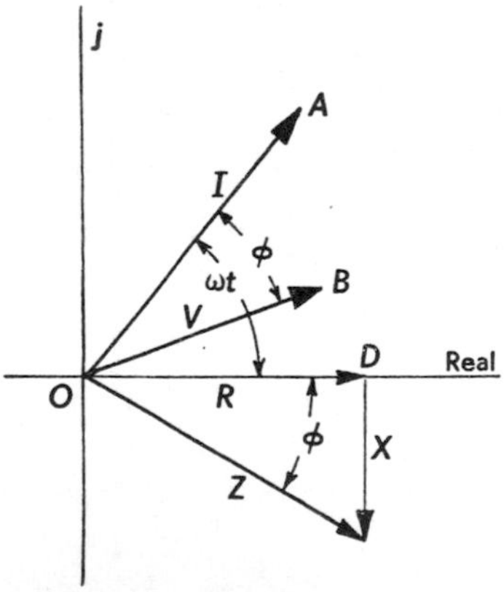

FIG. 6.2

For a circuit consisting of a resistor in series with a capacitor, the voltage lags the current and ϕ is negative, the complex impedance being $\mathbf{Z} = R - j(1/\omega C)$. The vector diagram for this case is shown in Fig. 6.2, the impedance vector having a negative imaginary component. It is convenient to consider that $\mathbf{Z} = (R + jX)$ for all series circuits, taking X as negative for a capacitance, namely $X = -(1/\omega C)$. For a circuit having resistance, inductance and capacitance in series, $X = (\omega L - 1/\omega C)$ as given in Chapter 3.

For a pure resistance, $\mathbf{Z} = R + j0 = R$ and $\phi = 0$.
For a pure inductance, $\mathbf{Z} = 0 + j\omega L = j\omega L$ and $\phi = +90^\circ$.
For a pure capacitance, $\mathbf{Z} = -j/(\omega C)$ and $\phi = -90^\circ$.

The vectors of voltage and current are usually considered to have moduli or magnitudes equal to the r.m.s. values, rather than peak values, and this convention is also applied to the moduli of the complex quantities representing the voltages and currents. The impedance, being the ratio of voltage to current, is not affected by this. Moreover, in practice it is usually unnecessary to consider the voltage and current as rotating vectors, since they rotate at the same speed, and it is their magnitudes and phase-relationships which are of importance. Most problems are simplified by taking either the current or voltage vector to lie along the real axis (see Chapter 3), so having zero 'j' component. This reduces the arithmetic considerably in the majority of cases.

Admittance

The complex-quantity technique is of greatest value in the analysis of circuits with parallel branches and in such problems, the admittance, symbol **Y** (modulus Y) is of service. **Y**, which is $1/\mathbf{Z}$ is therefore also a vector or a complex quantity. The terms 'vector admittance' or 'complex admittance' may be used to distinguish **Y** from the scalar admittance $Y = 1/Z$ where necessary.

For a circuit consisting of resistance and reactance in series, $\mathbf{Z} = (R + jX)$, and

$$\begin{aligned}\mathbf{Y} &= 1/(R + jX) = (R - jX)/(R^2 + X^2) \\ &= R/(R^2 + X^2) - jX/(R^2 + X^2) \\ &= R/Z^2 - jX/Z^2 \\ &= (1/Z)(\cos\phi - j\sin\phi) \\ &= Y(\cos\phi - j\sin\phi)\end{aligned}$$

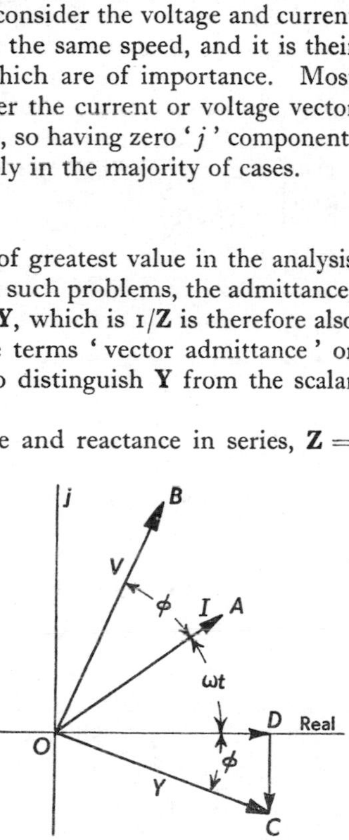

FIG. 6.3

Simple and direct slide-rule methods have been described for deriving an impedance from an admittance and vice-versa.* **Y** may also be written $Y\lfloor{-\phi}$ or $Y\exp(-j\phi)$ and may be represented by the *non-rotating* vector OC in Fig. 6.3, which shows the vector diagram for an inductive reactance and corresponds to Fig. 6.1.

The admittance vector is that vector by which the voltage is multiplied to obtain the current, *i.e.* $\mathbf{I} = \mathbf{V} \cdot \mathbf{Y} = \mathbf{V}/\mathbf{Z}$.

As already stated, X and ϕ are positive for an inductive circuit, and the corresponding admittance therefore has a negative imaginary component DC as shown in Fig. 6.3. For a circuit with resistance and

* See T. H. Barton, "Deriving Impedance from Admittance", *Electrical Review*, **159**, p. 1088 (1956), and E. Friedlander, "A New Vector Slide Rule", *G.E.C. Journal*, **20**, p. 91 (1953).

capacitance in series the admittance vector has a *positive* imaginary component, corresponding to the negative imaginary component of the impedance vector, in Fig. 6.2.

The real component of admittance is the conductance G, the imaginary component is the susceptance B, so that $\mathbf{Y} = G - jB$. Note that B is positive when X is positive. (Some authors prefer to write $\mathbf{Y} = G + jB$, taking B as negative when X is positive.)

The relation $\mathbf{Y} = Y(\cos \phi - j \sin \phi)$ was developed for a circuit consisting of resistance and reactance in series, but is true for any circuit or part of a circuit, and it therefore follows that the conductance $G = Y \cos \phi$ and that the susceptance $B = Y \sin \phi$ as shown already in Chapter 3.

Series circuits

For a circuit consisting of two impedances in series, as shown in Fig. 6.4, the total applied voltage is the vector sum of the voltages across

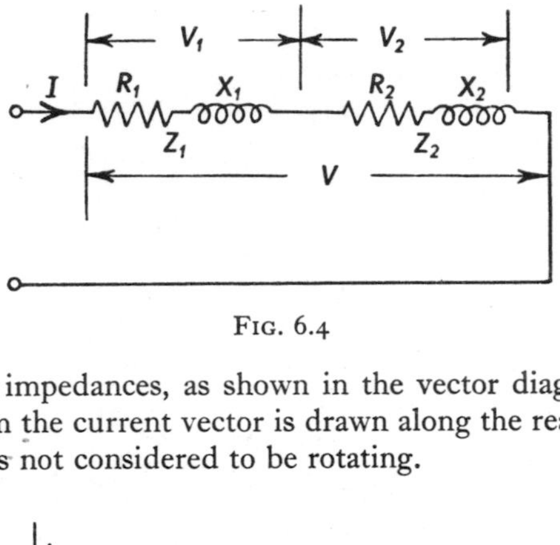

FIG. 6.4

the individual impedances, as shown in the vector diagram, Fig. 6.5. In this diagram the current vector is drawn along the real axis for convenience and is not considered to be rotating.

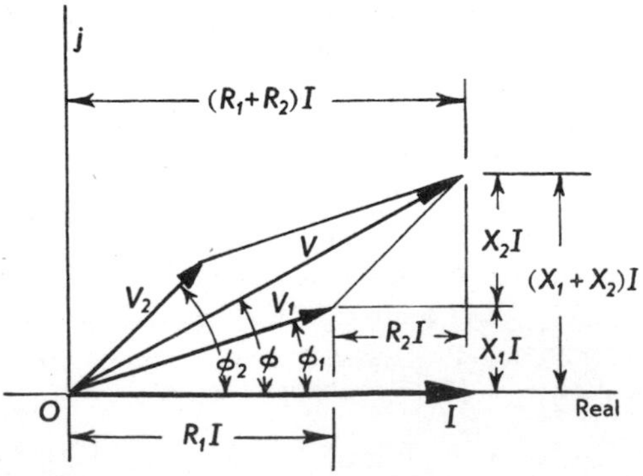

FIG. 6.5

The same results are obtained, however, in the more general case with the current vector at any angle to the real axis, the voltage vectors also being rotated through the same angle so that their phase relationships to the current remain as before.

The total applied voltage is given by:

$$\mathbf{V} = \mathbf{V}_1 + \mathbf{V}_2 = \mathbf{I}\mathbf{Z}_1 + \mathbf{I}\mathbf{Z}_2 = \mathbf{I}(\mathbf{Z}_1 + \mathbf{Z}_2)$$
$$= \mathbf{I}\{(R_1 + jX_1) + (R_2 + jX_2)\}$$
$$= \mathbf{I}\{(R_1 + R_2) + j(X_1 + X_2)\}$$

Thus, the total impedance is

$$\mathbf{Z} = \mathbf{V}/\mathbf{I} = (\mathbf{Z}_1 + \mathbf{Z}_2)$$

the total effective resistance being $(R_1 + R_2)$ and the total reactance $(X_1 + X_2)$.

Although both X_1 and X_2 are shown in Fig. 6.4 as inductive reactances, either or both could be capacitive and therefore negative, the sum being an algebraic sum and not merely arithmetical.

The above can be extended to any number of impedances in series, the total impedance, resistance and reactance being the sum of the impedances, resistances and reactances respectively.

Parallel circuits

For the parallel circuit shown in Fig. 6.6, the total current is the vector sum of the individual branch currents. That is,

$$\mathbf{I} = \mathbf{I}_1 + \mathbf{I}_2 = \mathbf{V}/\mathbf{Z}_1 + \mathbf{V}/\mathbf{Z}_2$$
$$= \mathbf{V}\mathbf{Y}_1 + \mathbf{V}\mathbf{Y}_2 = \mathbf{V}(\mathbf{Y}_1 + \mathbf{Y}_2).$$

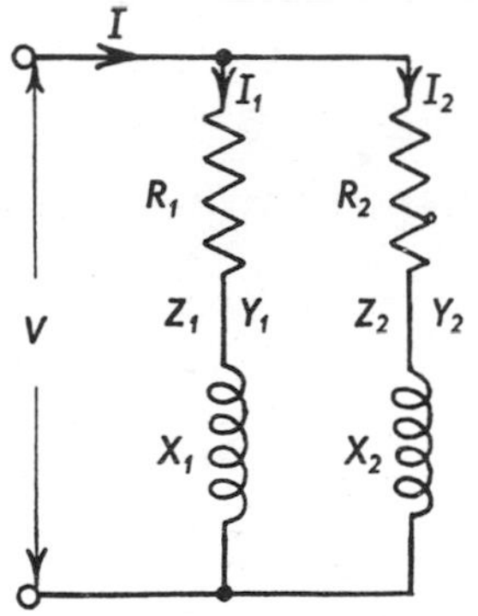

FIG. 6.6

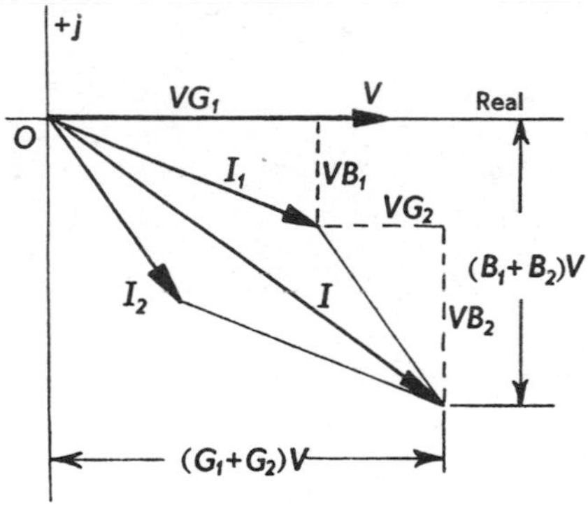

FIG. 6.7

The corresponding vector diagram is shown in Fig. 6.7. For the circuit shown $\mathbf{Z}_1 = (R_1 + jX_1)$ and $\mathbf{Z}_2 = (R_2 + jX_2)$,

$$\mathbf{Y}_1 = G_1 - jB_1 = R_1/(R_1^2 + X_1^2) - jX_1/(R_1^2 + X_1^2)$$
$$\mathbf{Y}_2 = G_2 - jB_2 = R_2/(R_2^2 + X_2^2) - jX_2/(R_2^2 + X_2^2)$$

Therefore, $\mathbf{Y} = \mathbf{I}/\mathbf{V} = (\mathbf{Y}_1 + \mathbf{Y}_2)$

or $$\mathbf{Y} = (G - jB) = (G_1 + G_2) - j(B_1 + B_2).$$

Thus, as stated already in Chapter 3 for a parallel circuit the individual conductances are added to give the total conductance and the susceptances are added to give the total susceptance. In terms of impedances,

since $$\mathbf{Y} = (\mathbf{Y}_1 + \mathbf{Y}_2),\ 1/\mathbf{Z} = 1/\mathbf{Z}_1 + 1/\mathbf{Z}_2$$
or $$\mathbf{Z} = \mathbf{Z}_1\mathbf{Z}_2/(\mathbf{Z}_1 + \mathbf{Z}_2).$$

This can be extended to include any number of parallel branches.

These results for series and parallel combinations of impedances or admittances, should be compared with those for such combinations of resistances in d.c. circuits, given in Chapter 2.

Series-parallel circuits

The methods of circuit analysis such as Kirchhoff's Laws, Maxwell's Cyclic-Current Rule, Thévenin's Theorem and so on are of great value for solving complicated a.c. circuit problems and their application is illustrated later. For circuits consisting of series and parallel combinations of impedances, however, the total effective impedance or admittance, the total current produced by a given applied voltage and the total power-factor, can readily be determined by iterative application of the simple rules given above for combining series and parallel impedances.

For example, the total impedance (or admittance) of the circuit illustrated in Fig. 6.8 (*a*) may be calculated as follows:

The two impedances connected across *BC* are first combined to give a single impedance. $\mathbf{Y}_2 = 1/\mathbf{Z}_2$ and $\mathbf{Y}_3 = 1/\mathbf{Z}_3$ are calculated and added to give $\mathbf{Y}_{BC} = (\mathbf{Y}_2 + \mathbf{Y}_3)$. The reciprocal of $\mathbf{Y}_{BC}$ is then calculated giving $\mathbf{Z}_{BC}$. (Alternatively, of course, $\mathbf{Z}_{BC}$ can be determined directly as $\mathbf{Z}_2\mathbf{Z}_3/(\mathbf{Z}_2 + \mathbf{Z}_3)$).

The parallel combination of $\mathbf{Z}_2$ and $\mathbf{Z}_3$ may then be replaced by $\mathbf{Z}_{BC}$ as shown in Fig. 6.8 (*b*) and the total impedance is then given by $\mathbf{Z}_{AD} = \mathbf{Z}_1 + \mathbf{Z}_{BC}$ and the total admittance is $\mathbf{Y}_{AD} = 1/\mathbf{Z}_{AD}$.

The real and imaginary parts of $\mathbf{Z}_{AD}$ give the total effective resistance and reactance, while the real and imaginary parts of $\mathbf{Y}_{AD}$ give the total conductance and susceptance. If these quantities are respectively R_{AD}, X_{AD}, G_{AD} and B_{AD}, equivalent series and parallel circuits can be drawn as shown in Fig. 6.8 (*c*) and (*d*).

The vector current for a given voltage $\mathbf{V}$ is $\mathbf{I} = \mathbf{V}/\mathbf{Z}$ or $\mathbf{I} = \mathbf{VY}$.

The power-factor can be calculated in several ways, since:

$$\cos\phi = R_{AD}/\sqrt{(R_{AD}^2 + X_{AD}^2)} = R_{AD}/Z_{AD}$$
or $$\cos\phi = G_{AD}/\sqrt{(G_{AD}^2 + B_{AD}^2)} = G_{AD}/Y_{AD}$$

i.e. cos ϕ is the component of current in phase with the voltage divided by the total current. In practice the voltage would probably be

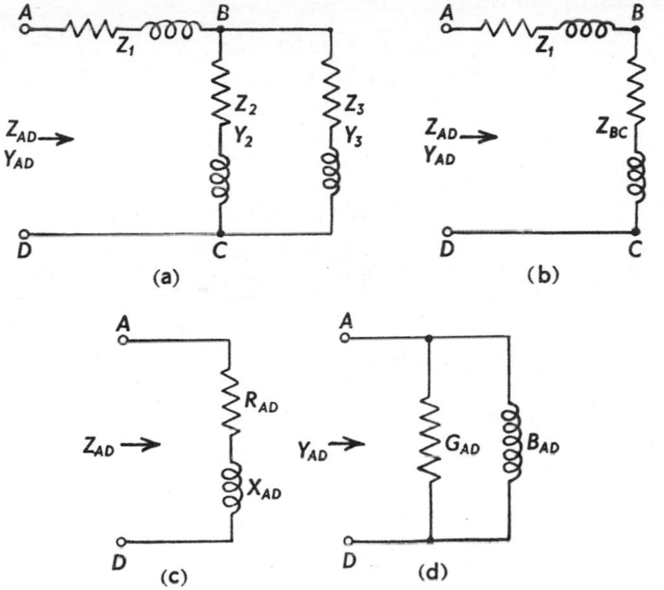

FIG. 6.8

assumed to be represented by a vector along the real axis, so that its imaginary component is zero and in this case cos ϕ is equal to the real component of current divided by the total current.

Note that the impedances furthest from the supply terminals are combined first to produce a single equivalent impedance.

EXAMPLE. Determine the input impedance, admittance, power-factor and current for the circuit illustrated in Fig. 6.9. Explain how the currents in the individual branches and the voltages between various points in the circuit can be found.

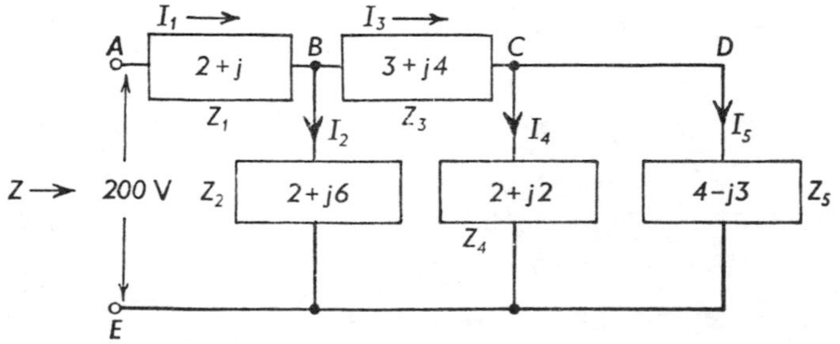

FIG. 6.9

Solution. Subscript figures will be used to indicate the impedances, for example, Z_{45} is the equivalent single impedance of the parallel combination of Z_4 and Z_5.

$$Z_5 = 4 - j3, \; Y_5 = (4 + j3)/25 = 0{\cdot}16 + j0{\cdot}12$$
$$Z_4 = 2 + j2, \; Y_4 = (2 - j2)/8 = 0{\cdot}25 - j0{\cdot}25$$
$$\therefore \quad Y_{45} = Y_4 + Y_5 = 0{\cdot}41 - j0{\cdot}13$$
$$Z_{45} = 1/Y_{45} = (0{\cdot}41 + j0{\cdot}13)/(0{\cdot}41^2 + 0{\cdot}13^2)$$
$$= 2{\cdot}22 + j0{\cdot}702$$
$$Z_{345} = Z_3 + Z_{45} = (3 + j4) + (2{\cdot}22 + j0{\cdot}702)$$
$$= 5{\cdot}22 + j4{\cdot}702.$$
$$Y_{345} = 1/Z_{345} = (5{\cdot}22 - j4{\cdot}702)/49{\cdot}4$$
$$= 0{\cdot}1057 - j0{\cdot}0953$$
$$Y_2 = (2 - j6)/40 = 0{\cdot}05 - j0{\cdot}15$$
$$Y_{2345} = 0{\cdot}05 - j0{\cdot}15 + 0{\cdot}1057 - j0{\cdot}0953$$
$$= 0{\cdot}1557 - j0{\cdot}2453$$
$$Z_{2345} = (0{\cdot}1557 + j0{\cdot}2453)/0{\cdot}0843$$
$$= 1{\cdot}845 + j2{\cdot}910$$
$$Z = 2 + j + 1{\cdot}845 + j2{\cdot}910$$

or

$$Z = (3{\cdot}845 + j3{\cdot}910)\ \Omega$$
$$|Z| = \sqrt{(3{\cdot}845^2 + 3{\cdot}910^2)} = \underline{5{\cdot}48\ \Omega}$$

Power-factor, $\cos\phi = 3{\cdot}845/5{\cdot}48 = \underline{0{\cdot}702}$

$$\phi = 45^\circ\, 23'$$
$$Y = (3{\cdot}845 - j3{\cdot}910)/30{\cdot}1 = (0{\cdot}128 - j0{\cdot}130)\ \text{mho}$$
$$|Y| = \sqrt{(0{\cdot}128^2 + 0{\cdot}130^2)} = \underline{0{\cdot}182}\ \text{mho}$$
$$1/|Y| = 5{\cdot}48\ \Omega = |Z|$$
$$\cos\phi = 0{\cdot}128/0{\cdot}182 = \underline{0{\cdot}702}\ \text{as before.}$$

Taking the applied voltage as

$$V = 200 + j\,.\,0 = 200.$$
$$I_1 = 200/(3{\cdot}845 + j3{\cdot}910)$$
$$= 200(3{\cdot}845 - j3{\cdot}910)/(3{\cdot}845^2 + 3{\cdot}910^2)$$
$$= 25{\cdot}6 - j26{\cdot}0$$
$$|I_1| = \sqrt{(25{\cdot}6^2 + 26{\cdot}0^2)} = \underline{36{\cdot}4\ \text{A}}$$

or

$$I_1 = 200(0{\cdot}128 - j0{\cdot}130)$$
$$= 25{\cdot}6 - j26{\cdot}0\ \text{as before.}$$
$$\cos\phi = 25{\cdot}6/36{\cdot}4 = \underline{0{\cdot}702}$$

The above solution has been set out deliberately without using heavy type to indicate vector quantities, to demonstrate that no confusion arises thereby. The only quantities specially distinguished, by the use of vertical lines, are the moduli of impedance, admittance and current. At every stage the quantities have been reduced to the simplest arithmetical form, leaving no unresolved fractions, as experience has shown that this is the best procedure for reducing the likelihood of errors.

The currents in the individual branches and the voltages between points in the circuit may be calculated by a process of re-expanding the circuit from the contracted equivalent circuit corresponding to the total effective impedance. At one stage the equivalent circuit (not actually drawn) consists of impedance $Z_1 = (2 + j)$ in series with $Z_{2345} = (1{\cdot}845 + j2{\cdot}910)$, the latter connected from B to E. Since the total current, $I_1 = (25{\cdot}6 - j26{\cdot}0)$ flows through both these impedances the voltage $V_{BE} = (25{\cdot}6 - j26{\cdot}0)(1{\cdot}845 + j2{\cdot}910) = (123 + j26{\cdot}4)$.

Alternatively this voltage can be calculated as

$$V_{BE} = 200(1{\cdot}845 + j2{\cdot}910)/(3{\cdot}845 + j3{\cdot}910)$$

The current I_2 is then given as

$$I_2 = (123 + j26{\cdot}4)/(2 + j6) = (10{\cdot}1 - j17{\cdot}1)$$
$$I_3 = I_1 - I_2 = (15{\cdot}5 - j8{\cdot}9)$$

The voltage V_{CE} is then given by

$$V_{CE} = Z_{45} \,.\, I_3 = 40{\cdot}7 \quad j8{\cdot}9$$

and the currents I_4 and I_5 are V_{CE}/Z_4 and V_{CE}/Z_5 respectively, *i.e.*

$$I_4 = 8{\cdot}0 - j12{\cdot}4,\ I_5 = 7{\cdot}5 + j3{\cdot}6.$$

EXAMPLE. Calculate the total current supplied to the circuit of Fig. 6.10. Determine also the voltages across the capacitor and the 10,000 Ω resistor.

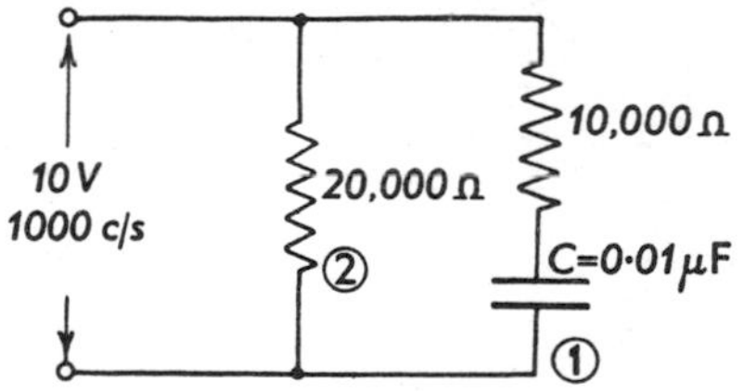

FIG. 6.10

Solution.

The reactance of C, $X_C = 10^6/(2\pi \times 1{,}000 \times 0{\cdot}01) = 15{,}900\ \Omega$

For branch 1, $\mathbf{Z_1} = (10 - j15{\cdot}9)10^3\ \Omega$

$$\therefore \quad \mathbf{Y}_1 = (10 + j15{\cdot}9)/(352 \times 10^3) \text{ mho}$$
$$= (0{\cdot}0285 + j0{\cdot}0452)/10^3 \text{ mho}$$

For branch 2, $\mathbf{Y}_2 = 1/(20 \times 10^3) \text{ mho} = 0{\cdot}05/10^3 \text{ mho}$

Total admittance $= (0{\cdot}0785 + j0{\cdot}0452)/10^3 \text{ mho}$

Current supplied $= (0{\cdot}785 + j0{\cdot}452)/10^3 \text{ A}$
$$= \underline{(0{\cdot}785 + j0{\cdot}452) \text{ mA}}$$

Voltage across $C = \{-j15{\cdot}9/(10 - j15{\cdot}9)\}10 = \underline{8{\cdot}46 \text{ V}}$

Voltage across 10,000 Ω resistor $= \{10/(10 - j15{\cdot}9)\}10 \text{ V}$
$$= \underline{5{\cdot}32 \text{ V}}$$

EXAMPLE. Evaluate the input impedance, admittance and power-factor for the circuit shown in Fig. 6.11.

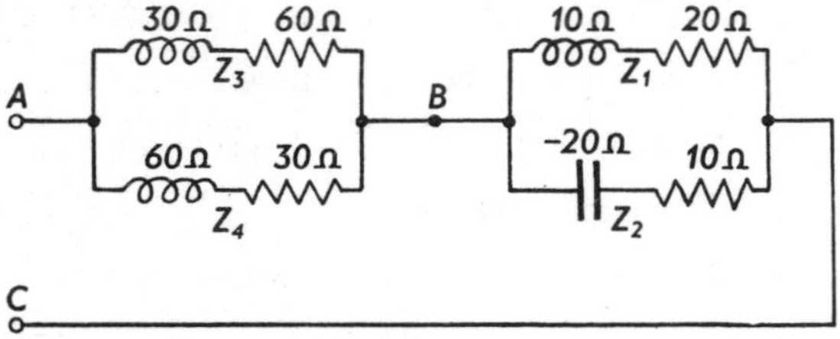

FIG. 6.11

Solution.

$$\mathbf{Z}_1 = (20 + j10),\ \mathbf{Y}_1 = (20 - j10)/500$$
$$\mathbf{Z}_2 = (10 - j20),\ \mathbf{Y}_2 = (10 + j20)/500$$
$$\mathbf{Y}_{12} = (30 + j10)/500$$
$$\mathbf{Z}_{12} = 500(30 - j10)/1{,}000 = 15 - j5$$
$$\mathbf{Z}_3 = (60 + j30),\ \mathbf{Y}_3 = (60 - j30)/4{,}500$$
$$\mathbf{Z}_4 = (30 + j60),\ \mathbf{Y}_4 = (30 - j60)/4{,}500$$
$$\mathbf{Y}_{34} = (90 - j90)/4{,}500 = (1 - j)/50$$
$$\mathbf{Z}_{34} = 50(1 + j)/2 = 25 + j25$$

Total $\mathbf{Z} = (40 + j20)$

$$Z = 10\sqrt{(16 + 4)} = 10\sqrt{20} = \underline{44{\cdot}7\ \Omega}$$
$$\cos\phi = 40/44{\cdot}7 = \underline{0{\cdot}895}$$
$$\mathbf{Y} = (40 - j20)/2{,}000 = (0{\cdot}02 - j0{\cdot}01)$$
$$Y = \underline{0{\cdot}0224}$$

[*Note*: $\cos\phi$ is also equal to $0{\cdot}02/0{\cdot}0224 = 0{\cdot}895$.]

Equivalent series and parallel circuits

In the example given above the existence of equivalent series and parallel circuits has been implied. For instance, the impedances $\mathbf{Z}_4$

and $\mathbf{Z}_5$ were converted to the equivalent admittances, which were then combined to give a single admittance. The latter was then inverted to provide the equivalent impedance. This technique of combining impedances or admittances is of such importance in solving a.c. circuit problems that it is worth a closer study.

Two circuits can be said to be equivalent when they take the same current at the same phase-angle relative to the voltage, when supplied at the same voltage and frequency. This is expressed very simply in terms of the complex impedances or admittances, since if two circuits have total impedances or admittances which are fully equal, with real and imaginary components separately equal, they satisfy the condition for equivalence.

While every circuit has an *infinite* number of equivalent circuits, based on the above definition, the only ones of interest and value are the simplest, consisting either of a resistance and reactance in series or of a resistance and reactance in parallel (Fig. 6.12).

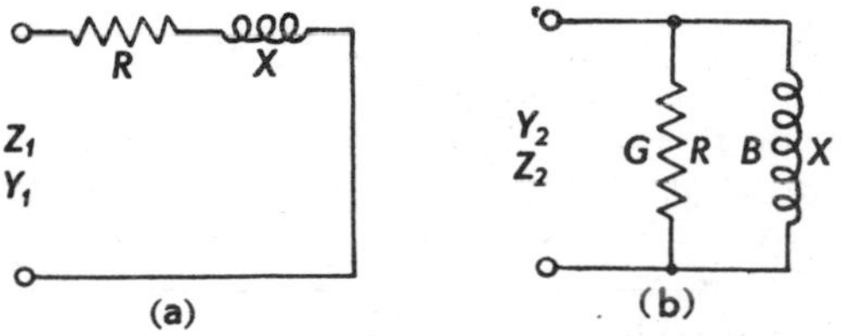

FIG. 6.12

The rules for combining series impedances to obtain a single impedance and for combining parallel admittances to obtain a single admittance have already been given. These rules, together with those given below, for converting a series circuit into its parallel equivalent or a parallel circuit into its series equivalent, are sufficient for the simplification of any static circuit, no matter how complicated.

The two circuits shown in Fig. 6.12 are equivalent provided that $\mathbf{Z}_1 = \mathbf{Z}_2$ or $\mathbf{Y}_1 = \mathbf{Y}_2$.

$$\mathbf{Z}_1 = R + jX,\ \mathbf{Y}_1 = R/(R^2 + X^2) - jX/(R^2 + X^2)$$
$$\mathbf{Y}_2 = G - jB,\ \mathbf{Z}_2 = G/(G^2 + B^2) + jB/(G^2 + B^2)$$

where $G = 1/R',\ B = 1/X'$.

Therefore, equating $\mathbf{Y}_1$ and $\mathbf{Y}_2$,

$$G = 1/R' = R/(R^2 + X^2)$$

or $$R' = (R^2 + X^2)/R$$

$$B = X/(R^2 + X^2)$$

or $$X' = (R^2 + X^2)/X$$

Equating $\mathbf{Z}_1$ and $\mathbf{Z}_2$,

$$R = G/(G^2 + B^2)$$

or

$$R = R'X'^2/(R'^2 + X'^2)$$

$$X = B/(G^2 + B^2)$$

$$= R'^2X'/(R'^2 + X'^2)$$

It is not suggested that an attempt should be made to apply the above formulae in practical problems, nor that they should be memorized. The conversion from a complex impedance to the equivalent complex admittance is easily carried out as required in a particular problem. However, it is worth noting that the change of one parameter in one circuit changes *both* parameters in the equivalent circuit. This means, for instance, that if the reactance of a series circuit changes, say due to a change of supply frequency, both the resistance and reactance of the equivalent parallel circuit are changed.

Therefore, two circuits which are equivalent to one another at a given frequency will not be equivalents at a different frequency. If X is positive (an inductive reactance) in one circuit it is also positive in the other.

A series circuit in which the resistance is *low* compared with the reactance transforms into a parallel circuit with a shunt resistance which is *high* compared with the reactance. Or, for a series circuit of high resistance and low reactance, the equivalent parallel circuit has a high reactance compared with the resistance.

Power and power-factor

The definitions of instantaneous and mean powers and of power-factor, for circuits with sinusoidal voltages and currents, are given in Chapter 3.

If v is the instantaneous voltage and $V_{\text{r.m.s.}}$ is the r.m.s. voltage, then

$$v = \sqrt{2}\, V_{\text{r.m.s.}} \cos \omega t, \text{ say.}$$

If i is the instantaneous current and $I_{\text{r.m.s.}}$ the r.m.s. current (both in ampères),

$$i = \sqrt{2}\, I_{\text{r.m.s.}} \cos (\omega t - \phi),$$

where ϕ is the phase-angle between the voltage and current.

The instantaneous power is:

$$p = vi = 2\, V_{\text{r.m.s.}}\, I_{\text{r.m.s.}} \cos \omega t \cos (\omega t - \phi) \text{ watts}$$

$$= V_{\text{r.m.s.}}\, I_{\text{r.m.s.}} \{\cos \phi + \cos (2\omega t - \phi)\} \text{ watts.}$$

The mean power (usually known simply as power) is

$$P = V_{\text{r.m.s.}} I_{\text{r.m.s.}} \cos \phi$$

and the power-factor is $\cos \phi$.

Where the equivalent series impedance $\mathbf{Z} = R + jX$ of an a.c. circuit, and the vector current $\mathbf{I}_{\text{r.m.s.}} = I_1 + jI_2$ have been calculated, the power may be determined very easily as $P = RI^2_{\text{r.m.s.}}$, where $I_{\text{r.m.s.}} = \sqrt{(I_1^2 + I_2^2)}$, I_1 and I_2 also being r.m.s. values.

The corresponding method where the equivalent parallel admittance $\mathbf{Y} = G - jB$ has been determined, together with the voltage, is to calculate the power as:

$$P = (V_{\text{r.m.s.}})^2 G$$

($G = 1/R'$ where R' is the shunt resistance in the parallel circuit of Fig. 6.12 (*b*).

These methods may not be convenient in some cases and an alternative method is simply to calculate the magnitudes of the r.m.s. current and voltage ($I_{\text{r.m.s.}}$ and $V_{\text{r.m.s.}}$) and the phase-angle ϕ between them and then use the formula $P = V_{\text{r.m.s.}} I_{\text{r.m.s.}} \cos\phi$.

For example, if the complex voltage and current for the circuit being considered are $(300 + j400)$ V and $(20 + j10)$ A respectively, the power is given by

$$P = \sqrt{(300^2 + 400^2)} \times \sqrt{(20^2 + 10^2)} \times \cos(\theta_1 - \theta_2)$$

where $\tan\theta_1 = 400/300$ and $\tan\theta_2 = 10/20$.

Thus, $P = 10{,}000$ watts and the power-factor,

$$\cos(\theta_1 - \theta_2) = \cos 26^\circ\, 34' = 0{\cdot}895.$$

This method is readily applicable also where the current and voltage appear in polar or exponential complex form.

Since the power is obtained from the product of the sinusoidal voltage and current, it is reasonable to ask whether it can also be obtained from the product of the vectors representing voltage and current. If, however, these vectors (expressed in complex form) are multiplied together the result is as follows:

$$\begin{aligned}
\mathbf{V}_{\text{r.m.s.}} &= V_{\text{r.m.s.}}(\cos\omega t + j\sin\omega t) = V_{\text{r.m.s.}}\exp(j\omega t)\\
\mathbf{I}_{\text{r.m.s.}} &= I_{\text{r.m.s.}}\{\cos(\omega t - \phi) + j\sin(\omega t - \phi)\}\\
&= I_{\text{r.m.s.}}\exp\{j(\omega t - \phi)\}\\
\therefore\quad \mathbf{V}_{\text{r.m.s.}}\mathbf{I}_{\text{r.m.s.}} &= V_{\text{r.m.s.}} I_{\text{r.m.s.}}\{\cos(2\omega t - \phi) + j\sin(2\omega t - \phi)\}\\
&= V_{\text{r.m.s.}} I_{\text{r.m.s.}}\exp\{j(2\omega t - \phi)\}
\end{aligned}$$

The average value of this product is zero, showing that the power cannot be calculated directly in this way. Even if the voltage and current vectors are stationary, for instance if

$$\mathbf{V}_{\text{r.m.s.}} = V\{\cos\theta + j\sin\theta\} \text{ and } \mathbf{I}_{\text{r.m.s.}} = I\{\cos(\theta - \phi) + j\sin(\theta - \phi)\}$$

giving $\mathbf{V}_{\text{r.m.s.}}\mathbf{I}_{\text{r.m.s.}} = VI\{\cos(2\theta - \phi) + j\sin(2\theta - \phi)\}$, the product does not give the power *unless* $\theta = 0$ or $\theta = \phi$, when the *real component* of $\mathbf{V}_{r.m.s.}\,\mathbf{I}_{r.m.s.}$ {(written $\mathcal{R}(\mathbf{V}_{r.m.s.}\,\mathbf{I}_{r.m.s.})$} becomes $V_{r.m.s.}\,I_{r.m.s.}\cos\phi$, namely the mean power.

When $\theta = 0$, the voltage vector lies along the real axis and when $\theta = \phi$ the current vector lies along the real axis.

Multiplying the vectors of voltage and current together fails to give the power because the analogy between a sinusoidal *real* quantity and a *single* rotating vector is not complete, and though the analogy serves for additions and subtractions it breaks down for multiplication.

The full representation of a sinusoid requires *two* conjugate vectors rotating in opposite directions as shown in Fig. 6.13 where a sinusoidal

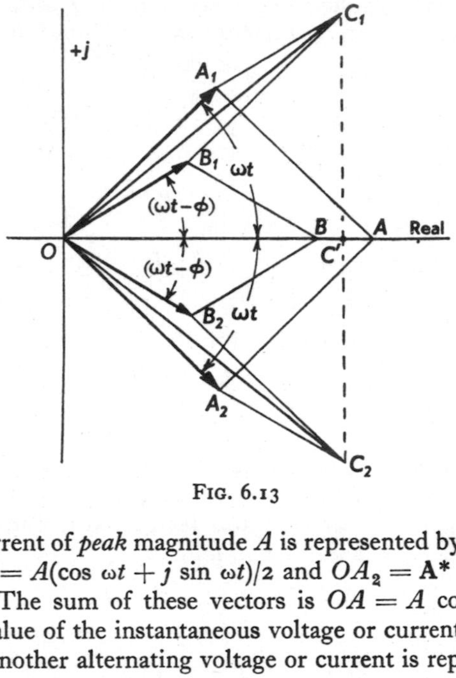

FIG. 6.13

voltage or current of *peak* magnitude A is represented by the ***vector sum*** of $OA_1 = \mathbf{A} = A(\cos\omega t + j\sin\omega t)/2$ and $OA_2 = \mathbf{A}^* = A(\cos\omega t - j\sin\omega t)/2$. The sum of these vectors is $OA = A\cos\omega t$, which is the correct value of the instantaneous voltage or current.

Similarly another alternating voltage or current is represented by

$$OB_1 = \mathbf{B} = B\{\cos(\omega t - \phi) + j\sin(\omega t - \phi)\}/2$$

and $$OB_2 = \mathbf{B}^* = B\{\cos(\omega t - \phi) - j\sin(\omega t - \phi)\}/2$$

The sum of the two sinusoids so represented is given by

$$\begin{aligned}\mathbf{D} &= \mathbf{A} + \mathbf{A}^* + \mathbf{B} + \mathbf{B}^* \\ &= (\mathbf{A} + \mathbf{B}) + (\mathbf{A}^* + \mathbf{B}^*) \\ &= \mathbf{C} + \mathbf{C}^*\end{aligned}$$

where $\mathbf{C}$ is the vector OC_1 and $\mathbf{C}^*$ is its conjugate OC_2.

$$\mathcal{R}(\mathbf{C}) = \mathcal{R}(\mathbf{C}^*) = OC' = \{A\cos\omega t + B\cos(\omega t - \phi)\}/2 = 1/2$$

the actual sinusoid represented by **D**. If the vectors OA_1 and OB_1 have moduli A and B instead of $A/2$ and $B/2$, the projection of the sum on the real axis equals the resultant sinusoid. Therefore, it is only necessary to consider OA_1 and OB_1 when performing additions, and this naturally holds also for subtractions.

If $(\mathbf{A} + \mathbf{A}^*)$ represents a sinusoidal voltage, v, and $(\mathbf{B} + \mathbf{B}^*)$ represents a sinusoidal current, i, the instantaneous power is given by

$$p = vi = (\mathbf{A} + \mathbf{A}^*)(\mathbf{B} + \mathbf{B}^*)$$
$$= \mathbf{AB} + \mathbf{A}^*\mathbf{B}^* + \mathbf{A}^*\mathbf{B} + \mathbf{AB}^*$$

It has already been proved that the average value of the product of two vectors rotating in the same direction at the same speed is zero, so that the average of **AB** and of $\mathbf{A}^*\mathbf{B}^*$ is zero. Therefore the average of $\mathbf{A}^*\mathbf{B} + \mathbf{AB}^*$ must be equal to the mean power, P.

$$\mathbf{A}^*\mathbf{B} = A\{\cos \omega t - j \sin \omega t\}B\{\cos (\omega t - \phi) + j \sin (\omega t - \phi)\}/4$$
$$= AB\{\cos \phi - j \sin \phi\}/4$$

Similarly, $\mathbf{AB}^* = AB\{\cos \phi + j \sin \phi\}/4$

and $\mathbf{A}^*\mathbf{B} + \mathbf{AB}^* = AB \cos \phi/2$

which is the mean power, since A and B are the peak voltage and current respectively.

If now the vectors OA_1, OA_2 and OB_1, OB_2 are of magnitude equal to the r.m.s. values of voltage and current respectively, instead of equal to half the peak value,

$$\mathbf{A}^*\mathbf{B} = AB\{\cos \phi - j \sin \phi\}/2$$

and $\mathbf{AB}^* = AB\{\cos \phi + j \sin \phi\}/2$

and the mean power P may be determined from *either* since the real parts, $\mathscr{R}(\mathbf{A}^*\mathbf{B}) = \mathscr{R}(\mathbf{AB}^*) = AB \cos \phi/2 = P$.

Furthermore the wattless volt-amps, or reactive volt-amps, $(VA)_r = AB \sin \phi/2$ equal the imaginary component of $\mathbf{AB}^*$, written $\mathscr{I}(\mathbf{AB}^*)$, or alternatively, $-\mathscr{I}(\mathbf{A}^*\mathbf{B})$. ($\phi$ is considered positive when the current, in this case represented by **B**, lags on the voltage, represented by **A**). Consider the example given on p. (105) where $\mathbf{V} = (300 + j400)$ V and $\mathbf{I} = (20 + j10)$ A

$$\mathbf{VI}^* = (300 + j400)(20 - j10) \text{ W} = (10{,}000 + j5{,}000) \text{ W}$$
$$P = \mathscr{R}(\mathbf{VI}^*) = 10{,}000 \text{ W}$$
$$(VA)_r = \mathscr{I}(\mathbf{VI}^*) = 5{,}000 \text{ VA.}$$

The volt-amps are given by $\sqrt{\{P^2 + (VA)_r^2\}} = 11{,}200$ VA.

The power-factor is $P/\sqrt{\{P^2 + (VA)_r^2\}} = 0{\cdot}895$.

Application of circuit laws and theorems to a.c. circuits

All the circuit laws and theorems previously enunciated for d.c. circuits (see Chapter 2) may be applied to a.c. circuits, by expressing the voltages and currents in complex form and by replacing resistance by complex impedance (see also Chapter 7). Some of these circuit laws have already been used, for instance,

$\mathbf{I} = \mathbf{V}/\mathbf{Z}$, which is the counterpart of Ohm's Law,

$\mathbf{Z} = \mathbf{Z}_1 + \mathbf{Z}_2 + \ldots + \mathbf{Z}_n$ for impedances in series

and $1/\mathbf{Z} = 1/\mathbf{Z}_1 + 1/\mathbf{Z}_2 + \ldots + 1/\mathbf{Z}_n$ for impedances in parallel.

The use of the progressive simplification technique described earlier in this chapter is the simplest way of solving some types of problem, but others require rather more elaborate methods such as Kirchhoff's Laws, Maxwell's Cyclic-Current Rule, Thévenin's Theorem, the Principle of Superposition and so on, though it is often useful to simplify a circuit to some extent by the simple method before adopting another one. The best method to be employed in a particular case depends on the form of circuit and on the information required. Facility in the solution of circuit problems can only come from practice and while the application of various methods is illustrated in the examples given below, it is suggested that the reader should also solve these in other ways.

EXAMPLE. Use Kirchhoff's Laws to find the currents $\mathbf{I}_1$, $\mathbf{I}_2$ and $\mathbf{I}_3$ in the network of Fig. 6.14. The generator voltage (10 V r.m.s.) should be taken as $(10 + j0)$V acting in a direction from F to A.

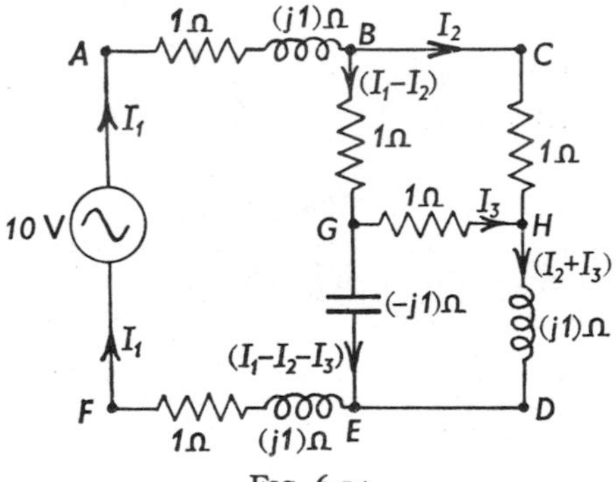

FIG. 6.14

Solution. Using Kirchhoff's first law the currents in all the branches of the network can be written down as shown in Fig. 6.14.

Kirchhoff's second law gives the following equations.

Loop ABGEFA,

$$10 + j0 = \mathbf{I}_1(1 + j1) + (\mathbf{I}_1 - \mathbf{I}_2)1 + (\mathbf{I}_1 - \mathbf{I}_2 - \mathbf{I}_3)(-j1) + \mathbf{I}_1(1 + j1)$$

or $$10 = \mathbf{I}_1(3 + j) + \mathbf{I}_2(-1 + j) + \mathbf{I}_3(0 + j) \quad . \quad . \quad . \quad . \quad (6.1)$$

Loop BCHGB,

$$0 = I_2 . 1 - I_3 . 1 - (I_1 - I_2) . 1$$

or $$0 = -I_1 + 2I_2 - I_3 \quad . \quad . \quad . \quad . \quad . \quad . \quad (6.2)$$

Loop GHDEG,

$$0 = I_3 . 1 + (I_2 + I_3)(j1) - (I_1 - I_2 - I_3)(-j1)$$

or $$0 = I_1 j + I_3 \quad . \quad . \quad . \quad . \quad . \quad . \quad . \quad . \quad . \quad . \quad . \quad . \quad (6.3)$$

From (6.3), $I_1 = -I_3/j = jI_3$ and substituting in (6.1)

$$10 = jI_3(3 + j) + I_2(-1 + j) + I_3 . j$$

or $$10 = I_3(-1 + j4) + I_2(-1 + j) \quad . \quad . \quad . \quad (6.4)$$

Substituting for I_1 in (6.2) gives

$$0 = -jI_3 + 2I_2 - I_3$$

or $$0 = -I_3(1 + j) + 2I_2$$

i.e. $$I_2 = I_3(1 + j)/2 \quad . \quad . \quad . \quad . \quad . \quad . \quad (6.5)$$

From (6.4) and (6.5),

$$10 = I_3(-1 + j4) + I_3(1 + j)(-1 + j)/2$$

or $$10 = I_3\{-1 + j4 + (-2)/2\} = I_3(-2 + j4)$$

$$\therefore \quad I_3 = -5/(1 - j2) = -5(1 + j2)/5 = \underline{-(1 + j2)\ A}$$

Substituting for I_3 in (6.5),

$$I_2 = -(1 + j2)(1 + j)/2 = \underline{(0{\cdot}5 - j1{\cdot}5)\ A}$$

From (6.3), $$I_1 = -j(1 + j2) = \underline{(2 - j)\ A.}$$

EXAMPLE. Determine the loop and branch currents for the network of Fig. 6.15 using Maxwell's Cyclic-Current Rule.

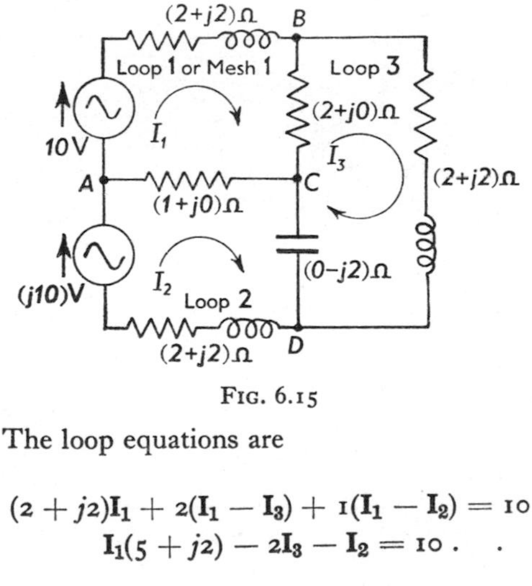

FIG. 6.15

Solution. The loop equations are

Loop 1,

$$(2 + j2)I_1 + 2(I_1 - I_3) + 1(I_1 - I_2) = 10$$

or $$I_1(5 + j2) - 2I_3 - I_2 = 10 \quad . \quad . \quad . \quad . \quad (6.6)$$

Loop 2,

$$1(\mathbf{I}_2 - \mathbf{I}_1) - j2(\mathbf{I}_2 - \mathbf{I}_3) + (2 + j2)\mathbf{I}_2 = j10$$

or

$$-\mathbf{I}_1 + 3\mathbf{I}_2 + \mathbf{I}_3(j2) = j10 \quad . \quad . \quad . \quad . \quad (6.7)$$

Loop 3,

$$2(\mathbf{I}_3 - \mathbf{I}_1) + (2 + j2)\mathbf{I}_3 - (j2)(\mathbf{I}_3 - \mathbf{I}_2) = 0$$

or

$$-\mathbf{I}_1 + j\mathbf{I}_2 + 2\mathbf{I}_3 = 0 \quad . \quad . \quad . \quad . \quad (6.8)$$

i.e.

$$\mathbf{I}_1 = j\mathbf{I}_2 + 2\mathbf{I}_3 \quad . \quad . \quad . \quad . \quad . \quad (6.9)$$

Substituting (6.9) in (6.6),

$$\mathbf{I}_2(-3 + j5) + \mathbf{I}_3(8 + j4) = 10 \quad . \quad . \quad . \quad (6.10)$$

Substituting (6.9) in (6.7),

$$\mathbf{I}_2(3 - j) + \mathbf{I}_3(-2 + j2) = j10$$

or

$$\mathbf{I}_3 = \{-j20 + 20 + \mathbf{I}_2(8 + j4)\}/8 \quad . \quad . \quad (6.11)$$

Substituting (6.11) in (6.10),

$$\begin{aligned} \mathbf{I}_2 &= (-20 + j10)/(3 + j13) \\ &= (-20 + j10)(3 - j13)/178 \\ &= (0{\cdot}393 + j1{\cdot}63) \text{ A} \end{aligned}$$

$$\therefore \quad \mathbf{I}_3 = (2{\cdot}078 - j0{\cdot}673) \text{ A}$$

and

$$\mathbf{I}_1 = (2{\cdot}526 - j0{\cdot}954) \text{ A}$$

The branch currents are then

$$\begin{aligned} AB &= \mathbf{I}_1 = (2{\cdot}526 - j0{\cdot}954) \text{ A} \\ CA &= (\mathbf{I}_1 - \mathbf{I}_2) = (2{\cdot}133 - j2{\cdot}584) \text{ A} \\ BC &= (\mathbf{I}_1 - \mathbf{I}_3) = (0{\cdot}448 - j0{\cdot}281) \text{ A} \\ CD &= (\mathbf{I}_2 - \mathbf{I}_3) = \underline{(-1{\cdot}685 + j2{\cdot}303) \text{ A}} \\ BD &= \mathbf{I}_3 = \underline{(2{\cdot}078 - j0{\cdot}673) \text{ A}} \end{aligned}$$

and

$$DA = \mathbf{I}_2 = \underline{(0{\cdot}393 + j1{\cdot}63) \text{ A.}}$$

EXAMPLE. Use the Principle of Superposition to find the current $\mathbf{I}_2$ in the network illustrated in Fig. 6.16.

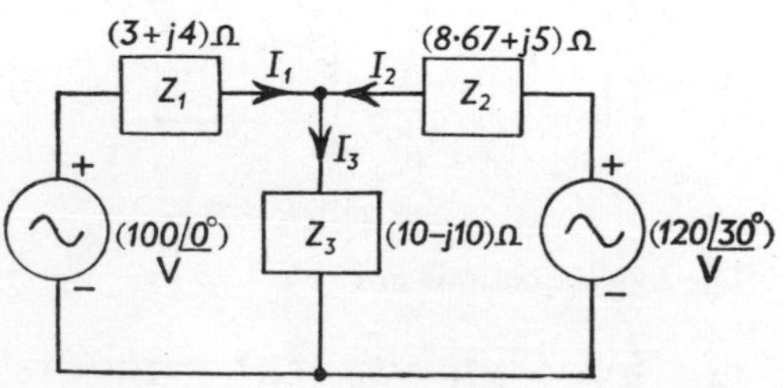

FIG. 6.16

Solution.

$$\mathbf{Z}_1 = (3 + j4)\ \Omega = (5\angle 53{\cdot}2^\circ)\ \Omega$$
$$\mathbf{Z}_2 = (8{\cdot}67 + j5)\ \Omega = (10\angle 30^\circ)\ \Omega$$
$$\mathbf{Z}_3 = (10 - j10)\ \Omega = (14{\cdot}14\angle -45^\circ)\ \Omega$$

First short-circuit the 100 V generator. The impedance presented to the other generator is then $\mathbf{Z}_2 + \mathbf{Z}_1\mathbf{Z}_3/(\mathbf{Z}_1 + \mathbf{Z}_3)$,

i.e. $(8{\cdot}67 + j5) + (70{\cdot}7\angle 8{\cdot}2^\circ)/(13 - j6)$

$$= (8{\cdot}67 + j5) + (70{\cdot}7\angle 8{\cdot}2^\circ)/(14{\cdot}3\angle -24{\cdot}8^\circ)$$
$$= (8{\cdot}67 + j5) + 4{\cdot}93\angle 33^\circ = \{(8{\cdot}67 + j5) + (4{\cdot}14 + j2{\cdot}69)\}\ \Omega$$
$$= (12{\cdot}81 + j7{\cdot}69)\ \Omega = (14{\cdot}9\angle 31^\circ)\ \Omega$$

The current through $\mathbf{Z}_2$ is then $\mathbf{I}_2' = \{(120\angle 30^\circ)/(14{\cdot}9\angle 31^\circ)\}$ A

$$= (8{\cdot}05\angle -1^\circ)\ \text{A}$$

Now short-circuit the 120 V generator. The impedance presented to the 100 V generator is then $\mathbf{Z}_1 + \mathbf{Z}_2\mathbf{Z}_3/(\mathbf{Z}_2 + \mathbf{Z}_3)$ which is found to be $(3 + j4) + 7{\cdot}33\angle 0^\circ = (10{\cdot}33 + j4)\ \Omega = (11{\cdot}1\angle 21{\cdot}2^\circ)\ \Omega$.

The current through $\mathbf{Z}_1$ is then $I_1'' = (100\angle 0^\circ)/(11{\cdot}1\angle 21{\cdot}2^\circ)$

$$= (9{\cdot}0\angle -21{\cdot}2^\circ)\ \text{A}$$

The voltage across $\mathbf{Z}_3 = \mathbf{V}_3' = \{\mathbf{Z}_2\mathbf{Z}_3/(\mathbf{Z}_2 + \mathbf{Z}_3)\}I_1''$

$$= (7{\cdot}33 \times 9\angle -21{\cdot}2^\circ)\ \text{V} = (65{\cdot}97\angle -21{\cdot}2^\circ)\ \text{V}$$

The current through $\mathbf{Z}_2$ is now $\mathbf{I}_2'' = -\mathbf{V}_3'/\mathbf{Z}_2$

$$= (-65{\cdot}97\angle -21{\cdot}2^\circ)/(10\angle 30^\circ) = -(6{\cdot}6\angle -51{\cdot}2^\circ)\ \text{A}$$

Thus, using the Principle of Superposition, $\mathbf{I}_2 = \mathbf{I}_2' + \mathbf{I}_2''$

$$= \{8{\cdot}05\angle -1^\circ + (-6{\cdot}6\angle -51{\cdot}2^\circ)\}\ \text{A} = (8{\cdot}05 - j0{\cdot}14 - 4{\cdot}13 + j5{\cdot}14)\ \text{A}$$
$$= (3{\cdot}92 + j5{\cdot}0)\ \text{A} = \underline{(6{\cdot}4\angle 52^\circ)\ \text{A.}}$$

EXAMPLE. Use Thévenin's Theorem to find the current in branch *CD* of the circuit of Fig. 6.17. [S.U.]

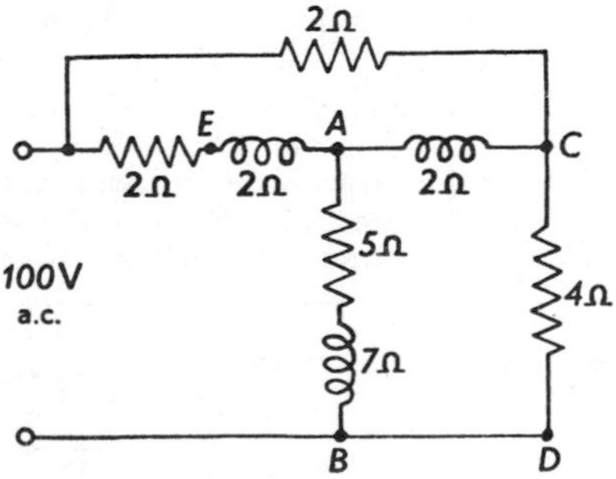

FIG. 6.17

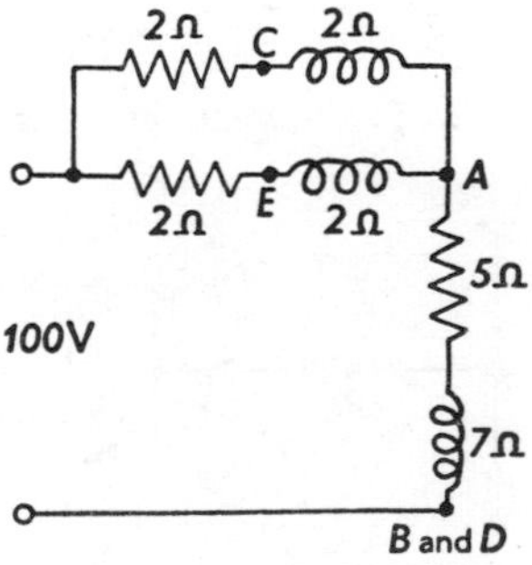

FIG. 6.18

Solution. To use Thévenin's Theorem remove branch CD giving the circuit of Fig. 6.18. The total impedance

$$= \{(1 + j1) + (5 + j7)\}\ \Omega$$
$$= (6 + j8)\ \Omega$$

Current supplied $= \{100/(6 + j8)\}$ A

$$= \{100(6 - j8)/100\}\ \text{A}$$
$$= (6 - j8)\ \text{A}$$

Voltage of C above D

$$= \{100 - (6 - j8)\}\ \text{V}$$
$$= (94 + j8)\ \text{V}.$$

It is next required to determine the impedance between points C and D with the input terminals short-circuited.

The combined impedance of $(2 + j2)\ \Omega$ and $(5 + j7)\ \Omega$ in parallel $=$ $(2 + j2)(5 + j7)/(7 + j9) = (1\cdot445 + j1\cdot72)\ \Omega$.

The impedance between C and D is therefore

$$2 \times (1\cdot445 \times j3\cdot72)/(3\cdot445 + j3\cdot72) = 1\cdot463 + j0\cdot579.$$

Thus, by Thévenin's Theorem,

Current through CD of original circuit ($\mathbf{I_{CD}}$)

$$= (94 + j8)/\{4 + (1\cdot463 + j0\cdot579)\}$$
$$\therefore\quad \underline{|\mathbf{I}_{CD}| = 17\cdot15\ \text{A}.}$$

PROBLEMS

1. Two impedances, each of 1 Ω resistance and 2 Ω inductive reactance, are connected in series. In parallel with one of these impedances is another, having a resistance of 2 Ω and a capacitive reactance of 4 Ω. What is the impedance of the complete circuit?

An alternating voltage source of $(5 + j0)$ V is connected to the circuit. Express the current taken by the circuit in the form $a + jb$. Does this current lead or lag on the applied voltage? Find also the phase-angle between the supply voltage and current.

[*Ans.* $(3\cdot31 + 3\cdot54j)\ \Omega$, $(0\cdot676 - 0\cdot723j)$ A, Current lags voltage, 46° 56′.]

2. The voltages and currents measured in the a.c. circuit shown in the diagram are as indicated. Draw a vector diagram for the arrangement and determine the values of the resistances and reactances. [S.U.]

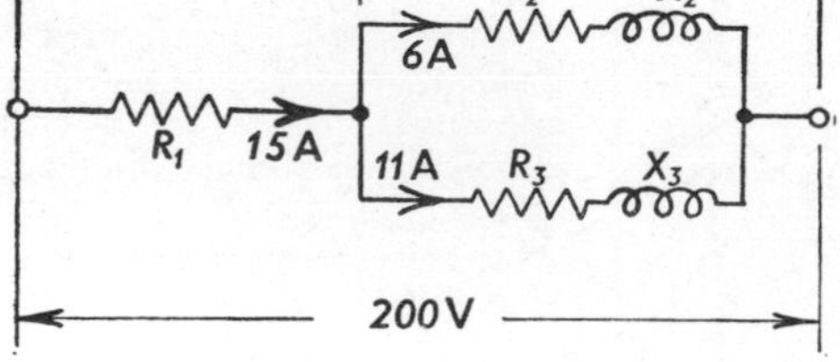

[*Ans.* $R_1 = 9\cdot33\ \Omega$, $R_2 = 13\ \Omega$, $R_3 = 2\cdot2\ \Omega$, $X_2 = 3\ \Omega$, $X_3 = 6\cdot9\ \Omega$.]

3. A circuit *ABD* consists of: *AB*, a 100 Ω resistor, *BCD*; a 50 Ω resistor *BC* in series with a 1 μF capacitor *CD*; *BED*, a 100 Ω resistor *BE* in series with a 25 mH inductor. A 100 V, 1,000 c/s a.c. supply is connected across *AD*. Determine the current taken and its power-factor. [S.U.]
[*Ans.* 0·328 A, 0·987.]

4. Two voltage sources, $\mathbf{V}_1 = 100(1 - j)$ V and $\mathbf{V}_2 = 100(1 + j)$ V, of internal impedance $\mathbf{Z}_1 = 30(1 + j)$ Ω and $\mathbf{Z}_2 = 50(1 + j0)$ Ω, respectively, are connected in parallel across an impedance $\mathbf{Z}_3 = 20(1 + j5)$ Ω. Find the magnitude of the current in $\mathbf{Z}_3$ and its phase relationship to $\mathbf{V}_2$. [S.U.]
[*Ans.* 0·503 A, 123° 6′.]

5. For the circuit illustrated evaluate the currents in *AB*, *BCE* and *BDE*. Calculate also the voltage between points *C* and *D*. [S.U.]
[*Ans.* 5·57 A, 3·71 A, 1·86 A, 52·5 V.]

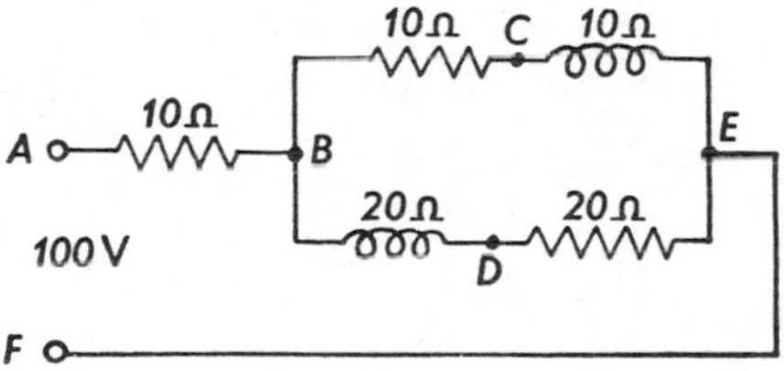

6. A series circuit consisting of a 20 Ω resistor and an inductor of 10 Ω reactance is connected in parallel with another circuit consisting of a 10 Ω resistor and a capacitor of 20 Ω reactance in series. Reduce the combination to a simple series circuit.
[*Ans.* A resistor of resistance 15 Ω in series with a capacitor of reactance 5 Ω.]

7. A variable capacitor connected in series with a circuit comprising a 20 Ω, non-inductive resistor in parallel with an inductor of resistance 15 Ω and inductance [illegible] H, is supplied from 200 V, 100 c/s mains. Determine the value of capacitance to give a total power-factor of unity, and the current then taken from the mains. [S.U.]
[*Ans.* 441 μF, 20·1 A.]

8. Calculate the admittance, impedance and power-factor of the following circuit when the supply frequency is 500 c/s.

Branches *A* and *B* are connected in parallel across the supply, where *A* is a 100 Ω resistor in series with a 2 μF capacitor, and *B* is a 100 Ω resistor in series with a 20 mH inductor. [S.U.]
[*Ans.* 0·01 mho, 100 Ω, 1.]

9. An a.c. circuit, *ABC*, consists of a capacitance of 1 μF in parallel with a resistance of 1,000 Ω (*AB*), in series with an inductance of 1 H in parallel with a resistance of 1,000 Ω (*BC*). Determine the impedance and power-factor of the circuit for a frequency of 50 c/s. Calculate also the phase-angle between the voltages *AB* and *BC*. [S.U.]
[*Ans.* 1,000 Ω, 1, 88° 25′.]

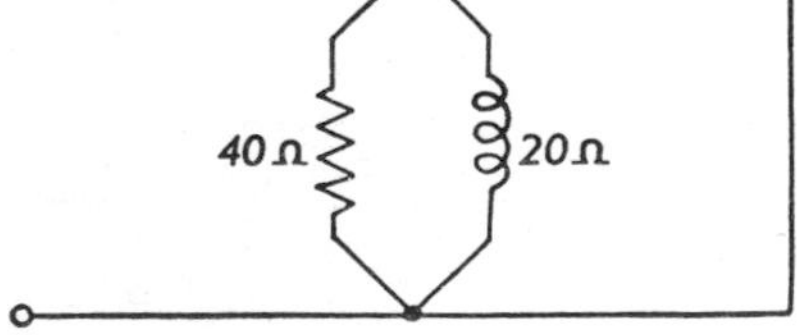

10. The circuit shown has values of resistance and reactance as illustrated. Determine the total admittance, conductance and susceptance; and the total effective resistance and reactance. [S.U.]
[*Ans.* 0·0467 mho, 0·0264 mho, 0·0385 mho, 12·1 Ω, 17·7 Ω.]

11. Find the values of L_S and R_S so that the arrangements shown at (*a*) and (*b*) are equivalent.

[*Ans.* $R_S = \omega^2 L_P{}^2 R_P/(R_P{}^2 + \omega^2 L_P{}^2)$
$L_S = L_P R_P{}^2/(R_P{}^2 + \omega^2 L_P{}^2)$.]

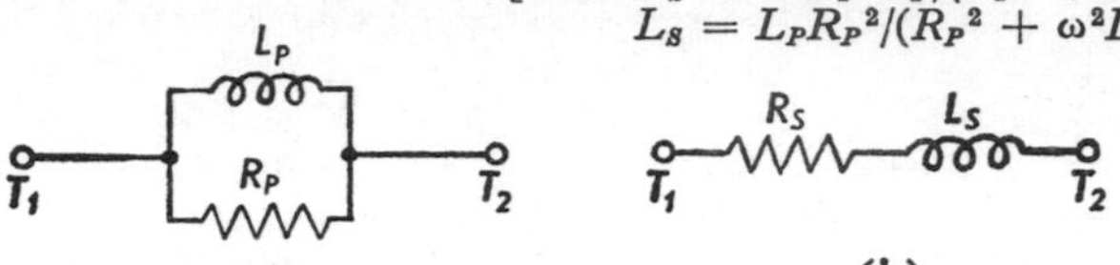

(a) (b)

12. Find the values of C_S and R_S so that the arrangements shown at (*a*) and (*b*) are equivalent.

[*Ans.* $R_S = R_P/\{1 + (\omega C_P R_P)^2\}$,
$C_S = C_P + 1/(\omega^2 R_P{}^2 C_P)$.]

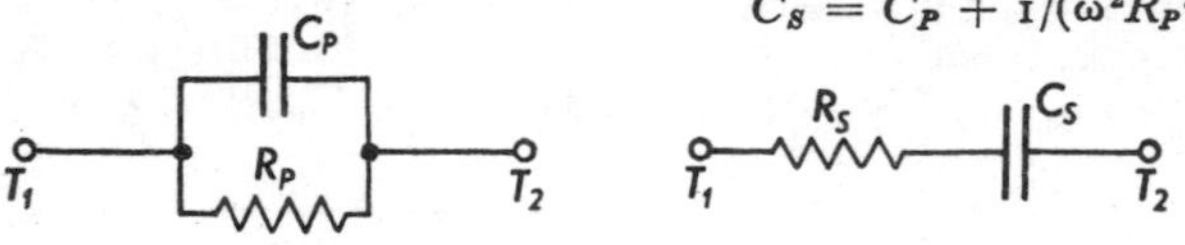

(a) (b)

13. Determine the values of L_2, C_3 and C_4 in terms of L_1, C_1 and C_2 if the arrangements shown at (*a*) and (*b*) are equivalent.

[*Ans.* $C_4 = C_1 + C_2$,
$C_3 = C_2(1 + C_2/C_1)$,
$L_2 = L_1/(1 + C_2/C_1)^2$.]

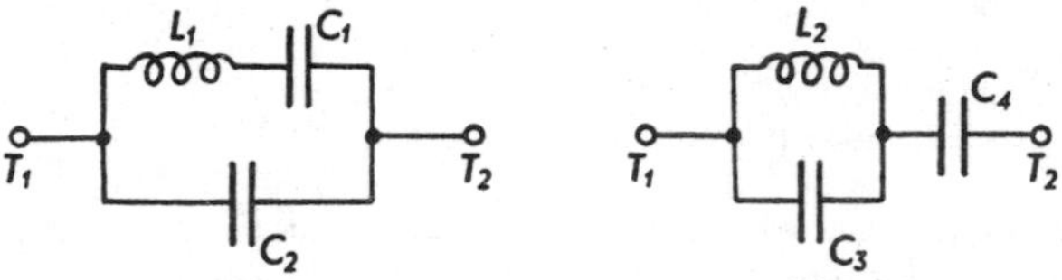

(a) (b)

14. Determine the values of L_3, L_4 and C_2 in terms of L_1, L_2 and C_1 if the arrangements shown at (*a*) and (*b*) are equivalent.

[*Ans.* $L_3 = (L_1)^2/(L_1 + L_2)$,
$L_4 = L_1 L_2/(L_1 + L_2)$,
$C_2 = C_1(L_1 + L_2)^2/L_2{}^2$.]

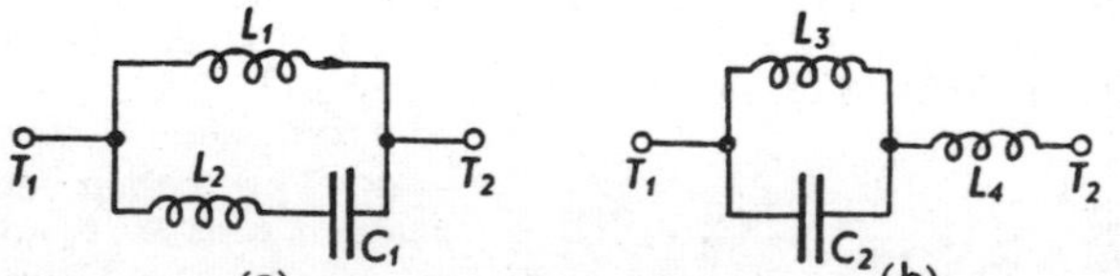

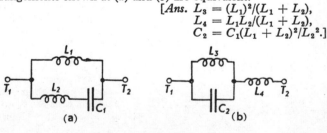

(a) (b)

15. Prove that if $R = \sqrt{L/C}$ the impedance of the circuit shown is independent of frequency, and determine the value of this impedance. [S.U.] [*Ans.* R.]

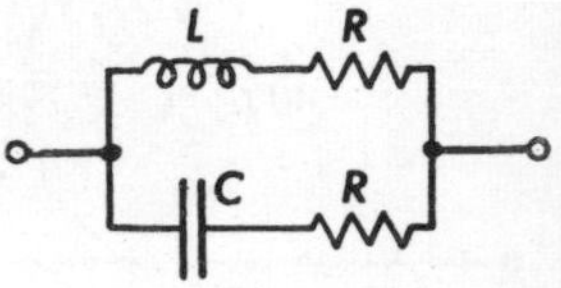

16. Prove that if $R = \sqrt{L/C}$ the impedance of the circuit illustrated is independent of frequency, and determine the value of this impedance. [*Ans.* *R*.]

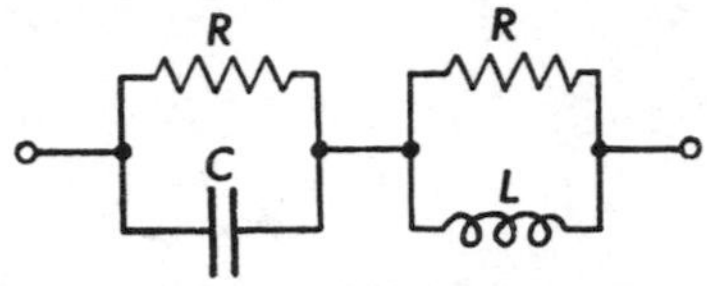

17. Three impedances of $(10 + j0)\ \Omega$, $(3 + j4)\ \Omega$ and $(0 - j4)\ \Omega$ are connected in parallel. This parallel combination is placed in series with an impedance of $(1 + j2)\ \Omega$ across a supply of 100 V. Calculate the voltage across the parallel branches and the total current taken from the supply. [*Ans.* 85·5 V, 20·4 A.]

18. Three coils *A*, *B* and *C* are provided. When all three are connected in series and a current of 2 A is passed through them the voltage drops across *A*, *B* and *C* are respectively, 100 V, 75 V and 50 V, while the power-factors are 0·5, 0·707 and 0·8. When *A* and *B* are joined in parallel and *C* is connected in series with the parallel combination, calculate the total power-factor and the applied voltage required to produce a total current of 2 A. [*Ans.* 0·724, 92·6 V.]

CHAPTER 7

SUBSIDIARY NETWORK THEOREMS AND PRINCIPLES

Millman's Theorem

Many circuits which are frequently encountered in both electronics and power applications can be solved by a very useful theorem due to Millman.*

Consider a number of admittances $\mathbf{Y}_1$, $\mathbf{Y}_2$, $\mathbf{Y}_3$, etc., which terminate at a common point O' (Fig. 7.1). The other ends of the admittances

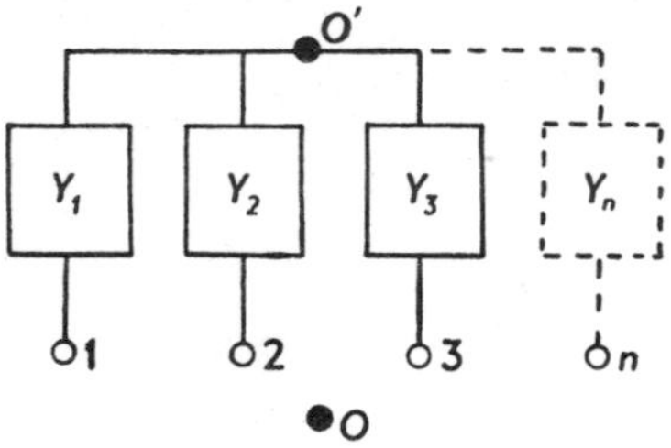

FIG. 7.1

are numbered 1, 2, 3, etc. O is any other point in the network. It is not necessary to know anything about the inter-connections between O, 1, 2, 3, etc., but only the voltage drops from O to 1, O to 2, etc.

The Theorem states that the voltage drop from O to O' ($\mathbf{V}_{00'}$) is given by

$$\mathbf{V}_{00'} = (\mathbf{V}_{01}\mathbf{Y}_1 + \mathbf{V}_{02}\mathbf{Y}_2 + \mathbf{V}_{03}\mathbf{Y}_3 + \ldots \mathbf{V}_{0n}\mathbf{Y}_n)/(\mathbf{Y}_1 + \mathbf{Y}_2 + \mathbf{Y}_3 + \ldots \mathbf{Y}_n)$$

where $\mathbf{V}_{0n}$ ($n = 1, 2, 3$, etc.) is the voltage drop from O to the nth impedance.

Proof.

Voltage drop across $\mathbf{Y}_1 = \mathbf{V}_{10'} = \mathbf{V}_{00'} - \mathbf{V}_{01}$ from 1 to O'

Current through $\mathbf{Y}_1 = \mathbf{I}_{10'} = (\mathbf{V}_{00'} - \mathbf{V}_{01})\mathbf{Y}_1$

Similarly, $\mathbf{I}_{20'} = (\mathbf{V}_{00'} - \mathbf{V}_{02})\mathbf{Y}_2$

$\mathbf{I}_{30'} = (\mathbf{V}_{00'} - \mathbf{V}_{03})\mathbf{Y}_3$

. . . .

and $\mathbf{I}_{n0'} = (\mathbf{V}_{00'} - \mathbf{V}_{0n})\mathbf{Y}_n$

* J. Millman, "A Useful Network Theorem", *Proc. I.R.E.*, **28**, p. 413 (1940). See also, F. A. Benson, *Electrical Engineering Problems with Solutions*, pp. 104–9 (Spon, 1954).

But Kirchhoff's first law applied at point O' gives:

$$I_{10'} + I_{20'} + I_{30'} + \dots + I_{n0'} = 0$$

i.e. $V_{00'} = (V_{01}Y_1 + V_{02}Y_2 + V_{03}Y_3 + \dots + V_{0n}Y_n)/(Y_1 + Y_2 + Y_3 + \dots + Y_n)$

The Theorem can also be proved by replacing each voltage source of Fig. 7.1 and its corresponding series admittance by a current-source equivalent to give the circuit of Fig. 7.2 (*a*) which can be redrawn as Fig. 7.2 (*b*).

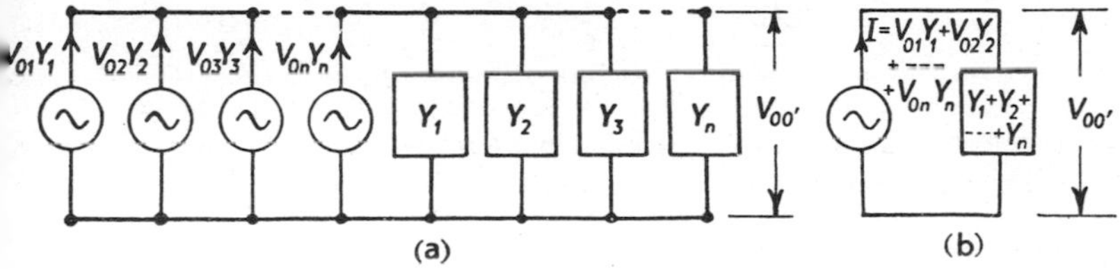

FIG. 7.2

Thus, $V_{00'} = I/\{Y_1 + Y_2 + Y_3 + \dots + Y_n\}$

$= (V_{01}Y_1 + V_{02}Y_2 + V_{03}Y_3 + \dots + V_{0n}Y_n)/(Y_1 + Y_2 + Y_3 + \dots + Y_n)$

A simple proof of the Theorem is provided by the Principle of Superposition. Thus, when voltage V_{01} acts alone,

$[V_{00'}]_1 = V_{01}Y_1(Y_2 + Y_3 + \dots + Y_n)/(Y_1 + Y_2 + Y_3 + \dots + Y_n)(Y_2 + Y_3 + \dots + Y_n)$

$= V_{01}Y_1/(Y_1 + Y_2 + Y_3 + \dots + Y_n)$

Similarly, when V_{02} acts alone,

$[V_{00'}]_2 = V_{02}Y_2/(Y_1 + Y_2 + Y_3 + \dots + Y_n)$

and when V_{0n} acts alone,

$[V_{00'}]_n = V_{0n}Y_n/(Y_1 + Y_2 + Y_3 + \dots + Y_n)$

Thus, when all the voltages act together

$V_{00'} = [V_{00'}]_1 + [V_{00'}]_2 + \dots + [V_{00'}]_n$

i.e. $V_{00'} = (V_{01}Y_1 + V_{02}Y_2 + V_{03}Y_3 + \dots + V_{0n}Y_n)/(Y_1 + Y_2 + Y_3 + \dots + Y_n)$

EXAMPLE. Use Millman's Theorem to find the current through Y_3 in the network of Fig. 7.3.

Solution. Choose points O, O', 1, 2 and 3 as shown on Fig. 7.3. Then Millman's Theorem gives:

$V_{00'} = (V_1Y_1 + V_2Y_2)/(Y_1 + Y_2 + Y_3)$ since $V_{03} = 0$.

$\therefore$ current through $\mathbf{Y_3} = \mathbf{Y_3 . V_{OO'}}$

$$= \mathbf{Y_3(V_1Y_1 + V_2Y_2)/(Y_1 + Y_2 + Y_3)}.$$

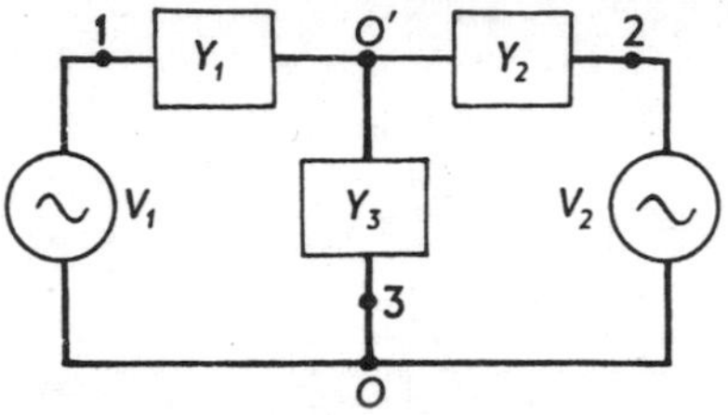

FIG. 7.3

EXAMPLE. Find the voltage between points O and O' in the network of Fig. 7.4 using Millman's Theorem.

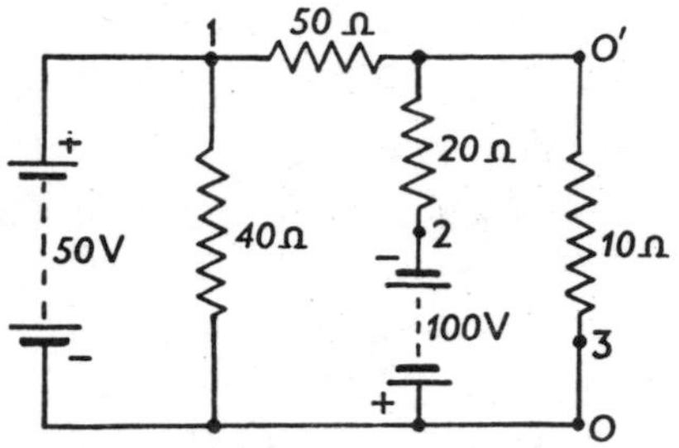

FIG. 7.4

Solution. Choose points 1, 2 and 3 as shown on Fig. 7.4. Then Millman's Theorem states:

$$\mathbf{V_{OO'}} = (\mathbf{V_{01}Y_1 + V_{02}Y_2 + V_{03}Y_3})/(\mathbf{Y_1 + Y_2 + Y_3})$$
$$= (-50/50 + 100/20 + 0)/(1/50 + 1/20 + 1/10)$$
$$= \underline{+ 23{\cdot}5\ \text{V}}$$

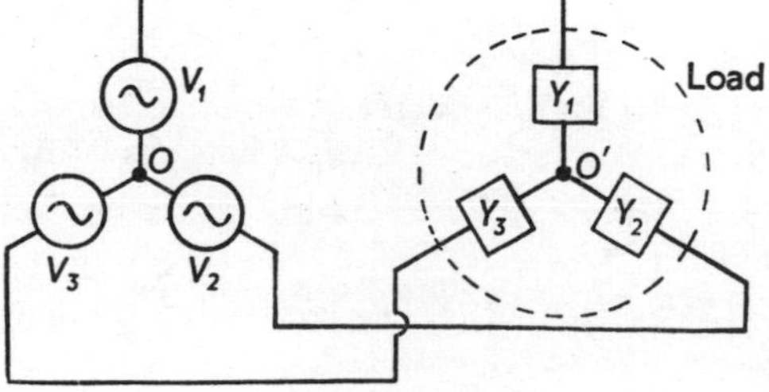

FIG. 7.5

Millman's Theorem is also useful for solving polyphase-circuit problems. Consider the arrangement of Fig. 7.5. The Theorem gives the voltage drop between points O and O' immediately, for

$$\mathbf{V}_{00} = (\mathbf{V}_1\mathbf{Y}_1 + \mathbf{V}_2\mathbf{Y}_2 + \mathbf{V}_3\mathbf{Y}_3)/(\mathbf{Y}_1 + \mathbf{Y}_2 + \mathbf{Y}_3)$$

The phase voltages of the load can then be easily calculated.

Millman's Theorem possesses great utility in solving many valve-circuit problems as shown in Chapter 13.

Norton's Theorem

Norton's Theorem is an alternative to Thévenin's Theorem and states that any linear network containing voltage sources is equivalent, when viewed from its output terminals, to a constant-current source and a shunt impedance. The constant current is equal to that current which would flow in a short-circuit placed between the terminals and the impedance is equal to the output impedance of the network. The constant-current source is assumed to have an infinite internal impedance.

Proof. Consider Fig. 7.6 where the output terminals A and B of

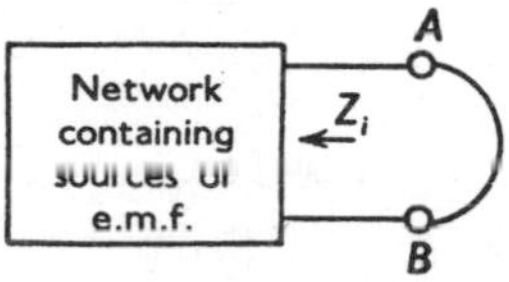

FIG. 7.6

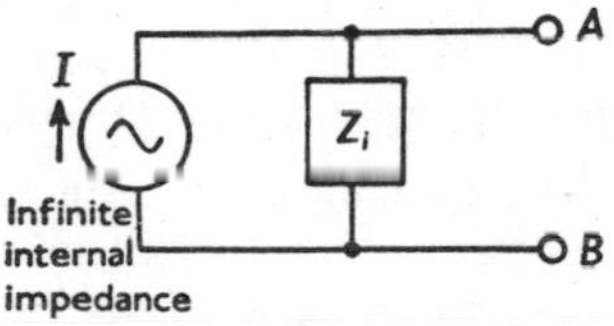

FIG. 7.7

the network are short-circuited. Then by Thévenin's Theorem the current $\mathbf{I}$ through the short-circuiting link is $\mathbf{V}_{AB}/\mathbf{Z}_i$ where $\mathbf{V}_{AB}$ is the open-circuit voltage between A and B.

Referring now to Fig. 7.7 it is seen that $\mathbf{V}_{AB} = \mathbf{Z}_i\mathbf{I}$, so Figs. 7.7 and 7.6 are equivalent.

Alternative statement of Norton's Theorem

Norton's Theorem can be stated in another useful generalized form * as follows:

The voltage between two points in a linear network is equal to the product $\mathbf{IZ}_i$, where $\mathbf{I}$ is the current which flows in a short-circuit placed between these terminals and $\mathbf{Z}_i$ is the impedance between these points (generators being replaced by their internal impedances).

Thévenin's and Norton's Theorems are often called the Helmholtz equivalent-source theorems.

* J. Millman and S. Seely, *Electronics*, 2nd Edition, pp. 515–18 (McGraw-Hill, 1951).

EXAMPLE. Apply Norton's Theorem to solve the problem on p. (117).

Solution. If a short-circuit is placed between O and O', the current in it due to $\mathbf{V}_1$ is $\mathbf{V}_1\mathbf{Y}_1$ and that due to $\mathbf{V}_2$ is $\mathbf{V}_2\mathbf{Y}_2$.

$$\therefore \quad \mathbf{I} = \mathbf{V}_1\mathbf{Y}_1 + \mathbf{V}_2\mathbf{Y}_2$$

Assume each generator has zero impedance, then

$$1/\mathbf{Z}_i = \mathbf{Y}_1 + \mathbf{Y}_2 + \mathbf{Y}_3$$

$$\therefore \quad \mathbf{V}_{00'} = \mathbf{I}\mathbf{Z}_i = (\mathbf{V}_1\mathbf{Y}_1 + \mathbf{V}_2\mathbf{Y}_2)/(\mathbf{Y}_1 + \mathbf{Y}_2 + \mathbf{Y}_3)$$

The current through $\mathbf{Y}_3 = \mathbf{Y}_3 \,.\, \mathbf{V}_{00'}$

$$= \underline{\mathbf{Y}_3(\mathbf{V}_1\mathbf{Y}_1 + \mathbf{V}_2\mathbf{Y}_2)/(\mathbf{Y}_1 + \mathbf{Y}_2 + \mathbf{Y}_3)}$$

EXAMPLE. Apply Norton's Theorem to solve the problem on p. 118.

Solution. If a short-circuit is placed between O and O', the current in it due to the 50 V battery = (50/50) A = 1 A. The current through the short-circuit due to the 100 V battery is —(100/20) A = —5 A.

$$\therefore \quad \mathbf{I} = (-5 + 1)\text{ A} = -4\text{ A}$$

Also, $$1/\mathbf{Z}_i = 1/50 + 1/20 + 1/10 = 17/100$$

$$\therefore \quad \mathbf{V}_{0'0} = \mathbf{I}\mathbf{Z}_i = -4/(17/100) = \underline{-23{\cdot}5\text{ V} = -\mathbf{V}_{00'}}$$

The Compensation Theorem

The Compensation Theorem may be stated as follows: When the impedance of a branch of a network which carries a current **I** is changed by an amount $\delta\mathbf{Z}$ all the currents in the network are altered by amounts equal to the currents which would arise if an e.m.f. $\mathbf{I}\delta\mathbf{Z}$ was acting independently in the modified branch.

Proof. Suppose the impedance of a branch of a network carrying a current **I** increases from **Z** to $\mathbf{Z} + \delta\mathbf{Z}$. Placing an e.m.f. $\mathbf{I}\delta\mathbf{Z}$ in the modified branch in the correct sense would cancel the voltage drop across $\delta\mathbf{Z}$ so that the network currents would return to their initial values. The Principle of Superposition then shows, however, that this compensating e.m.f. produces currents cancelling the changes due to $\delta\mathbf{Z}$. The Theorem is therefore proved because the alteration in current in any branch of the network caused by $\delta\mathbf{Z}$ is that which would flow in the branch due to an e.m.f. ($-\mathbf{I}\delta\mathbf{Z}$) acting alone in the branch originally modified.

Applications of the Compensation Theorem

The Compensation Theorem is helpful for solving problems connected with networks where component values are varied and is useful for studying the effects of tolerances on such values. It can also be employed for calculating the sensitivity of a bridge network. For example, suppose the balanced bridge of Fig. 7.8 (*a*) is unbalanced by changing $\mathbf{Z_1}$ to $\mathbf{Z_1}'$. The actual detector current in the unbalanced

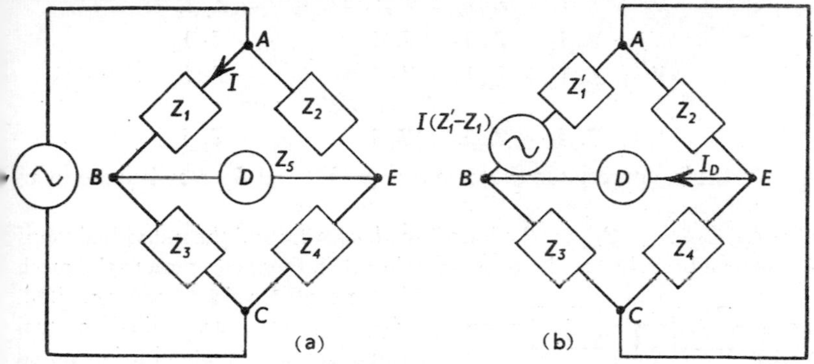

FIG. 7.8

circuit ($\mathbf{I_D}$) can then be calculated directly by using the Compensation Theorem because it is equal to the change in current in the detector arm which results from $\mathbf{I}(\mathbf{Z_1}' - \mathbf{Z_1})$ in arm *AB* (Fig. 7.8 (*b*)).

EXAMPLE. Calculate the change in current x in the network of Fig. 7.9, when the resistor R_3 increases by 10%.

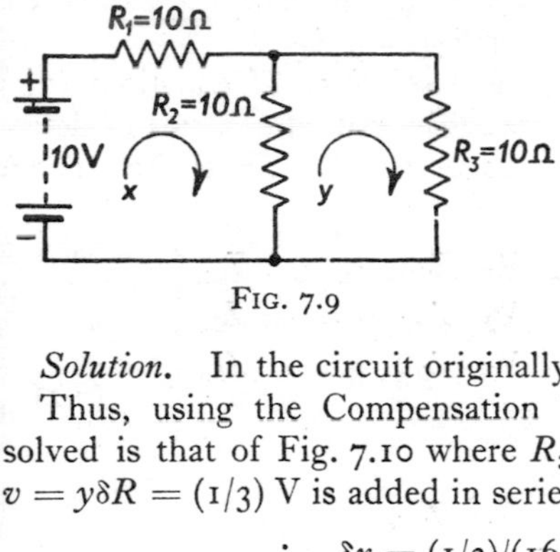

FIG. 7.9

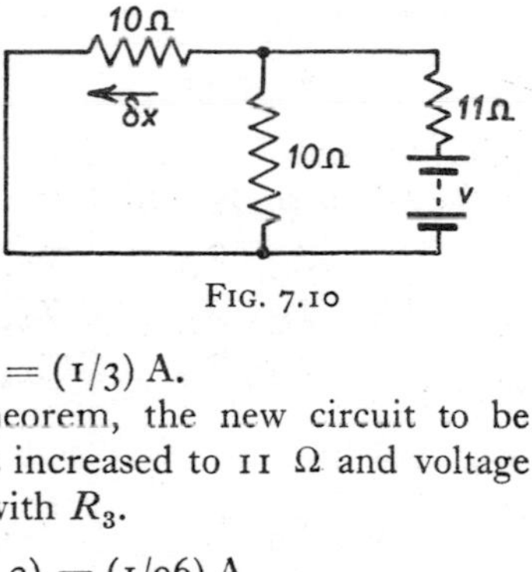

FIG. 7.10

Solution. In the circuit originally $y = (1/3)$ A.

Thus, using the Compensation Theorem, the new circuit to be solved is that of Fig. 7.10 where R_3 is increased to 11 Ω and voltage $v = y\delta R = (1/3)$ V is added in series with R_3.

$$\therefore \quad \delta x = (1/3)/(16 \times 2) = \underline{(1/96) \text{ A}}.$$

Mesh or loop analysis

Consider the network of Fig. 7.11. Then Maxwell's Cyclic Current Rule applied to the I_1 mesh gives

$$\mathbf{V_1} = (\mathbf{Z_1} + \mathbf{Z_2} + \mathbf{Z_4})\mathbf{I_1} - \mathbf{Z_2}\mathbf{I_2} - \mathbf{Z_4}\mathbf{I_3}$$

If $\quad (\mathbf{Z_1} + \mathbf{Z_2} + \mathbf{Z_4}) = \mathbf{Z_{11}}$ and $-\mathbf{Z_2} = \mathbf{Z_{12}}$ and $-\mathbf{Z_4} = \mathbf{Z_{13}}$.

then $\quad \mathbf{V_1} = \mathbf{Z_{11}}\mathbf{I_1} + \mathbf{Z_{12}}\mathbf{I_2} + \mathbf{Z_{13}}\mathbf{I_3}$

I

Thus, when an n-mesh network is analyzed in this way, simultaneous equations of the general form shown below result:

$$\left.\begin{aligned} \mathbf{V_1} &= \mathbf{Z_{11}I_1} + \mathbf{Z_{12}I_2} + \mathbf{Z_{13}I_3} + \ldots + \mathbf{Z_{1n}I_n} \\ \mathbf{V_2} &= \mathbf{Z_{21}I_1} + \mathbf{Z_{22}I_2} + \mathbf{Z_{23}I_3} + \ldots + \mathbf{Z_{2n}I_n} \\ \mathbf{V_3} &= \mathbf{Z_{31}I_1} + \mathbf{Z_{32}I_2} + \mathbf{Z_{33}I_3} + \ldots + \mathbf{Z_{3n}I_n} \\ &\cdots\cdots\cdots\cdots\cdots \\ \mathbf{V_n} &= \mathbf{Z_{n1}I_1} + \mathbf{Z_{n2}I_2} + \mathbf{Z_{13}I_3} + \ldots + \mathbf{Z_{nn}I_n} \end{aligned}\right\} \quad . \quad (7.1)$$

It will be appreciated that some of the **V**'s and **Z**'s may be zero in an actual case.

$\mathbf{Z_{11}}, \mathbf{Z_{22}} \ldots \mathbf{Z_{nn}}$ are the loop impedances around the individual loops when all branches of the network other than those common to the mesh being considered are open-circuited. $\mathbf{Z_{12}}$, $\mathbf{Z_{23}}$, etc., are called mutual impedances. It should be noted that $\mathbf{Z_{12}} = \mathbf{Z_{21}}$, $\mathbf{Z_{23}} = \mathbf{Z_{32}}$, etc. The coupling between two meshes may be due to either a common element or mutual inductance. It will be seen from Fig. 7.11 that if current $\mathbf{I_2}$ flowed in the reverse direction so that $\mathbf{I_1}$ and $\mathbf{I_2}$ are in the same direction in the common impedance $\mathbf{Z_2}$, then $\mathbf{Z_{12}} = +\mathbf{Z_2}$.

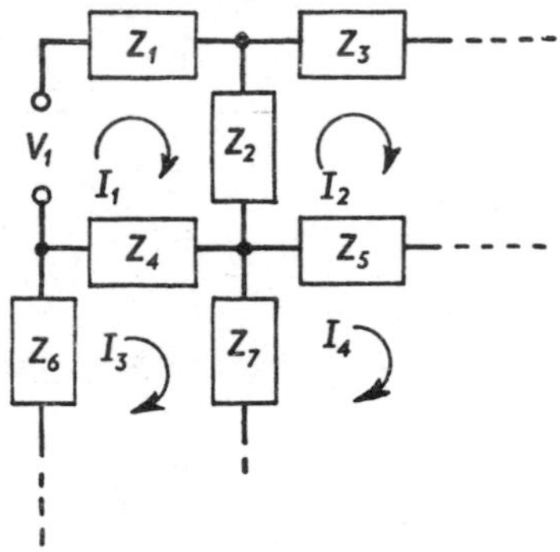

FIG. 7.11

The solutions of equations (7.1) are easily written in terms of determinants using Cramer's Rule (see Appendix 1). Thus, the current in the kth mesh, $\mathbf{I_k}$ is from (7.1),

$$\mathbf{I_k} = \frac{\begin{vmatrix} \mathbf{Z_{11}} & \mathbf{Z_{12}} & \ldots & \mathbf{Z_{1(k-1)}} & \mathbf{V_1} & \mathbf{Z_{1(k+1)}} & \ldots & \mathbf{Z_{1n}} \\ \mathbf{Z_{21}} & \mathbf{Z_{22}} & \ldots & \mathbf{Z_{2(k-1)}} & \mathbf{V_2} & \mathbf{Z_{2(k+1)}} & \ldots & \mathbf{Z_{2n}} \\ \mathbf{Z_{31}} & \mathbf{Z_{32}} & \ldots & \mathbf{Z_{3(k-1)}} & \mathbf{V_3} & \mathbf{Z_{3(k+1)}} & \ldots & \mathbf{Z_{3n}} \\ \vdots & \vdots & & & & & & \\ \mathbf{Z_{n1}} & \mathbf{Z_{n2}} & \ldots & \mathbf{Z_{n(k-1)}} & \mathbf{V_n} & \mathbf{Z_{n(k+1)}} & \ldots & \mathbf{Z_{nn}} \end{vmatrix}}{\mathbf{D}} \qquad (7.2)$$

where

$$\mathbf{D} = \begin{vmatrix} \mathbf{Z_{11}} & \mathbf{Z_{12}} & \ldots & \mathbf{Z_{1n}} \\ \mathbf{Z_{21}} & \mathbf{Z_{22}} & \ldots & \mathbf{Z_{2n}} \\ \mathbf{Z_{31}} & \mathbf{Z_{32}} & \ldots & \mathbf{Z_{3n}} \\ \vdots & \vdots & & \\ \mathbf{Z_{n1}} & \mathbf{Z_{n2}} & \ldots & \mathbf{Z_{nn}} \end{vmatrix} \quad . \quad . \quad . \quad . \quad . \quad (7.3)$$

The work required in solving a multi-mesh network problem can be reduced by writing down equations (7.2) and (7.3) directly from the network. It will be noticed that in the symbol for **D** the elements along the principal diagonal are the loop impedances $\mathbf{Z}_{11}, \mathbf{Z}_{22} \ldots \mathbf{Z}_{nn}$.

From equation (7.2), $\mathbf{I}_k$ can be written in the following form:

$$\mathbf{I}_k = \mathbf{V}_1\mathbf{B}_{1k}/\mathbf{D} + \mathbf{V}_2\mathbf{B}_{2k}/\mathbf{D} + \ldots + \mathbf{V}_j\mathbf{B}_{jk}/\mathbf{D} + \ldots + \mathbf{V}_n\mathbf{B}_{nk}/\mathbf{D} \quad . \quad (7.4)$$

where $\mathbf{B}_{jk}$ is the minor of the corresponding co-factor $\mathbf{V}_j$ and includes also the sign $(-1)^{k+j}$ (see Appendix 2).

When only generator $\mathbf{V}_j$ is present,

$$\mathbf{I}_k = \mathbf{B}_{jk}\mathbf{V}_j/\mathbf{D} \quad . \quad . \quad . \quad . \quad . \quad . \quad . \quad (7.5)$$

and when $j = k$,

$$\mathbf{I}_k = \mathbf{B}_{kk}\mathbf{V}_k/\mathbf{D} = \mathbf{V}_k \,.\, (\mathbf{B}_{kk}/\mathbf{D}) \quad . \quad . \quad . \quad (7.6)$$

Thus, $\mathbf{B}_{kk}/\mathbf{D}$ has the dimensions of admittance.

For the input mesh where $j = k = 1$, $\mathbf{I}_1/\mathbf{V}_1 = \mathbf{B}_{11}/\mathbf{D}$, which is called the *short-circuit input admittance* and will be denoted by $\mathbf{y}_{11}$ (the term short-circuit arises from the fact that all generators except $\mathbf{V}_1$ are short-circuited).

For the output mesh let $j = k = 2$, say. Then the *short-circuit output admittance* $\mathbf{y}_{22} = \mathbf{I}_2/\mathbf{V}_2 = \mathbf{B}_{22}/\mathbf{D}$. The ratio $\mathbf{I}_2/\mathbf{V}_1$, *i.e.* the current in mesh 2 due to a generator in mesh 1 is written as $\mathbf{y}_{12}$ and equals $\mathbf{B}_{12}/\mathbf{D}$. This is called the *transfer admittance* between the two meshes.

The expression for $\mathbf{I}_k$ which is given in terms of voltages and minors verifies the principle of superposition because each factor represents the current in the *k*th mesh due to one particular voltage source.

Nodal or junction analysis

Nodal network analysis has advantages over mesh analysis in solving certain types of network problem. When using such analysis all the sources are current ones. Consider the circuit of Fig. 7.12. One node is selected as a reference or datum node. This selection is arbitrary but the common side of a network, if one exists, is usually chosen as the reference node. Nodal analysis is based on Kirchhoff's current law. It will be assumed that the directions of the currents at each node are away from the junction. This choice is quite arbitrary just as the choice of the directions of the cyclic currents in mesh analysis is also arbitrary. Voltages $\mathbf{v}_{13}$ and $\mathbf{v}_{23}$ are those between nodes 1 and 2 and the reference node respectively. Constant-current sources are used in the circuit. Thus, using Norton's Theorem a source of open-circuit voltage $\mathbf{V}_1$ and internal impedance $\mathbf{Z}_1$ is replaced with a constant-current generator $\mathbf{V}_1\mathbf{Y}_1$ (of infinite internal impedance) in parallel with $\mathbf{Z}_1$. Then Kirchhoff's current law can be used to write down an equation for each node.

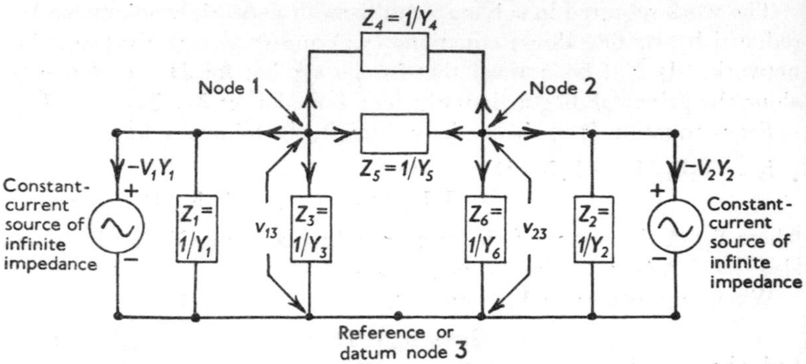

FIG. 7.12

Consider node 1 first. The constant-current generator $\mathbf{V_1Y_1}$ produces a current away from node 1 of $(-\mathbf{V_1Y_1})$. The current away from node 1 due to $\mathbf{v_{13}}$ is determined by short-circuiting all other node voltages, in this case only $\mathbf{v_{23}}$. Thus, $\mathbf{v_{13}}$ will produce a current $\mathbf{v_{13}(Y_1 + Y_3 + Y_4 + Y_5)}$ away from node 1. Similarly, the current away from node 1 due to $\mathbf{v_{23}}$ is found by short-circuiting $\mathbf{v_{13}}$; it is $-\mathbf{v_{23}(Y_4 + Y_5)}$.

Thus, for node 1,

$$-\mathbf{V_1Y_1} + \mathbf{v_{13}(Y_1 + Y_3 + Y_4 + Y_5)} - \mathbf{v_{23}(Y_4 + Y_5)} = 0 \quad (7.7)$$

The corresponding equation for node 2 is

$$-\mathbf{V_2Y_2} - \mathbf{v_{13}(Y_4 + Y_5)} + \mathbf{v_{23}(Y_2 + Y_4 + Y_5 + Y_6)} = 0 \quad (7.8)$$

In this particular case the node voltage $\mathbf{v_{23}}$ appears in the equation for node 1 and the node voltage $\mathbf{v_{13}}$ appears in the equation for node 2. If another node had been present between nodes 1 and 2, however, $\mathbf{v_{23}}$ would not appear in the node-1 equation and $\mathbf{v_{13}}$ would not appear in the node-2 equation.

Nodal analysis cannot be performed as described without modifications when mutual inductance is present between network elements although methods have been described to modify the procedure suitably.* When mutual inductance is present it is better to employ mesh analysis.

When an n-node network is analyzed in the above way simultaneous equations of the general form shown below result:

$$\left.\begin{aligned}
\mathbf{I_1} &= \mathbf{Y_{11}v_1} + \mathbf{Y_{12}v_2} + \mathbf{Y_{13}v_3} + \ldots + \mathbf{Y_{1n}v_n} \\
\mathbf{I_2} &= \mathbf{Y_{21}v_1} + \mathbf{Y_{22}v_2} + \mathbf{Y_{23}v_3} + \ldots + \mathbf{Y_{2n}v_n} \\
\mathbf{I_3} &= \mathbf{Y_{31}v_1} + \mathbf{Y_{32}v_2} + \mathbf{Y_{33}v_3} + \ldots + \mathbf{Y_{3n}v_n} \\
&\cdots\cdots\cdots\cdots \\
\mathbf{I_n} &= \mathbf{Y_{n1}v_1} + \mathbf{Y_{n2}v_2} + \mathbf{Y_{n3}v_3} + \ldots + \mathbf{Y_{nn}v_n}
\end{aligned}\right\} \quad (7.9)$$

* M. B. Reed, "Node Equations", *Proc. I.R.E.*, **32**, p. 355 (1944).

where $\mathbf{I}_1, \mathbf{I}_2, \mathbf{I}_3 \ldots \mathbf{I}_n$ are the generator currents at the various nodes and $\mathbf{v}_1, \mathbf{v}_2 \ldots \mathbf{v}_n$ are the respective node voltages referred to the reference node. Thus, using Cramer's rule, the voltage at the *k*th node is:

$$\mathbf{V}_k = \frac{\begin{vmatrix} \mathbf{Y}_{11} & \mathbf{Y}_{12} & \ldots & \mathbf{Y}_{1(k-1)} & \mathbf{I}_1 & \mathbf{Y}_{1(k+1)} & \ldots & \mathbf{Y}_{1n} \\ \mathbf{Y}_{21} & \mathbf{Y}_{22} & \ldots & \mathbf{Y}_{2(k-1)} & \mathbf{I}_2 & \mathbf{Y}_{2(k+1)} & \ldots & \mathbf{Y}_{2n} \\ \mathbf{Y}_{31} & \mathbf{Y}_{32} & \ldots & \mathbf{Y}_{3(k-1)} & \mathbf{I}_3 & \mathbf{Y}_{3(k+1)} & \ldots & \mathbf{Y}_{3n} \\ \cdot & \cdot & & & \cdot & & & \cdot \\ \cdot & \cdot & & & \cdot & & & \cdot \\ \cdot & \cdot & & & \cdot & & & \cdot \\ \mathbf{Y}_{n1} & \mathbf{Y}_{n2} & \ldots & \mathbf{Y}_{n(k-1)} & \mathbf{I}_n & \mathbf{Y}_{n(k+1)} & \ldots & \mathbf{Y}_{nn} \end{vmatrix}}{\mathbf{D}} \quad (7.10)$$

where

$$\mathbf{D} = \begin{vmatrix} \mathbf{Y}_{11} & \mathbf{Y}_{12} & \mathbf{Y}_{13} & \ldots & \mathbf{Y}_{1n} \\ \mathbf{Y}_{21} & \mathbf{Y}_{22} & \mathbf{Y}_{23} & \ldots & \mathbf{Y}_{2n} \\ \mathbf{Y}_{31} & \mathbf{Y}_{32} & \mathbf{Y}_{33} & \ldots & \mathbf{Y}_{3n} \\ \cdot & \cdot & \cdot & & \cdot \\ \cdot & \cdot & \cdot & & \cdot \\ \cdot & \cdot & \cdot & & \cdot \\ \mathbf{Y}_{n1} & \mathbf{Y}_{n2} & \mathbf{Y}_{n3} & \ldots & \mathbf{Y}_{nn} \end{vmatrix} \quad . \quad . \quad . \quad (7.11)$$

Equations (7.10) and (7.11) can be written down directly from the network.

Nodal analysis is particularly useful for solving problems connected with valve circuits because the equivalent circuits are similar to Fig. 7.12. One noteworthy feature of nodal analysis is that provided the number of nodes in a network remains the same, the number of nodal equations also stays the same, even if further branches are added in parallel with the elements already present.

Using minors and co-factors as in the mesh-analysis discussion $\mathbf{V}_k$ can be written as follows:

$$\mathbf{V}_k = \mathbf{I}_1\mathbf{B}_{1k}/\mathbf{D} + \mathbf{I}_2\mathbf{B}_{2k}/\mathbf{D} + \ldots + \mathbf{I}_j\mathbf{B}_{jk}/\mathbf{D} + \ldots + \mathbf{I}_n\mathbf{B}_{nk}/\mathbf{D} \quad . \quad (7.12)$$

When only current generator $\mathbf{I}_j$ is present (*i.e.* other generators are open-circuited)

$$\mathbf{v}_k = \mathbf{I}_j(\mathbf{B}_{jk}/\mathbf{D}) \quad . \quad . \quad . \quad . \quad . \quad . \quad (7.13)$$

$\mathbf{B}_{jk}/\mathbf{D}$ has the dimensions of impedance and is called the *open-circuit transfer impedance* $\mathbf{z}_{12}$.

The *open-circuit input impedance* $\mathbf{z}_{11} = \mathbf{v}_1/\mathbf{I}_1 = \mathbf{B}_{11}/\mathbf{D}$ and the *open-circuit output impedance* $\mathbf{z}_{22} = \mathbf{v}_2/\mathbf{I}_2 = \mathbf{B}_{22}/\mathbf{D}$.

Four-terminal networks

A four-terminal network possesses two input terminals and two output terminals. Four independent parameters, generally functions of frequency, may be used to specify the performance of such a linear network, whether it be passive or active. When the network is passive only three of these parameters are independent.

Consider the four-terminal network of Fig. 7.13. Various equations

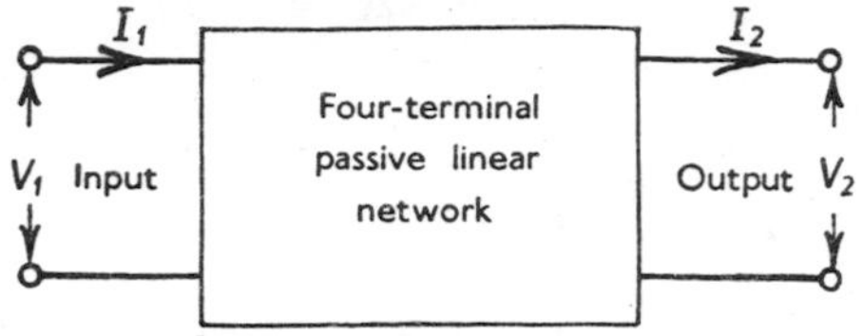

FIG. 7.13

can be written down giving relationships between the input and output voltages and currents. For example, mesh analysis gives

$$\left.\begin{aligned} \mathbf{V}_1 &= \mathbf{Z}_{11}\mathbf{I}_1 + \mathbf{Z}_{12}\mathbf{I}_2 \\ \mathbf{V}_2 &= \mathbf{Z}_{21}\mathbf{I}_1 + \mathbf{Z}_{22}\mathbf{I}_2 \end{aligned}\right\} \quad . \quad . \quad . \quad . \quad . \quad (7.14)$$

$\mathbf{Z}_{11}$, $\mathbf{Z}_{12}$, $\mathbf{Z}_{21}$ and $\mathbf{Z}_{22}$ are the parameters specifying the network.

Similarly, nodal analysis gives

$$\left.\begin{aligned} \mathbf{I}_1 &= \mathbf{Y}_{11}\mathbf{V}_1 + \mathbf{Y}_{12}\mathbf{V}_2 \\ \mathbf{I}_2 &= \mathbf{Y}_{21}\mathbf{V}_1 + \mathbf{Y}_{22}\mathbf{V}_2 \end{aligned}\right\} \quad . \quad . \quad . \quad . \quad . \quad (7.15)$$

The voltage and current at the input to the network can be related to the voltage and current at the output by the following equations:

$$\left.\begin{aligned} \mathbf{V}_1 &= \mathbf{A}\mathbf{V}_2 + \mathbf{B}\mathbf{I}_2 \\ \mathbf{I}_1 &= \mathbf{C}\mathbf{V}_2 + \mathbf{D}\mathbf{I}_2 \end{aligned}\right\} \quad . \quad . \quad . \quad . \quad . \quad . \quad (7.16)$$

It follows from the above equations that the impedance coefficients, $\mathbf{Z}_{11}$, $\mathbf{Z}_{12}$, $\mathbf{Z}_{21}$ and $\mathbf{Z}_{22}$, the admittance coefficients $\mathbf{Y}_{11}$, $\mathbf{Y}_{12}$, $\mathbf{Y}_{21}$ and $\mathbf{Y}_{22}$ and the **A**, **B**, **C** and **D** parameters can be determined by measurement, for:

$\mathbf{Z}_{11} = \mathbf{V}_1/\mathbf{I}_1$ with $\mathbf{I}_2 = 0$ (*i.e.* with the output terminals open-circuited)
$\mathbf{Z}_{21} = \mathbf{V}_2/\mathbf{I}_1$ with $\mathbf{I}_2 = 0$ (*i.e.* with the output terminals open-circuited)
$\mathbf{Z}_{12} = \mathbf{V}_1/\mathbf{I}_2$ with $\mathbf{I}_1 = 0$ (*i.e.* with the input terminals open-circuited)
$\mathbf{Z}_{22} = \mathbf{V}_2/\mathbf{I}_2$ with $\mathbf{I}_1 = 0$ (*i.e.* with the input terminals open-circuited)
$\mathbf{Y}_{11} = \mathbf{I}_1/\mathbf{V}_1$ with $\mathbf{V}_2 = 0$ (*i.e.* with the output terminals short-circuited)
$\mathbf{Y}_{21} = \mathbf{I}_2/\mathbf{V}_1$ with $\mathbf{V}_2 = 0$ (*i.e.* with the output terminals short-circuited)
$\mathbf{Y}_{12} = \mathbf{I}_1/\mathbf{V}_2$ with $\mathbf{V}_1 = 0$ (*i.e.* with the input terminals short-circuited)
$\mathbf{Y}_{22} = \mathbf{I}_2/\mathbf{V}_2$ with $\mathbf{V}_1 = 0$ (*i.e.* with the input terminals short-circuited)

$\mathbf{A} = \mathbf{V}_1/\mathbf{V}_2$ with $\mathbf{I}_2 = 0$ (*i.e.* with the output terminals open-circuited)
$\mathbf{B} = \mathbf{V}_1/\mathbf{I}_2$ with $\mathbf{V}_2 = 0$ (*i.e.* with the output terminals short-circuited)
$\mathbf{C} = \mathbf{I}_1/\mathbf{V}_2$ with $\mathbf{I}_2 = 0$ (*i.e.* with the output terminals open-circuited)

and

$\mathbf{D} = \mathbf{I}_1/\mathbf{I}_2$ with $\mathbf{V}_2 = 0$ (*i.e.* with the output terminals short-circuited)

Thus, **A** and **D** are dimensionless quantities, **B** has the dimensions of impedance and **C** has the dimensions of admittance. It can be shown that since only three parameters will completely specify a passive network **AD** − **BC** = 1. Further, for a lossless network **A** and **D** are real numbers but **B** and **C** are imaginary.

Apart from the three methods given above for specifying four-terminal networks there are three other important ones which are listed below:

(*a*) T-*section representation*

In the T-section representation three impedances, $\mathbf{T_1}$, $\mathbf{T_2}$ and $\mathbf{T_{12}}$ are connected as in Fig. 7.14.

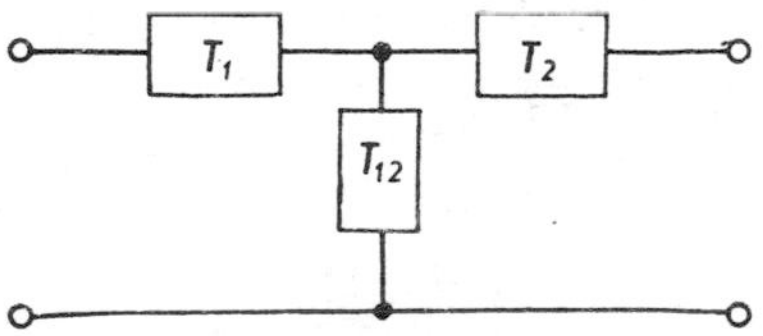

FIG. 7.14

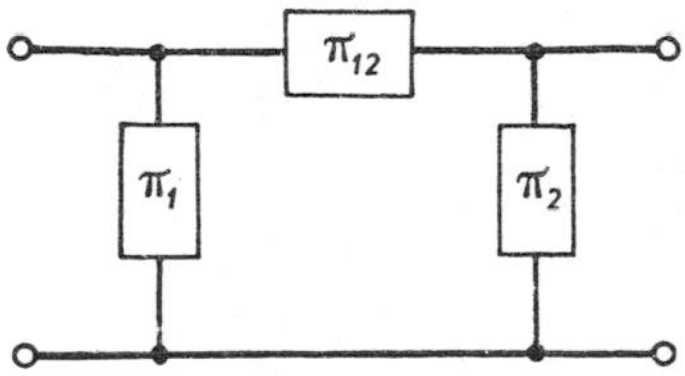

FIG. 7.15

(*b*) π-*section representation*

In the π-section representation three impedances $\boldsymbol{\pi_1}$, $\boldsymbol{\pi_2}$ and $\boldsymbol{\pi_{12}}$ are connected as in Fig. 7.15.

(*c*) *Image-parameter representation*

If $\mathbf{Z_{i1}}$ is the *image impedance* at the input to a network and $\mathbf{Z_{i2}}$ is the image impedance at the output then with $\mathbf{Z_{i2}}$ as the load the input impedance of the network is $\mathbf{Z_{i1}}$. Also, if $\mathbf{Z_{i1}}$ is the source impedance the network output impedance is $\mathbf{Z_{i2}}$.

A quantity $\boldsymbol{\theta}$ called the *image transfer constant* is defined as one half of the natural logarithm of the ratio of the input and output volt-ampères. Thus,

$$(\mathbf{V_2}/\mathbf{V_1}) = (\mathbf{Z_{i2}}/\mathbf{Z_{i1}})^{\frac{1}{2}}e^{-\theta}$$

The real and imaginary parts of the image transfer constant are called the *image attenuation constant* and the *image phase constant* respectively.

The relationships of the **Z** and **Y** coefficients, the **T** and $\boldsymbol{\pi}$ equivalents and the image parameters to the **A, B, C** and **D** parameters are shown in the following table. The reader may verify these relationships by interrelating some of the equations above.

Relationships Between Various Four-Terminal Network Parameters and the A, B, C and D Parameters

	A, B, C, D *Parameters*
$\mathbf{Z}_{11}$	$\mathbf{A/C}$
$\mathbf{Z}_{21}$	$\mathbf{1/C}$
$\mathbf{Z}_{22}$	$\mathbf{-D/C}$
$\mathbf{Y}_{11}$	$\mathbf{D/B}$
$\mathbf{Y}_{21}$	$\mathbf{1/B}$
$\mathbf{Y}_{22}$	$\mathbf{-A/B}$
$\mathbf{T}_{1}$	$\mathbf{(A - 1)/C}$
$\mathbf{T}_{12}$	$\mathbf{1/C}$
$\mathbf{T}_{2}$	$\mathbf{(D - 1)/C}$
π_{1}	$\mathbf{B/(D - 1)}$
π_{12}	$\mathbf{B}$
π_{2}	$\mathbf{B/(A - 1)}$
$\mathbf{Z}_{i1}$	$\pm\sqrt{\mathbf{AB/CD}}$
$\mathbf{Z}_{i2}$	$\pm\sqrt{\mathbf{BD/AC}}$
$\boldsymbol{\theta}$	$\cosh^{-1}(\pm\sqrt{\mathbf{AD}})$

EXAMPLE. Determine the Z, Y, T, π, A, B, C and D parameters of the network of Fig. 7.16. Find also the image parameters.

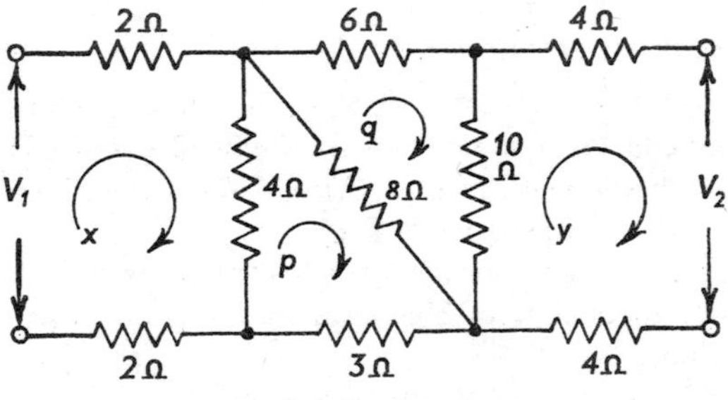

FIG. 7.16

Solution. Maxwell's Cyclic-Current Rule applied to the x, y, p and q meshes in turn gives

$$V_1 = 8x - 4p$$
$$V_2 = 18y - 10q$$
$$0 = -4x + 15p - 8q$$
$$0 = -10y - 8p + 24q$$

$$\therefore \text{ the determinant } D = \begin{vmatrix} 8 & 0 & -4 & 0 \\ 0 & 18 & 0 & -10 \\ -4 & 0 & 15 & -8 \\ 0 & -10 & -8 & 24 \end{vmatrix} = 25{,}312$$

$$\therefore\ Y_{11} = y_{11} = B_{11}/D = \begin{vmatrix} 18 & 0 & -10 \\ 0 & 15 & -8 \\ -10 & -8 & 24 \end{vmatrix} \Big/ 25{,}312 = 0{\cdot}1513 \text{ mho}$$

$$Y_{21} = y_{21} = B_{21}/D = \begin{vmatrix} 0 & -4 & 0 \\ 0 & 15 & -8 \\ -10 & -8 & 24 \end{vmatrix} \Big/ 25{,}312 = 0{\cdot}0126 \text{ mho}$$

$$Y_{22} = -y_{22} = -B_{22}/D$$

$$= -\begin{vmatrix} 8 & -4 & 0 \\ -4 & 15 & -8 \\ 0 & -8 & 24 \end{vmatrix} \Big/ 25{,}312 = -0{\cdot}0784 \text{ mho}$$

Thus, from the above table,

$A = -Y_{22}/Y_{21}$	$= 6{\cdot}222$	$T_{12} = 1/C$	$= 1{\cdot}078\ \Omega$
$B = 1/Y_{12}$	$= 79{\cdot}37\ \Omega$	$T_2 = (D-1)/C$	$= 11{\cdot}858\ \Omega$
$D = Y_{11}/Y_{12}$	$= 12{\cdot}0$	$\pi_1 = B/(D-1)$	$= 7{\cdot}215\ \Omega$
$C = (AD-1)/B$	$= 0{\cdot}928$ mho	$\pi_{12} = B$	$= 79{\cdot}37\ \Omega$
$Z_{11} = A/C$	$= 6{\cdot}704\ \Omega$	$\pi_2 = B/(A-1)$	$= 15{\cdot}2\ \Omega$
$Z_{12} = 1/C$	$= 1{\cdot}078\ \Omega$	$Z_{i1} = \sqrt{AB/CD}$	$= 6{\cdot}66\ \Omega$
$Z_{22} = -D/C$	$= 13{\cdot}006\ \Omega$	$Z_{i2} = \sqrt{BD/AC}$	$= 12{\cdot}84\ \Omega$
$T_1 = (A-1)/C$	$= 5{\cdot}628\ \Omega$	$\theta = \cosh^{-1}\sqrt{AD}$	$= 2{\cdot}846$

EXAMPLE. A symmetrical four-terminal network has an image impedance which is 600 Ω resistive. The image attenuation constant is 0·5 neper and the image phase constant is zero. A resistive load of 2,000 Ω is connected across the output terminals and a generator of 25 V is connected to the input terminals. If the internal impedance of the generator is 150 Ω resistive, calculate the load current. [S.U.]

Solution. Let the T-section of Fig. 7.17 represent the network. If the image impedance Z_i is connected across terminals 22′, the impedance measured between 1 and 1′ is also Z_i.

$$\therefore\ Z_i^2 = Z_a^2(1 + 2Z_b/Z_a) \quad \ldots \quad (7.17)$$

The image transfer constant is given by $e^\theta = (I_1/I_2)$ . . (7.18)

Voltage across 22′ $= I_2 Z_i$ . . . . (7.19)

Voltage across $Z_b = I_2(Z_i + Z_a)$ . . . . (7.20)

Current in $Z_b = I_2(Z_i + Z_a)/Z_b = I_1 - I_2$ . . . . . (7.21)

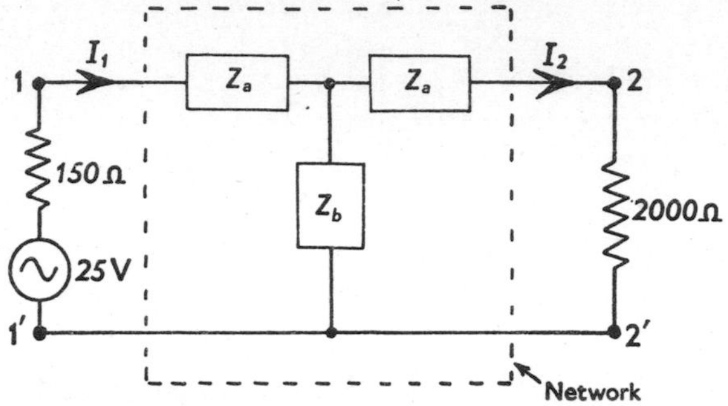

FIG. 7.17

From (7.18) and (7.21),

$$Z_i/Z_b = e^\theta - 1 - Z_a/Z_b = (Z_i/Z_a)(Z_a/Z_b) \quad . \quad (7.22)$$

∴ from (7.17) and (7.22),

$$Z_i^2 = Z_a^2\{1 + 2(Z_i/Z_a + 1)/(e^\theta - 1)\} \quad . \quad . \quad (7.23)$$

Here, $\theta = 0{\cdot}5$ and $Z_i = 600\ \Omega$, so $Z_a = 146{\cdot}8\ \Omega$ and $Z_b = 1{,}153\ \Omega$.

Using Thévenin's Theorem, the network can be replaced by the one shown in Fig. 7.18 where

$$E = 25 \times 1{,}153/(1{,}153 + 150 + 146{\cdot}8) = 19{\cdot}88\ \mathrm{V}$$

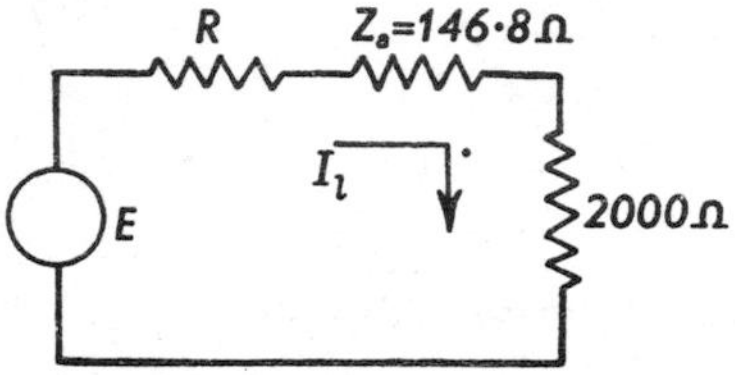

FIG. 7.18

and $\qquad R = 1{,}153 \times 296{\cdot}8/(1{,}153 + 296{\cdot}8) = 236\ \Omega$

$$\therefore \quad I_l = 19{\cdot}88/(2{,}000 + 146{\cdot}8 + 236)\ \mathrm{A}$$
$$= \underline{8{\cdot}34\ \mathrm{mA}}$$

Duality

The general simultaneous equations which were given above for voltages or currents when using mesh or nodal analysis respectively are seen to be of similar form. In fact, voltage in one set of equations is replaced by current in the other and impedance is.interchanged with admittance. Such circuits display the property of *duality*. Two circuits of this type may also have the additional property that inductance, capacitance and resistance in one are replaced by capacitance, inductance and conductance, respectively, in the other. The networks are then said to be *duals*. Consider Fig. 7.19.

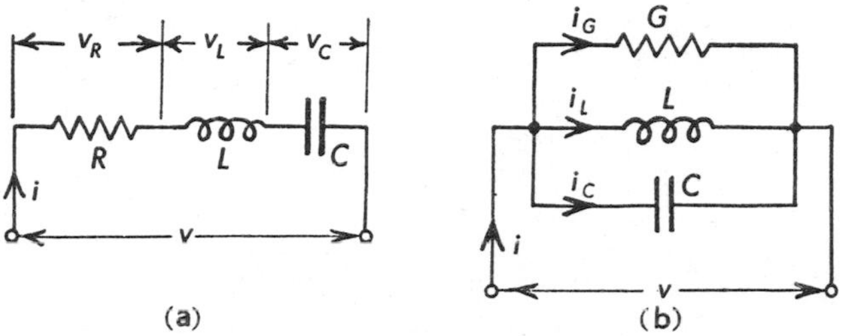

FIG. 7.19

For the series circuit of Fig. 7.19 (*a*),

$$v = v_R + v_L + v_C = R_i + L\, di/dt + \left(\int i\, dt\right)/C$$

For the parallel circuit of Fig. 7.19 (*b*),

$$i = i_G + i_L + i_C = Gv + C\, dv/dt + \left(\int v\, dt\right)/C$$

It will now be recognized that Norton's and Thévenin's Theorems are duals.

Duals will not be treated further here but it might be mentioned that the principle of duality covers a very wide field. For example, there is duality between the differential equations for electric circuits and for the motions of bodies under the actions of forces. These give analogies between e.m.f. and mechanical force, inductance and mass, current and velocity, capacitance and compliance and electrical resistance and normal frictional resistance.

Star–delta transformation

The star equivalents $\mathbf{Z}_1$, $\mathbf{Z}_2$ and $\mathbf{Z}_3$ in terms of the delta impedances $\mathbf{Z}_a$, $\mathbf{Z}_b$ and $\mathbf{Z}_c$ (Fig. 7.20) are easily obtained by writing down the impedances between pairs of external terminals in exactly the same way as was done in Chapter 2 for resistance networks. From these equations $\mathbf{Z}_a$, $\mathbf{Z}_b$ and $\mathbf{Z}_c$ can be found in terms of $\mathbf{Z}_1$, $\mathbf{Z}_2$ and $\mathbf{Z}_3$ but the calculations are fairly laborious. It is simpler to obtain the solution by using admittances instead of impedances as pointed out by Fleming.*

The procedure is to write down the admittance between each line in turn and the other two connected together.

* J. G. Fleming, "Star-Mesh Transformation", *Bull. Elect. Eng. Educ.*, No. 8, p. 17 (May, 1952).

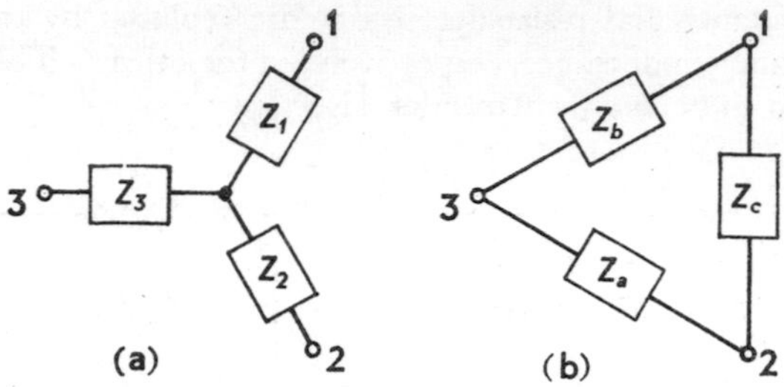

FIG. 7.20

Between terminal 1 *and terminals* 2 *and* 3 *connected,*

$$\mathbf{Y}_b + \mathbf{Y}_c = \mathbf{Y}_1(\mathbf{Y}_2 + \mathbf{Y}_3)/(\mathbf{Y}_1 + \mathbf{Y}_2 + \mathbf{Y}_3) \quad . \quad (7.24)$$

Between terminal 2 *and terminals* 1 *and* 3 *connected,*

$$\mathbf{Y}_c + \mathbf{Y}_a = \mathbf{Y}_2(\mathbf{Y}_1 + \mathbf{Y}_3)/(\mathbf{Y}_1 + \mathbf{Y}_2 + \mathbf{Y}_3) \quad . \quad (7.25)$$

Between terminal 3 *and terminals* 1 *and* 2 *connected,*

$$\mathbf{Y}_a + \mathbf{Y}_b = \mathbf{Y}_3(\mathbf{Y}_1 + \mathbf{Y}_2)/(\mathbf{Y}_1 + \mathbf{Y}_2 + \mathbf{Y}_3) \quad . \quad (7.26)$$

Add (7.24), (7.25) and (7.26):

$$2(\mathbf{Y}_a + \mathbf{Y}_b + \mathbf{Y}_c) = 2(\mathbf{Y}_1\mathbf{Y}_2 + \mathbf{Y}_2\mathbf{Y}_3 + \mathbf{Y}_1\mathbf{Y}_3)/(\mathbf{Y}_1 + \mathbf{Y}_2 + \mathbf{Y}_3) \quad (7.27)$$

Subtract from (7.27) each of the first three equations in turn:

$$\mathbf{Y}_a = \mathbf{Y}_2\mathbf{Y}_3/(\mathbf{Y}_1 + \mathbf{Y}_2 + \mathbf{Y}_3) \quad . \quad . \quad . \quad . \quad (7.28)$$

$$\mathbf{Y}_b = \mathbf{Y}_1\mathbf{Y}_3/(\mathbf{Y}_1 + \mathbf{Y}_2 + \mathbf{Y}_3) \quad . \quad . \quad . \quad . \quad (7.29)$$

and

$$\mathbf{Y}_c = \mathbf{Y}_1\mathbf{Y}_2/(\mathbf{Y}_1 + \mathbf{Y}_2 + \mathbf{Y}_3) \quad . \quad . \quad . \quad . \quad (7.30)$$

The corresponding impedance relationships can readily be found from these expressions if required but in many calculations the use of admittances is more convenient.

PROBLEMS

1. Determine the voltage across the 40 Ω resistor in the network shown using (*a*) Millman's Theorem, (*b*) the Generalized Form of Norton's Theorem. [*Ans.* 34·5 V.]

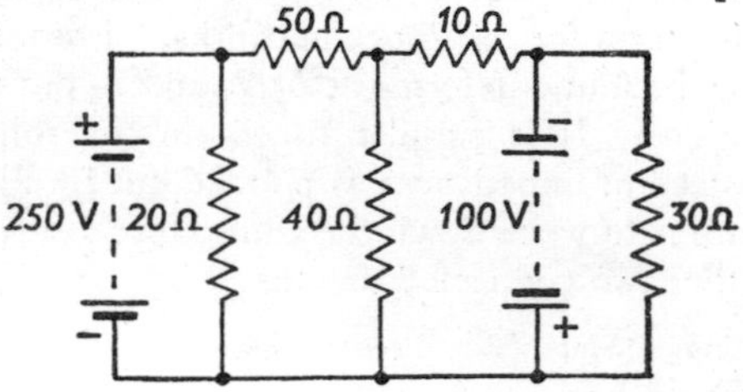

2. Calculate the voltage across the 10,000 Ω resistor in the network illustrated using (*a*) Millman's Theorem, (*b*) the Generalized Form of Norton's Theorem. [*Ans.* 21·4 V.]

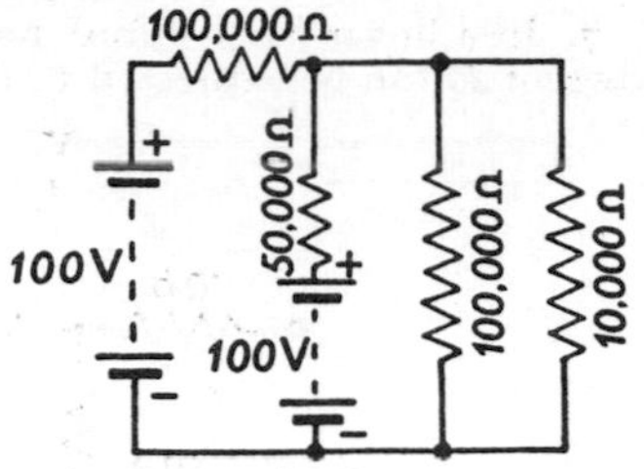

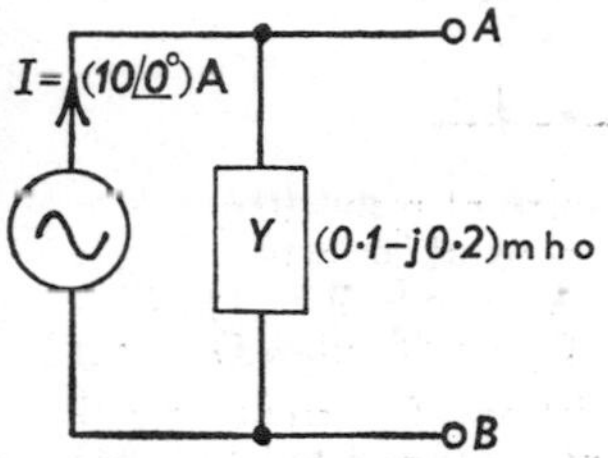

3. Replace the constant-current generator shown by a constant-voltage generator. [*Ans.* (44·7 |63·5°) V, (4·47 |63·5° Ω.]

4. A d.c. power supply has an output voltage of 240 V when the current is 130 mA and an output voltage of 300 V when the current is 40 mA. Show this supply in the form of (*a*) a voltage source, (*b*) a current source. [*Ans.* (*a*) $V = 327$ volts, $R = 667$ Ω, (*b*) $I = 490$ mA, $G = 0{\cdot}0015$ mho.]

5. Calculate the currents $\mathbf{I}_1$, $\mathbf{I}_2$ and $\mathbf{I}_3$ in the network illustrated using the nodal method of analysis.
[*Ans.*
$\mathbf{I}_1 = (1{\cdot}1 \,|\!-21°)$ A,
$\mathbf{I}_2 = (6{\cdot}4 \,|52°)$ A,
$\mathbf{I}_3 = (6{\cdot}8 \,|43°)$ A.]

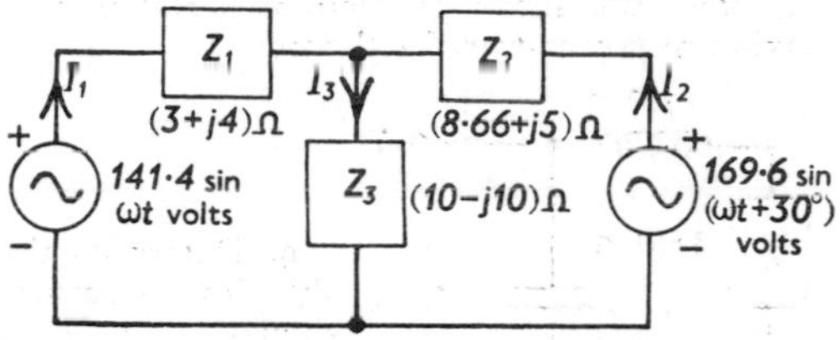

6. Open- and short-circuit tests are performed on the four-terminal network illustrated. An impedance of $(250 + j100)$ Ω is measured between terminals *A* and *B* with terminals *C* and *D* open-circuited. With *C* and *D* short-circuited the impedance between *A* and *B* is

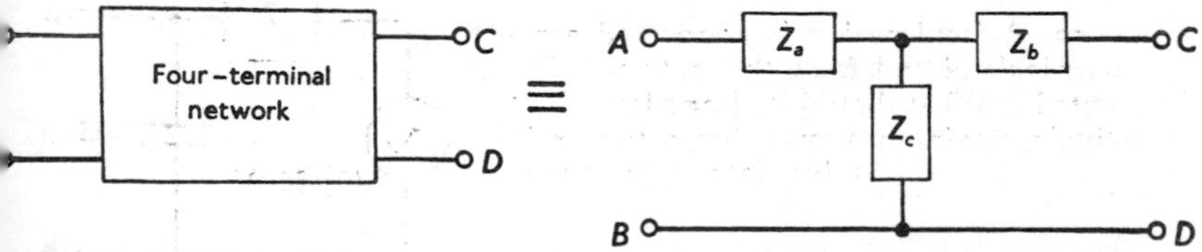

$(400 + j300)$ Ω. An impedance of $(200 + j0)$ Ω is measured between *C* and *D* with *A* and *B* open. Evaluate the impedances of the equivalent-T network.
[*Ans.* $\mathbf{Z}_a = (150 + j300)$ Ω,
$\mathbf{Z}_b = (100 + j200)$ Ω,
$\mathbf{Z}_c = (100 - j200)$ Ω.]

7. In a linear passive four-terminal network the input voltage V_1 and current I_1 can be expressed in the form:

$$\mathbf{V}_1 = \mathbf{A}\mathbf{V}_2 + \mathbf{B}\mathbf{I}_2$$
$$\mathbf{I}_1 = \mathbf{C}\mathbf{V}_2 + \mathbf{D}\mathbf{I}_2$$

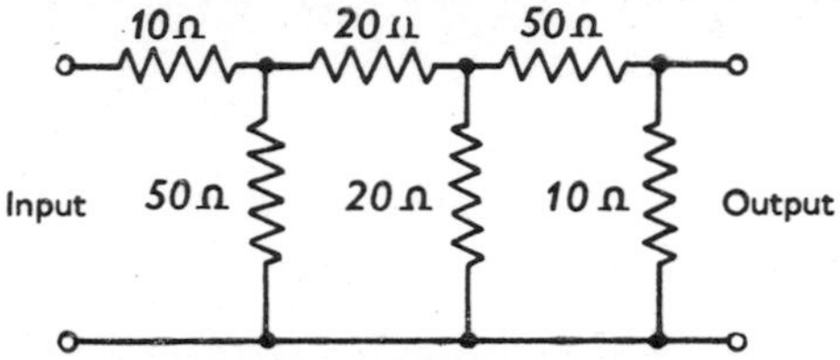

where $\mathbf{V}_2$ and $\mathbf{I}_2$ are the output voltage and current respectively.

Find the values of **A, B, C** and **D** for the network shown.

[*Ans.* **A** = 20·8, **B** = 179 Ω, **C** = 0·68 mho, **D** = 5·9.]

8. Prove that if an active network consisting of current or voltage sources and linear, bilateral, passive elements is connected to a passive network composed of similar elements, maximum power will be delivered to the passive network when its equivalent impedance is the conjugate of the equivalent impedance of the active network. Assume that the sources produce voltages and currents of constant amplitude and frequency.

[*Note*: the above problem is a statement of what is known as the maximum power-transfer theorem.]

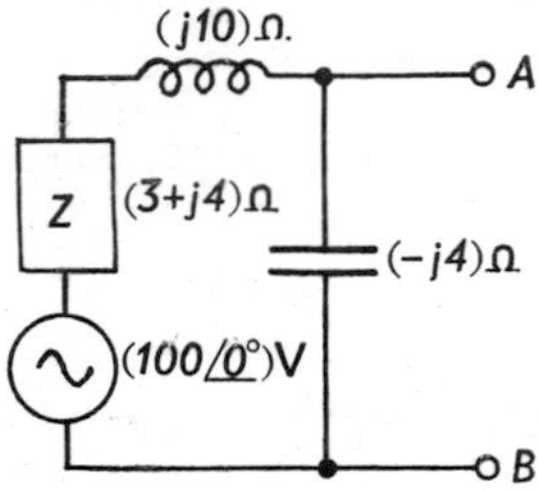

9. Determine the maximum power obtainable from terminals A and B of the circuit shown. [*Ans.* 828 W.]

10. A loudspeaker is connected across terminals A and B of the network illustrated. What should its impedance be to obtain maximum power dissipation in it? [*Ans.* (7·5 + j2·5) Ω.]

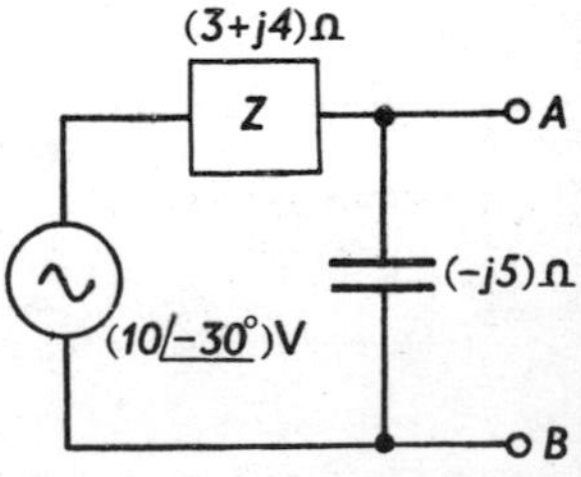

CHAPTER 8

COUPLED CIRCUITS AND TRANSFORMERS

Inductively-coupled circuits

When two circuits are inductively coupled energy is transferred from one to the other by transformer action. Consider the two coupled circuits of Fig. 8.1. Assume that the coils are wound on a single former in the same sense. Then

$$\mathbf{V} = (R_p + j\omega L_p)\mathbf{I_p} + j\omega M\mathbf{I_s}$$

and

$$0 = (R_s + j\omega L_s + \mathbf{Z})\mathbf{I_s} + j\omega M\mathbf{I_p}$$

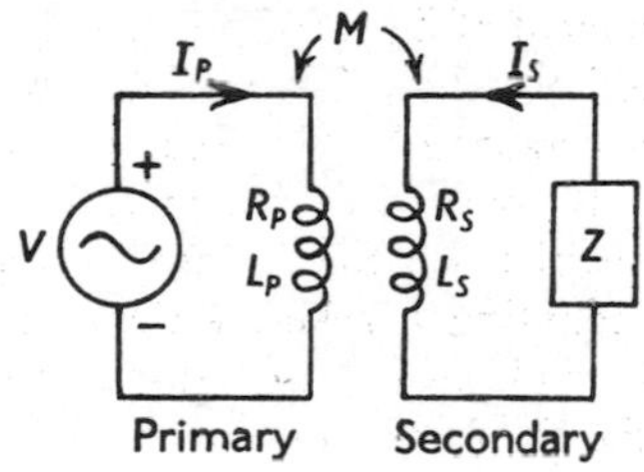

FIG. 8.1

For coils wound in the opposite sense with respect to each other M would be negative in both the above equations. In either case,

$$\mathbf{I_p} = \mathbf{V}/\{R_p + j\omega L_p + \omega^2M^2/(R_s + j\omega L_s + \mathbf{Z})\}$$

and

$$\mathbf{I_s} = -j\omega M\mathbf{I_p}/(R_s + j\omega L_s + \mathbf{Z})$$

Thus, the equivalent primary circuit is illustrated in Fig. 8.2. The secondary circuit can be ignored as far as the primary is concerned provided an impedance $\omega^2M^2/(R_s + j\omega L_s + \mathbf{Z})$ is added in series

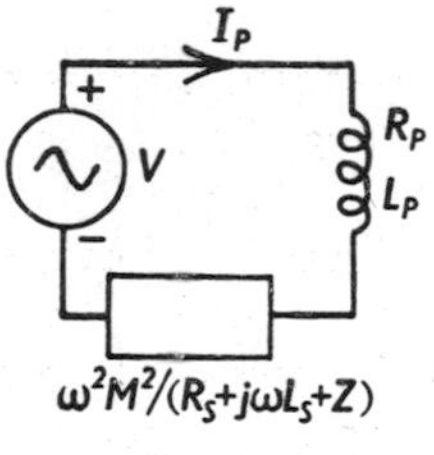

FIG. 8.2

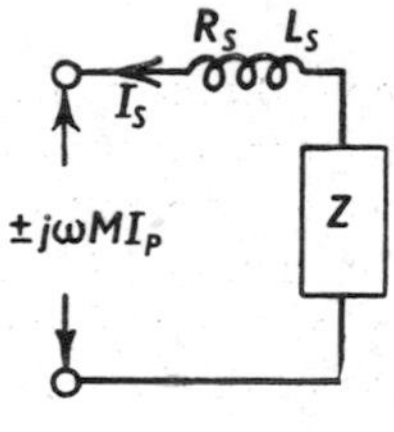

FIG. 8.3

with $(R_p + j\omega L_p)$. The voltage induced in the secondary circuit by current $\mathbf{I_p}$ is $\pm j\omega M\mathbf{I_p}$, so the equivalent secondary circuit is as shown in Fig. 8.3, the primary circuit being absent. The quantity $\omega^2M^2/(R_s + j\omega L_s + \mathbf{Z})$ is called the *coupled impedance* and many of the important characteristics of coupled circuits can be deduced by examining it. Consider, for example, the circuit of Fig. 8.1 when $Z = 0$.

Then from Fig. 8.2 it follows that the effective primary impedance $\mathbf{Z_p} = R_p + j\omega L_p + \omega^2 M^2/(R_s + j\omega L_s)$

$$i.e. \qquad \mathbf{Z_p} = R_p + j\omega L_p + \frac{\omega^2 M^2 R_s}{(R_s^2 + \omega^2 L_s^2)} - \frac{j\omega L_s(\omega^2 M^2)}{(R_s^2 + \omega^2 L_s^2)}$$

Thus, the secondary circuit couples into the primary circuit a resistive component $\omega^2 M^2 R_s/(R_s^2 + \omega^2 L_s^2)$, which adds to R_p, and also a capacitive component $j\omega L_s(\omega^2 M^2)/(R_s^2 + \omega^2 L_s^2)$, which neutralizes part of the primary inductive reactance. If $R_s = 0$, the reactive component of $\mathbf{Z_p}$ is $j\omega L_p(1 - k^2)$, where k is the coefficient of coupling. It follows that if $k = 1$ the primary inductance would be completely neutralized by the secondary capacitive component.

A coupled circuit of this type is encountered when a coil (primary circuit) is situated near a metal object, such as a screening can or mounting bracket, which forms the secondary circuit. If the object is made of good-conducting metal the added losses will be small and the chief effect on the coil will be a reduction of its effective inductance.

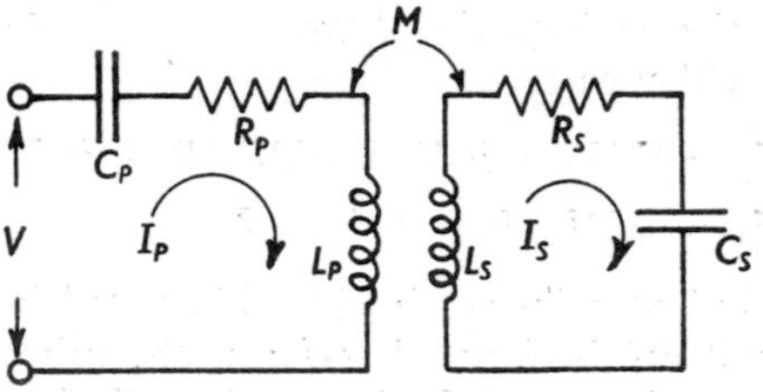

FIG. 8.4

Consider now the case where two resonant circuits (Fig. 8.4) are tuned to the same frequency and coupled together. The characteristics of the arrangement depend very much on the coefficient of coupling. Typical I_p/frequency and I_s/frequency curves are illustrated in Fig. 8.5.

The shapes of the I_p/f and I_s/f curves can be determined using equivalent circuits of the type already discussed. In practice the I_s/f curves are the more important. An expression for I_s can easily be obtained in terms of V, the circuit Q's, the coefficient of coupling (k) and the ratio of the actual frequency to the resonant frequency (α), in the following manner:

The impedance reflected into the primary circuit by the presence of the secondary $= \omega^2 M^2/\mathbf{Z_s}$

where $\quad \mathbf{Z_s} = R_s + j(\omega L_s - 1/\omega C_s) = R_s + j\omega L_s(1 - 1/\alpha^2)$

and $\quad \omega = 2\pi f.$

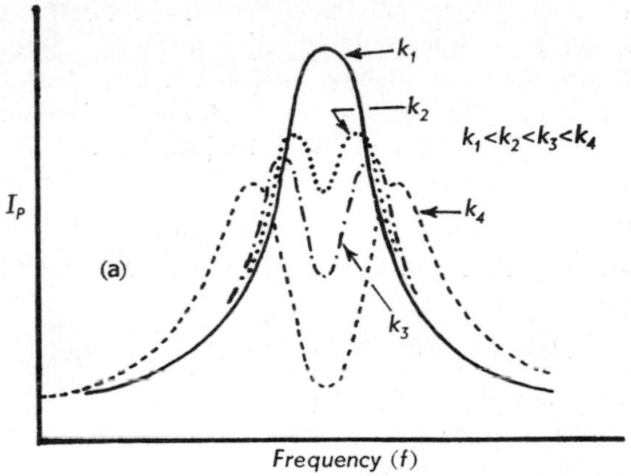

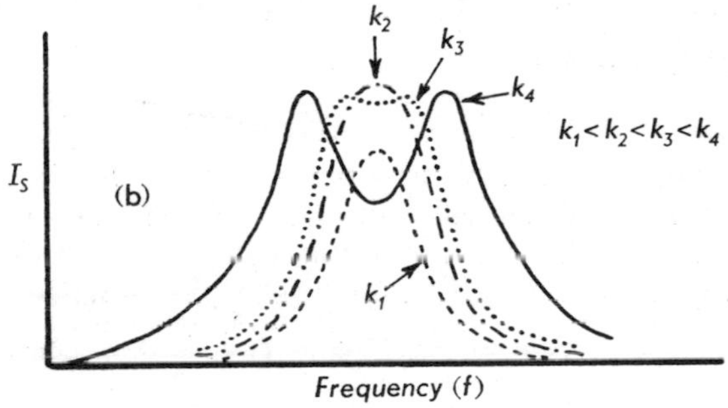

FIG. 8.5

The primary current

$$\mathbf{I_p} = \mathbf{V}/(Z_p + \omega^2 M^2/\mathbf{Z_s})$$

where $\mathbf{Z_p} = R_p + j(\omega L_p - 1/\omega C_p) = R_p + j\omega L_p(1 - 1/\alpha^2)$

The voltage induced in the secondary circuit $= -j\omega M\mathbf{I_p}$.

$$\therefore \text{ secondary current } \mathbf{I_s} = -j\omega M\mathbf{I_p}/\mathbf{Z_s}$$
$$= -j\omega M\mathbf{V}/(\mathbf{Z_p Z_s} + \omega^2 M^2)$$

i.e. $\mathbf{I_s} = -j\omega M\mathbf{V}/\{R_p R_s - (1 - 1/\alpha^2)^2\omega^2 L_p L_s + \omega^2 M^2 + j(1 - 1/\alpha^2)(\omega L_p R_s + \omega L_s R_p)\}$

Dividing the numerator and denominator by $\omega^2 L_p L_s$ and writing $Q_p = \omega L_p/R_p$ and $Q_s = \omega L_s/R_s$, also remembering that $M^2 = k^2 L_p L_s$ and $\omega = \alpha\omega_r$ where $\omega_r = 2\pi \times$ the resonant frequency,

$$\mathbf{I_s} = -j\mathbf{V}k/\alpha\omega_r\sqrt{L_p L_s}\{k^2 + 1/Q_p Q_s - (1 - 1/\alpha^2)^2 + j(1 - 1/\alpha^2)(1/Q_p + 1/Q_s)$$

This equation is complicated and the calculations necessary to determine I_s/frequency curves from it would be rather involved. Generally it is sufficient to find the conditions for critical coupling, I_s at resonance, I_s at the peaks if the coupling is greater than the critical value and the peak separation. The shape of the I_s/frequency curve can then be sketched in quite accurately.

$$\mathbf{I_s} = -j\omega M\mathbf{V}/[\{R_p + j(\omega L_p - 1/\omega C_p)\}\{R_s + j(\omega L_s - 1/\omega C_s)\} + \omega^2 M^2]$$

$\therefore$ I_s reaches a maximum value when the circuits are in resonance and $\omega^2 M^2 = R_p R_s$.

Thus, for maximum I_s, $\omega M = \sqrt{R_p R_s} = \omega\sqrt{L_p L_s}/\sqrt{Q_p Q_s}$.

i.e. the critical value of $k = 1/\sqrt{Q_p Q_s}$.

The value of I_s at resonance can be found from the above equation for I_s by putting $\alpha = 1$. Thus,

$$\mathbf{I}_{\mathbf{s}(\text{resonance})} = -j\mathbf{V}k/\omega_r\sqrt{L_p L_s}\{k^2 + 1/Q_p Q_s\}$$

If the coupling is critical,

$$\mathbf{I}_{\mathbf{s}(\text{resonance})} = -j\mathbf{V}\sqrt{Q_p Q_s}/2\omega_r\sqrt{L_p L_s} = -j\mathbf{V}/2\sqrt{R_p R_s}$$

The I_s/frequency curve shows two peaks when k is greater than the critical value. It is usually adequate to determine the width of the curve between the peaks by assuming the losses are negligible, *i.e.* Q_p and Q_s are infinite. Then from the equation for I_s,

$$\mathbf{I_s} = -j\mathbf{V}k/\alpha\omega_r\sqrt{L_p L_s}\{k^2 - (1 - 1/\alpha^2)^2\}$$

and so I_s becomes infinite when $(1 - 1/\alpha^2) = \pm k$.

$$\therefore \quad \frac{\text{Frequency at peak of } I_s}{\text{Resonant frequency}} = 1/\sqrt{1 \pm k} = \alpha_1$$

This expression is, of course, a special form of the general expression obtained when Q_p and Q_s are not infinite. In fact, it can be shown that

$$(\alpha_1)' = 1/\sqrt{1 \pm k\{1 - (1/Q_p^2 + 1/Q_s^2)/2k^2\}^{\frac{1}{2}}}$$

The values of I_s at the peaks are then not infinite but can be found by substituting $(\alpha_1)'$ in the equation for I_s. The peak heights of I_s are, however, both nearly equal to the resonant current with critical k.

EXAMPLE. A voltage of 200 V at a frequency of 159 kc/s is applied to the primary of the coupled circuit illustrated in Fig. 8.6. Determine the total effective resistance and reactance referred to the primary. Calculate also the primary and secondary currents.

Solution. The effective primary impedance $(\mathbf{Z_p})$ =

$$R_1 + j(\omega L_1 - 1/\omega C_1) + \omega^2 M^2/\{R_2 + j(\omega L_2 - 1/\omega C_2)\}$$

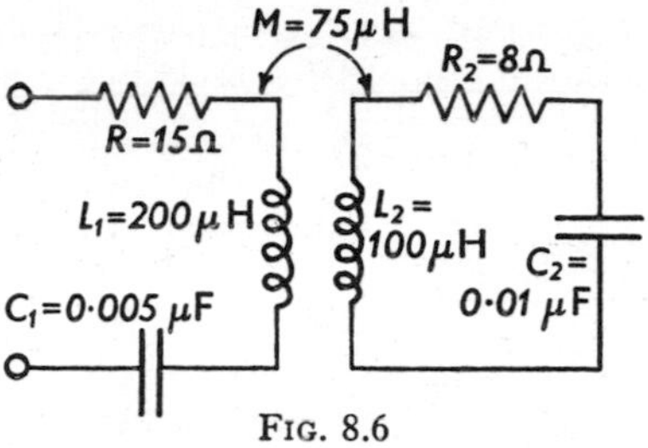

FIG. 8.6

Substituting the given values, $\mathbf{Z}_p$ is found to be $(718 + j0)\ \Omega$.

Therefore, the effective resistance $= \underline{718\ \Omega}$

and the effective reactance $= \underline{0}$

The primary current $= (200/718)\text{ A} = \underline{0{\cdot}278\text{ A}}$

The secondary current $= \omega M \times 0{\cdot}278/R_2$

$= \underline{2{\cdot}612\text{ A.}}$

Miscellaneous coupling methods

Energy can be transferred from one circuit to another without the aid of mutual inductance, three examples being shown in Fig. 8.7 (*a*),

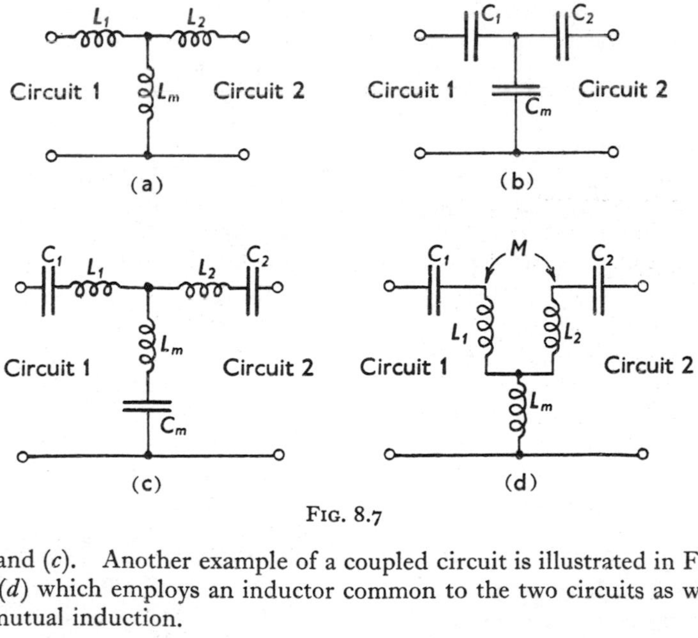

FIG. 8.7

(*b*) and (*c*). Another example of a coupled circuit is illustrated in Fig. 8.7 (*d*) which employs an inductor common to the two circuits as well as mutual induction.

All circuits of the type shown in Fig. 8.7 can be reduced to the simple coupled circuit shown in Fig. 8.8 by assigning suitable values to $\mathbf{Z_p}$ $\mathbf{Z_s}$ and M. The rules which determine these values are: (1) $\mathbf{Z_p}$ is the impedance measured between the primary terminals of the actual circuit when the secondary is on open-circuit. (2) $\mathbf{Z_s}$ is the impedance measured by opening the secondary of the actual circuit and finding the impedance between these open points when the primary is on open circuit. (3) M is calculated by assuming that a current $\mathbf{I_p}$ flows in the primary circuit. The voltage which appears across the open-circuited secondary is then $\pm j\omega M\mathbf{I_p}$.

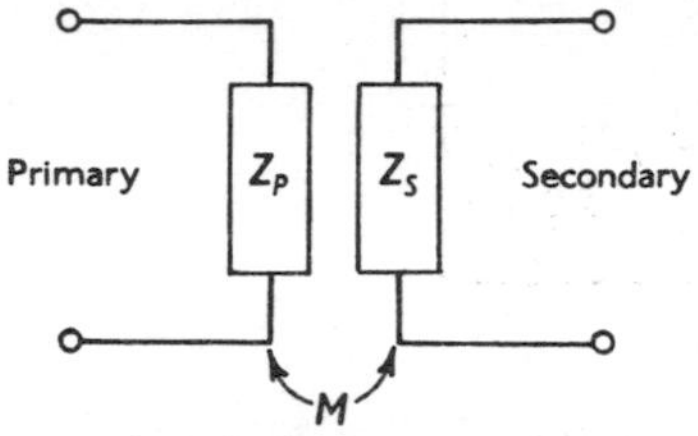

FIG. 8.8

Applying these rules to Fig. 8.7 (*a*), for example,

$$\mathbf{Z_p} = j\omega(L_1 + L_m),\ \mathbf{Z_s} = j\omega(L_2 + L_m) \text{ and } j\omega L_m\mathbf{I_p} = j\omega M\mathbf{I_p}$$

Thus, the coefficient of coupling is $L_m/\sqrt{(L_1 + L_m)(L_2 + L_m)}$

For the circuit of Fig. 8.7 (*b*) the rules give

$$\mathbf{Z_p} = (C_1 + C_m)/\omega C_1 C_m,\ \mathbf{Z_s} = (C_2 + C_m)/\omega C_2 C_m$$

and $$j\mathbf{I_p}/\omega C_m = j\omega M\mathbf{I_p}.$$

The coefficient of coupling in this case is therefore

$$\sqrt{C_1 C_2/(C_1 + C_m)(C_2 + C_m)}$$

The transformer

A transformer is a mutual inductor arranged so that the coefficient of coupling, $M/\sqrt{(L_p L_s)}$, is nearly unity. For use at power and audio frequencies the coils are placed on a core of laminated iron, so that all but a small fraction of the magnetic flux links with both coils, the values of M, L_p and L_s being very high, because a small current in one coil suffices to produce a large flux through the low-reluctance core. Laminated iron is not practicable for high frequencies because of the loss due to eddy currents and hysteresis, but cores of powdered iron and ferrite are commonly used.

Space does not permit a description of transformer construction to be given but transformers are employed so widely both in power and electronic circuits that an outline of the basic principles is appropriate here.

Although, in theory, a transformer may be analyzed as a mutual inductor by the method given earlier in this chapter, this is not convenient in practice, because the coefficient of coupling is so near to unity. The factor $(L_pL_s - M^2)$ occurs in many coupled-circuit equations, and though L_p, L_s and M are large in transformers, their difference is very small. Moreover, with an iron core, L_p, L_s and M are all non-linear functions of the effective magnetizing ampère-turns, but $(L_pL_s - M^2)$ is usually fairly constant. It is not possible to measure or calculate L_p, L_s and M separately with sufficient accuracy to obtain reasonable results for the factor $(L_pL_s - M^2)$.

The ideal transformer

In all actual transformers, the windings possess resistance, the fluxes due to the currents are not all mutual, and a small magnetizing current is required to maintain the flux in the core. However, the concept of an ideal transformer with none of these ' defects ' is very convenient, and is widely used in electrical-circuit theory. Such a transformer has no winding resistance, has a core of infinite permeance and all the flux links completely with both windings. Consider such an ideal transformer with N_p primary turns and N_s secondary turns, the primary being connected to an a.c. supply of voltage $v_p = V_p \cos \omega t$. Since there is no magnetizing current, the primary inductance being infinite, and moreover the winding resistance is zero, the resultant voltage in the primary circuit must be zero, so that $v_p + (-N_p d\Phi/dt) = 0$, where Φ is the core flux and the primary e.m.f. is $e_p = -N_p d\Phi/dt$. This equation is satisfied by $\Phi = \Phi_m \sin \omega t$, where $\Phi_m = V_p/N_p\omega$, giving $v_p = -e_p = +N_p\omega\Phi_m \cos \omega t$.

The flux Φ links with the secondary winding also, inducing therein an e.m.f. $e_s = -N_s d\Phi/dt = -N_s\omega\Phi_m \cos \omega t$

$$= N_s e_p/N_p$$

This secondary e.m.f. can be used as a source of voltage to supply a load, and for the ideal transformer, the secondary voltage v_s is equal to the e.m.f. e_s, so that the *numerical* voltage ratio is also $|v_s/v_p| = N_s/N_p$.

In the phase-relationships between the voltages, e.m.f.'s and the flux, implied in

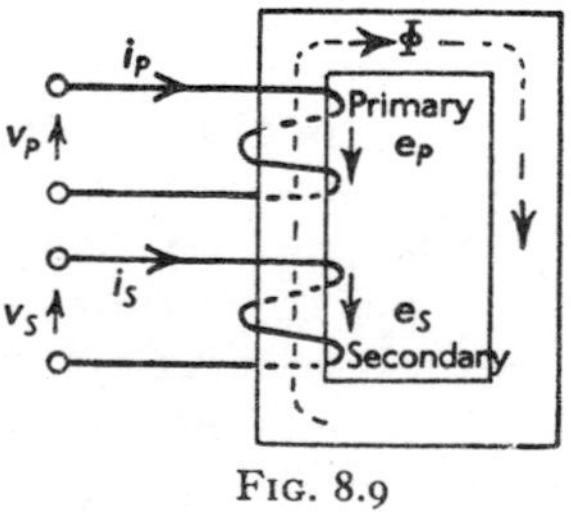

FIG. 8.9

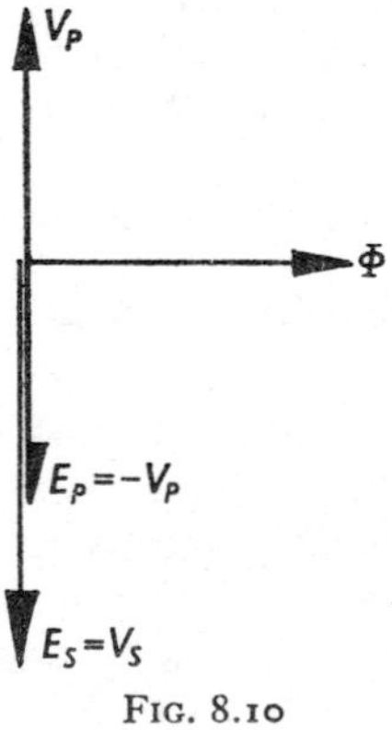

FIG. 8.10

the equations above, it is assumed that the two coils are wound in the same direction on the core, when the voltages, e.m.f.'s and flux are conventionally in the directions shown in Fig. 8.9. Obviously, if one of the coils was wound in the opposite direction to that shown the voltage and current for that coil would be reversed. The vector diagram corresponding to the above equations is shown in Fig. 8.10.

Magnetizing current

Since the permeance of the transformer core, though high, is not infinite, a small alternating magnetizing current flows in the primary winding. If the core had no eddy-current or hysteresis loss this current would be in phase with the flux and in quadrature with the e.m.f.'s as shown by I_μ in Fig. 8.11. The alternating flux does produce eddy currents in the core, however, and the iron has hysteresis, so there is a

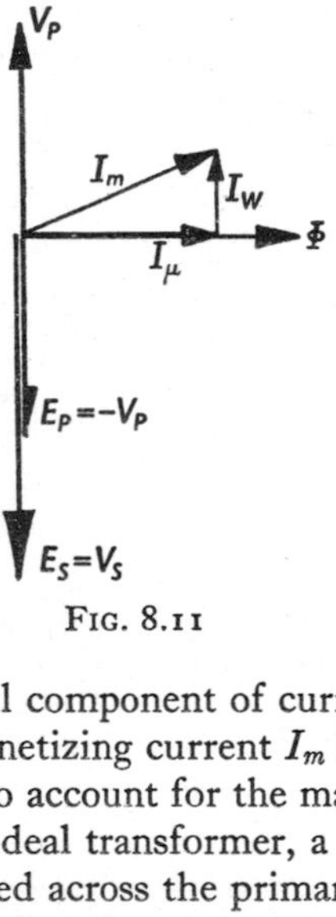

FIG. 8.11

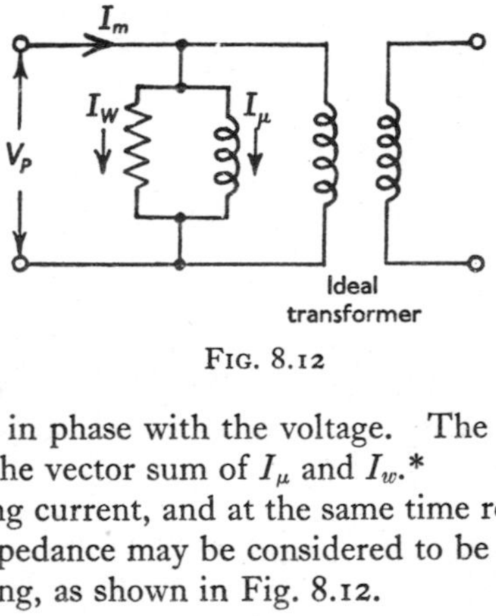

FIG. 8.12

small component of current, I_w, in phase with the voltage. The total magnetizing current I_m is then the vector sum of I_μ and I_w.*

To account for the magnetizing current, and at the same time retain the ideal transformer, a high impedance may be considered to be connected across the primary winding, as shown in Fig. 8.12.

Loaded transformer

When an impedance is connected across the secondary of a transformer with constant alternating primary voltage, an alternating current I_s will flow in the impedance and in the secondary winding, which will produce a magnetizing effect proportional to the ampère-turns N_sI_s. However, since in an ideal transformer, without winding resistances

* See T. H. Barton and F. A. Benson, "The Equivalent Circuit of the Single-Phase Transformer", *Electrical J.*, **153**, p. 117 (1954).

and in which the whole of the flux is mutual, the primary e.m.f. must be equal and opposite to the applied voltage, the flux must be a constant sinusoidal quantity so that the resultant ampère-turns must also be constant and equal to $N_p I_m$. Consequently an *extra* primary current I_p' flows, whose magnetizing effect is exactly opposite to that of I_s, that is, $N_p I_p' = -N_s I_s$, and the vector diagram will now be as shown in Fig. 8.13. The total primary current I_p is then the vector sum of I_p' and I_m, the resultant ampère-turns being still $N_p I_m$.

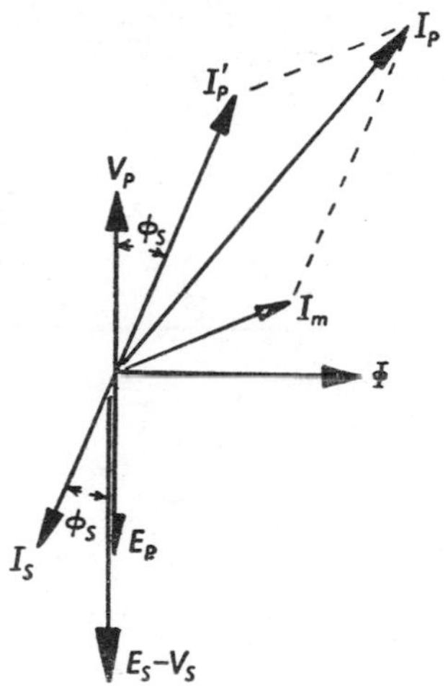

FIG. 8.13

The magnetizing current is usually much smaller than the full-load current, so that $I_p/I_s \simeq -N_s/N_p$, except for low load currents. Since $V_p/V_s = -N_p/N_s$ and $I_p'/I_s = N_s/N_p$, $V_p I_p' \cos \phi_s = V_s I_s \cos \phi_s$, thus satisfying the Law of the Conservation of Energy.

Resistance and leakage reactance

In an actual transformer the windings have resistance and the flux is not all mutual, since each coil produces, due to its own ampère-turns, fluxes of much less magnitude than the mutual flux, in the surrounding media. Some of these 'leakage' fluxes link only with the primary winding and some only with the secondary winding and some give partial mutual linkage. Three components of flux may therefore be recognized: the mutual flux Φ, flowing principally in the core, and produced by the resultant ampère-turns of primary and secondary; an effective primary leakage flux Φ_{lp} linking the primary winding only, proportional to the primary m.m.f., $N_p I_p$; and a similar secondary leakage flux Φ_{ls} linking the secondary winding only and produced by the secondary m.m.f. $N_s I_s$. This partition of the flux is convenient and logical, because the mutual flux in the iron core is a non-linear function of the resultant ampère-turns, while the leakage fluxes, flowing mainly in non-magnetic media, are nearly proportional to the individual winding ampère-turns.

A transformer may therefore be represented as a pair of coils with perfect coupling ($L_p' L_s' = M^2$), linked by the mutual flux Φ, together with 'leakage' inductors l_p and l_s and resistors R_p and R_s in series with primary and secondary to account for the e.m.f.'s produced by the leakage fluxes and for the voltages due to the winding resistances.

Thus, the complete equivalent circuit is as illustrated in Fig. 8.14 and the corresponding vector diagram is shown in Fig. 8.15.

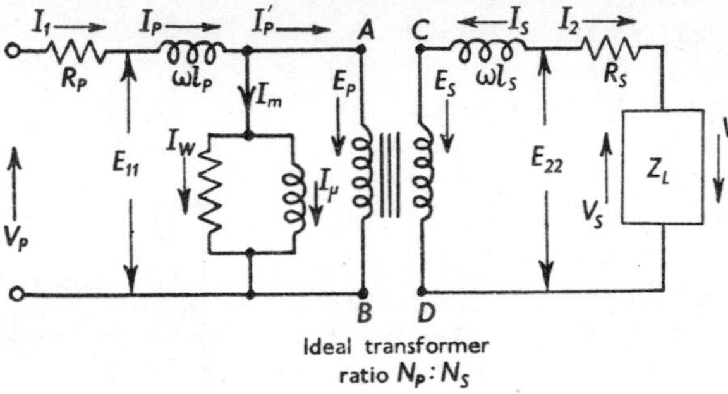

FIG. 8.14

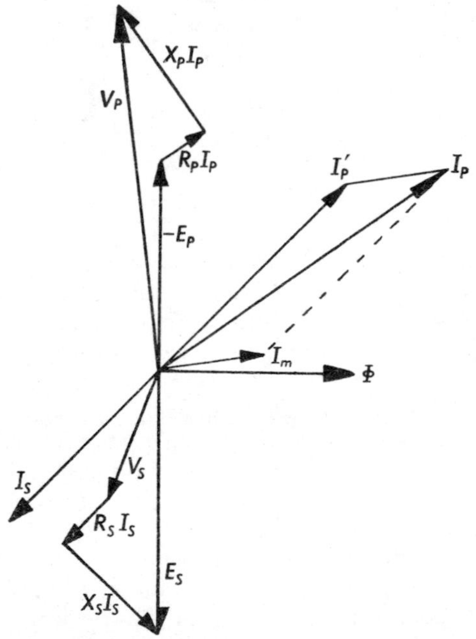

FIG. 8.15

In this vector diagram the leakage reactances are $X_p = \omega l_p$ and $X_s = \omega l_s$. R_pI_p, X_pI_p, R_sI_s and X_sI_s are the voltages required to drive the current through the resistors and leakage inductors. For clarity it is necessary to exaggerate the magnitudes of these voltages. In a power transformer R_pI_p and X_pI_p would be only a few per cent. of V_p, and R_sI_s and X_sI_s only a few per cent. of V_s.

Although the total e.m.f. E_{11} induced in the primary winding by the sinusoidally varying flux through it includes that due to the mutual or main flux Φ and that due to the leakage flux, it is customary to regard only the former component as the primary e.m.f. E_p, and similarly the secondary e.m.f. E_s is taken as that component due to Φ only, although strictly speaking the total secondary e.m.f. is E_{22}.

It is often convenient to consider the positive direction of flow of the secondary current in the opposite direction to I_s as shown on Fig. 8.14, that is, as $I_2 = -I_s$, and also to reverse the assumed direction of the voltage available to drive current through the load impedance. Thus, $V_2 = -V_s$. This gives a vector diagram as illustrated in Fig. 8.16, with I_2 and I_p' co-phasal. Thus, $N_pI_p' = N_sI_2$. It is still assumed that the primary winding starting at A (Fig. 8.14) and proceeding to B is wound on the core in the same direction as the secondary, starting at C and proceeding to D.

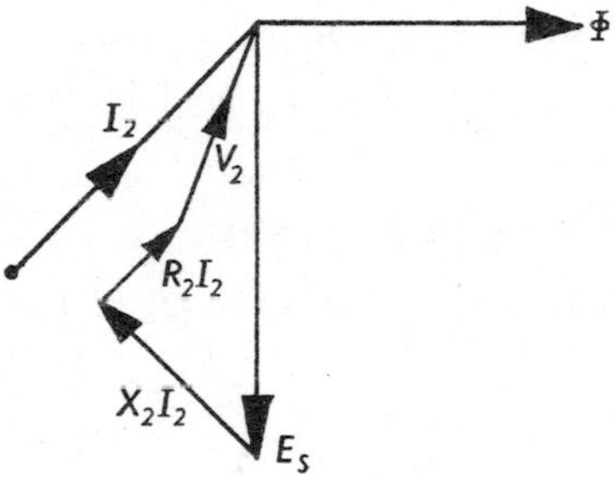

FIG. 8.16

The approximate equivalent circuit of the transformer

Since the magnetizing current I_m is small compared with the normal load current I_p', its contributions to the voltage drops in X_p and R_p are very small indeed, and little error is made if these are neglected and the shunt magnetizing impedance is considered to be connected directly across the primary input terminals as shown in Fig. 8.17. Using

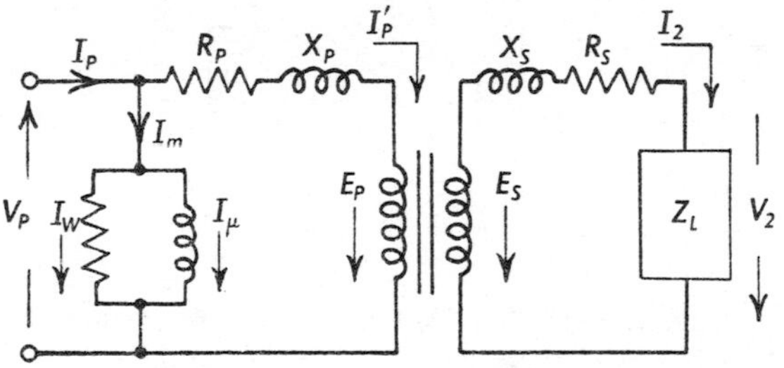

FIG. 8.17

square brackets for convenience here to represent vector quantities, the vector equations corresponding to the circuit of Fig. 8.17 are

$$[V_p] = [-E_p] + [R_pI_p'] + [X_pI_p'] \quad . \quad . \quad (8.1)$$

and

$$[V_2] = [-E_s] - [R_sI_2] - [X_sI_2] \quad . \quad . \quad (8.2)$$

Also, $I_{p'}/I_2 = N_s/N_p$ . . . . (8.3)

and $E_p/E_s = N_p/N_s$ . . . . (8.4)

From (8.1) and (8.4),

$$[V_p] = -[E_s](N_p/N_s) + [R_pI_p'] + [X_pI_p'] \quad . \quad . \quad . \quad (8.5)$$

From (8.2) and (8.5),

$$[V_p] = ([V_2] + [R_sI_2] + [X_sI_2])(N_p/N_s) + [R_pI_p'] + [X_pI_p'] \quad . \quad (8.6)$$

From (8.3) and (8.6),

$$[V_p] = [V_2](N_p/N_s) + [R_sI_p'](N_p/N_s)^2 + [X_sI_p'](N_p/N_s)^2 + [R_pI_p'] + [X_pI_p'] \quad . \quad (8.7)$$

i.e. $[V_p] = [V_2](N_p/N_s) + [R_s(N_p/N_s)^2 + R_p]I_p' + [X_s(N_p/N_s)^2 + X_p]I_p'$. (8.8)

$$= [V_2'] + [R_p'I_p'] + [X_p'I_p'] \quad . \quad . \quad . \quad . \quad . \quad . \quad (8.9)$$

Also, since $I_2 = V_2/Z_L$, $I_p' = N_sV_2/Z_LN_p$

$$\therefore \quad I_p'(N_p/N_s)V_2/Z_L(N_p/N_s)^2 = V_2'/Z_L'$$

Thus, an equivalent circuit, corresponding to the above equations can be drawn as shown in Fig. 8.18.

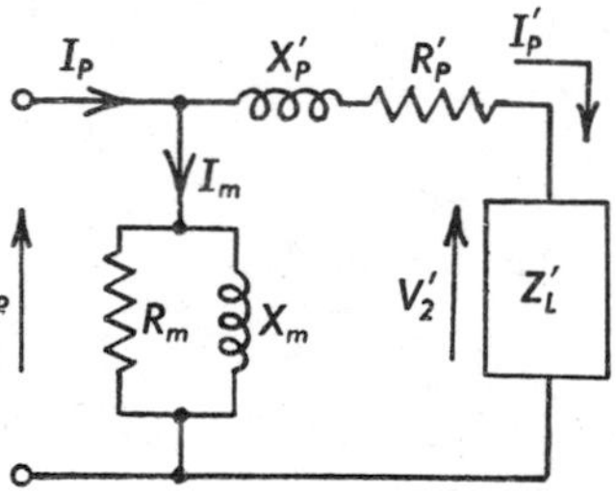

FIG. 8.18

$$X_p' = X_p + X_s(N_p/N_s)^2$$

and $$R_p' = R_p + R_s(N_p/N_s)^2$$

are the total leakage reactance and resistance referred to the primary, $X_s(N_p/N_s)^2$ being the secondary leakage reactance referred to the primary and $R_s(N_p/N_s)^2$ being the secondary resistance referred to the primary. $Z_L' = Z(N_p/N_s)^2$ is the load impedance referred to the primary, while $I_p' = I_2(N_s/N_p)$ and $V_2' = V_2(N_p/N_s)$ are the secondary current and voltage referred to the primary.

A circuit similar to that of Fig. 8.18, but with all quantities referred to the secondary side may readily be found by manipulating the above equations so as to eliminate V_p, I_p', X_p and R_p. Such a circuit is illustrated in Fig. 8.19.

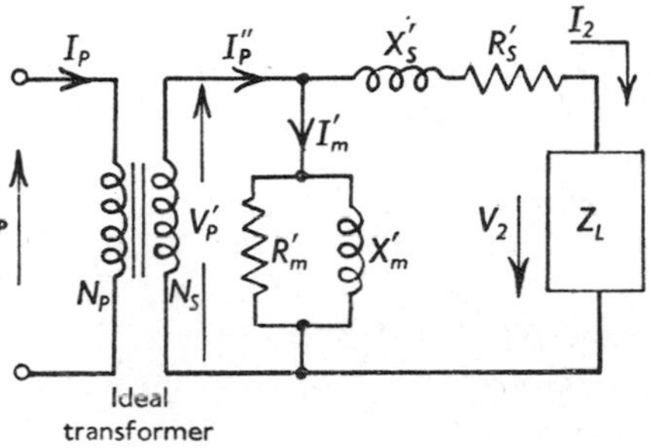

FIG. 8.19

$$R_m' = R_m(N_s/N_p)^2, \ X_m' = X_m(N_s/N_p)^2$$
$$I_p'' = I_p(N_p/N_s), \ I_m' = I_m(N_p/N_s)$$
$$V_p' = V_p(N_s/N_p), \ X_s' = X_s + X_p(N_s/N_p)^2$$
$$R_s' = R_s + R_p(N_s/N_p)^2, \ I_2 = I_p'(N_p/N_s)$$

The quantities I_p'', I_m' and V_p' are the primary current, magnetizing current and primary voltage referred to the secondary; R_s' and X_s' are the total resistance and leakage reactance referred to the secondary and $R_p(N_s/N_p)^2$ and $X_p(N_s/N_p)^2$ are the primary resistance and leakage reactance referred to the secondary.

Matching

In an electronic amplifier it may be desirable to connect a load of a given impedance in the output circuit, whereas the actual load (*e.g.* a loudspeaker coil) may have a very different impedance. By using an output transformer with the correct turns ratio this can be accomplished. For example, if the desired load impedance is 6,000 Ω and the actual load impedance (of a loudspeaker coil) is 15 Ω, a transformer of primary/secondary turns ratio of 20 to 1 would give the correct match because $15 \times 20^2 = 6{,}000$.

Measurement of transformer parameters

The significant transformer parameters can be determined reasonably accurately from the results of the two following simple tests:

(*a*) *Open-circuit test.*

The transformer primary is supplied at normal rated voltage and frequency, with the secondary on open-circuit. The input current and power are measured, giving the magnetizing current and its power-factor. A voltmeter connected to the secondary enables the voltage ratio to be determined.

(*b*) *Short-circuit test.*

The secondary terminals are short-circuited and a low voltage (preferably adjustable) of normal frequency is applied to the primary. The voltage V volts the current I ampères and the power P watts are measured. Since the shunt magnetizing impedance is so very much higher than the resistance R_p' and the leakage reactance X_p', the effective impedance $Z_p' = V/I$ is very nearly equal to $\sqrt{\{(R_p')^2 + (X_p')^2\}}$. Now $R_p' = P/I^2$ and $X_p' = \sqrt{\{(Z_p')^2 - (R_p')^2\}}$.

Both the open-circuit and short-circuit tests may also be carried out on the secondary side, so obtaining I_m', R_s' and X_s'.

Secondary voltage of loaded transformer

By definition, an ideal transformer is effectively impedanceless, so that load currents can produce no voltage drops in it. The only voltage drops due to load currents are in the effective leakage reactance X_p' or X_s' and resistance R_p' or R_s'. Considering Fig. 8.19, where all the quantities are referred to the secondary side, the vector diagram for the arrangement is as shown in Fig. 8.20, where the voltages $R_s'I_2$ and

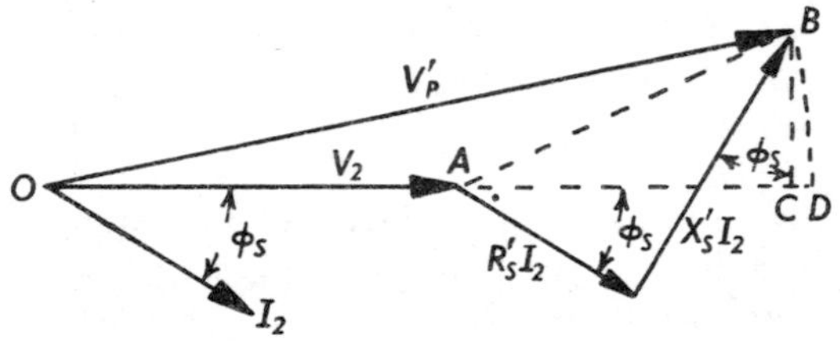

FIG. 8.20

$X_s'I_2$ are respectively parallel to and perpendicular to the current vector I_2. If BD is the arc of the circle, centre O and radius OB, meeting OA produced at D, the difference in the *magnitudes* (not the vector difference) of V_p' and V_2 is AD. However, since $R_s'I_2$ and $X_s'I_2$ are usually very small compared with V_2 and V_p', CD is very small and may be neglected. Therefore, $|V_p'| - |V_2| \simeq AC = R_s'I_2 \cos \phi_s + X_s'I_2 \sin \phi_s$.

When the transformer load current I_2 is zero, $V_2 = V_p'$, so that the difference in the secondary voltage between no-load and when loaded is $R_s'I_2 \cos \phi_s + X_s'I_2 \sin \phi_s$. If I_{2f} is the full-load current, the percentage regulation is $(R_s'I_{2f} \cos \phi_s + X_s'I_{2f} \sin \phi_s) \times 100/V_p'$ %, because the percentage regulation of a transformer is defined as the difference between the no-load secondary voltage and the voltage with full-load current, expressed as a percentage of the no-load voltage.

The vector diagram corresponding to Fig. 8.18, where all parameters are referred to the primary side is shown in Fig. 8.21. When the

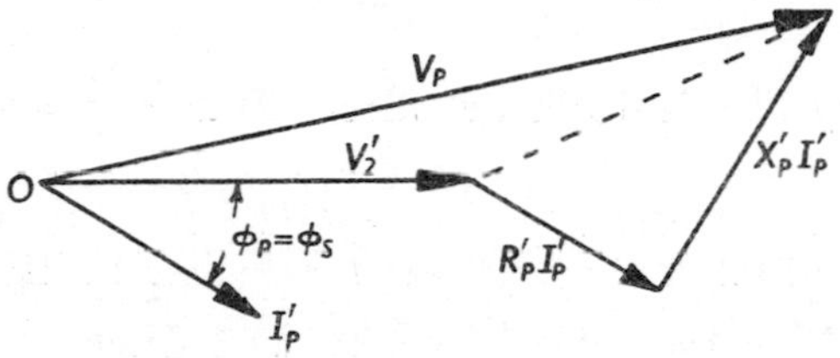

FIG. 8.21

parameters referred to the primary are known, there is no need to convert to secondary values as the percentage regulation is given by $(R_p'I_p' \cos \phi_p + X_p'I_p' \sin \phi_p) \times 100/V_p$ %.

Percentage and per-unit resistance and reactance

Instead of expressing the leakage reactances and resistances of a transformer in ohms, they may conveniently be expressed as percentages or 'per-unit' (*p.u.*).

For example, the *p.u.* primary resistance of a transformer is given by

$$R_p(\text{p.u.}) = R_p(\text{ohms}) \times (\text{full-load current})/(\text{rated voltage})$$

and the percentage value is 100 times the *p.u.* value. The total *p.u.* or percentage resistance and the individual or total *p.u.* or percentage reactances are determined in a similar way.

The percentage regulation is readily calculated from the percentage resistance and leakage reactance, since regulation is in general $= (RI \cos \phi + XI \sin \phi)100/V$ where I is the full-load current and V the rated voltage. Thus, the regulation = (percentage total resistance) cos ϕ + (percentage total reactance) sin ϕ.

In comparing transformers of different ratings, comparison of the *p.u.* or percentage impedances is more helpful than comparison of actual impedances. For instance, if two transformers have the same percentage leakage reactances and resistances, their regulations are the same for all load power-factors, although their actual resistances and reactances may be very different.

Furthermore, *p.u.* or percentage resistance and reactance are unchanged when referred from primary to secondary, or vice-versa. Thus, suppose the full-load secondary current is I_{2f}, the rated secondary voltage is V_s and the leakage reactance is X_s. The percentage reactance is then $100X_sI_{2f}/V_s$. If the corresponding primary voltage is V_p.

the ratio is V_p/V_s and the full-load primary current (neglecting magnetizing current) is $I_p = I_{2f}V_s/V_p$ and the secondary reactance referred to the primary is $X_s(V_p/V_s)^2$. The percentage reactance, on these primary figures is $X_s(V_p/V_s)^2(I_{2f}V_s/V_p)100/V_p = 100X_sI_{2f}/V_s$, as before.

Voltage drop in a transformer direct from kVA load and kVA rating

The percentage voltage drop $= (\%R)I \cos\phi/I_{f.l.} + (\%X)I \sin\phi/I_{f.l.}$ where $I_{f.l.}$ is the full-load current and I is the actual current.

$$\therefore \quad \text{percentage voltage drop} = (\%R)\text{kW}/\text{kVA rating} + (\%X)(\text{kVA})_r/\text{kVA rating}.$$

EXAMPLE. Determine the percentage voltage drop for a transformer with a percentage resistance of 1% and a percentage reactance of 5%, of rating 500 kVA, when it is delivering 400 kVA at 0·6 p.f. lagging.

Solution. For this transformer,

$$\text{kW} = 400 \times 0{\cdot}6 = 240$$

$$(\text{kVA})_r = 400 \times 0{\cdot}8 = 320$$

$$\therefore \quad \text{percentage voltage drop} = \{(1 \times 240/500) + (5 \times 320/500)\}\% = \underline{3{\cdot}68\%}$$

Polyphase transformers

Voltage transformations in a two-phase circuit require two single-phase transformers, and in a three-phase circuit three single-phase transformers (or a special three-phase transformer combination) are used. It is possible, however, to use only two transformers in a three-phase circuit, the so-called Vee-connection. Phase transformation as well as voltage transformation may be readily obtained by special transformer connections.

Three-phase transformers

Attention will be confined here to star- and delta-connected three-phase transformers; reference should be made to specialist texts for more elaborate connections. Either primary or secondary may be connected in star or in delta, giving four possible types, namely: star–star, delta–delta, star–delta and delta–star. Note that a star–delta transformer means one with primaries connected in star and secondaries in delta. As shown later, the possibility of parallel operation of three-phase transformers depends, among other things, on their connections.

When the connections of the primaries and secondaries are the same, namely both either in star or in delta, the ratio of the line voltages is the same as the ratio of the phase voltages. When the connections are different the line-voltage ratio is $\sqrt{3}$ or $1/\sqrt{3}$ times the phase-voltage ratio, *e.g.* for a star–delta transformer the line-voltage ratio, primary to secondary, is $\sqrt{3}$ times the phase-voltage ratio.

There is no difficulty in referring primary impedances to the secondary or vice-versa if it is borne in mind that the three-phase transformer is really three single-phase transformers. For example, consider a delta–star transformer whose line-voltage ratio is 3,200 : 415. The phase-voltage ratio is 3,200 : $415/\sqrt{3}$ or 3,200 : 240. If the primary resistance is 1·6 Ω/phase and its leakage reactance is 4 Ω/phase, the values referred to the secondary/phase are $1{\cdot}6 \times 240^2/3{,}200^2 = 0{\cdot}009$ Ω and $4 \times 240^2/3{,}200^2 = 0{\cdot}0225$ Ω respectively. As mentioned earlier percentage or *p.u.* values are transferred unchanged.

Equivalent star and delta connections

It is often very convenient to transform a balanced delta-connected impedance, or a delta-connected set of transformer windings, into the equivalent star-connected arrangement. For example, consider a delta–star transformer, of line-voltage ratio 2 : 1, fed from a balanced three-phase source of line voltage 400 V, through lines of resistance 1 Ω and reactance 2 Ω, per phase. The resistance and leakage reactance of the transformer will be assumed to be 3 Ω and 6 Ω per phase respectively, referred to the primary. Replacement of the delta-connected transformer primaries by star-connected ones, means reducing the voltage/phase to $1/\sqrt{3}$ of its previous value, so that the impedances are reduced to 1/3 of their previous values, namely 1 Ω resistance and 2 Ω reactance. Thus, the total impedances of lines and transformer/phase are now 2 Ω resistance in series with 4 Ω reactance, the voltage across each phase being $400/\sqrt{3}$. If a star-connected load of resistance 5 Ω and reactance 2 Ω is connected across the secondary winding, the values of these impedances referred to the primary are 20 Ω and 8 Ω respectively, because the phase-to-phase transformation ratio is now 2 : 1, since both primary and secondary are star-connected. Thus, the primary current/phase is $400/\sqrt{3}(22^2 + 12^2)$, neglecting magnetizing current. This is also the line current. The *percentage* values of resistance and leakage reactance are *not* changed by converting from star to delta or vice-versa.

Phase transformation

For special purposes, two-phase and six-phase, or even more complicated systems are required (six-phase is commonly used in power rectifiers). These transformations are usually obtained with transformers from the standard three-phase supply system.

(a) Three-phase to two-phase transformation

The Scott connection for obtaining a two-phase supply from a three-phase one (or three-phase from two-phase) is shown in Fig. 8.22 (*a*).

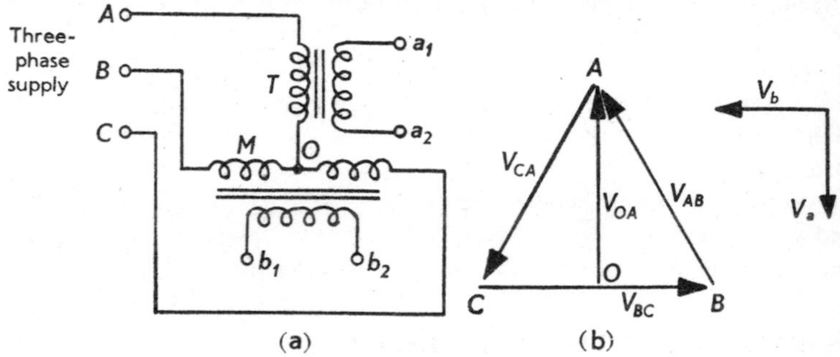

FIG. 8.22

Two single-phase transformers are used, one with a centre-tapped primary winding, known as the main transformer M and another T, of different ratio, known as the ‘ teaser ’. The vector diagram is as shown in Fig. 8.22 (*b*).

The primary winding of T is wound for a voltage of $(\sqrt{3}/2)$ times the three-phase line voltage, while both secondaries, from which the two-phase supply is taken, are wound for the same voltage.

(b) Three-phase to six-phase transformation

One method of obtaining a six-phase supply is by connecting together, to form a star-point, the centre taps of the three secondary windings of a three-phase transformer as illustrated in Fig. 8.23 (*a*). The vector diagrams are shown in Fig. 8.23 (*b*) and (*c*). This is really a three-

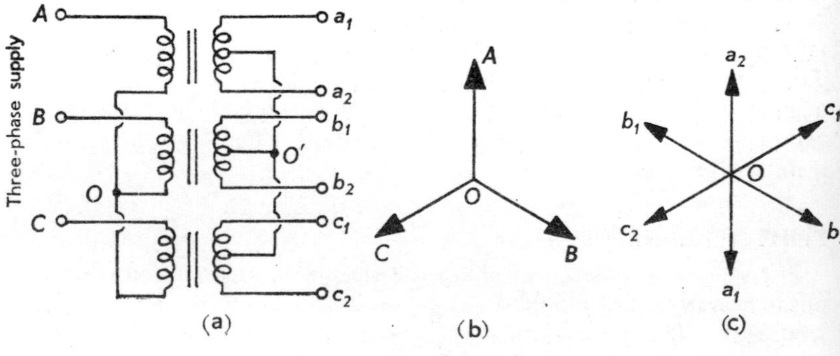

FIG. 8.23

phase version of the bi-phase transformer connection used for rectifiers (see Chapter 13).

Parallel operation of transformers

It is often necessary to connect transformers in parallel on both the primary and secondary sides so that they share the total load. For satisfactory performance the following conditions must be fulfilled: (*a*) the no-load voltage ratios must be the same, or only very slightly different, otherwise appreciable circulating currents flow and losses occur even under no-load conditions, (*b*) the transformers must be correctly connected to have the same ' polarity ', (*c*) in the case of three-phase transformers certain conditions regarding the connection arrangements of the two transformers must be fulfilled (see later) in order to satisfy condition (*b*), (*d*) for the load to be equitably shared in proportion to the ratings, the transformers should have approximately the same *percentage* resistances and leakage reactances.

When paralleling two single-phase transformers, of equal no-load voltage ratio, both primaries are first connected in parallel to the supply. A secondary terminal A_1 of one is then connected to a secondary terminal B_1 of the other, and a voltmeter capable of withstanding twice the secondary voltage is connected between the other secondary terminals, A_2 and B_2. If the correct connections are A_1 to B_1 and A_2 to B_2, the voltmeter will read zero. If the correct connection is A_1 to B_2 and A_2 to B_1, however, the voltmeter will read twice the secondary voltage of each transformer. The remedy is obvious.

For three-phase transformers which are suitable for parallel operation (see later), the primaries are first connected to the three-phase supply and two secondary terminals A_1 and B_1, say, are connected together. A voltmeter is then used to determine which of the remaining terminals A_2, A_3 and B_2, B_3 are at the same potential. If no such indication is obtained, the connection between A_1 and B_1 is broken and A_1 is connected to B_2 and the test is repeated. Then, if necessary, A_1 is joined to B_3 and the test again performed. If there is no combination of connections which gives zero-voltage indication, it means that the transformers are not suitable for parallel operation at all.

As mentioned earlier, there are four possible types of three-phase transformer using star and/or delta connections, namely, star–star, delta–delta, star–delta and delta–star. Provided the other conditions necessary for parallel operation are fulfilled, transformers of identical connection arrangement may be operated in parallel, but transformers with different connections may not be suitable for paralleling. Fig. 8.24 shows the simple voltage vector diagram of a star–star transformer, the primary phase voltages being OA_1, OB_1 and OC_1 and the line voltages B_1A_1, C_1B_1 and A_1C_1. The no-load secondary phase and line voltages OA_2, OB_2, OC_2 and B_2A_2, C_2B_2 and A_2C_2, respectively, are each in anti-phase with the corresponding primary voltages. Thus, the phase difference between primary and secondary line voltages is 180°. If the transformer is connected in star–delta, the secondary line

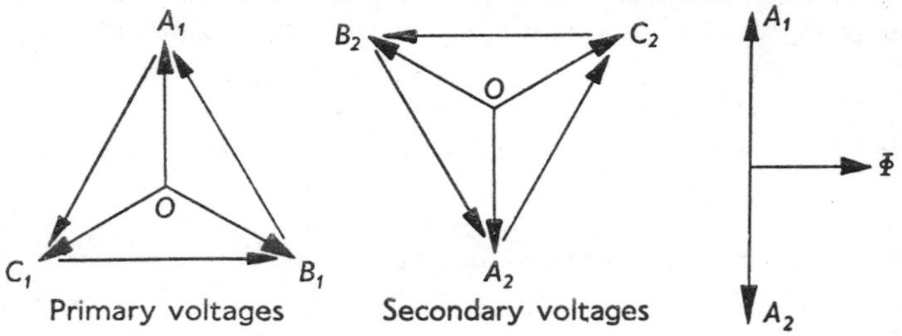

FIG. 8.24

voltages are the same as the phase voltages, namely OA_2, OB_2, OC_2, so that OA_2, for instance, lags by 210° on B_1A_1. Therefore, even though the line-voltage ratios of a star–star and star–delta transformer are the same, they cannot be operated in parallel because there is always a phase difference between the secondary line voltages. Thus, star–star and delta–delta transformers will operate in parallel, but neither of these may be paralleled with star–delta or delta–star transformers.

Load sharing by parallel transformers

When two single-phase or suitable three-phase transformers of the same no-load voltages are correctly paralleled, the equivalent circuit for the single-phase pair or for one phase of the three-phase pair with balanced loading, is as shown in Fig. 8.25. The total leakage reactance and the total resistance per phase are referred to the secondary side as shown (all the quantities can also be referred to the primary if this is

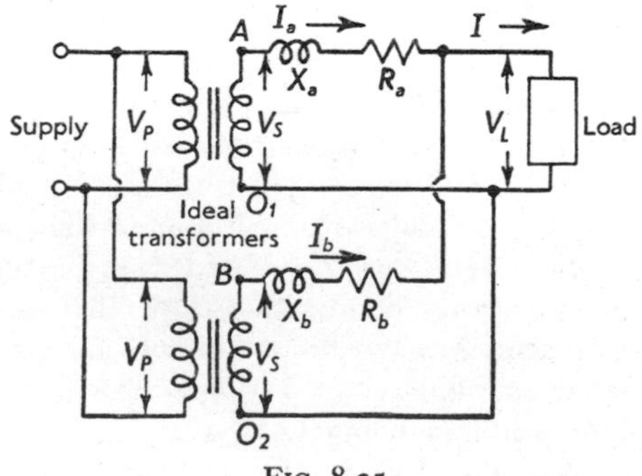

FIG. 8.25

more convenient). Since the secondary voltages V_s of the ideal transformers are equal in magnitude and phase and since O_1 and O_2 are joined together, A and B must be equipotential points and may therefore be connected without changing the current distribution. A simplified equivalent circuit, as shown in Fig. 8.26 can thus be drawn.

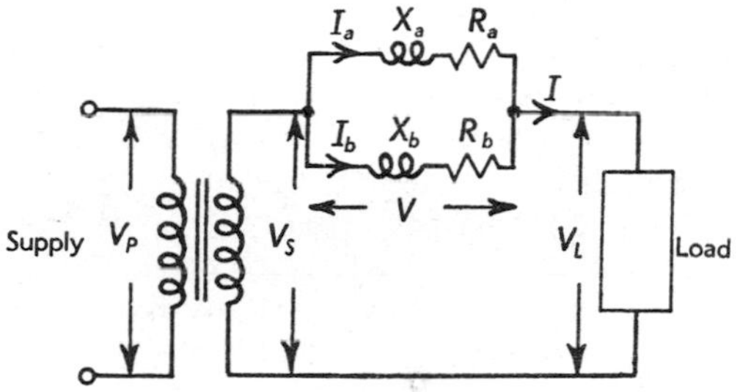

FIG. 8.26

The vector equations corresponding to this circuit are

$$\mathbf{I} = \mathbf{I_a} + \mathbf{I_b} \quad (8.10)$$

and
$$\mathbf{V} = \mathbf{I_a Z_a} = \mathbf{I_b Z_b} \quad (8.11)$$

where
$$\mathbf{Z_a} = R_a + jX_a \text{ and } \mathbf{Z_b} = R_b + jX_b$$

From equation (8.11), $\mathbf{I_a} = \mathbf{I_b Z_b}/\mathbf{Z_a}$ . . . . (8.12)

Substituting (8.12) in (8.10) gives

$$\mathbf{I_b} = \mathbf{IZ_a}/(\mathbf{Z_a} + \mathbf{Z_b}) \quad (8.13)$$

Similarly,
$$\mathbf{I_a} = \mathbf{IZ_b}/(\mathbf{Z_a} + \mathbf{Z_b}) \quad (8.14)$$

The *magnitudes* of the individual currents are given by:

$$I_a = IZ_b/|\mathbf{Z_a} + \mathbf{Z_b}| \quad (8.15)$$

and
$$I_b = IZ_a/|\mathbf{Z_a} + \mathbf{Z_b}| \quad (8.16)$$

where I is the magnitude of the total current, $Z_a = \sqrt{(R_a^2 + X_a^2)}$, $Z_b = \sqrt{(R_b^2 + X_b^2)}$ and $|\mathbf{Z_a} + \mathbf{Z_b}| = \sqrt{\{(R_a + R_b)^2 + (X_a + X_b)^2\}}$.

[Note carefully that $|\mathbf{Z_a} + \mathbf{Z_b}|$ is *not* equal to $Z_a + Z_b$ unless $R_a/X_a = R_b/X_b$.]

Equations (8.15) and (8.16) show that the currents in the transformers are determined by the ratio of impedances, so that the latter may be expressed either in actual ohms or in percentage (or *p.u.*) values, *provided the latter are referred to the same basis.* For transformers of the same rating, the percentage impedances are in the same ratio as the actual impedances, but if the transformers have different ratings, either the actual values of resistances and reactances must be calculated, or one or both of the given percentage impedances must be modified to give the same ratio as the actual impedances.

The percentage impedance is proportional to the actual impedance multiplied by the rated current, *i.e.* to the actual impedance multiplied by the rated kVA. Therefore, if for the purposes of calculation the rated current or kVA is changed, the percentage impedance must be altered in proportion. The method is illustrated in the following example, which also shows how the kVA loading may be determined directly.

EXAMPLE. Two three-phase transformers, A and B, of the same no-load line-voltage ratio 3,300/400 V, are connected in parallel to supply a total load of 600 kVA at 0·8 power-factor lagging. Transformer A is rated at 400 kVA, its resistance being 2% and its leakage reactance 2%. B is rated at 200 kVA, its resistance being 1% and its leakage reactance 4%. Assume that both transformers have star-connected secondary windings. Calculate the load taken by each transformer.

Determine, also, the power-factor of the current in each transformer.

Solution. The load taken by each transformer will be calculated in two ways:

(*a*) *Method 1*

The rated secondary voltage per phase $= (400/\sqrt{3})$ V $= 231$ V.

The full-load secondary current of A is, therefore, $400{,}000/(3 \times 231) = (1{,}000/\sqrt{3})$ A/phase, and that of B is $(500/\sqrt{3})$ A/phase.

Thus, the actual transformer impedances per phase referred to the secondary are

$$R_A = 2 \times 231/\{100 \times 1{,}000/\sqrt{3}\} = 0{\cdot}008\ \Omega$$

$$X_A = 0{\cdot}008\ \Omega$$

$$R_B = 1 \times 231/\{100 \times 500/\sqrt{3}\} = 0{\cdot}008\ \Omega$$

and $$X_B = 0{\cdot}032\ \Omega.$$

The total current is $600{,}000/(\sqrt{3} \times 400) = 867$ A, or expressed in complex form, with voltage as the reference vector, $0{\cdot}8 \times 867 - j(0{\cdot}6 \times 867) = (694 - j520)$.

From equations (8.13) and (8.14) therefore,

$$\mathbf{I_b} = (694 - j520)(0{\cdot}008 + j0{\cdot}008)/\{0{\cdot}016 + j0{\cdot}040\}. \qquad (8.17)$$

$$\therefore \quad I_b = 227 \text{ A and } (\text{kVA})_b = 227 \times 400 \times \sqrt{3}/1{,}000 = \underline{157 \text{ kVA}}$$

$$\mathbf{I_a} = (694 - j520)(0{\cdot}008 + j0{\cdot}032)/\{0{\cdot}016 + j0{\cdot}040\}. \qquad (8.18)$$

$$\therefore \quad I_a = 663 \text{ A and } (\text{kVA})_a = \underline{460 \text{ kVA}}$$

(*b*) *Method 2*

$\mathbf{Z_a} = (2 + j2)\%$ on a 400-kVA basis, or $(1 + j1)\%$ on a 200-kVA basis.

$\mathbf{Z_b} = (1 + j4)\%$ on a 200-kVA basis.

$\therefore \quad \mathbf{Z_a} + \mathbf{Z_b} = (2 + j5)\%$ and $|\mathbf{Z_a} + \mathbf{Z_b}| = (\sqrt{29})\% = 5{\cdot}38\%$.

Expressing the kVA as a *vector*, with voltage as reference, **kVA** = $(600 \times 0{\cdot}8 - j600 \times 0{\cdot}6) = 480 - j360$, (480 kW and 360 kVA_r).

Therefore, $\quad (\mathbf{kVA})_\mathbf{b} = (480 - j360)(1 + j)/(2 + j5) \quad . \quad . \quad (8.19)$

or $\quad (kVA)_b = \underline{157\ kVA}$

and $\quad (\mathbf{kVA})_\mathbf{a} = (480 - j360)(1 + j4)/(2 + j5) \quad . \quad . \quad (8.20)$

or $\quad (kVA)_a = \underline{460\ kVA}$

To determine the power-factor of the current in each transformer, equations (8.17) and (8.18) or (8.19) and (8.20) must be worked out in full. Equation (8.20) when fully simplified becomes $(\mathbf{kVA})_\mathbf{a} = 401 - j223$) kVA, from which $(kVA)_a = 460$ kVA and $\cos \phi_a = 401/460 = \underline{0{\cdot}872}$. Equation (8.19) gives $(\mathbf{kVA})_\mathbf{b} = 79 - j137$, from which $(kVA)_b = 157$ kVA and $\cos \phi_b = 79/157 = \underline{0{\cdot}5}$.

When the transformer primaries are supplied from a common source through individual cables of appreciable resistance and reactance, the latter are added to the resistance and reactance of the transformer when calculating the load on each transformer. Similarly, allowance can be made for secondary cables. If one is working in terms of percentage impedances, the cable impedances, usually given in actual ohms, are converted to percentage values.

If the secondary terminal voltage of a pair of paralleled transformers, supplying a given load, at a given power-factor, is required, two methods of calculation may be adopted as illustrated by the following example.

EXAMPLE. Determine the secondary line voltage of the pair of paralleled transformers in the example given on p. 156.

Solution

(*a*) *Method 1*

The load and power-factor of *one* transformer will be calculated and from this the voltage drop (which must be the same for both transformers).

Thus, for transformer A, $R_A = 1\%$ and $X_A = 1\%$ on a 200-kVA basis. Since the kW = 401 corresponding to the $I \cos \phi$ component of current,

The percentage resistance drop $= (401 \times 1)/200 = 2{\cdot}005\%$

The percentage reactance drop $= (223 \times 1)/200 = 1{\cdot}115\%$

The total voltage drop is therefore $3{\cdot}12\%$ and the secondary line voltage is $400 - (0{\cdot}0312 \times 400) = \underline{387{\cdot}5\ V}$.

(*b*) *Method 2*

The transformer impedances will be converted to a single impedance, that of the equivalent single transformer. Since the equivalent circuit of the paralleled transformers shows that $(R_A + jX_A)$ and $(R_B + jX_B)$ are simply in parallel the parameters of the single equivalent transformer are given by

$$R + jX = (R_A + jX_A)(R_B + jX_B)/\{R_A + R_B) + j(X_A + X_B)\}$$

In this example, using the percentage impedance values (200-kVA basis)

$$R + jX = (1 + j)(1 + j4)/(2 + j5) = 0{\cdot}655 + j0{\cdot}863$$

The percentage voltage drop is therefore,

$$0{\cdot}655 \times 480/200 + 0{\cdot}863 \times 360/200 = 3{\cdot}12\%$$

and the secondary line voltage is 387·5 V, as before.

Transformers of different no-load voltage ratios

Although it is not good practice to operate in parallel two transformers of different voltage ratios, it is possible to do so without undue loss if the ratios are only slightly different. This may be useful as a temporary measure in an emergency.

As an example, consider two 100 kVA, three-phase transformers with star-connected secondaries, whose no-load secondary line voltages are 400 V and 404 V when supplied at the rated primary voltage. The first transformer will be assumed to have a leakage reactance of 0·08 Ω and a total resistance of 0·02 Ω, and the second a reactance of 0·06 Ω and a resistance of 0·04 Ω, these impedances being referred to the secondary per phase.

The equivalent circuit per phase of the paralleled transformers is as shown in Fig. 8.27.

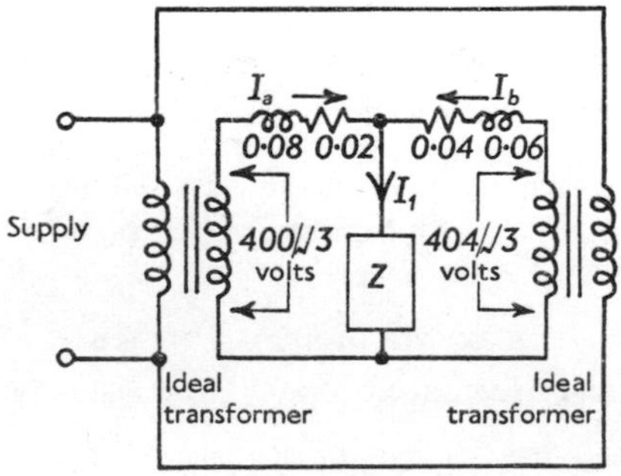

FIG. 8.27

The no-load secondary voltages of $400/\sqrt{3}$ and $404/\sqrt{3}$ V/phase can be considered to be co-phasal if the very small magnetizing-current voltage drop is neglected. Therefore, on no-load, when $Z = \infty$, $I_b = -I_a = (4/\sqrt{3})/\sqrt{(0{\cdot}14^2 + 0{\cdot}06^2)} = 15{\cdot}2$ A which is not unreasonable.

If the common load impedance consists of a resistor of 0·925 Ω in series with a reactor of 0·695 Ω (power-factor 0·8), the following vector equations can be written

$$400/\sqrt{3} = (0{\cdot}02 + j0{\cdot}08)\mathbf{I_a} + (0{\cdot}925 + j0{\cdot}695)\mathbf{I_1}$$

and

$$404/\sqrt{3} = (0{\cdot}04 + j0{\cdot}06)\mathbf{I_b} + (0{\cdot}925 + j0{\cdot}695)\mathbf{I_1}$$

Also,

$$\mathbf{I_1} = \mathbf{I_a} + \mathbf{I_b}.$$

From these equations,

$$\mathbf{I_a} = 55{\cdot}4 - j54{\cdot}8 \text{ and } I_a = 77{\cdot}5 \text{ A}$$

$$\mathbf{I_b} = 98{\cdot}5 - j64{\cdot}5 \text{ and } I_b = 117{\cdot}5 \text{ A}$$

and

$$\mathbf{I_1} = 153{\cdot}9 - j119{\cdot}3 \text{ and } I_1 = 195{\cdot}0 \text{ A}.$$

If the current I_1 and its power-factor with respect to the *terminal* voltage are given, little error is made in assuming that the power-factor is with respect to the supply voltage. Thus, if $I_1 = 195$ A at 0·8 power-factor lagging, $\mathbf{I_1} = (156 - j117)$ A.

$$\mathbf{I_a} + \mathbf{I_b} = \mathbf{I_1} = 156 - j117$$

$$\mathbf{I_b}(0{\cdot}04 + j0{\cdot}06) - \mathbf{I_a}(0{\cdot}02 + j0{\cdot}08) = 4/\sqrt{3} = 2{\cdot}31$$

$$\therefore \quad \mathbf{I_a} = 56{\cdot}7 - j54 \text{ and } I_a = 78 \text{ A}$$

and

$$\mathbf{I_b} = 99{\cdot}2 - j63 \text{ and } I_b = 117 \text{ A}.$$

Further discussion of the equivalent circuit of the transformer *

It is shown below that the 'approximate' equivalent circuits of a transformer (Figs. 8.17, 8.18) are not necessarily approximations, provided that the parameters are measured on the assumption that these circuits are correct.

If all the impedances are referred to the primary side of a single-phase transformer, the equivalent circuit may be represented as in Fig. 8.28, where $\mathbf{Z_p} = R_p + jX_p$, $\mathbf{Z_s}' = (R_s + jX_s)(N_p/N_s)^2$, $\mathbf{Z_L}' = \mathbf{Z_L}(N_p/N_s)^2$ and $\mathbf{Z_m}$ is the magnetising impedance.

Fig. 8.29 shows the so-called approximate circuit, with $\mathbf{Z_0}$ as the no-load or effective magnetizing impedance and $\mathbf{Z_s}''$ the impedance due to the winding resistances and leakage reactances. If these circuits

* D. Harrison, "The Equivalent Circuit of the Transformer and Induction Motor", *Electrical Energy*, 1, p. 208 (1957).

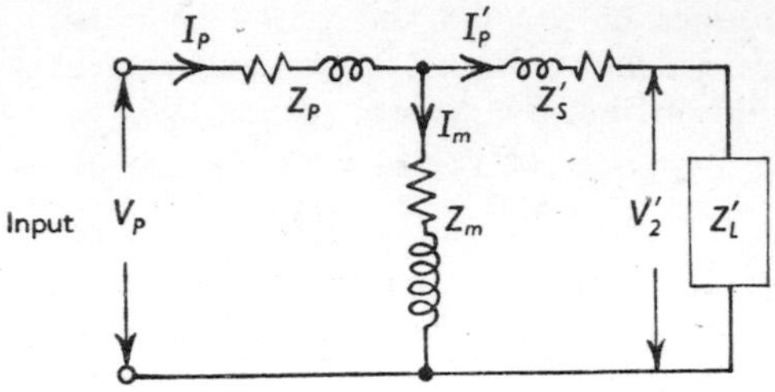

FIG. 8.28

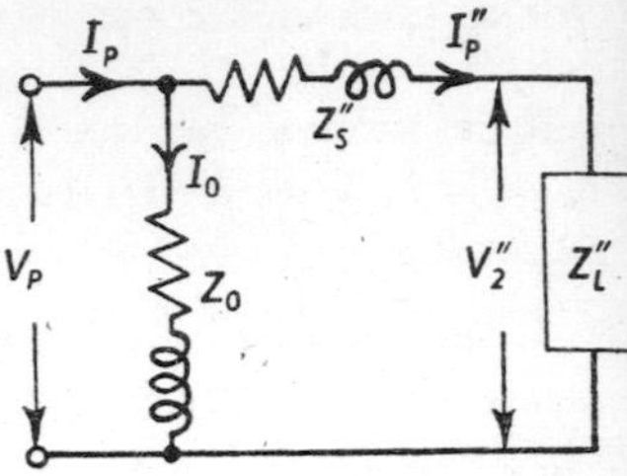

FIG. 8.29

are equivalent for all values of $\mathbf{Z_L}'$ and $\mathbf{Z_L}''$, the input impedances must be identical. When $\mathbf{Z_L}'$ and $\mathbf{Z_L}''$ are infinite (no-load condition), the input impedances are respectively $(\mathbf{Z_p} + \mathbf{Z_m})$ and $\mathbf{Z_o}$, so that $\mathbf{Z_o} = \mathbf{Z_p} + \mathbf{Z_m} = \mathbf{kZ_m}$, where $\mathbf{k} = (\mathbf{Z_p} + \mathbf{Z_m})/\mathbf{Z_m}$ which is a *complex* ratio.

For finite values of $\mathbf{Z_L}'$ and $\mathbf{Z_L}''$, the input impedance of the first circuit is

$$\mathbf{Z_i} = \mathbf{Z_p} + \mathbf{Z_m}(\mathbf{Z_s}' + \mathbf{Z_L}')/(\mathbf{Z_m} + \mathbf{Z_s}' + \mathbf{Z_L}')$$

The input impedance of the second circuit is now:

$$\mathbf{Z_i}' = \mathbf{Z_o}(\mathbf{Z_s}'' + \mathbf{Z_L}'')/(\mathbf{Z_o} + \mathbf{Z_s}'' + \mathbf{Z_L}'')$$

and since $\mathbf{Z_o} = \mathbf{Z_p} + \mathbf{Z_m}$,

$$\mathbf{Z_i}' = (\mathbf{Z_p} + \mathbf{Z_m})(\mathbf{Z_s}'' + \mathbf{Z_L}'')/\{(\mathbf{Z_p} + \mathbf{Z_m}) + (\mathbf{Z_s}'' + \mathbf{Z_L}'')\}$$

Therefore, if the two circuits are truly equivalent, so that $\mathbf{Z_i} = \mathbf{Z_i}'$,

$$\{\mathbf{Z_p}(\mathbf{Z_m} + \mathbf{Z_s}' + \mathbf{Z_L}') + \mathbf{Z_m}(\mathbf{Z_s}' + \mathbf{Z_L}')\}\{(\mathbf{Z_p} + \mathbf{Z_m}) + (\mathbf{Z_s}'' + \mathbf{Z_L}'')\}$$
$$= (\mathbf{Z_m} + \mathbf{Z_s}' + \mathbf{Z_L}')(\mathbf{Z_p} + \mathbf{Z_m})(\mathbf{Z_s}'' + \mathbf{Z_L}'')$$

i.e. $(\mathbf{Z_s}'' + \mathbf{Z_L}'')\{-\mathbf{Z_p}(\mathbf{Z_m} + \mathbf{Z_s}' + \mathbf{Z_L}') -$
$$\mathbf{Z_m}(\mathbf{Z_s}' + \mathbf{Z_L}') + (\mathbf{Z_p} + \mathbf{Z_m})(\mathbf{Z_m} + \mathbf{Z_s}' + \mathbf{Z_L}')\}$$
$$= (\mathbf{Z_p} + \mathbf{Z_m})\{\mathbf{Z_p}(\mathbf{Z_m} + \mathbf{Z_s}' + \mathbf{Z_L}') + \mathbf{Z_m}(\mathbf{Z_s}' + \mathbf{Z_L}')\}$$

$$\therefore \quad (\mathbf{Z_s}'' + \mathbf{Z_L}'')\mathbf{Z_m}^2 = (\mathbf{Z_p} + \mathbf{Z_m})\{(\mathbf{Z_p} + \mathbf{Z_m})(\mathbf{Z_s}' + \mathbf{Z_L}') + \mathbf{Z_p}\mathbf{Z_m}\}$$

Thus, $(\mathbf{Z_s}'' + \mathbf{Z_L}'') = \{(\mathbf{Z_p} + \mathbf{Z_m})^2(\mathbf{Z_s}' + \mathbf{Z_L}')/\mathbf{Z_m}^2\} +$
$$\{\mathbf{Z_p}(\mathbf{Z_p} + \mathbf{Z_m})/\mathbf{Z_m}\}$$
$$= \mathbf{k}^2(\mathbf{Z_s}' + \mathbf{Z_L}') + \mathbf{kZ_p}$$

This expression corresponds to the equivalent circuit of Fig. 8.30. It is left as an exercise for the reader to show that $\mathbf{I_p}'' = \mathbf{I_p}'/\mathbf{k}$, and $\mathbf{V_2}'' = \mathbf{kV_2}'$.

When making the usual open-circuit and short-circuit tests on a transformer, it is tacitly assumed that the equivalent circuit is that of Fig. 8.29 and not that of Fig. 8.28. Thus the open-circuit test gives the impedance $\mathbf{Z_o}$ and not $\mathbf{Z_m}$, and the short-circuit test gives $\mathbf{Z_s}''$ and not $(\mathbf{Z_p} + \mathbf{Z_s}')$. Furthermore, the measured open-circuit voltage ratio V_2/V_p is not simply the turns ratio N_2/N_1 but N_2/N_1k. (In practice the phase-angle of $\mathbf{k}$ is usually ignored, but this introduces negligible error.)

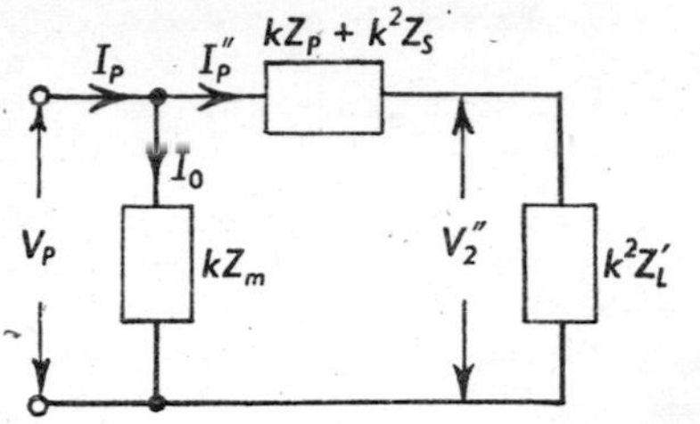

FIG. 8.30

Using the measured ratio, the secondary current is referred to the primary by multiplying by N_2/N_1k and the secondary voltage is referred to the primary by multiplying by N_1k/N_2. These results are consistent with the assumption that the equivalent circuit is that of Fig. 8.29.

PROBLEMS

1. An intermediate-frequency transformer has identical primary and secondary circuits; each winding is tuned by a capacitor of 150 pF. If the transformer has a bandwidth of 9 kc/s centred on a frequency of 470 kc/s and there is critical coupling, find: (*a*) the inductance of each winding, (*b*) the coefficient of coupling, (*c*) the mutual inductance between the windings, (*d*) the Q-factor of each winding.
[*Ans.* (*a*) 768 μH, (*b*) 0·019, (*c*) 14·6 μH, (*d*) 52·2.]

2. A transformer has a tuned primary winding and an untuned secondary. The inductance of each winding is 1 mH and the mutual inductance between them is 0·5 mH. The primary winding is tuned with the secondary open-circuited, and resonates at a frequency of 500 kc/s. If the secondary is now short-circuited find the change of tuning capacitance required to keep the same resonant frequency. Neglect the resistances of the windings. [S.U.] [*Ans.* 34 μμF.]

3. Two tuned circuits are coupled together magnetically. The inductance, resistance and capacitance of the two circuits are respectively, 500 μH, 25 Ω, 800 μμF and 800 μH, 40 Ω, 500 μμF. The mutual inductance is 90 μH. An e.m.f. of 2 V of varying frequency is induced in the first circuit. Plot a curve showing the current amplitude in the second circuit as the frequency is varied through resonance.

4. Two identical tuned circuits, having self-inductance of 500 μH and capacitance 200 μμF are inductively coupled, the mutual inductance being 30 μH. What are the two resonant frequencies of each circuit?
[*Ans.* 488 kc/s, 518 kc/s.]

5. Two identical coils have each an inductance of 1,000 μH and a Q factor of 50. The coefficient of coupling between them is 0·01. Each coil is tuned by a 500 μμF capacitor. A source of 1 V at a variable frequency is placed in series with one circuit.

Determine the frequency at which the current in the second circuit is a maximum and this value of current. [*Ans.* 225 kc/s, 14·1 mA.]

6. Two circuits, each consisting of an inductor of 0·005 H inductance and a 0·003 μF capacitor, are coupled together by a 0·1 μF capacitor which forms a branch common to the two circuits. What is the coefficient of coupling for the arrangement? [*Ans.* 0·029.]

7. Two circuits, each consisting of a 2 mH inductor a 200 Ω resistor and a 0·002 μF capacitor, are coupled by a mutual inductance of 10 μH. At what frequency will a voltage of 1 V in one circuit produce maximum current in the other? What will then be the values of the currents in each circuit? [*Ans.* 80 kc/s, 5 mA, 0·125 mA.]

8. A single-phase transformer has 100 primary turns and 25 secondary turns and is supplied at 400 V. With the secondary open-circuited, the primary current is 5 A at 0·2 power-factor lagging. Determine the total primary current and its power-factor when the secondary current is 200 A at 0·6 power-factor lagging. [S.U.] [*Ans.* 54·5 A, 0·57.]

9. If the primary and secondary resistances of the above transformer are 0·05 Ω and 0·004 Ω respectively, determine the total losses and the efficiency with the load specified, assuming (*a*) that the primary resistance carries the total primary current, and (*b*) that it only carries the load component of current as implied by the circuit of Fig. 8.17.
[*Ans.* (*a*) 709 W, 94·3%, (*b*) 685 W, 94·47%.]

10. A 100 kvA, three-phase transformer has a no-load ratio of *line* voltages of 3,300 to 400 V. When the secondary is on open-circuit, with rated primary voltage applied, the input power is 1 kW. With the secondary short-circuited and with a primary *line* voltage of 200 V, the primary *line* current is 18 A and the total input power is 2·5 kW. Determine the efficiency at full-load and at half-full-load at 0·8 power-factor lagging, and the percentage regulation at 0·8 power-factor lagging. [S.U.] [*Ans.* 95·97%, 96·18%, 5·1%.]

11. A 150 kVA, three-phase transformer of no-load voltage ratio 3,300 : 500 and with leakage reactance and resistance of 5% and 2% respectively, is supplied from a 3,300 V, three-phase source through a cable of 1 Ω resistance per phase and 3 Ω reactance per phase. The transformer secondary supplies two balanced loads as follows: (*a*) 50 A at 0·8 power-factor lagging through a short cable of negligible impedance, (*b*) 100 A at 0·7 power-factor lagging through a cable of 0·1 Ω resistance per phase and 0·2 Ω reactance per phase. Determine the line voltage at each load. [S.U.] [*Ans.* (*a*) 462 V, (*b*) 425 V.]

12. Two transformers *A* and *B*, both of no-load ratio 1,000 : 500 V are connected in parallel and supplied at 1,000 V. *A* is rated at 100 kVA, its total resistance and reactance being 1% and 5% respectively. *B* is rated at 250 kVA, with 2% resistance and 2% reactance. Determine the load on each transformer and the secondary voltage, when a total load of 300 kVA at 0·8 power-factor lagging is supplied. [S.U.]
[*Ans.* 55·7 kVA, 251 kVA, 486·2 V.]

13. A 750 kVA transformer having 1% resistance and 5% leakage reactance, is connected in parallel with a 250 kVA transformer of 3% resistance and 3% reactance, both transformers having the same no-load ratio. Determine the maximum continuous load which can safely be supplied by the parallel combination. [S.U.] [*Ans.* 842 kVA.]

14. A three-phase transformer with star-connected primary and delta-connected secondary windings has a no-load *line* voltage ratio of 2 : 1 and supplies a balanced delta-connected load, each phase of which consists of a 9 Ω reactor in series with a 9 Ω resistor. The leakage reactances and resistances per phase of the transformer are: primary reactance and resistance are 2 Ω and 1 Ω respectively; secondary reactance and resistance are 1·5 Ω and 0·5 Ω respectively. Determine (*a*) the secondary line current and line voltage, and (*b*) the readings of two wattmeters connected to measure the total power in the load, when the transformer is supplied from 1,000 V, three-phase mains. [S.U.]

[*Ans.* 54·8 A, 402 V, 5,700 W, 21,280 W.]

CHAPTER 9

CIRCLE DIAGRAMS AND INVERSION

Vector loci

In some a.c. circuit problems, where it is necessary to determine the magnitudes and phase-angles of the current (or voltage) for a given applied voltage (or current), over a wide range of values of one of the parameters (*e.g.* resistance) of the circuit, it is often possible to reduce the amount of labour required by plotting vector loci. For example, if it can be shown that the extremity of the current vector (using the voltage vector as reference) lies on a circle, this can easily be drawn. Probably the commonest and most useful form of vector locus is the circle which may be used to investigate the behaviour of circuits as the frequency of the applied voltage is varied, to determine the performance of the induction motor and so on.

Circle diagrams for simple series circuits

(*a*) *Variable Reactance and Fixed Resistance*

For a circuit consisting of a variable reactance X in series with a fixed resistance R, to which a constant alternating voltage is applied, the vector diagram is as shown in Fig. 9.1.

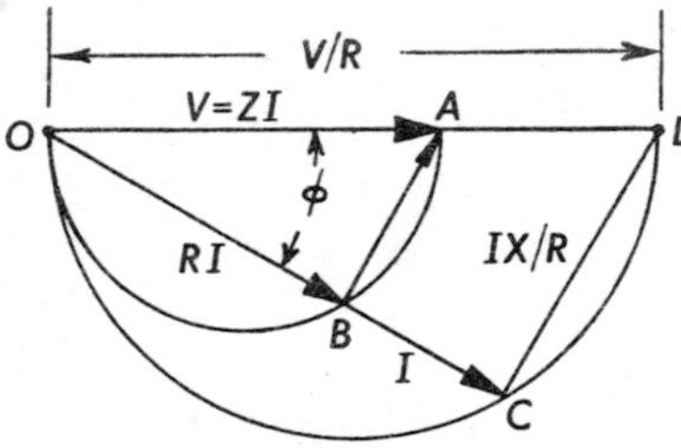

FIG. 9.1

The current vector OC is shown lagging by the angle ϕ on the voltage vector OA, the latter being the vector sum of the two components $OB = RI$ and $BA = XI$, in phase and in quadrature with the current respectively. Since OA, which equals V, is fixed and angle $OBA = 90°$, B must lie on the semi-circle OBA having diameter $OA = V$.

The current vector OC is derived from the voltage vector OB on dividing by the constant resistance R. If CD is drawn perpendicular to OC, *i.e.* parallel to BA, to meet OA produced at D, then since the triangles OBA and OCD are similar $CD = IX/R$ and $OD = V/R$ which is a constant. Thus, the extremity of the current vector, C, also lies on a semi-circle of diameter $OD = V/R$ as illustrated. If the reactance is capacitive instead of inductive, as considered above, the semi-circles lie above the line of the voltage vector.

EXAMPLE. A circuit consisting of a 50 Ω resistor in series with a variable reactor is shunted by a 100 Ω resistor. Draw the locus of the extremity of the total-current vector to scale and determine the reactance and current corresponding to the minimum overall power-factor, the supply voltage being 100 V. [S.U.]

Solution. Drawing the voltage vector OV (Fig. 9.2), the current

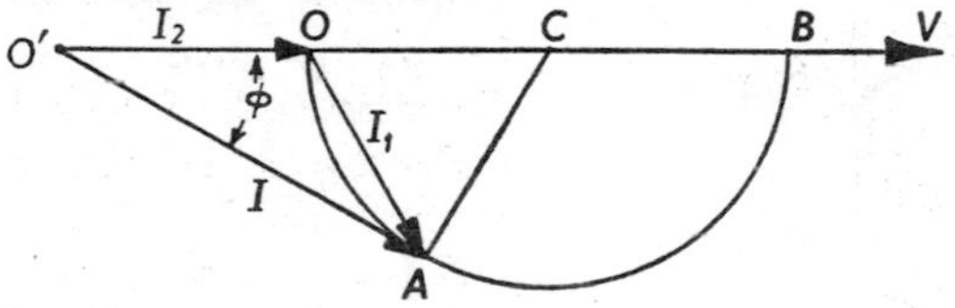

FIG. 9.2

I_1, in the reactive circuit, has a semi-circular locus OAB as shown, the diameter OB being of length corresponding to 2 A.

To add the fixed current, $I_2 = 1$ A, in the 100 Ω resistor, the origin is shifted to the left to O' by this amount, and, as clearly seen, $O'A$ represents the total current I, the vector sum of I_1 and I_2.

The minimum power-factor, corresponding to the maximum phase-angle occurs when $O'A$ is tangential to the circle, and $O'A$ is therefore perpendicular to the radius CA.

Thus, $\sin \phi = AC/O'C = 0{\cdot}5$ and $\phi = 30°$.

The power-factor, $\cos \phi = \sqrt{3}/2 = 0{\cdot}866$

$$\therefore \quad I = \sqrt{3} = \underline{1{\cdot}732 \text{ A}}$$

Angle $COA = 60°$, so that $OA = I_1 = 1$ A.

If X is the reactance,

$$\sqrt{(50^2 + X^2)} = 100/1$$

giving $$X = \underline{86{\cdot}5\ \Omega.}$$

(b) *Variable Resistance and Fixed Reactance*

For a circuit consisting of a fixed reactor in series with a variable resistor, supplied at constant voltage, the voltage vector diagram is again a right-angled triangle OAB as illustrated in Fig. 9.3, the applied-voltage vector being OA which equals ZI. Since angle OBA is a right-angle and V is fixed, point B, the extremity of the RI vector, moves on a semi-circle of diameter OA. However, since R is now variable, the current vector is not directly proportional to $OB = RI$ as in the previous case, although I and RI are co-phasal.

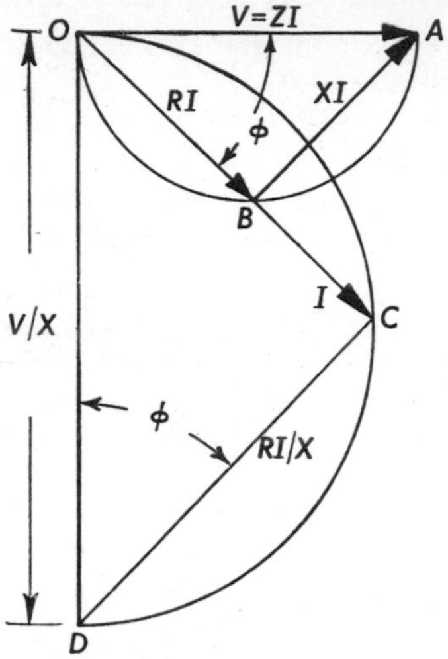

FIG. 9.3

Since the reactance X is constant, the vector $BA = XI$ is proportional in magnitude (but not in phase) to the current. Vector I is obtained from vector XI by dividing the magnitude of the latter by X to give its magnitude, and by rotating *clockwise* by 90° to give its correct phase. Dividing each of the sides of triangle OBA by X in this way, provides triangle OCD, which is similar to OBA and since angle OCD is a right-angle and $OD = V/X$, a fixed quantity, C moves on the semi-circle OCD as R varies.

EXAMPLE. Draw the locus of the total-current vector in the circuit shown in Fig. 9.4 to scale, then determine the maximum power and the corresponding values of R and the power-factor. [S.U.]

Solution. The locus diagram is illustrated in Fig. 9.5. The diameter of the semi-circle $OPQ = 200/X_1 = 200/10 = 20$ A. $I_1 = 10$ A and is in phase with the voltage. $I_2 = 4$ A and lags the voltage by 90°.

Point P is the one to give maximum power. At this point $R = X_1 = 10\ \Omega$.

Maximum power

$= V(I \cos\phi) = 200 \times 20 = \underline{4{,}000 \text{ W}}$

Total current I

$= \{\sqrt{(20^2 + 14^2)}\}$ A $= 24{\cdot}4$ A

$\therefore$ total power-factor

$= 20/24{\cdot}4 = \underline{0{\cdot}82}.$

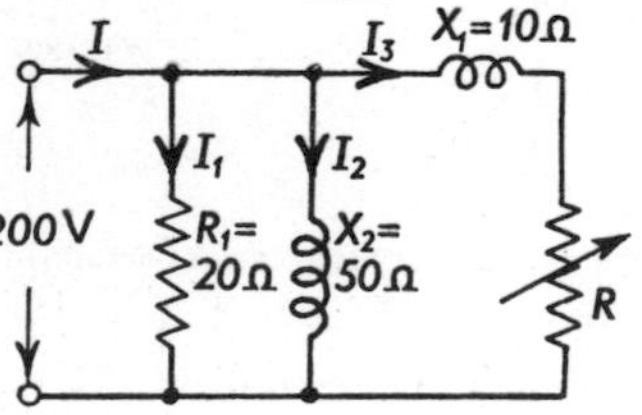

FIG. 9.4

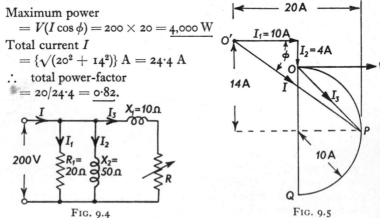

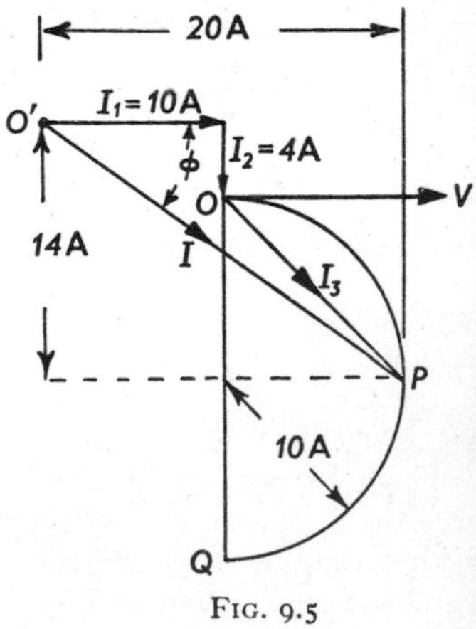

FIG. 9.5

Admittance loci

In the vector diagrams described above the vectors were either of voltage or current, but admittance diagrams and vector loci are often used. These can be regarded as current loci for unit voltage and the general theory given above is applicable.

Parallel circuits with constant total current

Consider the parallel circuit of Fig. 9.6 where the total current I is constant. Then, if R or X is varied the extremity of the V vector moves on a semi-circle, the current being taken as the basic reference vector.

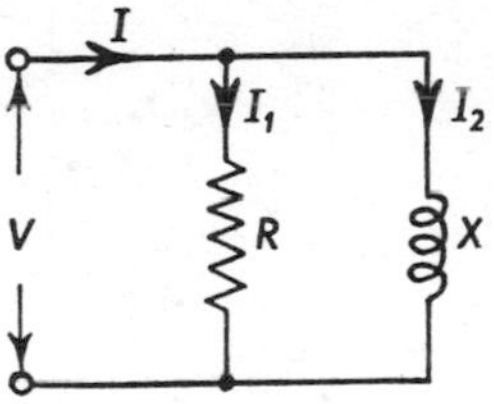

FIG. 9.6

Case (a). Variable reactance and constant resistance

The current-vector diagram is the right-angled triangle OAB of Fig. 9.7 and it is clear that A moves on a semi-circle with $OB = I$ as diameter. Multiplying OA, OB and AB by R, the similar vector triangle $OA'B'$ is obtained, OA' being the V vector. Since angle $OA'B'$ is a right-angle and $OB' = RI$, a constant, A' moves on the semi-circle shown with OB' as diameter.

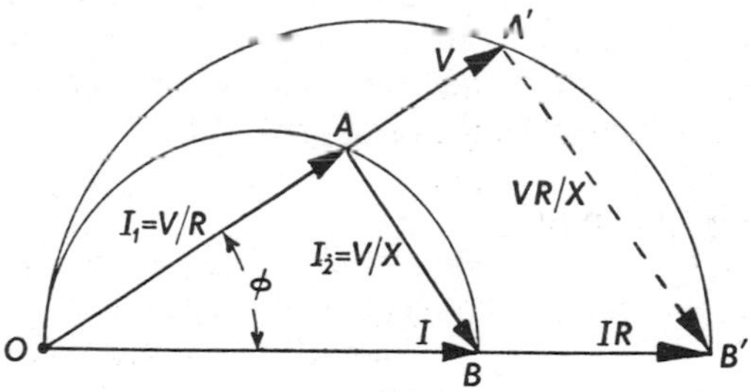

FIG. 9.7

If a circuit of constant impedance is connected in series with the parallel arrangement shown, the voltage across it will be constant and the total voltage will be the vector sum of the fixed voltage and the variable voltage V. The technique of shifting the origin, as used in the solution to the example on p. 166, may then be adopted.

If the reactance is capacitive, instead of inductive, the vector triangles lie below the horizontal axis.

Case (b). Variable resistance and constant reactance

The current-vector diagram is the right-angled triangle OAB (Fig. 9.8) as before. The voltage vector is in phase with I_1 and therefore lies in the direction OA, but since R is variable $OA = V/R$ is not proportional to V. The vector $AB = I_2 = V/X$ is proportional to V, however, since X is constant. Hence, on multiplying the triangle OAB by X and turning through 90° *counter-clockwise*, the triangle OCD

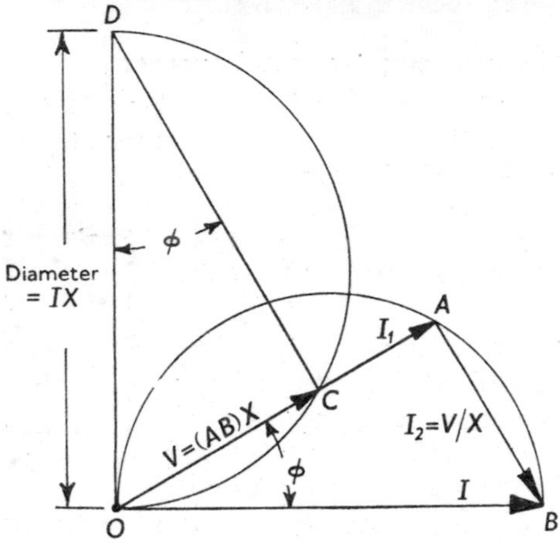

FIG. 9.8

is obtained, with OC being the vector V. Since A moves on the original semi-circle, C must move on the semi-circle OCD. Again, with capacitive reactance, the complementary semi-circles to those shown on Fig. 9.8, are obtained as the loci of A and C.

More complex circuits

Circular vector loci are obtained for some circuits which are more complex than the simple series and parallel circuits already discussed. Some such circuits may be translated into an equivalent simple form, while others are best analyzed by the use of co-ordinate geometry or by the method of geometrical inversion, both these topics being discussed later in the chapter. As an example of a circuit which can be re-arranged, consider Fig. 9.9 which is often known as a 'phase-lead' circuit and is widely used in feedback control systems. Although the reactance is shown as capacitive, the analysis presented below is applicable for any variable reactor.

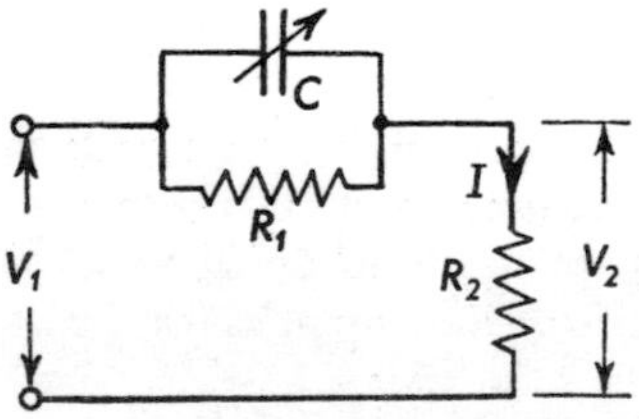

FIG. 9.9

The current I and the voltage $V_2 = R_2 I$ will vary with the frequency of the applied voltage V_1. If the reactance of the capacitor is denoted by the variable quantity X, then the total impedance of the circuit

$$Z = R_2 + R_1(jX)/(R_1 + jX) = \{R_1R_2 + jX(R_1 + R_2)\}/(R_1 + jX).$$

The admittance is

$$\begin{aligned} Y &= (R_1 + jX)/\{R_1R_2 + jX(R_1 + R_2)\} \\ &= \{1/(R_1 + R_2)\}\{R_1^2 + R_1R_2 + jX(R_1 + R_2\}/ \\ &\qquad \{R_1R_2 + jX(R_1 + R_2)\} \\ &= [1/(R_1 + R_2)][1 + R_1^2/\{R_1R_2 + jX(R_1 + R_2)\}] \\ &= Y_1 + Y_2 \\ &= 1/Z_1 + 1/Z_2 \end{aligned}$$

where $Y_1 = 1/Z_1 = 1/(R_1 + R_2)$
and $Y_2 = 1/Z_2 = 1/\{R_1 + R_2\}\{R_2/R_1 + jX(R_1 + R_2)/R_1^2\}$.

Thus, an equivalent circuit, valid for all values of X, consists of a fixed resistive impedance Z_1 in parallel with an impedance Z_2 composed of a fixed resistor in series with a variable reactor. The current-vector locus, as X varies, is therefore circular as shown in Fig. 9.10, where V is now the applied voltage.

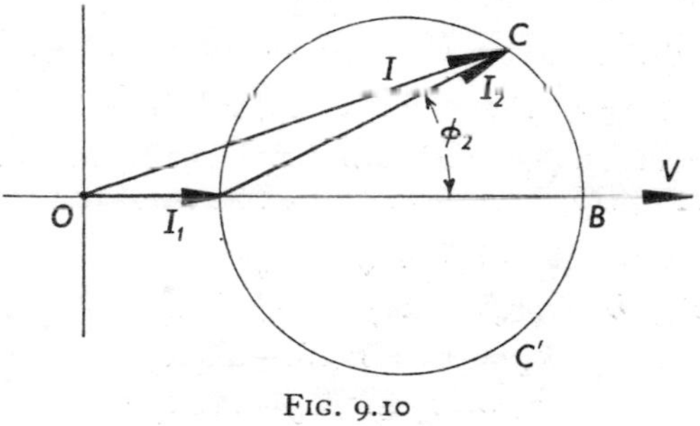

FIG. 9.10

In Fig. 9.10, $I_1 = V/(R_1 + R_2)$.

The diameter of the circle $= VR_1/R_2(R_1 + R_2)$. When X is capacitive the locus is the semi-circle above V and when X is inductive the locus is the semi-circle below V. Angle ϕ_2 may be calculated for a range of values of X and the circle can then be marked in terms of X.

Use of co-ordinate geometry

As an example of the use of co-ordinate geometry in circuit analysis consider an arrangement consisting of a resistor $(R_1 + R_2s)$ in series with a reactor $(X_1 + X_2s)$ where s is a variable parameter. The complex impedance is then $\mathbf{Z} = (R_1 + R_2s) + j(X_1 + X_2s)$ and the admittance

$\mathbf{Y} = 1/\{(R_1 + R_2s) + j(X_1 + X_2s)\}$. Plotting the admittance on the complex plane as in Fig. 9.11, $\mathbf{Y} = h + jk$, where h and k are the co-ordinates of the extremity A of the admittance vector.

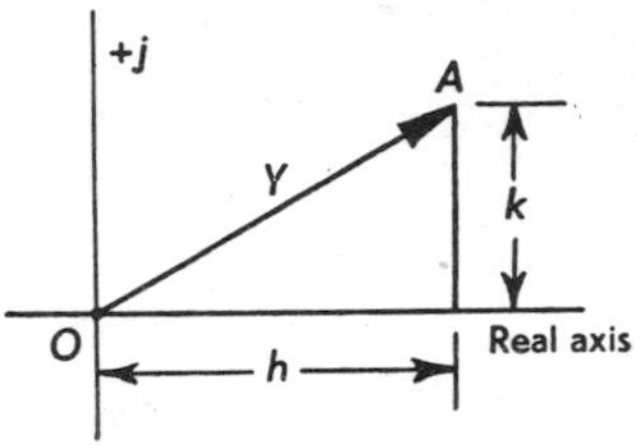

FIG. 9.11

Then $$(h + jk) = 1/\{(R_1 + R_2s) + j(X_1 + X_2s)\}$$
or $$(h + jk)\{(R_1 + R_2s) + j(X_1 + X_2s)\} = 1$$

Equating real and imaginary parts of this expression separately:

$$h(R_1 + R_2s) - k(X_1 + X_2s) = 1$$
and $$h(X_1 + X_2s) + k(R_1 + R_2s) = 0$$

Eliminating s from these equations gives:

$$(R_1X_2 - X_1R_2)(h^2 + k^2) - X_2h - R_2k = 0$$
or $$h^2 + k^2 - X_2h/(R_1X_2 - X_1R_2) - R_2k/(R_1X_2 - X_1R_2) = 0.$$

This is the equation of a circle and may be compared with that for a circle of radius r, whose centre has co-ordinates h_0 and k_0, which is:

$$(h - h_0)^2 + (k - k_0)^2 = r^2$$
or $$h^2 + k^2 - 2h_0h - 2k_0k + h_0^2 + k_0^2 - r^2 = 0.$$

Thus, $$h_0 = X_2/2(R_1X_2 - X_1R_2)$$
$$k_0 = R_2/2(R_1X_2 - X_1R_2)$$

and $r^2 = h_0^2 + k_0^2$ so that the circle passes through the origin.

A circuit as above with a fixed impedance in parallel would still have a circular admittance locus, but the origin would be shifted by the amount of the parallel admittance. Such a circuit applies to the induction motor (Chapter 15).

Geometrical inversion

Two points such as P and P_1 in Fig. 9.12 are 'inverse' points if they lie on a straight line through O, the 'pole' or centre of inversion, and if $OP \, . \, OP_1 = k$, where k is the constant of inversion. Then, if P follows a particular locus, P_1 will follow another locus so as to satisfy the above condition, giving the 'inverse locus'. Although such loci may be of any form, the most useful in practice are circular or straight-line ones, because they occur fairly frequently in circuit theory and simple rules govern them.

Let P move on the circle APB, centre C, shown and let $OABB_1A_1$ be the straight line through O and C extended. Then, if $OA \,.\, OA_1 =$

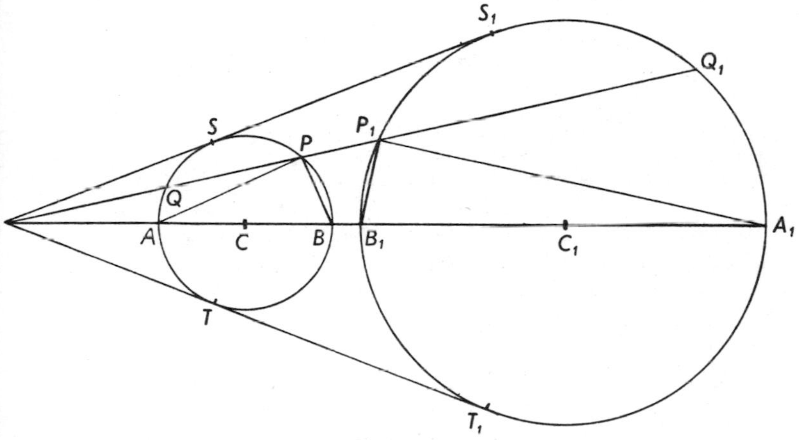

FIG. 9.12

$OB \,.\, OB_1 = OP \,.\, OP_1 = k$, A_1 and B_1 are fixed points. Since $OP/OA = OA_1/OP_1$, triangles OPA and OA_1P_1 are similar, since angle POA is common, and so angle OPA = angle OA_1P_1. Also, triangles OBP and OB_1P_1 are similar so that angle OPB = angle OB_1P_1.

Therefore, angle $APB = 90° = OPB - OPA = OB_1P_1 - OA_1P_1 =$ angle $B_1P_1A_1$. It follows that P_1 lies on the circle illustrated in Fig. 9.12, whose diameter is B_1A_1.

The inverse of a circle with respect to a given pole and with a given constant k is therefore another circle which is easily constructed because the ends of the diameter A_1 and B_1 are determined from $OA_1 = k/OA$ and $OB_1 = k/OB$. The circles have common tangents OSS_1 and OTT_1. It should be noted that $OC \,.\, OC_1$ is *not* equal to k, so that the centre of the circle C_1 cannot be found directly but must be determined by bisecting B_1A_1.

A special case arises when O lies on the circle and is coincident with A (Fig. 9.13). In this case $OA = 0$ and $OA_1 = \infty$. The circle $B_1P_1A_1$ of Fig. 9.12 becomes a straight line through B_1 and perpendicular to OAB.

Since $OB \,.\, OB_1 = OP \,.\, OP_1$ or $OB/OP = OP_1/OB_1$, triangles OPB and OB_1P_1 are similar and angle OB_1P_1 is a right-angle. The

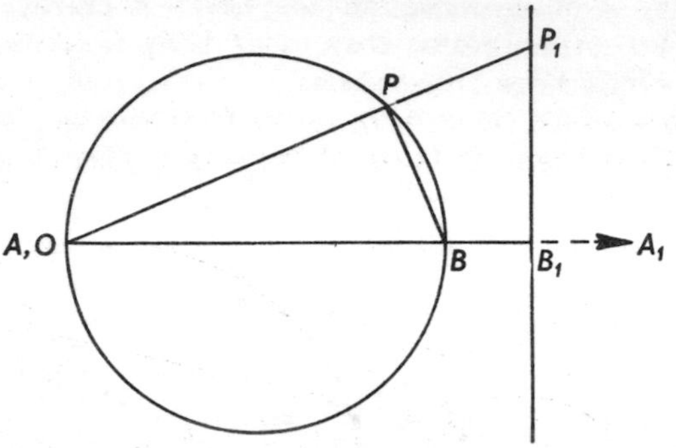

FIG. 9.13

circle and line may or may not intersect. The relationships between inverse points and inverse loci are reciprocal, *i.e.* if P_1 is the inverse of P then P is the inverse of P_1.

Impedance and admittance

Admittance is the reciprocal of impedance, so that $\mathbf{Y} \, . \, \mathbf{Z} = 1$, or more generally if **Y** and **Z** are expressed in units such that they are not reciprocals of each other then $\mathbf{Y} \, . \, \mathbf{Z} = k$ where k is a constant. For example, if Z is expressed in ohms and Y in millimhos, $k = 1{,}000$.

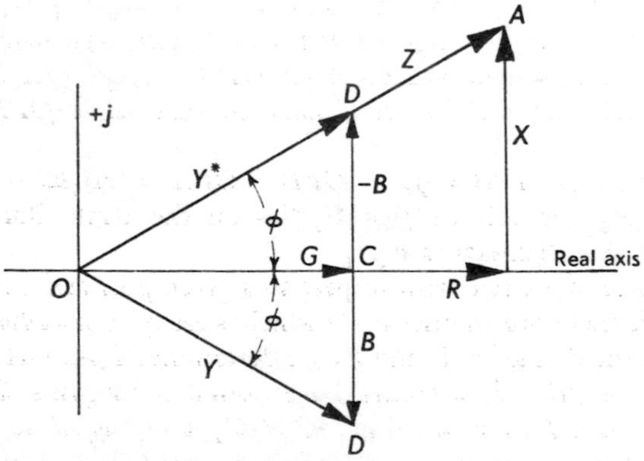

FIG. 9.14

Fig. 9.14 shows the relation between the vectors of impedance and the corresponding admittance. $\mathbf{Z} = OA = R + jX$. $\mathbf{Y} = OD = G - jB$.

The points A and D satisfy the conditions for inverse points given above except that OA and OD are not collinear. However, **Z** and the conjugate of **Y**, $\mathbf{Y}^* = OD'$, fully satisfy the conditions, so that if A

moves on a circle, then so does D' and clearly so does D. Thus, for a given locus of A, that of D' may be drawn and then that of D which is the image of D' in the real axis. In practice it is unnecessary to actually draw the locus of D, OD' being treated as the admittance and remembering that for admittance, but not for impedance, CD' is a negative ordinate.

The following examples will serve to illustrate the application of geometrical inversion to circuit problems.

EXAMPLE. An a.c. circuit, supplied at constant frequency, has two parallel branches, one consisting of a 10 Ω resistor in series with a variable inductive reactor, the other consisting of a 20 Ω resistor in series with a 15 Ω inductor. Draw to scale the vector locus of the total admittance and determine the value of admittance when the variable reactance is 30 Ω. Explain how the total-impedance locus could be constructed. [S.U.]

Solution. The impedance of the first branch is $\mathbf{Z}_1 = (10 + jX_L)\ \Omega$, where X_L is the reactance of the variable reactor. The vector locus of $\mathbf{Z}_1$ with respect to the origin O is the straight line AB shown in Fig. 9.15. $OA = \mathbf{Z}_1$ when $X_L = 0$, *i.e.* $OA = 10\ \Omega$. The values of

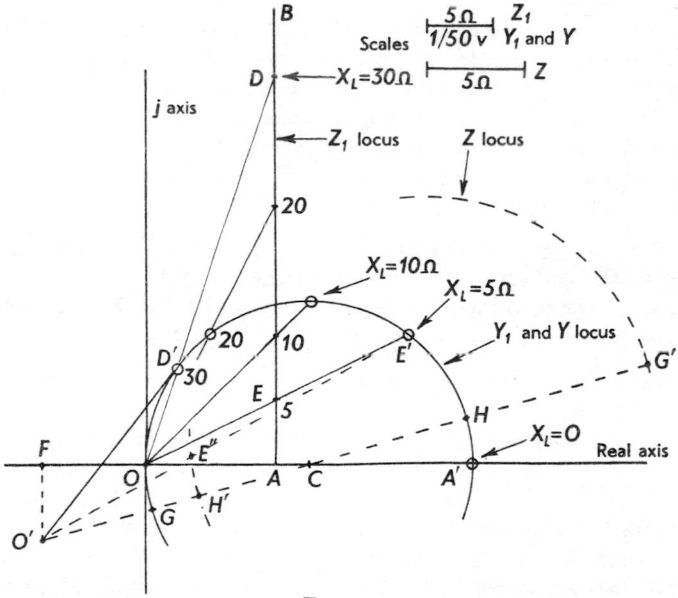

FIG. 9.15

X_L are marked on AB, so that, for example, the $\mathbf{Z}_1$ vector for $X_L = 30\ \Omega$ is represented by OD. The inverse of AD with respect to O is a circle passing through O and this, drawn to a suitable scale, represents the locus of the admittance $\mathbf{Y}_1 = 1/\mathbf{Z}_1$ (strictly $\mathbf{Y}_1^*$ as discussed above).

The inverse of OA is $OA' = (1/10)$ mho, so that if the diameter of the $\mathbf{Y}_1$ circle is made 10″ for instance, the scale of $\mathbf{Y}_1$ is 1″ = (1/100) mho. Lines are drawn from O through the different X_L points on AB to obtain the corresponding points on the $\mathbf{Y}_1$ locus (*e.g.* D' corresponding to D and E' corresponding to E). The impedance of the second branch is $\mathbf{Z}_2 = (20 + j15)\ \Omega$, giving $\mathbf{Y}_2 = (0{\cdot}032 - j0{\cdot}024)$ mho. The total admittance is $\mathbf{Y} = \mathbf{Y}_1 + \mathbf{Y}_2$, so that the origin is shifted to O', where $FO = 0{\cdot}032$ mho and $O'F = 0{\cdot}024$ mho (remember that negative susceptance is measured upwards for convenience). For any particular value of X_L, $\mathbf{Y}$ is given by the vector from O' to the corresponding point on the $\mathbf{Y}_1$ locus. Thus, for $X_L = 30\ \Omega$, $\mathbf{Y} = O'D'$. By measurement, $O'D' = (0{\cdot}042 - j0{\cdot}054)$ mho.

If the locus of the total impedance, $\mathbf{Z} = 1/\mathbf{Y}$, is required, the $\mathbf{Y}_1$ locus is inverted with respect to the point O', choosing any suitable scale, not necessarily the same as that used for the $\mathbf{Z}_1$ locus. The $\mathbf{Z}$ locus will be another circle whose diameter lies along $O'C$, where C is the centre of the $\mathbf{Y}_1$ circle. The maximum and minimum values of $\mathbf{Y}$ are given by $O'H = 0{\cdot}135$ mho and $O'G = 0{\cdot}035$ mho, so that the corresponding values of $\mathbf{Z}$ are $7{\cdot}4\ \Omega$ minimum and $28{\cdot}6\ \Omega$ maximum. These are represented by $O'H'$ and $O'G'$, measured along $O'C$ to a suitable scale, the circular $\mathbf{Z}$ locus then being drawn on $H'G'$ as diameter. (For clarity, only part of this locus is shown.) The points on the $\mathbf{Z}$ locus corresponding to the different values of the variable reactance X_L are then found by drawing straight lines from O' through the appropriate reactance points on the $\mathbf{Y}_1$ locus. For example, when $X_L = 5\ \Omega$, $\mathbf{Y} = O'E'$ and $\mathbf{Z} = O'E''$.

EXAMPLE. In the circuit shown in Fig. 9.16 (*a*), $\mathbf{Z}_1 = (8 + j10)\ \Omega$, $\mathbf{Z}_m = j20\ \Omega$, $\mathbf{Z}_2 = (R_2 + j10)\ \Omega$, R_2 being a variable.

Construct the total input-impedance locus and determine the magnitude and phase-angle of this impedance for $R_2 = 5\ \Omega$.

Solution. Repeated inversion is required in this case, as illustrated in Fig. 9.16 (*b*).

The locus of $\mathbf{Z}_2$ is the straight line PQ parallel to the real axis, with $O_1P = X_2 = 10\ \Omega$. Values of R_2 are scaled along PQ as shown. Thus, for $R_2 = 40\ \Omega$, $\mathbf{Z}_2 = O_1Q = (40 + j10)\ \Omega$. The locus of $\mathbf{Y}_2 = 1/\mathbf{Z}_2$ is the inverse of PQ and is therefore the circle shown, centre C_1, passing through O_1, of diameter $O_1B_1 = 1/X_2 = 1/10$ mho. Straight lines are drawn from O_1 through the points on the $\mathbf{Z}_2$ locus to give the corresponding points on the $\mathbf{Y}_2$ locus. For example, for $R_2 = 5\ \Omega$, $\mathbf{Z}_2 = O_1A_1$ and $\mathbf{Y}_2 = O_1A_2$.

The locus of the combined parallel admittance, $\mathbf{Y}_{2m} = (\mathbf{Y}_2 + \mathbf{Y}_m)$, is the same as that of $\mathbf{Y_2}$ alone, but the origin is shifted to O_2, where $O_1O_2 = \mathbf{Y_m} = 1/20$ mho. Thus, $\mathbf{Y_{2m}}$ for $R_2 = 5\ \Omega$ is given by O_2A_2.

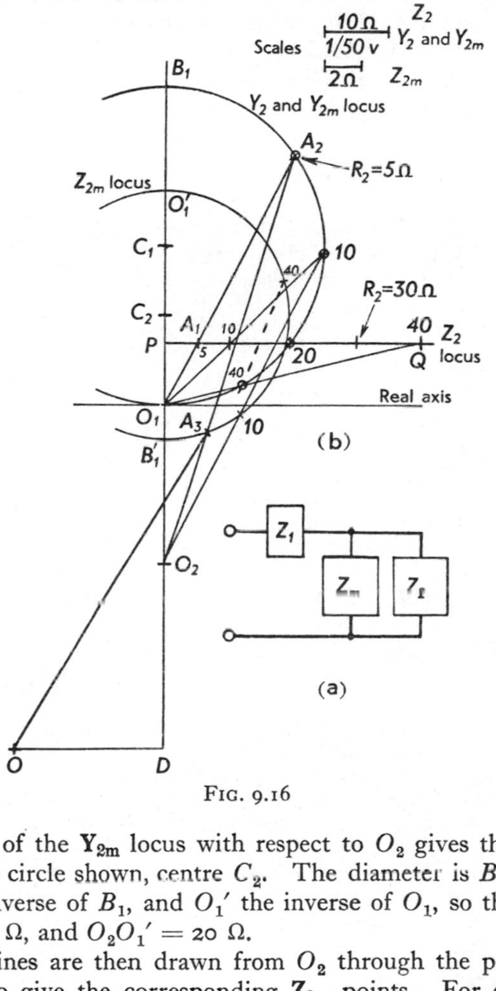

FIG. 9.16

Inversion of the $\mathbf{Y_{2m}}$ locus with respect to O_2 gives the $\mathbf{Z_{2m}}$ locus, which is the circle shown, centre C_2. The diameter is $B_1'O_1'$, where B_1' is the inverse of B_1, and O_1' the inverse of O_1, so that $O_2B_1' = 20/3 = 6{\cdot}67\ \Omega$, and $O_2O_1' = 20\ \Omega$.

Straight lines are then drawn from O_2 through the points on the $\mathbf{Y_{2m}}$ locus to give the corresponding $\mathbf{Z_{2m}}$ points. For example, for $R_2 = 5\ \Omega$, $\mathbf{Z_{2m}}$ is given by O_2A_3. Since the total impedance is $\mathbf{Z} = (\mathbf{Z_1} + \mathbf{Z_{2m}})$, the origin is now moved to O, where $OD = R_1 = 8\ \Omega$, and $DO_2 = X_1 = 10\ \Omega$. The values of $\mathbf{Z}$ are then given by the lines from O to the $\mathbf{Z_{2m}}$ locus. Thus, when $R_2 = 5\ \Omega$, $Z = OA_3 = 19{\cdot}9\ \Omega$, the phase-angle being $A_3OD = 59°$.

If the locus of the total input-admittance is required, the circle on diameter $B_1'O_1'$ is inverted with respect to O, to give another circle whose diameter lies along OC_2, the ends of the diameter being determined in the manner described in the previous example in inverting **Y** to obtain **Z**.

If the reactance X_1 had been capacitive, O_2D would be drawn upwards from O_2 in Fig. 9.16 (*b*). In such a case, with a suitable value of R_1, O could lie *inside* the **Z** locus. This would mean that **Z** might be inductive or capacitive, depending on the value of R_2.

PROBLEMS

1. Two circuits are connected in parallel. One circuit consists of a 100 Ω resistor and the other of a 25 Ω resistor in series with a fixed capacitor. An alternating-current supply of 100 V amplitude and variable frequency is connected across the combination.

Draw to scale the locus of the total current vector and determine the capacitor reactance when the phase-angle between the supply voltage and current is a maximum. [S.U.] [*Ans.* 56 Ω.]

2. Two impedances Z_1 and Z_2 are connected in parallel across a 200 V, 50 c/s supply. The impedance Z_1 consists of a 50 Ω resistor in series with a 0·2 H inductor, while Z_2 consists of a variable resistor R ohms in series with a 0·1 H inductor.

Show that the extremity of the total-current vector describes a circular locus as R is varied and draw the vector diagram to scale. Find the value of R to give maximum power. [S.U.] [*Ans.* 31·4 Ω.]

3. A 20 Ω reactor is connected in parallel with a series circuit consisting of a reactor of reactance 10 Ω and a variable resistor R. Prove that the extremity of the total-current vector moves on a circle if the supply voltage is constant at 100 V r.m.s. What is the maximum power-factor? Determine also the value of R when the power-factor has its maximum value. [S.U.] [*Ans.* 0·5; 17·3 Ω.]

4. A 200 V, single-phase supply is connected to a 100 Ω resistor, shunted across which is a variable resistor in series with a 40 Ω inductor. Show that the extremity of the total-current vector describes an arc of a circle as the resistance is varied, taking the voltage vector as a fixed reference. Calculate the maximum power and the corresponding power-factor.

If the resistor in the series branch is set to a fixed value, and the shunt resistor is made variable, while the total current is now maintained at a constant value, show that the extremity of the voltage vector has a circular locus, with the total-current vector taken as reference. [S.U.]
[*Ans.* 900 W, 0·873.]

5. An a.c. circuit, supplied at 100 V, 50 c/s, consists of a variable resistor in series with a fixed 100 μF capacitor.

Show that the extremity of the current vector moves on a circle. Determine the maximum power dissipated in the circuit and the corresponding power-factor and value of the resistor. [S.U.]
[*Ans.* 157 W, 0·707, 31·8 Ω.]

6. A variable non-inductive resistor R of maximum value 10 Ω is placed in series with a coil which has a resistance of 3 Ω and a reactance of 4 Ω. The arrangement is supplied from a 240 V, a.c. supply. Show that the locus of the extremity of the current vector is a semi-circle. From the locus diagram calculate the current supplied when R is 5 Ω. [S.U.] [*Ans.* 26·7 A.]

7. An inductive reactance of 5 Ω and a capacitive reactance of 8 Ω each have a variable resistor in series with them. These two circuits are joined in parallel across a 200 V supply. Plot the circle diagram for the arrangement and evaluate the voltage across the terminals of the reactors which are not connected together, when each resistor is fixed at 10 Ω. [*Ans.* 181 V.]

8. Two impedances Z_1 and Z_2 are connected in parallel across a 230 V, 50 c/s supply. Z_1 consists of a 40 Ω resistor in series with a 0·2 H inductor and Z_2 consists of a variable resistor R ohms in series with a 0·073 H inductor.

Show that the extremity of the total-current vector describes a circular locus as R is varied and draw the locus diagram to scale. Use the diagram to determine the value of R to give maximum power-factor for the circuit and the corresponding power dissipated in each branch. [S.U.] [*Ans.* 67 Ω, 384 W, 705 W.]

9. A coil of 20 Ω reactance at the supply frequency is connected in series with a variable non-inductive resistor, across 200 V a.c. mains. Draw the locus of the extremity of the current vector and hence find the magnitude of the current when the resistance of the circuit is 20 Ω. [*Ans.* 7·07 A.]

10. If the circuit described in the previous problem is shunted by a capacitor of 50 Ω reactance at the supply frequency, determine from the locus diagram the total current supplied when the resistance is 20 Ω. [*Ans.* 5·1 A.]

11. An impedance of $\{2s + j(4 + s)\}$ Ω is connected in parallel with another impedance, whose admittance in (0·06 − j0·06) mho, s being variable. By geometrical inversion construct the admittance locus and determine the values of the total admittance for s. = 0·5, 1·0, 2·0, 3·0. Check the position of the centre and the radius of the circular locus by the co-ordinate geometry method. [*Ans.* 0·29, 0·27, 0·22, 0·19 mho.]

12. An inductor of resistance 10 Ω and variable reactance X ohms, is shunted by a 40 Ω resistor, the combination being connected in series with an inductor of reactance 10 Ω and negligible resistance. Construct the locus of the total impedance and determine the values of this for X = 5, 10, 20 and 30 Ω. Determine also the minimum impedance of the circuit if the 10 Ω inductor is replaced by a capacitor of 10 Ω reactance. [*Ans.* 15·6 Ω, 18·8 Ω, 25·2 Ω, 34·4 Ω; 10 Ω.]

13. Construct the locus of the input admittance for the example illustrated in Fig. 9.16 and determine the values of the admittance for R_2 = 10, 20, 30 and 40 Ω. [*Ans.* 0·046, 0·040, 0·036, 0·032 mho.]

14. The parameters of a circuit of the type shown in Fig. 9.16 (*a*) are:

$$\mathbf{Z_1} = (8 - j10)\ \Omega,\ \mathbf{Z_m} = (20 + j20)\ \Omega,$$
$$\mathbf{Z_2} = (R_2 + j10)\ \Omega,\ R_2 \text{ being variable.}$$

Draw the locus of the total input impedance to scale and determine the impedance values for R_2 = 5 Ω and R_2 = 40 Ω. [*Ans.* 12·6, 22·7 Ω.]

CHAPTER 10

NON-SINUSOIDAL WAVES

Non-sinusoidal waves

Waveforms observed in practice often differ somewhat from the standard sine wave and this difference, if large, has to be taken into account. A non-sinusoidal waveform is still periodic and it is shown in this chapter that any periodic waveform can be split up into a number of pure sine waves of different frequencies and amplitudes. One of these component waves has the frequency of the complex wave and is called the *fundamental*, the remaining components have frequencies which are integral multiples of the fundamental frequency and are called *harmonics*, *e.g.* a second harmonic is a component wave which has a frequency twice that of the fundamental. Harmonics may be *odd* or *even*. An odd harmonic is one that has a frequency which is an odd number of times the fundamental frequency while an even harmonic is one that has a frequency which is an even number of times the fundamental frequency. The amplitudes of the various harmonics usually decrease as the frequency increases although frequently one particular harmonic may be well developed due to the circumstances. Any harmonic may be specified by (*a*) its frequency, (*b*) its amplitude and (*c*) its phase relative to the fundamental. Therefore, the instantaneous value of a complex voltage waveform may be expressed as:

$$v = V_1 \sin(\omega t + \phi_1) + V_2 \sin(2\omega t + \phi_2) + V_3 \sin(3\omega t + \phi_3) + \dots$$

where V_1, V_2, V_3, etc. are the maximum values of the fundamental and the various harmonics, respectively, and ϕ_1, ϕ_2, ϕ_3, etc. are phase-angles.

Waveforms may contain only *odd* harmonics, or only *even* harmonics. For example, machines usually produce only odd harmonics while even harmonics, as well as odd ones, arise in electronic amplifiers due to curvature of valve characteristics. There are many cases where only one of the harmonics is of significant amplitude.

It is interesting to consider the effect of the presence of various harmonics superimposed on a sine wave, because this helps to decide what are the likely harmonics in a given complex waveform. Four cases will be dealt with:

(1) *Presence of an odd sine harmonic*

Consider, as an example, the presence of a third harmonic. It is seen from Fig. 10.1 that this gives a flat-topped wave which is symmetrical about $\pi/2$ and also about π with reversed sign. The waveform shown is for a positive third harmonic. The waveform for a negative third harmonic has a peaked top.

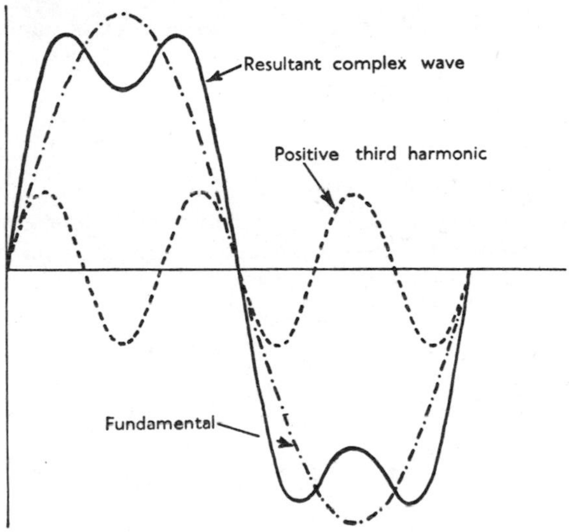

FIG. 10.1

(2) *Presence of an odd cosine harmonic*

Consider, as an example, the presence of a positive third harmonic. It is found, by drawing out waveforms similar to those of Fig. 10.1, that this gives a waveform which is neither symmetrical about $\pi/2$ nor π.

Similar conclusions are reached for a negative third harmonic.

(3) *Presence of an even sine harmonic*

Consider, as an example, the presence of a second harmonic. This is found to give a resultant waveform which is not symmetrical about $\pi/2$ but is symmetrical about π with reversed sign.

(4) *Presence of an even cosine harmonic*

Consider, as an example, the presence of a positive second harmonic. This gives a waveform which has a flat-topped positive portion symmetrical about $\pi/2$ and a peaked negative portion symmetrical about $3\pi/2$. The waveform is not, however, symmetrical about π. A negative even cosine harmonic would give a similar result except that the peaked part would now be positive and the flat-topped section negative.

It will be evident that when the area of the positive part of the complex wave is not equal to the area of the negative portion, the curve has a mean height A which may be either positive or negative.

Fourier series

For any waveform which is cyclic, repeating itself at intervals of 2π,

$$f(\theta) = A + a_1 \sin \theta + a_2 \sin 2\theta + \ldots + a_n \sin n\theta + \ldots$$
$$+ b_1 \cos \theta + b_2 \cos 2\theta + \ldots + b_n \cos n\theta + \ldots \text{ ad inf.}$$

The area under one cycle of the curve is $\int_0^{2\pi} f(\theta)\, d\theta$ and this equals $2\pi A$ because the integrals of all the sine and cosine terms, which arise from the right-hand side of the above expression, are zero.

Thus, the value of the constant term $f(\theta)$ of any wave is

$$A = \frac{1}{2\pi} \int_0^{2\pi} f(\theta)\, d\theta$$

It also follows from the expression for $f(\theta)$ that

$$\int_0^{2\pi} f(\theta) \sin n\theta\, d\theta = \int_0^{2\pi} a_n \sin^2 n\theta\, d\theta = \frac{a_n}{2} \int_0^{2\pi} (1 - \cos 2n\theta) d\theta = \pi a_n$$

$$\therefore \quad a_n = \frac{1}{\pi} \int_0^{2\pi} f(\theta) \sin n\theta\, d\theta$$

Similarly, the amplitude of the nth cosine harmonic is

$$b_n = \frac{1}{\pi} \int_0^{2\pi} f(\theta) \cos n\theta\, d\theta.$$

When the dependent variable is not expressible as a simple function of the independent variable, an approximate graphical solution for finding the coefficient of the Fourier series is possible, by replacing the above integration processes, by summations over a number of equal measureable increments of the independent variable. Thus, the expression for A becomes

$$(1/2\pi) \sum_1^N \{f(\theta)_N\, \Delta\theta\}$$

where $\Delta\theta$ is the measurable counterpart of $d\theta$ and equals $2\pi/N$. Therefore,

$$A = (1/2\pi) \sum_1^N \{f(\theta)_N\, 2\pi/N\} = \sum_1^N f(\theta)_N/N.$$

(This expression for the average height of the waveform will probably be well known to the reader.) Similar procedures can be applied to the expressions for a_n and b_n.

EXAMPLE. Find the Fourier series for the waveform produced by a half-wave rectifier.

Solution. Consider the waveform shown in Fig. 10.2.

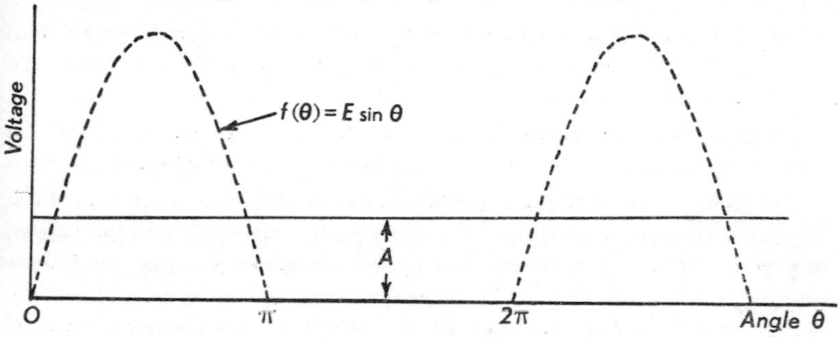

FIG. 10.2

It is evident from the foregoing discussion that it contains (i) a constant term, (ii) negative even cosine harmonics together with (iii) a fundamental sine. Due to the complete agreement of this waveform with case (4) above one would expect that no other harmonics are present. Let us now test this conclusion mathematically.

The amplitude of the constant term is

$$A = \frac{1}{2\pi}\int_0^{2\pi} f(\theta)\, d\theta = \frac{1}{2\pi}\left[\int_0^{\pi} E \sin\theta\, d\theta + \int_{\pi}^{2\pi} 0\, d\theta\right]$$

because $f(\theta) = E \sin\theta$ from 0 to π and $f(\theta) = 0$ from π to 2π.

$$\therefore \quad A = E/\pi.$$

The amplitude of the nth sine harmonic is

$$a_n = \frac{1}{\pi}\int_0^{\pi} E \sin\theta \sin n\theta\, d\theta$$

which is zero except for $n = 1$, in which case

$$a_1 = \frac{1}{\pi}\int_0^{\pi} E \sin^2\theta\, d\theta = E/2.$$

Similarly, the amplitude of the nth cosine harmonic is:

$$b_n = \frac{1}{\pi}\int_0^{\pi} E \sin\theta \cos n\theta\, d\theta$$

$$= \frac{E}{2\pi}\int_0^{\pi} \{\sin (n + 1)\theta - \sin (n - 1)\theta\} d\theta$$

When n is odd, $b_n = 0$.
When n is even, $b_n = -2E/\pi(n^2 - 1)$.

The Fourier expansion is therefore

$$E\left[\frac{1}{\pi}+\frac{1}{2}\sin\theta-\frac{2}{\pi}\sum_{n=2,4,6\ldots}^{n=\infty}\frac{\cos n\theta}{(n^2-1)}\right]$$

Thus, the waveform consists of a constant term, a fundamental sine and negative even cosine harmonics as previously deduced from the appearance of the waveform.

EXAMPLE. Deduce from the solution to the previous example the Fourier expansion for the waveform produced by a full-wave rectifier.

Solution. The full-wave circuit consists essentially of two half-wave circuits, one circuit operates during one half-cycle and the second operates during the next half-cycle. Analyzing each half-wave separately using the result of the previous example, it is seen from Fig. 10.3, that for the full-wave circuit the component fundamentals cancel

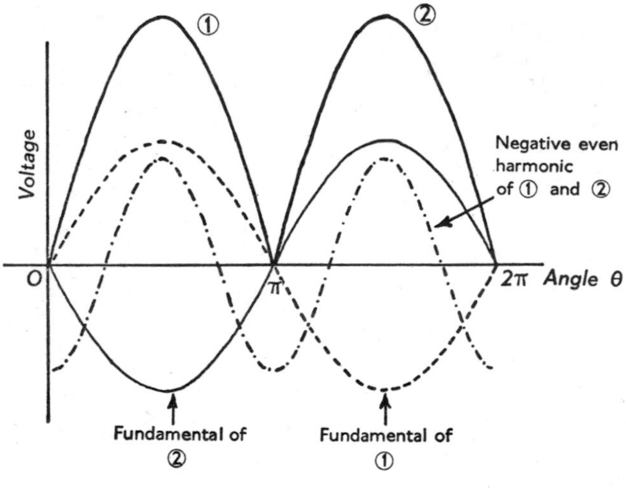

FIG. 10.3

out, the negative even cosine harmonics are coincident and are therefore present with twice the amplitude. It is also evident that the value of the constant term is twice the value for the previous case.

The Fourier expansion for the full-wave rectifier waveform is therefore

$$E\left[\frac{2}{\pi}-\frac{4}{\pi}\sum_{n=2,4,6\ldots}^{n=\infty}\frac{\cos n\theta}{(n^2-1)}\right]$$

EXAMPLE. Find the Fourier series for the waveform of Fig. 10.4 produced by an m-phase rectifier.

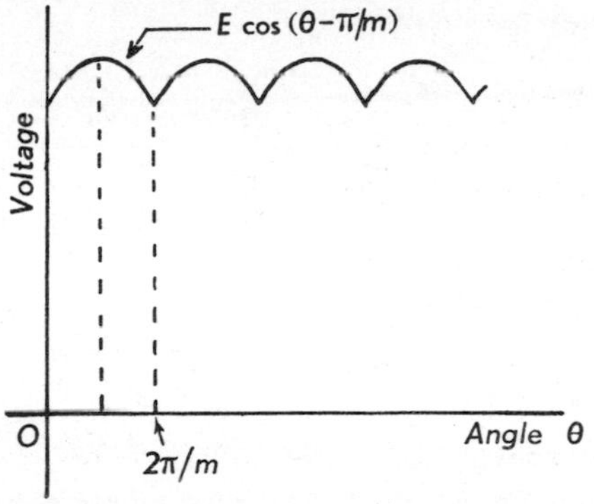

FIG. 10.4

Solution. When the cyclic interval is only $2\pi/m$ then the frequency of each harmonic is increased m times and therefore the Fourier expansion is

$$f(\theta) = A + a_1 \sin m\theta + a_2 \sin 2m\theta + \ldots + a_n \sin mn\theta + \ldots$$
$$+ b_1 \cos m\theta + b_2 \cos 2m\theta + \ldots + b_n \cos mn\theta + \ldots$$

where
$$A = \frac{1}{(2\pi/m)} \int_0^{2\pi/m} f(\theta)\, d\theta$$

$$a_n = \frac{m}{\pi} \int_0^{2\pi/m} f(\theta) \sin mn\theta\, d\theta$$

and
$$b_n = \frac{m}{\pi} \int_0^{2\pi/m} f(\theta) \cos mn\theta\, d\theta.$$

In this case
$$A = \frac{1}{(2\pi/m)} \int_0^{2\pi/m} E \cos(\theta - \pi/m) d\theta$$
$$= (mE/\pi) \sin(\pi/m).$$

Also,
$$a_n = \frac{m}{\pi} \int_0^{2\pi/m} E \cos(\theta - \pi/m) \sin mn\theta\, d\theta$$
$$= \frac{mE}{2\pi} \int_0^{2\pi/m} \{\sin(\theta - \pi/m + mn\theta) - \sin(\theta - \pi/m - mn\theta)\} d\theta$$
$= 0$ for all values of n.

Similarly,

$$b_n = \frac{m}{\pi} \int_0^{2\pi/m} E \cos(\theta - \pi/m) \cos mn\theta\, d\theta$$
$$= \frac{mE}{2\pi} \int_0^{2\pi/m} \{\cos(\theta - \pi/m + mn\theta) + \cos(\theta - \pi/m - mn\theta)\} d\theta$$
$$= -2E/(m^2n^2 - 1)(m/\pi) \sin(\pi/m).$$

Hence, for an m-phase rectifier,

$$f(\theta) = (mE/\pi)\sin(\pi/m) - \sum_{n=1}^{n=\infty}\left(\frac{2E}{m^2n^2 - 1}\right)\frac{m}{\pi}\sin\frac{\pi}{m}\cdot\cos mn\theta$$

$$= (mE/\pi)\sin(\pi/m)\left[1 - \sum_{n=1}^{n=\infty}\frac{2}{(m^2n^2-1)}\cos mn\theta\right].$$

If $m = 2$,

$$f(\theta) = (2E/\pi)[1 - 2\cos 2\theta/3 - 2\cos 4\theta/15 \ldots]$$

as proved already.

If $m = 6$,

$$f(\theta) = (6E/\pi)\sin(\pi/6)[1 - 2\cos 6\theta/35 - 2\cos 12\theta/143 \ldots]$$

Thus, the chief harmonic present in a six-phase rectifier is the sixth and the percentage of this harmonic is

$$(2/35) \times 100\% = \underline{5{\cdot}71\%}.$$

EXAMPLE. Prove that for the waveform illustrated in Fig. 10.5,

$$y = (4E/\pi)(\cos x - \tfrac{1}{3}\cos 3x + \tfrac{1}{5}\cos 5x - \tfrac{1}{7}\cos 7x + \ldots)$$

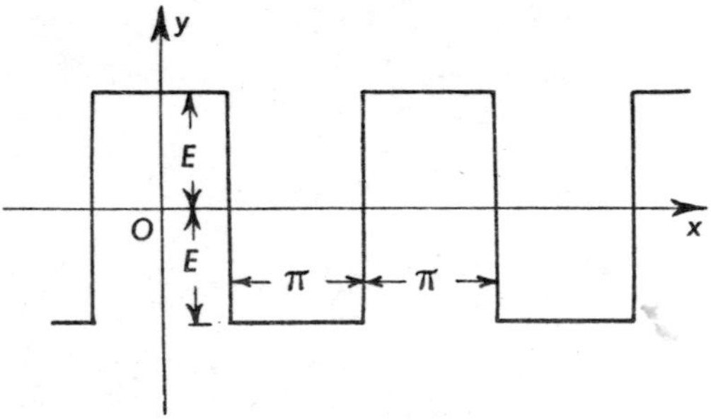

FIG. 10.5

Solution.

From 0 to $\pi/2$, $y = f(x) = E$.
From $\pi/2$ to $3\pi/2$, $y = f(x) = -E$.
From $3\pi/2$ to 2π, $y = f(x) = E$.

It is evident from the waveform that $A = 0$ (the average value of the waveform over the period 0 to 2π is zero).

Now

$$a_n = (1/\pi)\int_0^{2\pi} f(x)\sin nx\,dx$$

$$= (1/\pi)\left[\int_0^{\pi/2} E\sin nx\,dx + \int_{\pi/2}^{3\pi/2}(-E)\sin nx\,dx + \int_{3\pi/2}^{2\pi} E\sin nx\,dx\right]$$

$$= 0.$$

Similarly,

$$b_n = (1/\pi)\int_0^{2\pi} f(x)\cos nx\,dx$$

$$= (E/\pi)\left[\int_0^{\pi/2}\cos nx\,dx + \int_{3\pi/2}^{2\pi}\cos nx\,dx - \int_{\pi/2}^{3\pi/2}\cos nx\,dx\right]$$

$$= (2E/n\pi)[\sin(n\pi/2) - \sin(3n\pi/2)].$$

When n is even, $b_n = 0$.

When n is odd, $b_n = 4E/n\pi$, when n is 1, 5, 9, etc.

$b_n = -4E/n\pi$, when n is 3, 7, 11, etc.

$$\therefore \quad y = \underline{(4E/\pi)(\cos x - \tfrac{1}{3}\cos 3x + \tfrac{1}{5}\cos 5x - \tfrac{1}{7}\cos 7x + \ldots)}$$

Simplification of Fourier analysis due to certain types of symmetry

The example just considered shows that a given waveform may not need all the terms which are specified by Fourier's series, for no sine terms appear in the result. It is convenient to be able to recognize waveforms which do not require all the terms of the series because then by inspection the amount of work required to arrive at the result can be considerably reduced. The necessary inspection can be performed quite readily as indicated below.

It has been shown that a cyclic waveform can be represented as

$$f(\theta) = A + \textstyle\sum_1^\infty a_n \sin n\theta + \sum_1^\infty b_n \cos n\theta$$

Thus,

$$f(-\theta) = A - \textstyle\sum_1^\infty a_n \sin n\theta + \sum_1^\infty b_n \cos n\theta$$

$$\therefore \quad \{f(\theta) + f(-\theta)\}/2 = A + \textstyle\sum_1^\infty b_n \cos n\theta$$

and

$$\{f(\theta) - f(-\theta)\}/2 = \textstyle\sum_1^\infty a_n \sin n\theta.$$

Also

$$f(\theta) = \{f(\theta) + f(-\theta)\}/2 + \{f(\theta) - f(-\theta)\}/2.$$

If $f(\theta) = f(-\theta)$, then $f(\theta)$ is said to be an *even function* and

$$f(\theta) = \{f(\theta) + f(-\theta)\}/2 = A + \textstyle\sum_1^\infty b_n \cos n\theta$$

and no sine terms appear in the series.

Similarly, if $f(\theta) = -f(-\theta)$, $f(\theta)$ is an *odd function* and

$$f(\theta) = \{f(\theta) - f(-\theta)\}/2 = \textstyle\sum_1^\infty a_n \sin n\theta.$$

In this case there is no constant term and there are no cosine terms in the series.

There are further types of symmetry but these will not be

discussed here. For further information the reader should consult other texts.*

R.M.S. value of a complex wave

The r.m.s. value of a periodic function, $f(t)$, in accordance with the general definition given in Chapter 3, is

$$\sqrt{\left[(1/T_1)\int_0^{T_1}\{f(t)\}^2 dt\right]},$$

where T_1 is the time for a complete cycle (if the function is symmetrical about the t axis it is only necessary to integrate over one half-cycle). The integration may be carried out graphically by measuring the area under the curve of $\{f(t)\}^2$ or by tabulating the ordinates of $\{f(t)\}^2$ and obtaining a mean value. These methods, while of general application and of great importance, are often tedious and where the wave has been analyzed as described above into its fundamental and harmonic components, the r.m.s. value can be obtained as is evident from Chapter 3 and as shown again below.

In general, a non-sinusoidal waveform will be made up of a steady component, a fundamental component and both sine and cosine harmonics which may be evaluated by the methods described already. The sine and cosine harmonics of a given frequency may be combined to give a single sinusoidal component of that frequency. Thus, $B_1 \sin \beta t + B_2 \cos \beta t = B \sin (\beta t + \phi)$ where $B = \sqrt{(B_1^2 + B_2^2)}$ and $\tan \phi = B_2/B_1$.

Therefore, the instantaneous magnitude of the wave (a voltage, say), may be expressed as

$$v = A + a \sin \alpha t + b \sin (\beta t + \phi) + c \sin (\gamma t + \theta) + \ldots$$

and

$$v^2 = A^2 + a^2 \sin^2 \alpha t + b^2 \sin^2 (\beta t + \phi) + c^2 \sin^2 (\gamma t + \theta) + \ldots$$
$$+ 2A\{a \sin \alpha t + b \sin (\beta t + \phi) + \ldots\} +$$
$$2ab \sin \alpha t \sin (\beta t + \phi) + \ldots$$

i.e. $$v^2 = A^2 + \tfrac{1}{2}a^2(1 - \cos 2\alpha t) + \tfrac{1}{2}b^2\{1 - \cos 2(\beta t + \phi)\} + \ldots$$
$$+ \text{other sinusoidal terms.}$$

In the usual case where $b = 2a$, $c = 3a$, etc., the average value of all the sinusoidal terms in this expression, over one cycle of the fundamental, that is over a time $1/a$, is zero. Even if b, c, etc., are not integral multiples of a, the long-time average of the sinusoidal terms will be zero. Therefore, the average value of v^2 is $(A^2 + a^2/2 + b^2/2 + \ldots)$ and the r.m.s. value of the wave is given by

$$V_{\text{r.m.s.}} = \sqrt{(A^2 + a^2/2 + b^2/2 + \ldots)}$$

* For example, see W. H. Middendorf, *Analysis of Electric Circuits*, **Chapter 17** (John Wiley, 1956).

Since $a/\sqrt{2}$, $b/\sqrt{2}$, etc., are the r.m.s. values of the separate sinusoidal components, which may be designated a_r, b_r, etc.,

$$V_{\text{r.m.s.}} = \sqrt{(A^2 + a_r^2 + b_r^2 + \ldots)}$$

Two important general deductions can be drawn from this formula:

(1) The relative phase-angles (ϕ, θ, etc.) of the components have no significance in the r.m.s. value.

(2) If the harmonics are of small magnitude compared with the fundamental, their effect on the r.m.s. value of the whole wave will be quite small. For example, consider a wave having no steady component, a fundamental of r.m.s. magnitude 100 units and a single harmonic of r.m.s. magnitude 20 units. The r.m.s. value of the wave is $\sqrt{(100^2 + 20^2)} = 102$ units, *i.e.* a 20% harmonic contributes only 2% to the r.m.s. magnitude of the complex waveform.

EXAMPLE. Determine the r.m.s. value of the full-wave rectifier waveform shown in Fig. 10.3 from the Fourier-series formula

$$f(\theta) = 2E/\pi[1 - 2\cos 2\theta/3 - 2\cos 4\theta/15 \ldots].$$

Solution. The r.m.s. value

$$\begin{aligned} &= E\sqrt{[4/\pi^2 + 16/2\pi^2\{(1/3)^2 + (1/15)^2 + \ldots\}]} \\ &= E\sqrt{[0{\cdot}405 + 0{\cdot}090 + 0{\cdot}0045 + 0{\cdot}0008 + \ldots]} \\ &= E\sqrt{0{\cdot}4993} = 0{\cdot}707E \\ &= \underline{E/\sqrt{2}}. \end{aligned}$$

Electric circuits with non-sinusoidal voltages and currents

(a) Circuit having resistance only

The form of the current wave (i) passing through a resistor is the same as that of the voltage (v_R) across it, since the instantaneous values are related by Ohm's Law.

i.e. $i = v_R/R$, where R is the resistance.

Thus, if $i = I_1 \sin \omega_1 t + I_2 \sin (\omega_2 t + \phi) + \ldots$

$$\begin{aligned} v_R &= RI_1 \sin \omega_1 t + RI_2 \sin (\omega_2 t + \phi) + \ldots \\ &= V_1 \sin \omega_1 t + V_2 \sin (\omega_2 t + \phi) + \ldots \end{aligned}$$

(b) Circuit having inductance only

If the current wave has the form given under (*a*) above, the voltage across the inductor v_L is $L\,di/dt$

i.e.

$$\begin{aligned} v_L &= I_1 L\omega_1 \cos \omega_1 t + I_2 L\omega_2 \cos (\omega_2 t + \phi) + \ldots \\ &= V_{L_1} \cos \omega_1 t + V_{L_2} \cos (\omega_2 t + \phi) + \ldots \end{aligned}$$

(c) *Circuit having capacitance only*

If the current wave has the form given under (a) above, the voltage across the capacitor v_C is $(\int i\,dt)/C$, so that

$$v_C = (I_1/C)\int \sin \omega_1 t\,dt + (I_2/C)\int \sin(\omega_2 t + \phi)dt + \dots$$
$$= -(I_1/\omega_1 C)\cos \omega_1 t - (I_2/\omega_2 C)\cos(\omega_2 t + \phi) - \dots$$
$$= -V_{C_1}\cos \omega_1 t - V_{C_2}\cos(\omega_2 t + \phi)\dots$$

(d) *LCR series circuit*

For a circuit with resistance, inductance and capacitance in series, carrying the current given under (a) above, the instantaneous applied voltage must be the sum of the voltages across each component.

Taking the components for each frequency separately,

$$v_1 = I_1\{R \sin \omega_1 t + (L\omega_1 - 1/\omega_1 C)\cos \omega_1 t\}$$

and if $(L\omega_1 - 1/\omega_1 C) = X_1$ and $\sqrt{(R^2 + X_1^2)} = Z_1$,

$$v_1 = I_1 Z_1 \sin(\omega_1 t + \phi_1), \text{ where } \tan \phi_1 = X_1/R_1.$$

Similarly, if $X_2 = (L\omega_2 - 1/\omega_2 C)$ and $Z_2 = \sqrt{(R^2 + X_2^2)}$,

$$v^2 = I_2 Z_2 \sin(\omega_2 t + \phi_2), \text{ and so on.}$$

It follows that each sinusoidal component of current may be calculated separately as though the corresponding voltage was the only component present, the total current being simply the sum of all the instantaneous currents so calculated. The converse holds in determining the voltage for a given current.

EXAMPLE. The voltage $v = 100 \cos 314t + 50 \sin(1{,}570t - 30°)$ is applied to a series circuit consisting of a 10 Ω resistor, a 0·02 H inductor and a 50 μF capacitor. Determine the instantaneous current and the r.m.s. values of voltage and current. [S.U.]

Solution. Consider first the fundamental for which $\omega = 314$.

The inductive reactance $= 0{\cdot}02 \times 314 = 6{\cdot}28\ \Omega$

The capacitive reactance $= -10^6/(50 \times 314) = -63{\cdot}8\ \Omega$

The combined reactance $= -57{\cdot}32\ \Omega$

Impedance $= \sqrt{(10^2 + 57{\cdot}32^2)} = 58{\cdot}3\ \Omega$

$\therefore\ I_1 = 100/58{\cdot}3 = 1{\cdot}71$ A and $\tan \phi_1 = -5{\cdot}732$, so $\phi_1 = -80°\ 10'$

Thus, $i_1 = 1{\cdot}71 \cos(314t + 80°\ 10')$ A

Consider now the harmonic (5th)

The inductive reactance $= 5 \times 6{\cdot}28 = 31{\cdot}4\ \Omega$
The capacitive reactance $= -63{\cdot}8/5 = -12{\cdot}76\ \Omega$
The total reactance $= 18{\cdot}64\ \Omega$
Impedance $= \sqrt{(10^2 + 18{\cdot}64^2)} = 21{\cdot}2\ \Omega$

$\therefore\quad I_5 = 50/21{\cdot}2 = 2{\cdot}36$ A and $\tan\phi_5 = 1{\cdot}864$, so $\phi_5 = 61°\ 48'$

Thus, $$i_5 = 2{\cdot}36 \sin(5\omega t - 30° - 61°\ 48')\ \text{A}$$
$$= 2{\cdot}36 \sin(1{,}570t - 91°\ 48')\ \text{A}$$

The total current

$$= i_1 + i_5$$
$$= \underline{\{1{\cdot}71 \cos(314t + 80°\ 10') + 2{\cdot}36 \sin(1{,}570t - 91°\ 48')\}\text{A}}$$

The r.m.s. voltage $= \sqrt{(100^2 + 50^2)}/\sqrt{2} = \underline{79{\cdot}2\ \text{V}}$

The r.m.s. current $= \sqrt{(1{\cdot}71^2 + 2{\cdot}36^2)}/\sqrt{2} = \underline{2{\cdot}06\ \text{A}}$

Power and power-factor

Consider a circuit in which an applied voltage of instantaneous value

$$v = V_0 + V_1 \sin\omega_1 t + V_2 \sin(\omega_2 t + \theta)$$

gives a current of instantaneous value (in ampères)

$$i = I_0 + I_1 \sin(\omega_1 t - \phi_1) + I_2 \sin(\omega_2 t + \theta - \phi_2)$$

The instantaneous power is then

$$vi = V_o I_o + V_1 I_1 \sin\omega_1 t \sin(\omega_1 t - \phi_1) + V_2 I_2 \sin(\omega_2 t + \theta) \sin(\omega_2 t + \theta - \phi_2) + V_o I_1 \sin(\omega_1 t - \phi_1) + V_1 I_2 \sin\omega_1 t \sin(\omega_2 t + \theta - \phi_2) + \ldots$$

giving $$vi = V_o I_o + \tfrac{1}{2} V_1 I_1 \{\cos\phi_1 - \cos(2\omega_1 t - \phi_1)\} + \tfrac{1}{2} V_2 I_2 \{\cos\phi_2 - \cos(2\omega_2 t + 2\theta - \phi_2)\} + \ldots$$

The remaining terms in the above expression are all sinusoidal periodic terms.

The mean value of vi is the mean power and this is $V_o I_o + \frac{1}{2} V_1 I_1 \cos\phi_1 + \frac{1}{2} V_2 I_2 \cos\phi_2$, all the other terms being periodic sinusoidal having zero mean values.

Thus, a voltage of one frequency in association with a current of another frequency produces no mean power, the only contributions to the power being from voltages and currents of the same frequency. Therefore, the power due to each voltage and current of the same frequency is calculated in the normal way, as though they were the only voltage and current present, the total mean power being the simple sum of all the component powers so calculated.

Thus, in the example on p. 188, the power due to the fundamental is $(100/\sqrt{2}) \cdot (1{\cdot}71/\sqrt{2}) \cos 80^\circ 10' = 14{\cdot}5$ W and the power due to the harmonic is $(50/\sqrt{2})(2{\cdot}36/\sqrt{2}) \cos 61^\circ 48' = 27{\cdot}8$ W, giving a total power of 42·3 W.

In a static circuit the power taken is dissipated as the loss in the resistors and for each resistor is $RI^2_{\text{r.m.s.}}$, where $I_{\text{r.m.s.}}$ is the resultant r.m.s. current through the resistor. This follows from the definition of r.m.s. current. In the example under consideration the r.m.s. current is 2·06 A and the resistor has a resistance of 10 Ω, so that the power is $10 \times (2{\cdot}06)^2 = 42{\cdot}3$ W as before.

By the general definition power-factor = (power in watts)/(r.m.s. voltage × r.m.s. current in ampères). It is only for voltages and currents of pure sinusoidal waveforms that the power-factor is equal to $\cos \phi$, where ϕ is the angle of phase-difference between voltage and current. If either the voltage or the current or both are non-sinusoidal, no single value of ϕ exists and $\cos \phi$ is meaningless (except in the special case when the voltage and current waves are of identical form, which is only true for a pure resistance, when the power-factor is unity).

The power-factor in the example given above is $42{\cdot}3/(79{\cdot}2 \times 2{\cdot}06) = 0{\cdot}26$.

Non-linear circuits

The analysis of non-linear circuits, which have parameters varying in value with the magnitude of the current, is very difficult and beyond the scope of this book. A few brief remarks, however, are not inappropriate here. Unlike linear circuits, in which the current magnitudes are directly proportional to voltage magnitudes, general solutions are not possible for non-linear circuits because the parameters change with current or voltage magnitude.

The form of attack depends on the type of problem and approximate solutions obtained by graphical constructions or by repeated trial-and-error methods are used. It may be possible to obtain the impressed voltage required to produce a given waveform of current, but not, except by trial-and-error, to do the converse. As an example of this, consider a non-linear inductor in series with a resistor, carrying a current of given waveform. It is assumed that the relation between the inductor flux-linkage ψ and the current i is known (from the saturation curve). By constructing a series of tangents to the $\psi - i$ curve the relation between $d\psi/di$ and i can be determined in the form of a table, or plotted as a curve.

A table can then be drawn up with columns of corresponding values of time (t), current i, di/dt, Ri, $d\psi/di$, $d\psi/dt = (d\psi/di)(di/dt)$ and the applied voltage which is given by $v = Ri + d\psi/dt$.

The determination of the current waveform for a given applied voltage waveform is very much more difficult, the method being essentially one of trial-and-error, assuming a current waveform, determining the corresponding voltage waveform and comparing this with the actual applied voltage. The comparison would indicate the form of correction necessary in the assumed current and the operation would be repeated until the calculated and actual voltages agreed.

The case of a simple non-linear resistor is of interest. A resistor of the type used in lightning arrestors (Thyrite, Metrosil, etc.), has a resistance which falls as the applied voltage and current increase. A sinusoidal alternating voltage applied to this kind of resistor gives a peaky current with a prominent third harmonic, together with other odd harmonics. Thus, if the voltage is $v = V \sin \omega t$, the current would be, to a first approximation, neglecting harmonics other than the third, $i = I_1 \sin \omega t - I_3 \sin 3\omega t$. Neither I_1 nor I_3 would be directly proportional to V. The power dissipated in the resistor is simply $VI_1/2$ while the r.m.s. voltage and current are $V/\sqrt{2}$ and $\sqrt{\{I_1^2 + I_3^2\}}/\sqrt{2}$ respectively. Thus, the power-factor is $I_1/\sqrt{\{I_1^2 + I_3^2\}}$ and is therefore less than unity, although the current is in phase with the voltage in the sense that they are zero and reach their maximum values at the same time.

A sinusoidal current flowing through such a resistor will require a flat-topped voltage waveform with a positive third harmonic amongst others. Low power-factors of this kind, due to non-linearities, cannot be corrected by the usual means such as the use of parallel capacitors.

PROBLEMS

1. Show that the Fourier series of the sawtooth waveform illustrated is

$$y = (2E/\pi)\left(\sin x - \frac{\sin 2x}{2} + \frac{\sin 3x}{3} - \frac{\sin 4x}{4} \cdots\right)$$

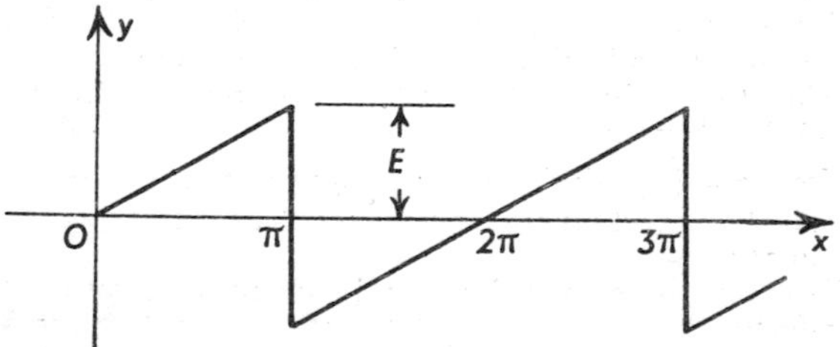

2. Show that the Fourier series of the triangular waveform illustrated is

$$y = (8E/\pi^2)\left(\cos x + \frac{\cos 3x}{9} + \frac{\cos 5x}{25} + \ldots\right)$$

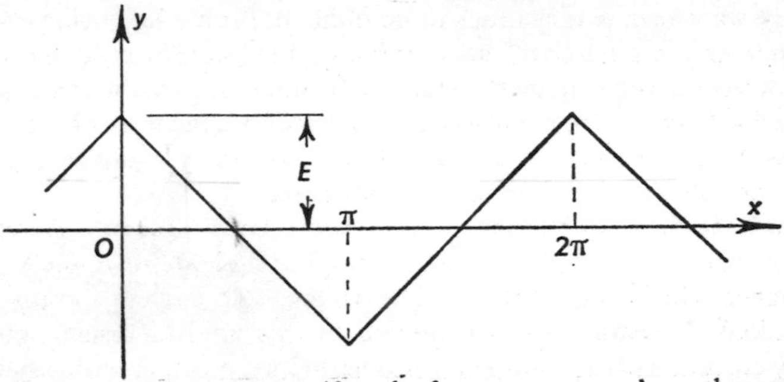

3. A current i increases uniformly from zero to 5 A as the angular displacement θ in radius changes from zero to 2π. The current then abruptly falls to zero and repeats the cycle of changes. Show that the Fourier series of the waveform is

$$i = 5\left(0{\cdot}5 - \frac{\sin x}{\pi} - \frac{\sin 2x}{2\pi} - \frac{\sin 3x}{3\pi} \ldots\right).$$

Plot the result of adding the first four terms of the series.

Determine also the first four terms of the series graphically.

4. The periodic time of a certain current wave is divided into 12 equal parts, the corresponding instantaneous values of current (i) being 3·370, 4·340, 5·315, 5·980, 5·315, 3·175, 1·187, 0·739, 1·260, 1·562, 1·710, 2·358. Show that the waveform can be represented by the following expression:

$$i = 3{\cdot}025 + 2{\cdot}210 \sin\theta - 0{\cdot}132 \sin 2\theta + \ldots$$
$$+ 0{\cdot}804 \cos\theta - 0{\cdot}746 \cos 2\theta + \ldots$$

where θ is the angular displacement.

5. Use the 12-ordinate method of Problem **4** to solve Problems **1** and **2**.

6. What are the fundamental and harmonic frequencies of a voltage represented by the expression $v = \{141 \sin 377t + 28{\cdot}3 \sin (754t - 60°)\}$ V? Calculate the r.m.s. value of this voltage.

[*Ans.* 60 c/s, 120 c/s, 102 V.]

7. Calculate the r.m.s. value of the voltage $v = \{10{\cdot}2 \sin (\omega t - 11{\cdot}3°) + 2 \sin (3\omega t + 90°) + \sin 5\omega t\}$ V. [*Ans.* 7·4 V.]

8. A current which can be represented by the expression $i = \{10{\cdot}2 \sin (\omega t - 11{\cdot}3°) + 2 \sin (3\omega t + 90°) + \sin 5\omega t\}$ A flows through a circuit element and gives a voltage drop across the element of $v = \{141 \sin \omega t + 11 \sin (3\omega t + 30°)\}$ V. Determine the average power delivered to the element. [*Ans.* 710 W.]

9. A voltage $v = \{156 \sin(\omega t + 30°) + 50 \sin (3\omega t - 60°) + 2 \sin (5\omega t + 45°)\}$ V applied to a certain circuit produces a current $i = \{31{\cdot}1 \sin (\omega t + 25°) + 5 \sin 5\omega t\}$ A.

Find the r.m.s. values of voltage and current, the power supplied and the power-factor. [*Ans.* 116 V, 22·3 A, 2,420 W, 0·94.]

10. A voltage which can be represented by the expression $v = \{200 \cos 314t - 40 \sin 628t\}$ V is connected to a circuit consisting of a

20 Ω resistor in series with a 100 μF capacitor. Derive the expression for the steady-state current and determine its r.m.s. value.

[*Ans.* {5·33 cos (314t + 57° 48′) − 1·565 sin (628t + 38° 33′)} A; 3·94 A.]

11. A current represented by the expression $i = \{5 \sin 105t + 2 \sin (315t + 30°)\}$ A is flowing in a circuit consisting of a 60 Ω resistor in series with a 0·9 H inductor and a 100 μF capacitor. Derive an expression for the voltage across the circuit as a function of time and calculate the total power dissipated. [S.U.]

[*Ans.* {300 sin (105t − 40′) + 516 sin (315t + 106° 36′)} V; 870 W.]

12. A voltage represented by the expression $v = \{100 \sin 314t - 25 \sin (628t - 60°)\}$ V is connected to a circuit consisting of a 20 Ω resistor in series with a 0·1 H inductor and a 40 μF capacitor. Obtain an expression for the steady-state current flowing in the circuit and find its r.m.s. value. [S.U.]

[*Ans.* {1·915 sin (314t + 67·5°) + 0·82 cos (628t − 19° 6′)} A; 1·47 A.]

13. A circuit consisting of a 100 μF capacitor in series with a 20 Ω resistor is supplied with a voltage whose instantaneous value is {100 sin 314t − 50 cos 942t} V. Derive an expression for the steady-state instantaneous current and determine its r.m.s. value and the total power. [S.U.]

[*Ans.* {2·66 sin (314t + 57° 50′) − 2·21 cos (942t + 27° 55′)} A; 2·445 A; 120 W.]

14. A circuit consisting of a 10 Ω resistor in series with a 0·015 H inductor, carries a current represented by $i = (10 \sin 314t + 5 \cos 942t)$ A. Determine the expression for the voltage across the circuit and calculate its r.m.s. value and the power-factor. What is the total power absorbed? [S.U.]

[*Ans.* {110·5 sin (314t + 25° 13′) + 86·5 cos (942t + 54° 39′)} V; 99 V; 0·8; 625 W.]

15. A circuit consisting of a 200 μF capacitor in series with a 7 Ω resistor is supplied with a voltage whose instantaneous value is given by {200 sin 314t + 20 sin (942t − 90°)} V.

Derive an expression for the current in the circuit and evaluate the total r.m.s. current, the total power and the power-factor. [S.U.]

[*Ans.* {11·5 sin (314t + 66° 14′) + 2·28 sin (942t − 52° 57′)} A; 8·3 A; 483 W; 0·41.]

16. A 10 Ω resistor is connected across a source of voltage $v = \{10 + 20 \sin 250t + 15 \sin (500t + 30°)\}$ V. Calculate the average current, the r.m.s. current and the total power absorbed.

[*Ans.* 1 A; 2·03 A; 41·2 W.]

17. Determine the sum and difference of the following two non-sinusoidal current waves:

$$i_1 = \{10 \sin \omega t + 5 \sin (3\omega t - 30°) - 3 \sin (5\omega t + 60°)\} \text{ A}$$
$$i_2 = \{20 \sin (\omega t - 30°) + 10 \sin (5\omega t + 45°)\} \text{ A.}$$

[*Ans.* {29·1 sin (ωt − 21·5°) + 5 sin (3ωt − 30°) + 7·2 sin (5ωt + 38·7°)} A; {12·4 sin (ωt + 126·3°) + 5 sin (3ωt − 30°) + 12·9 sin (5ωt − 131·5°)} A.]

CHAPTER 11

UNBALANCED POLYPHASE CIRCUITS

Introduction

In polyphase circuits with balanced impedances to which balanced polyphase voltages are applied, the voltage and current magnitudes and the phase-angles between them are the same for each phase. It is therefore only necessary to analyze one of the phase circuits. When the impedances or the voltages, or both, are not symmetrical, however, the whole circuit must be analyzed. (In some cases the use of symmetrical components, which are briefly dealt with later, enables the calculation to be simplified.)

Attention is confined here to three-phase circuits, in which unbalance, or disymmetry, means that the three line voltages or currents, and the three phase voltages or currents are not equal in magnitude, or are not displaced from one another by 120°. Unbalanced currents are necessarily present in many distribution circuits where single-phase loads are supplied, although these are distributed between the phases to equalize the loads at the substations as far as possible. Heavy unbalanced currents may also arise due to system faults, when short-circuits occur between two phases or between one phase and earth. Such unbalanced currents give rise to unbalanced voltages because of the unequal line impedance voltage drops.

The behaviour of polyphase machines under unbalanced conditions is much more complex than under balanced conditions and, in fact, symmetrical components were first devised by Fortesque * as an aid to the analysis of machines under unbalanced conditions. The method is now widely used in the study of fault conditions on networks.†

Simple static unbalanced three-phase circuits

The currents flowing through unbalanced polyphase impedances, connected either in star or delta with known applied voltages, may be calculated by the application of some of the circuit laws already given in Chapters 2 and 7 in terms of complex quantities. For example, consider the unbalanced delta-connected load shown in Fig. 11.1 (*a*) to which a balanced set of three-phase voltages of r.m.s. line value 400 V is applied. It is necessary in unbalanced-circuit problems to specify carefully the

* C. L. Fortesque, " Method of Symmetrical Co-ordinates Applied to the Solution of Polyphase Networks ", *Trans. American I.E.E.*, **37**, p. 1027 (1918).

† E. Clarke, *Circuit Analysis of A.C. Power Systems*, Vols. I and II (John Wiley, 1948 and 1950).

'phase-sequence' of voltages and currents. For the set of line voltages whose vectors are shown as 'positive phase-sequence' in Fig. 11.1 (*b*) the phase-sequence, or order in which the voltages attain their maximum value, is V_{AB}, V_{BC}, V_{CA}. A set of voltages of opposite or 'negative-phase-sequence' is such that the voltages attain their maximum values in the order V_{AB}, V_{CA}, V_{BC} (see Fig. 11.1 (*c*)).

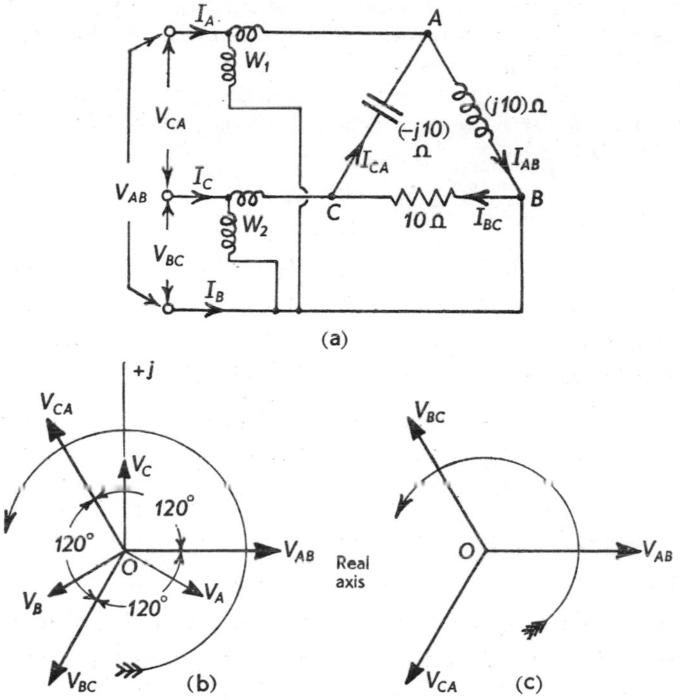

FIG. 11.1

To save unnecessary arithmetic the vector $\mathbf{V_{AB}}$ is taken as lying along the real axis in the complex plane. Then, considering the positive phase-sequence system of Fig. 11.1 (*b*), $\mathbf{V_{CA}} = \{\exp(j2\pi/3)\}\mathbf{V_{AB}} = (-1/2 + j\sqrt{3}/2)\mathbf{V_{AB}}$ and $\mathbf{V_{BC}} = \{\exp(j4\pi/3)\}\mathbf{V_{AB}} = \{\exp(j2\pi/3)\}^2\mathbf{V_{AB}} = \{\exp(-j2\pi/3)\}\mathbf{V_{AB}} = (-1/2 - j\sqrt{3}/2)\mathbf{V_{AB}}$.

It is convenient here to define the '120° operator' as:

$$a = \exp(j2\pi/3) = (-1/2 + j\sqrt{3}/2)$$

This complex operator, *a*, when multiplied by a vector, turns the latter through 120° in a counter-clockwise direction. The above expressions for $\mathbf{V_{CA}}$ and $\mathbf{V_{BC}}$ therefore become

$$\mathbf{V_{CA}} = a\mathbf{V_{AB}},\ \mathbf{V_{BC}} = a^2\mathbf{V_{AB}}.$$

Also, since $\mathbf{V_{AB}} = a\mathbf{V_{BC}}$, $a^3 = 1$ and because the vector sum of the three vectors is zero $(1 + a + a^2) = 0$.

The phase-to-neutral voltages, $\mathbf{V_A}$, $\mathbf{V_B}$ and $\mathbf{V_C}$ are as shown in Fig. 11.1 (*b*), the relations being $\mathbf{V_{AB}} = (\mathbf{V_A} - \mathbf{V_B})$, $\mathbf{V_{BC}} = (\mathbf{V_B} - \mathbf{V_C})$ and $\mathbf{V_{CA}} = (\mathbf{V_C} - \mathbf{V_A})$. It should be noted that the phase-sequence of the phase-to-neutral voltages is $\mathbf{V_A}$, $\mathbf{V_B}$, $\mathbf{V_C}$.

For the negative phase-sequence system $\mathbf{V_{BC}} = a\mathbf{V_{AB}}$ and $\mathbf{V_{CA}} = a^2\mathbf{V_{AB}}$ and the phase-to-neutral voltages in order of phase-sequence are now $\mathbf{V_A}$, $\mathbf{V_C}$, $\mathbf{V_B}$.

With the positive phase-sequence voltages applied to the circuit of Fig. 11.1 (*a*), the following vector equations may be obtained using Kirchhoff's first law:

$$\mathbf{I_A} + \mathbf{I_B} + \mathbf{I_C} = 0 \quad \ldots \quad (11.1)$$

$$\mathbf{I_A} = \mathbf{I_{AB}} - \mathbf{I_{CA}} \quad \ldots \quad (11.2)$$

$$\mathbf{I_B} = \mathbf{I_{BC}} - \mathbf{I_{AB}} \quad \ldots \quad (11.3)$$

and

$$\mathbf{I_C} = \mathbf{I_{CA}} - \mathbf{I_{BC}} \quad \ldots \quad (11.4)$$

[Note how any one equation of the last three may be derived from another by transposing suffixes in cyclic order *A*, *B*, *C*.]

Now

$$\mathbf{I_{AB}} = \mathbf{V_{AB}}/(j10) = -j\mathbf{V_{AB}}/10 \quad \ldots \quad (11.5)$$

$$\mathbf{I_{BC}} = \mathbf{V_{BC}}/10 = a^2\mathbf{V_{AB}}/10 \quad \ldots \quad (11.6)$$

and

$$\mathbf{I_{CA}} = \mathbf{V_{CA}}/(-j10) = +ja\mathbf{V_{AB}}/10 \quad \ldots \quad (11.7)$$

Taking $\mathbf{V_{AB}} = (400 + j0)$ as suggested:

$$\mathbf{I_{AB}} = -j400/10 = -j40, \text{ so } I_{AB} = 40 \text{ A}$$

$$\mathbf{I_{BC}} = (-1/2 - j\sqrt{3}/2)40 = (-20 - j20\sqrt{3}), \text{ so } I_{BC} = 40 \text{ A}$$

$$\mathbf{I_{CA}} = j(-1/2 + j\sqrt{3}/2)40 = (-j20 - 20\sqrt{3}), \text{ so } I_{CA} = 40 \text{ A}$$

Thus,

$$\mathbf{I_A} = -j20 + 20\sqrt{3}, \text{ so } I_A = 40 \text{ A}$$

$$\mathbf{I_B} = -20 + j(40 - 20\sqrt{3}) = (-20 + j5{\cdot}4), \text{ so } I_B = 20{\cdot}7 \text{ A}$$

and

$$\mathbf{I_C} = -20(\sqrt{3} - 1) + j20(\sqrt{3} - 1), \text{ so } I_C = 20{\cdot}7 \text{ A.}$$

The above quantities can also easily be found graphically, as illustrated in Fig. 11.2.

With negative phase-sequence voltages applied to the same circuit, equations (11.1) to (11.5) still hold but now

$$\mathbf{I_{BC}} = \mathbf{V_{BC}}/10 = a\mathbf{V_{AB}}/10 \quad \ldots \quad (11.8)$$

and

$$\mathbf{I_{CA}} = \mathbf{V_{CA}}/(-j10) = ja^2\mathbf{V_{AB}}/10 \quad \ldots \quad (11.9)$$

Thus, $\mathbf{I_{AB}} = -j40$ as before

$$\mathbf{I_{BC}} = (-1/2 + j\sqrt{3}/2)40 = -20 + j20\sqrt{3}$$

$$\mathbf{I_{CA}} = j(-1/2 - j\sqrt{3}/2)40 = -j20 + 20\sqrt{3}$$

$$\mathbf{I_A} = -j20 - 20\sqrt{3},\ \text{so } I_A = 40 \text{ A}$$

$$\mathbf{I_B} = -20 + j(40 + 20\sqrt{3}),\ \text{so } I_B = 77{\cdot}2 \text{ A}$$

and $\mathbf{I_C} = 20(\sqrt{3} + 1) - j20(\sqrt{3} + 1)$, so $I_C = 77{\cdot}2$ A.

It is left to the reader to solve this case graphically.

EXAMPLE. Determine the two wattmeter readings in the circuit of Fig. 11.1 (*a*) and the total power supplied, remembering that the

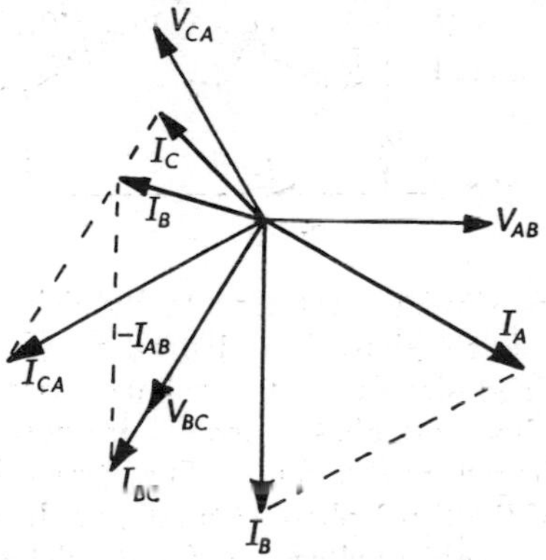

FIG. 11.2

balanced set of three-phase voltages applied have an r.m.s. line value of 400 V. Assume the phase-sequence is positive.

Solution. Using the information derived in the above analysis and referring to Fig. 11.2:

Wattmeter W_1 reads

$$I_A V_{AB} \cos \phi_{AB} = \underline{13{,}856 \text{ W}}$$

Wattmeter W_2 reads

$$I_C V_{CB} \cos \phi_{BC} = \underline{2{,}130 \text{ W}}$$

Alternatively, W_1 reads

$$\mathscr{R}[\mathbf{V_{AB}} \,.\, \mathbf{I_A}^*] = \mathscr{R}[400\{j20 + 20\sqrt{3}\}] = \underline{13{,}856 \text{ W}}$$

and W_2 reads

$$\mathscr{R}[\mathbf{V_{CB}} \,.\, \mathbf{I_C}^*] = \mathscr{R}[(1/2 + j\sqrt{3}/2)(-14{\cdot}64 - j14{\cdot}64)400]$$
$$= \underline{2{,}130 \text{ W}}$$

The total power $= (13{,}856 + 2{,}130)$ W
$= 15{,}986$ W
$= \underline{I_{BC}{}^2 10 \text{ W}}.$

An unbalanced star-connected set of impedances, as shown in Fig. 11.3, supplied from a balanced three-phase supply, *with a neutral*

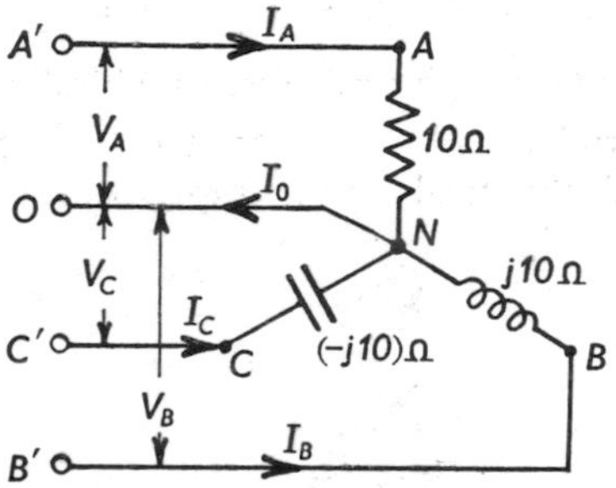

FIG. 11.3

connection, requires similar treatment to the delta-connected system described above. Each phase is independent of the others and its current is determined simply by the voltage across it divided by its impedance. The line and phase currents are now the same, but the line and phase voltages are different. The current in the neutral wire is the *vector sum* of the three phase currents, *i.e.* $\mathbf{I_O} = \mathbf{I_A} + \mathbf{I_B} + \mathbf{I_C}$.

Taking the same supply voltages as for the delta-connected system of Fig. 11.1 and considering positive phase-sequence with V_A as the reference voltage,

$$\mathbf{V_A} = (400/\sqrt{3})(1 + j0) = 231 \text{ V}$$
$$\mathbf{V_B} = a^2 . 231 = (-1/2 - j\sqrt{3}/2)231 \text{ V}$$
$$\mathbf{V_C} = a . 231 = (-1/2 + j\sqrt{3}/2)231 \text{ V}$$
$$\mathbf{I_A} = \mathbf{V_A}/10 = (23{\cdot}1 + j0) \text{ A, so } I_A = 23{\cdot}1 \text{ A}$$
$$\mathbf{I_B} = \mathbf{V_B}/(j10) = \{(+j/2 - \sqrt{3}/2)23{\cdot}1\}\text{A, so } I_B = 23{\cdot}1 \text{ A}$$
$$\mathbf{I_C} = \mathbf{V_C}/(-j10) = \{(-j/2 - \sqrt{3}/2)23{\cdot}1\}\text{A, so } I_C = 23{\cdot}1 \text{ A}$$
$$\therefore \quad \mathbf{I_O} = \mathbf{I_A} + \mathbf{I_B} + \mathbf{I_C} = (1 - \sqrt{3})23{\cdot}1 + j0 = -16{\cdot}9 \text{ A}.$$

A problem of this kind is easily solved graphically, the construction being as shown in Fig. 11.4.

For the opposite phase-sequence of voltages, the vector diagram is as shown in Fig. 11.5 and $I_O = 63$ A.

Unbalanced star-connected impedances without neutral connector

The problem of unbalanced star-connected impedances supplied from a balanced three-phase supply, but *without* a neutral connection is more complicated than the case just described. Consider, for example, the circuit of Fig. 11.3, but without the neutral connection, so that $\mathbf{I}_O = 0$ and $\mathbf{I}_A + \mathbf{I}_B + \mathbf{I}_C = 0$. Designating the line voltages $\mathbf{V}_{AB}$, $\mathbf{V}_{BC}$ and $\mathbf{V}_{CA}$, the following equations are then derived using Kirchhoff's second law:

$$\mathbf{V}_{AB} = 10\mathbf{I}_A - j10\mathbf{I}_B$$
$$\mathbf{V}_{BC} = j10\mathbf{I}_B - (-j10)\mathbf{I}_C = j10(\mathbf{I}_B + \mathbf{I}_C)$$
$$\mathbf{V}_{CA} = -j10\mathbf{I}_C - 10\mathbf{I}_A.$$

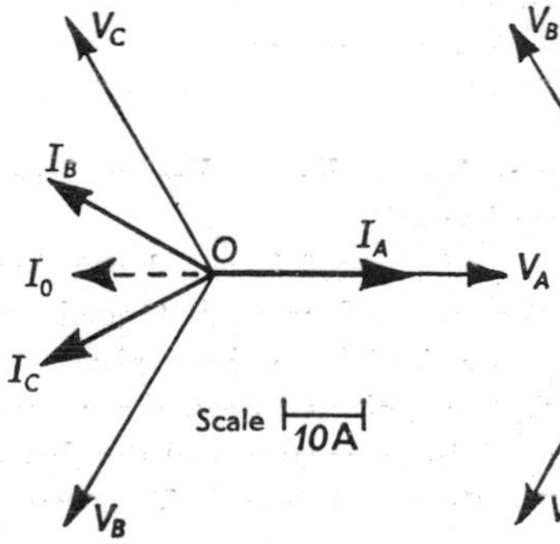

FIG. 11.4

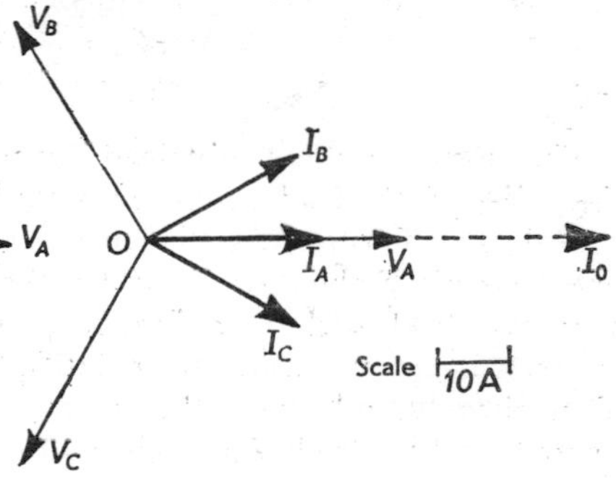

FIG. 11.5

Thus, taking $\mathbf{V}_{AB}$ as the reference voltage and with the positive phase-sequence ($\mathbf{V}_{AB}$, $\mathbf{V}_{BC}$, $\mathbf{V}_{CA}$),

$$400 = 10\mathbf{I}_A - j10\mathbf{I}_B \text{ or } \mathbf{I}_A - j\mathbf{I}_B = 40$$

$$400(-1/2 - j\sqrt{3}/2) = j10(\mathbf{I}_B + \mathbf{I}_C), \text{ or } \mathbf{I}_B + \mathbf{I}_C = 40(j/2 - \sqrt{3}/2)$$
$$400(-1/2 + j\sqrt{3}/2) = -j10\mathbf{I}_C - 10\mathbf{I}_A, \text{ or } \mathbf{I}_A + j\mathbf{I}_C = 40(1/2 - j\sqrt{3}/2)$$

Only two of these equations are really independent, as it will be found that the third can be derived from them. Therefore, consider the first two and the equation $\mathbf{I}_A + \mathbf{I}_B + \mathbf{I}_C = 0$, or $\mathbf{I}_C = -(\mathbf{I}_A + \mathbf{I}_B)$.

Eliminating $\mathbf{I}_C$ from the second equation,

$$\mathbf{I}_B - (\mathbf{I}_A + \mathbf{I}_B) = 40(j/2 - \sqrt{3}/2)$$

Using the first equation, $\mathbf{I}_A$ is found to be $20(\sqrt{3} - j)$, *i.e.* $I_A = 40$ A.

$$\therefore \quad j\mathbf{I}_B = \mathbf{I}_A - 40 = (20\sqrt{3} - 40) - 20j$$

i.e. $\quad \mathbf{I}_B = j(40 - 20\sqrt{3}) - 20$, so $I_B = 20{\cdot}7$ A

Thus, $\quad \mathbf{I}_C = -20\sqrt{3} + 20 - j(40 - 20\sqrt{3})$

$$= -20(\sqrt{3} - 1) + j20(\sqrt{3} - 1)$$

so $\quad I_C = 20{\cdot}7$ A.

The voltage of point A with respect to N, $\mathbf{V_{AN}}$ is $+10\mathbf{I_A} = +200(\sqrt{3}-j)$ and $|\mathbf{V_{AN}}| = 400$ V.

Similarly, $\mathbf{V_{BN}} = j10\mathbf{I_B} = -j200 - (400 - 200\sqrt{3})$ and $|\mathbf{V_{BN}}| = 270$ V.

$$\mathbf{V_{CN}} = -j10\mathbf{I_C} = -j10\{-20(\sqrt{3}-1) + j20(\sqrt{3}-1)\}$$
$$= 200(\sqrt{3}-1)(1+j) \text{ and } |\mathbf{V_{CN}}| = 207 \text{ V}.$$

The voltage between point N and the neutral point of the supply, $\mathbf{V_{NO}}$, is

$$\mathbf{V_{NO}} = \mathbf{V_{AO}} - \mathbf{V_{AN}} = (400/\sqrt{3})(\sqrt{3}/2 - j/2) - 200(\sqrt{3}-j)$$
$$= 200(\sqrt{3}-1)(-1 + j/\sqrt{3})$$

and $$|\mathbf{V_{NO}}| = 168{\cdot}5 \text{ V}.$$

The same result is obtained from $\mathbf{V_{NO}} = \mathbf{V_{BO}} - \mathbf{V_{BN}}$ or $\mathbf{V_{NO}} = \mathbf{V_{CO}} - \mathbf{V_{CN}}$, as the reader may check for himself.

Millman's Theorem (see Chapter 7) is often useful for solving three-phase circuit problems. Consider the case of an unbalanced star-connected load, such as in Fig. 11.3, supplied by a three-phase star-connected generator, with star-point O, but *without a neutral connection.* The voltage drop between the neutral of the generator and the floating neutral N of the load, $\mathbf{V_{ON}}$ is given directly by Millman's Theorem as:

$$\mathbf{V_{ON}} = (\mathbf{V_A Y_A} + \mathbf{V_B Y_B} + \mathbf{V_C Y_C})/(\mathbf{Y_A} + \mathbf{Y_B} + \mathbf{Y_C})$$

where $\mathbf{Y_A}$, $\mathbf{Y_B}$ and $\mathbf{Y_C}$ are the admittances between points A and N, B and N and C and N respectively. The currents are then calculated from

$$\mathbf{I_A} = (\mathbf{V_A} - \mathbf{V_{ON}})\mathbf{Y_A}$$
$$\mathbf{I_B} = (\mathbf{V_B} - \mathbf{V_{ON}})\mathbf{Y_B}$$

and $$\mathbf{I_C} = (\mathbf{V_C} - \mathbf{V_{ON}})\mathbf{Y_C}$$

These currents can be found in a somewhat simpler fashion if the generator is considered to be delta-connected. The voltage drop across any one of the load impedances can be found directly by applying the Theorem.

Special cases of Millman's Theorem applied to three-phase circuits can be found in the literature,* but the method is not as widely used as it should be considering that it is the simplest way of solving unbalanced three-phase star-connected load problems. It should also be noted that the expressions just given for $\mathbf{V_{ON}}$, $\mathbf{I_A}$, $\mathbf{I_B}$ and $\mathbf{I_C}$ are valid even if the applied voltages are unbalanced, or if the generators are not the component parts of a three-phase system.

* See, for example, H. Sherman, "Letter to the Editor", *Electrical Engng.*, **59**, p. 166 (1940), and V. G. Smith, "Letter to the Editor", *ibid.*, **59**, p. 166 (1940).

Two loads from one supply

Where two loads are taken from the same supply, either or both being unbalanced, the most straightforward method is to calculate the currents for each circuit separately, in vector or complex form, and add the results to determine the total current. If both loads are mesh-connected the impedances in parallel between each pair of lines may be combined to give a single impedance, so that the two meshes are replaced by a single mesh. If both sets of impedances are connected in star, *without a neutral connection from the supply*, the individual phases *cannot* be simply combined because the two star points are *not* necessarily at the same potential. Two methods of calculation are available in this case.

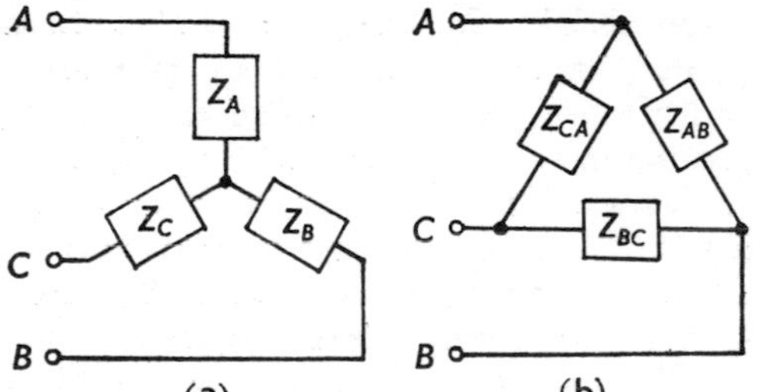

FIG. 11.6

Either the individual currents are calculated for each star-connected load and combined to give total line currents, or each star-connected set of impedances may be transformed into the equivalent delta set, the two being then combined into a single delta. The formulae for delta–star and star–delta transformations for resistor networks are given in Chapter 2 and the same formulae, with resistances replaced by complex impedances, are used in a.c. circuits. These formulae are listed below (see Fig. 11.6).

$$\mathbf{Z}_A = (\mathbf{Z}_{AB}\mathbf{Z}_{CA})/(\mathbf{Z}_{AB} + \mathbf{Z}_{BC} + \mathbf{Z}_{CA})$$
$$\mathbf{Z}_B = (\mathbf{Z}_{BC}\mathbf{Z}_{AB})/(\mathbf{Z}_{AB} + \mathbf{Z}_{BC} + \mathbf{Z}_{CA})$$
$$\mathbf{Z}_C = (\mathbf{Z}_{CA}\mathbf{Z}_{BC})/(\mathbf{Z}_{AB} + \mathbf{Z}_{BC} + \mathbf{Z}_{CA})$$
$$\mathbf{Z}_{AB} = \mathbf{Z}_A\mathbf{Z}_B(1/\mathbf{Z}_A + 1/\mathbf{Z}_B + 1/\mathbf{Z}_C)$$
$$\mathbf{Z}_{BC} = \mathbf{Z}_B\mathbf{Z}_C(1/\mathbf{Z}_A + 1/\mathbf{Z}_B + 1/\mathbf{Z}_C)$$
$$\mathbf{Z}_{CA} = \mathbf{Z}_C\mathbf{Z}_A(1/\mathbf{Z}_A + 1/\mathbf{Z}_B + 1/\mathbf{Z}_C)$$

Although the use of these transformations is rarely justified for problems where unbalanced loads are supplied from sources through lines of negligible impedance, they may be useful when line impedance has to be taken into account. For instance, if a delta-connected set of unequal impedances is supplied through lines of appreciable impedance, the delta may be transformed to the equivalent star so that the impedance of a line and a phase are then simply in series.

Line impedances with unbalanced currents

In power-circuit problems and particularly during fault conditions, the line impedances may be of importance. Usually the three 'line' conductors are symmetrically disposed with respect to each other and with respect to the neutral conductor, if present. In some overhead conductor lines the conductors are not symmetrically disposed, but are transposed at intervals so that each conductor occupies each position in turn, thus equalizing the impedances.

Consider a symmetrically-arranged set of three-phase conductors A, B, C, *without neutral.* The resistances will be the same for each line, naturally, but, under unbalanced-load conditions, it is not so obvious that the effective reactances will be the same. If the instantaneous currents flowing towards the load are i_A, i_B and i_C, then since the circuit is a three-wire one, $i_A + i_B + i_C = 0$. The instantaneous voltage induced in A due to the magnetic fields is $v = -L_A(Di_A) - M_{AB}(Di_B) - M_{AC}(Di_C)$, where L_A, M_{AB} and M_{AC} are constant and $D = d/dt$. With a symmetrical disposition, $M_{AB} = M_{AC} = M$, say, so that $v = -L_A(Di_A) - MD(i_C + i_B) = -(L_A - M)Di_A$.

Thus, the effective inductance of line A is $(L_A - M)$, which is independent of whether the current is balanced or not, provided $i_A + i_B + i_C = 0$. The same argument holds for the other lines and since $L_A = L_B = L_C$, the effective inductances under unbalanced conditions (with no neutral current) are the same as for balanced conditions.

When a neutral conductor is present and carries a finite current, the above is not true. Let the instantaneous currents be i_A, i_B and i_C as before and the neutral current flowing *away* from the load be i_N. Then $i_N = i_A + i_B + i_C$.

The voltage now induced in line A is

$$v_A = -L_A Di_A - MD(i_B + i_C) + M_0 Di_N$$

where M_0 is the mutual inductance between a line and the neutral conductor. This equation indicates that there is now no simple effective line inductance which will account for the self and mutual effects. (As shown later, this difficulty is eased by the use of symmetrical components.)

EXAMPLE. Determine the line currents for the circuit of Fig. 11.7 with the applied voltages: $\mathbf{V_{AB}} = 400$ V, $\mathbf{V_{BC}} = a^2 400$ V and $\mathbf{V_{CA}} = a400$ V.

Solution. In order to determine the currents by the normal circuit laws, *e.g.* Kirchhoff's Laws, six simultaneous equations must be solved for the six currents in each of the phases. This is a tedious process. The alternative method is to transform each of the star-connected loads

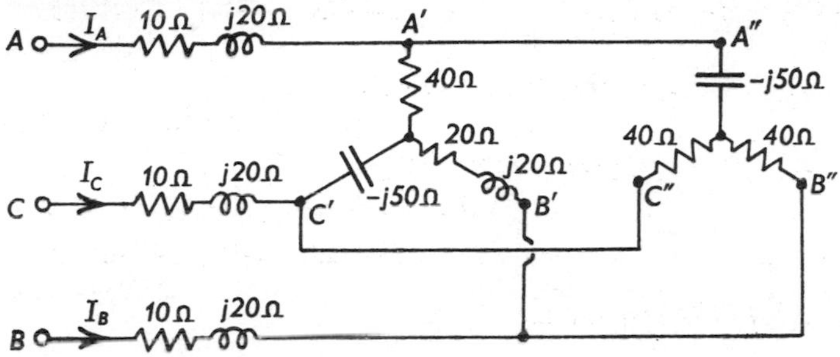

FIG. 11.7

into deltas, combine these into one delta, retransform into a single star and then solve as shown previously. Thus, for the A', B', C' impedances,

$$1/\mathbf{Z}_A' + 1/\mathbf{Z}_B' + 1/\mathbf{Z}_C' = 1/40 + (1 - j)/40 + j/50 = (10 - j)/200 \text{ mho.}$$

$$\mathbf{Z}_{A'B'} = 40(20 + j20)(10 - j)/200 = 4(11 + j9)\ \Omega$$
$$\mathbf{Z}_{B'C'} = (20 + j20)(-j50)(10 - j)/200 = 5(9 - j11)\ \Omega$$
$$\mathbf{Z}'_{C'A'} = (-j50)(40)(10 - j)/200 = -10(1 + j10)\ \Omega$$

For the A'', B'', C'' impedances,

$$1/\mathbf{Z}_A'' + 1/\mathbf{Z}_B'' + 1/\mathbf{Z}_C'' = j/50 + 1/40 + 1/40 = (5 + j2)/100 \text{ mho.}$$

$$\mathbf{Z}_{A''B''} = (-j50)(40)(5 + j2)/100 = 20(2 - j5)\ \Omega$$
$$\mathbf{Z}_{B''C''} = (40)(40)(5 + j2)/100 = 16(5 + j2)\ \Omega$$
$$\mathbf{Z}_{C''A''} = (40)(-j50)(5 + j2)/100 = 20(2 - j5)\ \Omega$$

Combining the impedances between lines,

$$\mathbf{Z}_{ab} = \mathbf{Z}_{A'B'}\mathbf{Z}_{A''B''}/(\mathbf{Z}_{A'B'} + \mathbf{Z}_{A''B''}) = (64{\cdot}2 + j17{\cdot}4)\ \Omega$$
$$\mathbf{Z}_{bc} = (38{\cdot}4 - j24{\cdot}4)\ \Omega$$
$$\mathbf{Z}_{ca} = (17{\cdot}3 + j19{\cdot}8)\ \Omega$$

The circuit now consists of these three impedances connected in delta across the points A', B', C'. The equations are

$$\mathbf{V}_{AB} = (10 + j20)\mathbf{I}_A + (64{\cdot}2 + j17{\cdot}4)\mathbf{I}_{AB} - (10 + j20)\mathbf{I}_B$$

or $$400 = (10 + j20)(\mathbf{I}_{AB} - \mathbf{I}_{CA}) + (64{\cdot}2 + j17{\cdot}4)\mathbf{I}_{AB} - (10 + j20)(\mathbf{I}_{BC} - \mathbf{I}_{AB})$$

i.e. $$400 = (84{\cdot}2 + j57{\cdot}4)\mathbf{I}_{AB} - (10 + j20)\mathbf{I}_{BC} - (10 + j20)\mathbf{I}_{CA}$$

$$a^2\mathbf{V}_{AB} = \mathbf{V}_{BC} = (10 + j20)\mathbf{I}_B + (38{\cdot}4 - j24{\cdot}4)\mathbf{I}_{BC} - (10 + j20)\mathbf{I}_C$$

$$\text{or } 400(-1/2 - j\sqrt{3}/2) = (10 + j20)(\mathbf{I}_{BC} - \mathbf{I}_{AB}) + (38{\cdot}4 - j24{\cdot}4)\mathbf{I}_{BC} - (10 + j20)(\mathbf{I}_{CA} - \mathbf{I}_{BC})$$

$$\text{i.e. } 400(-1/2 - j\sqrt{3}/2) = -(10 + j20)\mathbf{I}_{AB} + (58{\cdot}4 - j64{\cdot}4)\mathbf{I}_{BC} - (10 + j20)\mathbf{I}_{CA}$$

$$a\mathbf{V}_{AB} = \mathbf{V}_{CA} = (10 + j20)\mathbf{I}_C + (17{\cdot}3 + j19{\cdot}8)\mathbf{I}_{CA} - (10 + j20)\mathbf{I}_A$$

$$\text{or } 400(-1/2 + j\sqrt{3}/2) = (10 + j20)(\mathbf{I}_{CA} - \mathbf{I}_{BC}) + (17{\cdot}3 + j19{\cdot}8)\mathbf{I}_{CA} - (10 + j20)(\mathbf{I}_{AB} - \mathbf{I}_{CA})$$

$$= -(10 + j20)\mathbf{I}_{AB} - (10 + j20)\mathbf{I}_{BC} + (37{\cdot}3 + j59{\cdot}8)\mathbf{I}_{CA}$$

From the above equations,

$$\mathbf{I}_{AB} = (3{\cdot}21 - j2{\cdot}16)\text{ A}$$
$$\mathbf{I}_{BC} = (0{\cdot}67 - j3{\cdot}96)\text{ A}$$
$$\mathbf{I}_{CA} = (-0{\cdot}72 + j4{\cdot}14)\text{ A}$$
$$\therefore\ \mathbf{I}_A = \mathbf{I}_{AB} - \mathbf{I}_{CA} = (3{\cdot}93 - j6{\cdot}30)\text{ A}$$
$$\mathbf{I}_B = \mathbf{I}_{BC} - \mathbf{I}_{AB} = (-2{\cdot}54 - j1{\cdot}80)\text{ A}$$
$$\mathbf{I}_C = \mathbf{I}_{CA} - \mathbf{I}_{BC} = (-1{\cdot}39 + j8{\cdot}10)\text{ A}$$

If the individual currents in the original load impedances in the above example had been required, probably the simplest procedure would have been first to calculate the voltages across the loads. Thus, $\mathbf{V}_{A'B'} = \mathbf{V}_{AB} - \mathbf{I}_A(10 + j20) + \mathbf{I}_B(10 + j20)$, and so on. The currents in the individual impedances of the *mesh* equivalents of the original load, $\mathbf{I}_{A'B'}$, etc. can then readily be determined, from which the line currents $\mathbf{I}_A'$, etc. for each load may be calculated. These are then the phase currents of the original loads. Only one such set of currents needs to be evaluated by this procedure, for $\mathbf{I}_A'' = \mathbf{I}_A - \mathbf{I}_A'$, etc.

Problems with *unbalanced* voltages applied, provided the impedances remain the same as under balanced conditions, may be solved in a similar fashion. Alternatively, the symmetrical components of the voltages may be calculated, and used separately to give components of current. This is of little advantage if the impedances are unbalanced.

Symmetrical components

The Principle of Superposition states that for a linear circuit, or circuits, the currents produced by each component of the resultant voltage may be added to give the total current. Thus, if an unsymmetrical set of polyphase voltages can be resolved into a number of symmetrical sets, the currents produced by each of the latter may be added to give the resultant currents.

The *symmetrical components* of a set of three-phase voltages (or currents) are defined as:

(1) The positive-sequence components $\mathbf{V}_{A1}$, $\mathbf{V}_{B1}$, $\mathbf{V}_{C1}$ which form a balanced three-phase set of phase-sequence A, B, C.

(2) The negative-sequence components $\mathbf{V}_{A2}$, $\mathbf{V}_{B2}$, $\mathbf{V}_{C2}$ which also form a balanced three-phase set of phase-sequence A, C, B.

(3) The zero-sequence components $\mathbf{V}_{AO}$, $\mathbf{V}_{BO}$, $\mathbf{V}_{CO}$, which are equal and in phase, *i.e.* $\mathbf{V}_{AO} = \mathbf{V}_{BO} = \mathbf{V}_{CO} = \mathbf{V}_O$.

Then,

$$\mathbf{V}_A = \mathbf{V}_{A1} + \mathbf{V}_{A2} + \mathbf{V}_{AO} \quad . \quad . \quad . \quad (11.10)$$

$$\mathbf{V}_B = \mathbf{V}_{B1} + \mathbf{V}_{B2} + \mathbf{V}_{BO} \quad . \quad . \quad . \quad (11.11)$$

$$\mathbf{V}_C = \mathbf{V}_{C1} + \mathbf{V}_{C2} + \mathbf{V}_{CO} \quad . \quad . \quad . \quad (11.12)$$

From the given definitions,

$$\mathbf{V}_{B1} = a^2\mathbf{V}_{A1}, \ \mathbf{V}_{C1} = a\mathbf{V}_{A1}$$

$$\mathbf{V}_{B2} = a\mathbf{V}_{A2}, \ \mathbf{V}_{C2} = a^2\mathbf{V}_{A2}$$

where, as before, $a = -1/2 + j\sqrt{3}/2$ and $a^2 = -1/2 - j\sqrt{3}/2$.

For simplicity, writing $\mathbf{V}_{A1} = \mathbf{V}_1$ and $\mathbf{V}_{A2} = \mathbf{V}_2$,

$$\mathbf{V}_A = \mathbf{V}_1 + \mathbf{V}_2 + \mathbf{V}_O \quad . \quad . \quad . \quad . \quad (11.13)$$

$$\mathbf{V}_B = a^2\mathbf{V}_1 + a\mathbf{V}_2 + \mathbf{V}_O \quad . \quad . \quad . \quad (11.14)$$

$$\mathbf{V}_C = a\mathbf{V}_1 + a^2\mathbf{V}_2 + \mathbf{V}_O \quad . \quad . \quad . \quad (11.15)$$

Adding (11.13), (11.14) and (11.15),

$$(\mathbf{V}_A + \mathbf{V}_B + \mathbf{V}_C) = \mathbf{V}_1(1 + a + a^2) + \mathbf{V}_2(1 + a + a^2) + 3\mathbf{V}_O$$

and since $1 + a + a^2 = 0$

$$\mathbf{V}_O = (\mathbf{V}_A + \mathbf{V}_B + \mathbf{V}_C)/3 \quad . \quad . \quad . \quad (11.16)$$

Multiplying (11.14) by a and (11.15) by a^2,

$$a\mathbf{V}_B = a^3\mathbf{V}_1 + a^2\mathbf{V}_2 + a\mathbf{V}_O$$

$$a^2\mathbf{V}_C = a^3\mathbf{V}_1 + a^4\mathbf{V}_2 + a^2\mathbf{V}_O$$

and since $a^3 = 1$ and $a^4 = a$

$$a\mathbf{V}_B = \mathbf{V}_1 + a^2\mathbf{V}_2 + a\mathbf{V}_O \quad . \quad . \quad . \quad . \quad (11.17)$$

$$a^2\mathbf{V}_C = \mathbf{V}_1 + a\mathbf{V}_2 + a^2\mathbf{V}_O \quad . \quad . \quad . \quad . \quad (11.18)$$

Adding (11.13), (11.17) and (11.18),

$$\mathbf{V}_A + a\mathbf{V}_B + a^2\mathbf{V}_C = 3\mathbf{V}_1 + (1 + a + a^2)\mathbf{V}_2 + (1 + a + a^2)\mathbf{V}_O$$

or

$$\mathbf{V}_1 = (\mathbf{V}_A + a\mathbf{V}_B + a^2\mathbf{V}_C)/3 \quad . \quad . \quad . \quad . \quad (11.19)$$

Similarly, multiplying (11.15) by a and (11.14) by a^2 and adding to (11.13)

$$\mathbf{V}_2 = (\mathbf{V}_A + a^2\mathbf{V}_B + a\mathbf{V}_C)/3 \quad . \quad . \quad (11.20)$$

Since equations (11.16), (11.19) and (11.20) give unique values for $\mathbf{V}_O$, $\mathbf{V}_1$ and $\mathbf{V}_2$, it follows that *any* set of three-phase voltages or currents, balanced or not, can be resolved into symmetrical components as defined above (for a balanced set of positive phase-sequence $\mathbf{V}_0$ and $\mathbf{V}_2$ are zero).

Equations (11.16), (11.19) and (11.20) can be interpreted in a graphical resolution into symmetrical components. Equation (11.16) means that the vector sum of the voltages or currents is three times the zero-sequence component in each phase. Equation (11.19) shows that by adding the vector $\mathbf{V}_A$ to $\mathbf{V}_B$ advanced by 120° and to $\mathbf{V}_C$ advanced by 240°, three times the positive-sequence component is obtained. For equation (11.20) $\mathbf{V}_B$ is advanced by 240° and $\mathbf{V}_C$ by 120° and added to $\mathbf{V}_A$ to give $3\mathbf{V}_2$.

EXAMPLE. If $\mathbf{V}_A = 100 + j0$, $\mathbf{V}_B = -100 - j100$ and $\mathbf{V}_C = +j50$ determine the symmetrical components of voltage $\mathbf{V}_A$.

Solution.

$$\mathbf{V}_0 = -j50/3 = \underline{-j16 \cdot 67}$$

$$\mathbf{V}_1 = \{100 + (-1/2 + j\sqrt{3}/2)(-100 - j100) + (-1/2 - j\sqrt{3}/2)(j50)\}/3$$

$$= \underline{(93 \cdot 3 - j20 \cdot 5)}$$

$$\mathbf{V}_2 = \{100 + (-1/2 - j\sqrt{3}/2)(-100 - j100) + (-1/2 + j\sqrt{3}/2)(j50)\}/3$$

$$= \underline{6 \cdot 70 + j37 \cdot 19}$$

The components of voltage $\mathbf{V}_B$ can be found since they are $\mathbf{V}_0 + a^2\mathbf{V}_1 + a\mathbf{V}_2$ and of voltage $\mathbf{V}_C$ similarly are $\mathbf{V}_0 + a\mathbf{V}_1 + a^2\mathbf{V}_2$.

The graphical construction is shown in Fig. 11.8.

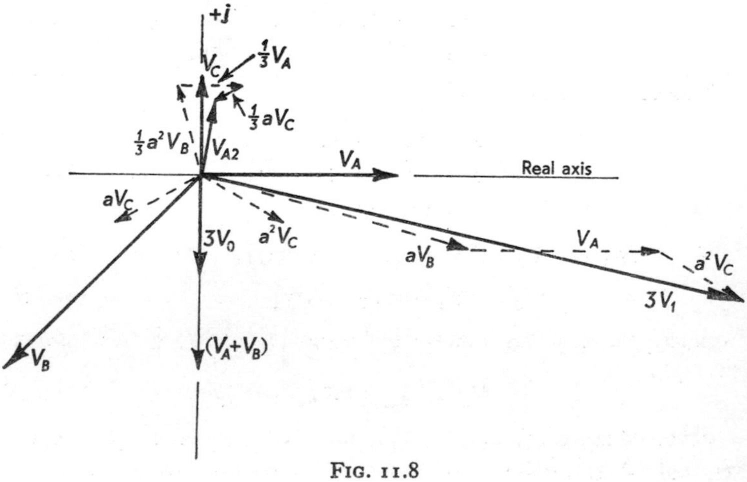

FIG. 11.8

The equations giving the relationships between total phase currents and the symmetrical components of these currents are of exactly the same form as those for voltages. Thus,

$$\begin{aligned} \mathbf{I_A} &= \mathbf{I_1} + \mathbf{I_2} + \mathbf{I_0} \\ \mathbf{I_B} &= a^2\mathbf{I_1} + a\mathbf{I_2} + \mathbf{I_0} \\ \mathbf{I_C} &= a\mathbf{I_1} + a^2\mathbf{I_2} + \mathbf{I_0} \\ \mathbf{I_0} &= (\mathbf{I_A} + \mathbf{I_B} + \mathbf{I_C})/3 \\ \mathbf{I_1} &= (\mathbf{I_A} + a\mathbf{I_B} + a^2\mathbf{I_C})/3 \\ \mathbf{I_2} &= (\mathbf{I_A} + a^2\mathbf{I_B} + a\mathbf{I_C})/3 \end{aligned}$$

The zero-sequence components $\mathbf{V_0}$ may be determined analytically or graphically and subtracted from the original voltages to give,

$$\mathbf{V_A}' = \mathbf{V_A} - \mathbf{V_0},\ \mathbf{V_B}' = \mathbf{V_B} - \mathbf{V_0},\ \mathbf{V_C}' = \mathbf{V_C} - \mathbf{V_0}.$$

The voltages $\mathbf{V_A}'$, $\mathbf{V_B}'$ and $\mathbf{V_C}'$ can then be analyzed as shown above into positive- and negative-sequence components.

Other methods of analysis may also be derived. For instance,

$$\mathbf{V_A}' = \mathbf{V_1} + \mathbf{V_2} \quad . \quad . \quad . \quad . \quad . \quad (11.21)$$

$$\mathbf{V_B}' = a^2\mathbf{V_1} + a\mathbf{V_2} \quad . \quad . \quad . \quad . \quad (11.22)$$

$$\mathbf{V_C}' = a\mathbf{V_1} + a^2\mathbf{V_2} \quad . \quad . \quad . \quad . \quad (11.23)$$

giving

$$a\mathbf{V_B}' = a^3\mathbf{V_1} + a^2\mathbf{V_2} = \mathbf{V_1} + a^2\mathbf{V_2}$$

Subtracting this from (11.23),

$$(\mathbf{V_C}' - a\mathbf{V_B}') = \mathbf{V_1}(a - 1) \quad . \quad . \quad . \quad . \quad . \quad . \quad . \quad (11.24)$$

or

$$(\mathbf{V_C}' - a\mathbf{V_B}') = \mathbf{V_1}(1/2 + j\sqrt{3}/2) = \mathbf{V_1}\underline{|60^\circ}.$$

Thus, for calculation when the complex expressions for $\mathbf{V_C}'$ and $\mathbf{V_B}'$ are known,

$$\begin{aligned} \mathbf{V_1} &= \{\mathbf{V_C}' - (-1/2 + j\sqrt{3}/2)\mathbf{V_B}'\}/(1/2 + j\sqrt{3}/2) \\ &= \mathbf{V_C}'(1/2 - j\sqrt{3}/2) - (1/2 + j\sqrt{3}/2)\mathbf{V_B}' \quad . \quad . \quad (11.25) \end{aligned}$$

Graphically, $\mathbf{V_B}'$ advanced by 120° is subtracted from $\mathbf{V_C}'$, the resultant then being retarded (moved clockwise) by 60° to give $\mathbf{V_1}$. Many graphical methods of analysis have been devised.*

Similarly, $\mathbf{V_2}$ may be determined by eliminating $\mathbf{V_1}$ from any pair of the three equations (11.21), (11.22), (11.23).

Three-phase line voltages

Even if the *phase* voltages of a three-phase system contain zero-sequence components, the *line* voltages do not. For if

$$\mathbf{V_A} = \mathbf{V_0} + \mathbf{V_1} + \mathbf{V_2}$$

$$\mathbf{V_B} = \mathbf{V_0} + a^2\mathbf{V_1} + a\mathbf{V_2}$$

and

$$\mathbf{V_C} = \mathbf{V_0} + a\mathbf{V_1} + a^2\mathbf{V_2}$$

* R. Neumann, *Symmetrical Component Analysis of Unsymmetrical Polyphase Systems* (Pitman, 1939).

$$\mathbf{V_{AB}} = \mathbf{V_A} - \mathbf{V_B} = \mathbf{V_1}(1 - a^2) + \mathbf{V_2}(1 - a)$$
$$\mathbf{V_{BC}} = \mathbf{V_B} - \mathbf{V_C} = \mathbf{V_1}(a^2 - a) + \mathbf{V_2}(a - a^2)$$
$$\mathbf{V_{CA}} = \mathbf{V_C} - \mathbf{V_A} = \mathbf{V_1}(a - 1) + \mathbf{V_2}(a^2 - 1)$$

Thus, in a three-wire system without neutral no zero-sequence voltages are applied to the load.

Three-phase line currents

For a three-wire system, the sum of the line currents $(\mathbf{I_A} + \mathbf{I_B} + \mathbf{I_C})$, is zero, so there is no zero-sequence component of line current. A neutral connection is essential if a zero-sequence current is to exist.

Single-phase currents

Important special cases are those with single-phase currents flowing between two lines, or between line and neutral.

For a single impedance connected between lines A and B,

$$\mathbf{I_A} = -\mathbf{I_B} \quad \text{and} \quad \mathbf{I_C} = 0.$$

$\mathbf{I_A} + \mathbf{I_B} + \mathbf{I_C} = 0$ so that $\mathbf{I_0}$, the current in the neutral wire, is zero.

$$\mathbf{I_1} = (\mathbf{I_A} + a\mathbf{I_B})/3 = \mathbf{I_A}(1 - a)/3 = \mathbf{I_A}(3/2 - j\sqrt{3}/2)/3$$
$$= (\mathbf{I_A}/\sqrt{3})\,\underline{|-30^\circ}$$
$$\mathbf{I_2} = (\mathbf{I_A} + a^2\mathbf{I_B})/3 = \mathbf{I}\ (3/2 + j\sqrt{3}/2)/3 = (\mathbf{I_A}/\sqrt{3})\,\underline{|+30^\circ}$$

For a single impedance between line A and neutral, $\mathbf{I_B} = \mathbf{I_C} = 0$.

$$\therefore \quad \mathbf{I_0} = \mathbf{I_A}/3$$
$$\mathbf{I_1} = \mathbf{I_A}/3$$
$$\mathbf{I_2} = \mathbf{I_A}/3$$
$$\mathbf{I_A} = \mathbf{I_0} + \mathbf{I_1} + \mathbf{I_2} = \mathbf{I_A}$$
$$\mathbf{I_B} = \mathbf{I_0} + a^2\mathbf{I_1} + a\mathbf{I_2} = \mathbf{I_A}(1 + a^2 + a)/3 = 0$$
$$\mathbf{I_C} = \mathbf{I_0} + a\mathbf{I_1} + a^2\mathbf{I_2} = \mathbf{I_A}(1 + a + a^2)/3 = 0$$

Note that the neutral current in a three-phase, four-wire system is $3\mathbf{I_0}$.

Symmetrical-component impedances of lines

It has been shown earlier that for a three-wire cable or transmission line with symmetrically-arranged conductors, that is, for a system in which no zero-sequence currents can flow, the effective inductance of each line is not dependent on whether the currents are balanced or not. This means that the *effective positive and negative-sequence reactances are the same.* However, with a neutral conductor, in which current flows, the effective inductance of the lines is of a more complicated nature, owing to the mutual inductances between line and neutral conductors. This means, in effect, that the zero-sequence inductance or reactance is not the same as the positive- or negative-sequence ones. If the positive-, negative- and zero-sequence components of current are considered separately, however, this difficulty is largely resolved.

Thus, for zero-sequence currents of i_O in each line, giving a neutral current of $3i_O$, the induced voltage in line A is $v_A = -L_A Di_O - 2MDi_O + 3M_O Di_O$ and the effective inductance of line A to zero-sequence currents is:

$$L_{AO} = (L_A + 2M - 3M_O)$$

The voltage induced in the neutral conductor itself is

$$\begin{aligned} v_N &= -L_N Di_N + 3M_O Di_O \\ &= -L_N Di_N + M_O Di_N \end{aligned}$$

where L_N is the self-inductance of the neutral conductor and $i_N = 3i_O$ is the neutral current.

Therefore, the effective zero-sequence inductance of the neutral wire is

$$L_{NO} = (L_N - M_O)$$

The reactances corresponding to these inductances can readily be measured for a cable or overhead line. The positive- and negative-sequence reactances are measured by connecting the three phase cores of the cable to a balanced three-phase supply of suitable voltage with the other ends short-circuited. Measurements of voltage, current and power enable the reactance and resistance to be calculated. The zero-sequence impedance is measured by connecting all three phase cores together at one end and supplying with single-phase voltage between these and the neutral core, all four cores being shorted at the far end.

Symmetrical-component power

The mean power in any three-phase circuit in terms of phase voltage and current vectors is given by

$$P = \mathscr{R}[\mathbf{V_A I_A}^* + \mathbf{V_B I_B}^* + \mathbf{V_C I_C}^*]$$

where $\mathbf{I_A}^*$, $\mathbf{I_B}^*$ and $\mathbf{I_C}^*$ are the conjugates of $\mathbf{I_A}$, $\mathbf{I_B}$ and $\mathbf{I_C}$ respectively.

In terms of the symmetrical components of voltage and current, the expression inside the brackets is

$$\begin{aligned} \sum \mathbf{VI}^* = (\mathbf{V_0} + \mathbf{V_1} + \mathbf{V_2})(\mathbf{I_0}^* + \mathbf{I_1}^* + \mathbf{I_2}^*) + \\ (\mathbf{V_0} + a^2\mathbf{V_1} + a\mathbf{V_2})\{\mathbf{I_0}^* + (a^2\mathbf{I_1})^* + (a\mathbf{I_2})^*\} \\ + (\mathbf{V_0} + a\mathbf{V_1} + a^2\mathbf{V_2})\{\mathbf{I_0}^* + (a\mathbf{I_1})^* + (a^2\mathbf{I_2})^*\} \end{aligned}$$

Since the conjugate of the product of two vectors is the product of the conjugates, and since $a^* = (a^2)$ and $(a^2)^* = a$

$$\begin{aligned}\sum \mathbf{VI}^* &= (\mathbf{V}_0 + \mathbf{V}_1 + \mathbf{V}_2)(\mathbf{I}_0^* + \mathbf{I}_1^* + \mathbf{I}_2^*) + \\ &\qquad (\mathbf{V}_0 + a^2\mathbf{V}_1 + a\mathbf{V}_2)(\mathbf{I}_0^* + a\mathbf{I}_1^* + a^2\mathbf{I}_2^*) \\ &\qquad\qquad + (\mathbf{V}_0 + a\mathbf{V}_1 + a^2\mathbf{V}_2)(\mathbf{I}_0^* + a^2\mathbf{I}_1^* + a\mathbf{I}_2^*) \\ &= 3\mathbf{V}_0\mathbf{I}_0^* + 3\mathbf{V}_1\mathbf{I}_1^* + 3\mathbf{V}_2\mathbf{I}_2^* \\ &\quad + \mathbf{V}_0\mathbf{I}_1^*(1 + a + a^2) + \mathbf{V}_0\mathbf{I}_2^*(1 + a^2 + a) \\ &\quad + \mathbf{V}_1\mathbf{I}_0^*(1 + a + a^2) + \mathbf{V}_1\mathbf{I}_2^*(1 + a + a^2) + \dots \\ &= 3\mathbf{V}_0\mathbf{I}_0^* + 3\mathbf{V}_1\mathbf{I}_1^* + 3\mathbf{V}_2\mathbf{I}_2^*\end{aligned}$$

Therefore, the mean power is

$$P = \mathscr{R}[3\mathbf{V}_0\mathbf{I}_0^* + 3\mathbf{V}_1\mathbf{I}_1^* + 3\mathbf{V}_2\mathbf{I}_2^*]$$

It is clear that the mean power given by the association of the voltages of one phase-sequence, with the currents of a different phase-sequence, is zero.

Unbalanced three-phase voltages applied to symmetrical three-phase impedances

Although the use of symmetrical components is scarcely justified for simple static circuits, it will be useful to illustrate the method by a simple example, before outlining the procedure adopted in more complex cases.

EXAMPLE. The three *phase* voltages of an unbalanced three-phase supply are: $\mathbf{V}_A = (200 + j0)$ V; $\mathbf{V}_B = (-j200)$ V; $\mathbf{V}_C = (-100 + j200)$ V. Connected in star across this supply are three equal impedances of $(20 + j10)$ Ω, there being no connection between the star-point and the supply neutral. Evaluate the symmetrical components of the A-phase currents and the three line currents.

Solution. The symmetrical components of the A-phase voltage are

$$\mathbf{V}_0 = (200 - j200 - 100 + j200)/3 = (100/3) \text{ V}.$$

(This component is not actually required in this problem because there is no zero-sequence current.)

$$\begin{aligned}\mathbf{V}_1 &= \{200 + (-1/2 + j\sqrt{3}/2)(-j200) + \\ &\qquad (-1/2 - j\sqrt{3}/2)(-100 + j200)\}/3 \\ &= 199 + j28{\cdot}9\end{aligned}$$

$$\begin{aligned}\mathbf{V}_2 &= \{200 + (-1/2 - j\sqrt{3}/2)(-j200) + \\ &\qquad (-1/2 + j\sqrt{3}/2)(-100 + j200)\}/3 \\ &= -32{\cdot}3 - j28{\cdot}9\end{aligned}$$

The component currents in phase A are therefore

$$\mathbf{I}_{A1} = \mathbf{V}_1/(20 + j10) = (199 + j28{\cdot}9)(20 - j10)/500$$
$$= \underline{(8{\cdot}56 - j2{\cdot}82)\ \text{A}}$$

$$\mathbf{I}_{A2} = \mathbf{V}_2/(20 + j10) = (-32{\cdot}3 - j28{\cdot}9)(20 - j10)/500$$
$$= \underline{(-1{\cdot}87 - j0{\cdot}51)\ \text{A}}$$

$$\therefore \quad \mathbf{I}_A = \mathbf{I}_{A1} + \mathbf{I}_{A2} = \underline{(6{\cdot}69 - j3{\cdot}33)\ \text{A}}$$

$$\mathbf{I}_B = \mathbf{I}_{B1} + \mathbf{I}_{B2} = (-1/2 - j\sqrt{3}/2)(8{\cdot}56 - j2{\cdot}82) + (-1/2 + j\sqrt{3}/2)(-1{\cdot}87 - j0{\cdot}51)$$
$$= \underline{(-5{\cdot}344 - j7{\cdot}365)\ \text{A}}$$

$$\mathbf{I}_C = \mathbf{I}_{C1} + \mathbf{I}_{C2} = (-1/2 + j\sqrt{3}/2)(8{\cdot}56 - j2{\cdot}82) + (-1/2 - j\sqrt{3}/2)(-1{\cdot}87 - j0{\cdot}51)$$
$$= \underline{(-1{\cdot}347 + j10{\cdot}685)\ \text{A}}$$

Note that, within the limits of calculation accuracy, $\mathbf{I}_A + \mathbf{I}_B + \mathbf{I}_C = 0$.

Machines with unbalanced loads

In the analysis of many power circuits under unbalanced conditions it is often necessary to take account of the behaviour of the machines included in the system.

Synchronous machines (see also Chapter 15)

The three-phase alternators, which produce the driving voltages in a power system, normally work with load currents which are very nearly balanced, but under fault conditions, such as an earth on one line, or a short-circuit between two lines, the currents are very unbalanced and in the worst cases are single-phase ones. Symmetrical components simplify calculations in such cases.

With balanced armature currents it is often sufficiently accurate to take account of the armature-reaction and leakage-reactance effects in an alternator by invoking the concept of synchronous reactance and resistance. (The latter is often negligible.) Thus, as far as positive-sequence currents are concerned, the alternator phases may be considered to have internal e.m.f.'s of $\mathbf{E}_1$, $a^2\mathbf{E}_1$ and $a\mathbf{E}_1$, each having an internal impedance, the synchronous impedance, $\mathbf{Z}_S$ or $\mathbf{Z}_1$ (positive-sequence impedance). *The e.m.f.'s of rotation are necessarily of positive phase-sequence.*

Balanced three-phase currents of negative phase-sequence produce an armature field rotating in the opposite direction to that of the poles, and produce therein, or in the damper windings, thereof, opposing currents which tend to neutralize this rotating field. The effective reactance under these circumstances is much smaller than the synchronous reactance and is of the nature of a leakage reactance. This reactance is the ' negative-sequence reactance ', designated $\mathbf{Z_2}$.

Zero-phase-sequence currents produce no rotating field and, in a ' perfect ' three-phase machine, would produce no magnetic field whatever. In practice, however, they do produce small alternating fields, giving the effect of a small reactance, the ' zero-sequence reactance ' $\mathbf{Z_0}$.

Unbalanced currents also produce harmonic e.m.f.'s in a synchronous machine, but these are usually neglected in system-fault studies.

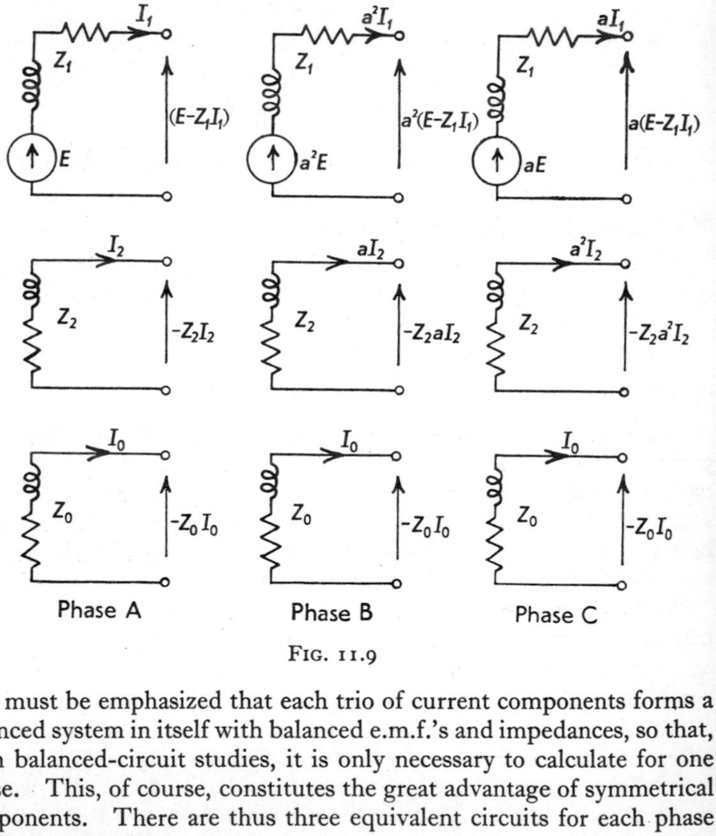

FIG. 11.9

It must be emphasized that each trio of current components forms a balanced system in itself with balanced e.m.f.'s and impedances, so that, as in balanced-circuit studies, it is only necessary to calculate for one phase. This, of course, constitutes the great advantage of symmetrical components. There are thus three equivalent circuits for each phase as illustrated in Fig. 11.9.

Polyphase induction motor

The effective input impedance per phase of a three-phase induction motor, supplied with balanced three-phase voltages and operating at slip s_1 is $\mathbf{Z_1} = (R_1 + R_2/s_1) + jX$, where R_1 is the primary resistance, R_2 the secondary resistance (referred to the primary) and X the total leakage reactance (referred to the primary), per phase. $s_1 = (N_S - N)/N_S$ where N_S, is the normal synchronous speed and N is the operating speed. (See Chapter 15.)

When the motor is supplied with unbalanced voltages, these may be split into the positive- and negative-sequence components. The zero-sequence components of the phase voltages are not required, because the primary winding is either delta-connected, or if star-connected has no neutral connection. The positive-sequence components of voltage produce a positive-sequence set of balanced currents in the stator which produce a forward-rotating field, so that the effective impedance is as above. The negative-sequence components of the voltage also produce a balanced set of currents, giving a backward-rotating field of speed $-N_S$. Thus, the slip with respect to this field is $s_2 = (-N_S - N)/(-N_S)$, and since $N = N_S(1 - s_1)$, $s_2 = 2 - s_1$. This negative-sequence rotating field produces a torque opposing that of the positive-sequence field, but at normal operating speeds when $s_1 < 1$, the backward torque is much smaller than the forward torque. However, $\mathbf{Z_2} = \{R_1 + R_2/(2 - s_1)\} + jX$, and is much smaller than $\mathbf{Z_1}$ when s_1 is very small, for example, at normal speeds ($s_1 = 0{\cdot}05$ say, or less). It follows that the negative-sequence current, for a given magnitude of negative-sequence voltage, is much greater than the positive-sequence current for the same positive-sequence voltage. Thus, induction machines are very sensitive to unbalance in the supply voltages.

In the case of an induction motor supplied with a single-phase voltage, the phase currents are $\mathbf{I_A} = -\mathbf{I_B}$ and $\mathbf{I_C} = 0$ (the machine being considered star-connected) and as shown on p. 208,

$$\mathbf{I_1} = (\mathbf{I_A}/\sqrt{3})\,\underline{|-30^\circ}, \quad \mathbf{I_2} = (\mathbf{I_A}/\sqrt{3})\,\underline{|+30^\circ}.$$

Therefore, $\mathbf{V_1} = \mathbf{I_1 Z_1} = (\mathbf{I_A}/\sqrt{3})\,\underline{|-30^\circ}\{(R_1 + R_2/s_1) + jX\}$

$$\mathbf{V_2} = \mathbf{I_2 Z_2} = (\mathbf{I_A}/\sqrt{3})\,\underline{|+30^\circ}[\{R_1 + R_2/(2 - s_1)\} + jX]$$

If, for example, $R_1 = R_2 = 1\ \Omega$, $X = 4\ \Omega$ and $s = 0{\cdot}05$,

$$\mathbf{V_1} = (\mathbf{I_A}/\sqrt{3}\,\underline{|-30^\circ}(21 + j4)$$

$$\mathbf{V_2} = (\mathbf{I_A}/\sqrt{3})\,\underline{|+30^\circ}(1{\cdot}53 + j4)$$

$$\therefore \quad V_2/V_1 = 4{\cdot}3/21{\cdot}3 = 0{\cdot}2$$

It should be noted, that it *cannot* be assumed that a single-phase motor is supplied with a *single-phase* voltage, which would have equal magnitudes of positive- and negative-sequence components. It is the *current* relationship, $\mathbf{I_A} = -\mathbf{I_B}$, given above, which is determined by the method of connection. A potential appears at the open-circuited terminal of phase C due to the rotating fields inducing an e.m.f. in this phase winding, and the machine behaves as though its supply was such that the voltage across phase C is exactly equal to the e.m.f. in C, so that no current flows in that winding.* A similar situation arises when a single-phase fault occurs on a power network (see below).

Calculation of fault currents in a supply system

It has been shown above how the currents flowing in a symmetrical three-phase network, to which unbalanced voltages are applied, may be calculated by using the symmetrical components of the voltages. When the impedances are unbalanced, and the voltages are either balanced or unbalanced, there is little advantage in using the symmetrical-component method, because it is not possible to calculate the current for one phase only, for each symmetrical component. It is therefore difficult, at first sight, to see why the symmetrical-component method is so useful, both for single-phase machine operation or for the calculation of fault currents in a power network due to single-phase short-circuits. However, it is easy to show that such cases can be represented as being the application of *unbalanced* voltages to *balanced* impedances.† Thus, in the single-phase operation of the induction motor discussed above, the phase impedances are equal for each symmetrical component of current, and although no voltage is actually applied to one phase, a voltage is present at that phase. Even if the actual winding did not exist it could be imagined.

Earth fault on alternator

Consider a single-phase short-circuit on an alternator with positive-, negative- and zero-sequence impedances $\mathbf{Z}_1$, $\mathbf{Z}_2$, $\mathbf{Z}_0$ and phase e.m.f.'s, $\mathbf{E}_1$, $a^2\mathbf{E}_1$ and $a\mathbf{E}_1$. The circuit arrangement is shown in Fig. 11.10. The impedances $\mathbf{Z}$ illustrated have the above values depending on the phase-sequence being considered.

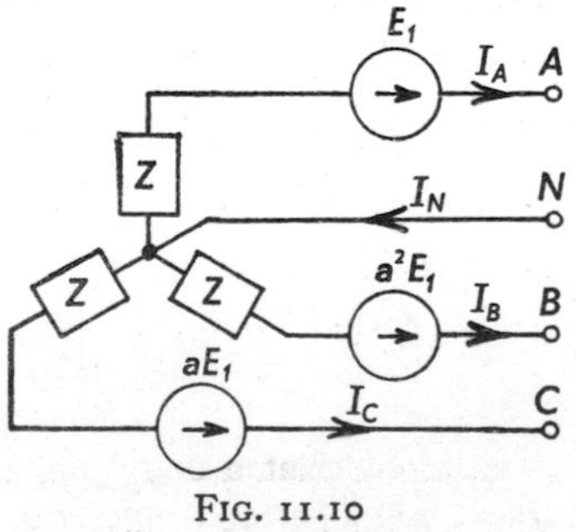

FIG. 11.10

If points A and N are short-circuited, while B and C remain open, then $\mathbf{I_B} = \mathbf{I_C} = 0$, but $\mathbf{I_A}$ flows. If there were no interaction between the phase windings of the machine, *i.e.*, if the positive-, negative- and zero-sequence impedances were all the same, the e.m.f.'s in phases B and C

* K. Sing-Yui and R. Tsao, " Some Notes on the Torque-slip Characteristics of Single-phase Induction Motors ", *Bull. Elect. Eng. Educ.*, No. 12, p. 29 (June, 1954).

† H. Tropper, *Electric Circuit Theory* (Longmans, Green & Co., 1949).

would remain the same as on open-circuit. However, extra e.m.f.'s are induced due to the current in phase *A*, and the voltages across *BN* and *CN* will be $\mathbf{V}_B'$ and $\mathbf{V}_C'$, say. Thus, the short-circuit is equivalent to the application of unsymmetrical voltages to the balanced three-phase impedances **Z**, the voltages being such that current flows only in phase *A* and returns via the neutral connector. It is not actually necessary to calculate these voltages in order to find $\mathbf{I}_A$, but they are implicit in the following analysis.

$\mathbf{I}_A = \mathbf{I}_0 + \mathbf{I}_1 + \mathbf{I}_2$, and since the voltage between *A* and *N* is zero, the sum of the three symmetrical-component voltages is zero, so that, from Fig. 11.9,

$$(\mathbf{E} - \mathbf{Z}_1\mathbf{I}_1) + (-\mathbf{Z}_2\mathbf{I}_2) + (-\mathbf{Z}_0\mathbf{I}_0) = 0,$$

or

$$\mathbf{E}_1 = \mathbf{I}_0\mathbf{Z}_0 + \mathbf{I}_1\mathbf{Z}_1 + \mathbf{I}_2\mathbf{Z}_2$$
$$\mathbf{I}_B = \mathbf{I}_0 + a^2\mathbf{I}_1 + a\mathbf{I}_2 = 0$$
$$\mathbf{I}_C = \mathbf{I}_0 + a\mathbf{I}_1 + a^2\mathbf{I}_2 = 0$$

and, as shown previously for this condition,

$$\mathbf{I}_0 = \mathbf{I}_1 = \mathbf{I}_2 = \mathbf{I}_A/3$$

Thus, $\mathbf{I}_0 = \mathbf{I}_1 = \mathbf{I}_2 = \mathbf{E}_1/(\mathbf{Z}_0 + \mathbf{Z}_1 + \mathbf{Z}_2)$

and $\mathbf{I}_A = 3\mathbf{E}_1/(\mathbf{Z}_0 + \mathbf{Z}_1 + \mathbf{Z}_2)$

$$\begin{aligned}\mathbf{V}_{BN} &= a^2\mathbf{E}_1 - \mathbf{I}_0\mathbf{Z}_0 - a^2\mathbf{I}_1\mathbf{Z}_1 - a\mathbf{I}_2\mathbf{Z}_2 \\ &= a^2\mathbf{E}_1 - \mathbf{E}_1\mathbf{Z}_0/(\mathbf{Z}_0 + \mathbf{Z}_1 + \mathbf{Z}_2) - a^2\mathbf{E}_1\mathbf{Z}_1/(\mathbf{Z}_0 + \mathbf{Z}_1 + \mathbf{Z}_2) \\ &\qquad - a\mathbf{E}_1\mathbf{Z}_2/(\mathbf{Z}_0 + \mathbf{Z}_1 + \mathbf{Z}_2) \\ &= \mathbf{E}_1\{\mathbf{Z}_0(a^2 - 1) + \mathbf{Z}_2(a^2 - a)\}/(\mathbf{Z}_0 + \mathbf{Z}_1 + \mathbf{Z}_2) \\ &= -\mathbf{E}_1\{3\mathbf{Z}_0 + j\sqrt{3}(\mathbf{Z}_0 + 2\mathbf{Z}_2)\}/2(\mathbf{Z}_0 + \mathbf{Z}_1 + \mathbf{Z}_2)\end{aligned}$$

Similarly, $\mathbf{V}_{CN}$ which equals $a\mathbf{E}_1 - \mathbf{I}_0\mathbf{Z}_0 - a\mathbf{I}_1\mathbf{Z}_1 - a^2\mathbf{I}_2\mathbf{Z}_2$ can be shown to be: $\mathbf{E}_1\{-3\mathbf{Z}_0 + j\sqrt{3}(\mathbf{Z}_0 + 2\mathbf{Z}_2)\}/2(\mathbf{Z}_0 + \mathbf{Z}_1 + \mathbf{Z}_2)$

Phase-to-phase fault

If a short-circuit occurs between phases *A* and *B* (Fig. 11.10), the conditions are $\mathbf{I}_C = 0$, $\mathbf{I}_A = -\mathbf{I}_B$ and so, as shown previously, $\mathbf{I}_0 = 0$, $\mathbf{I}_1 = \mathbf{I}_A(1 - a)/3$, $\mathbf{I}_2 = \mathbf{I}_A(1 - a^2)/3$.

Equating the voltages and impedance drops around the *AB* circuit,

$$\begin{aligned}\mathbf{E}_1 - a^2\mathbf{E}_1 &= \mathbf{I}_0\mathbf{Z}_0 + \mathbf{I}_1\mathbf{Z}_1 + \mathbf{I}_2\mathbf{Z}_2 - \mathbf{I}_0\mathbf{Z}_0 - a^2\mathbf{I}_1\mathbf{Z}_1 - a\mathbf{I}_2\mathbf{Z}_2 \\ &= \mathbf{I}_1\mathbf{Z}_1(1 - a^2) + \mathbf{I}_2\mathbf{Z}_2(1 - a)\end{aligned}$$

i.e. $\mathbf{E}_1(1 - a^2) = \mathbf{I}_A(1 - a)(1 - a^2)\mathbf{Z}_1/3 + \mathbf{I}_A(1 - a^2)(1 - a)\mathbf{Z}_2/3$

i.e. $\mathbf{I}_A = 3\mathbf{E}_1/\{(1 - a)(\mathbf{Z}_1 + \mathbf{Z}_2)\}$

$\therefore\ \mathbf{I}_1 = \mathbf{E}_1/(\mathbf{Z}_1 + \mathbf{Z}_2)$

and $\mathbf{I}_2 = -a^2\mathbf{E}_1/(\mathbf{Z}_1 + \mathbf{Z}_2)$

Thus, $\mathbf{V_{AN}} = -a\mathbf{E_1Z_2}/(\mathbf{Z_1} + \mathbf{Z_2}) = \mathbf{V_{BN}}$

and $\mathbf{V_{CN}} = a\mathbf{E_1} - \mathbf{Z_1}a\mathbf{I_1} - \mathbf{Z_2}a^2\mathbf{I_2}$

$$= 2a\mathbf{E_1Z_2}/(\mathbf{Z_1} + \mathbf{Z_2})$$

Double phase-to-neutral fault

Suppose A and B (Fig. 11.10) are both connected to N. The conditions then are

$$\mathbf{I_C} = 0, \ \mathbf{V_{AN}} = \mathbf{V_{BN}} = 0.$$

Now, $\mathbf{E_1} = \mathbf{ZI_A} = \mathbf{Z_0I_0} + \mathbf{Z_1I_1} + \mathbf{Z_2I_2}$

$$a^2\mathbf{E_1} = \mathbf{ZI_B} = \mathbf{Z_0I_0} + \mathbf{Z_1}a^2\mathbf{I_1} + \mathbf{Z_2}a\mathbf{I_2}$$

and since $\mathbf{I_C} = 0$, $\mathbf{I_0} + a\mathbf{I_1} + a^2\mathbf{I_2} = 0$.

From these three equations the values of $\mathbf{I_0}$, $\mathbf{I_1}$ and $\mathbf{I_2}$, and then of $\mathbf{I_A}$, $\mathbf{I_B}$ and the voltage $\mathbf{V_{CN}}$, may be determined. It is found that

$$\mathbf{I_0} = -\mathbf{E_1}a\mathbf{Z_2}/\{\mathbf{Z_0Z_1} + \mathbf{Z_1Z_2} + \mathbf{Z_2Z_0}\}$$
$$\mathbf{I_1} = \mathbf{E_1}(\mathbf{Z_0} + \mathbf{Z_2})/\{\mathbf{Z_0Z_1} + \mathbf{Z_1Z_2} + \mathbf{Z_2Z_0}\}$$
$$\mathbf{I_2} = \mathbf{E_1}(a + 1)\mathbf{Z_0}/\{\mathbf{Z_0Z_1} + \mathbf{Z_1Z_2} + \mathbf{Z_2Z_0}\}$$
$$= -\mathbf{E_1}a^2\mathbf{Z_0}/\{\mathbf{Z_0Z_1} + \mathbf{Z_1Z_2} + \mathbf{Z_2Z_0}\}$$
$$\mathbf{V_{CN}} = a\mathbf{E_1} - \mathbf{Z_0I_0} - \mathbf{Z_1}a\mathbf{I_1} - \mathbf{Z_2}a^2\mathbf{I_2}$$
$$= 3a\mathbf{E_1Z_2Z_0}/\{\mathbf{Z_0Z_1} + \mathbf{Z_1Z_2} + \mathbf{Z_2Z_0}\}.$$

Faults on power networks

In the case of a power network supplied by several alternators, and with transformers, transmission lines, interconnectors, feeders and so on, an extension of Thévenin's Theorem shows that the methods used above for a single alternator may be applied. In other words, a network of symmetrical impedances with symmetrical generated voltages can be replaced by a single set of symmetrical impedances and a single set of symmetrical generated voltages. In practice there may be some difficulty in determining the values of the equivalent impedances, but the principle remains true. Alternatively, any of the methods of circuit analysis may be employed for each of the symmetrical components of current separately, the relationships between the components of current being determined by the fault conditions, as in the case of the single alternator discussed above.

Special consideration must be given to three-phase transformers in fault analysis, as the zero-sequence impedance depends on the type of connection. For positive- and negative-sequence currents, each of which forms by definition a balanced system, the transformer reactances are the normal leakage reactances. For the zero-sequence set of currents, however, the reactance may be much greater, depending on the connections. For example, consider a star–star transformer supplied from a generator with unearthed neutral, the transformer-primary neutral also being unearthed, while its secondary neutral is earthed (Fig. 11.11). If the transformer is assumed to be ideal, in so far as the magnetizing impedance is infinite, the ampère-turns on the primary and secondary must balance for each phase separately. Thus,

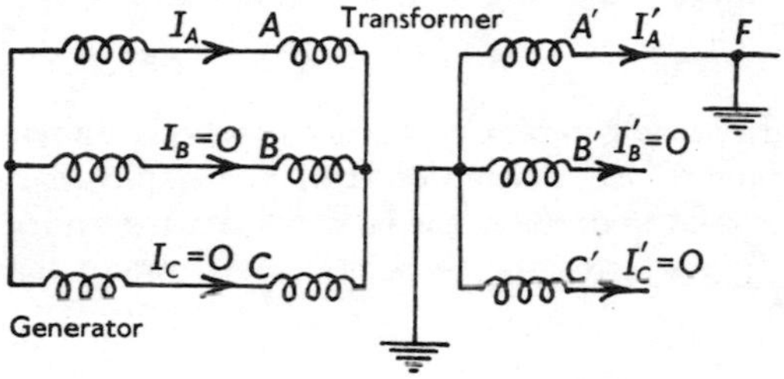

FIG. 11.11

if the secondary phase A' is earthed, so that current $\mathbf{I_A}'$ flows, then $\mathbf{I_A}$ should flow in the primary A phase and $\mathbf{I_A}N_1 = \mathbf{I_A}'N_2$ where N_1 and N_2 are the numbers of primary and secondary turns per phase. At the same time the currents in phases B and C should be zero to match the zero secondary currents. This is obviously incorrect (on the assumption made) since Kirchhoff's first law is violated. Therefore, $\mathbf{I_A}$ and $\mathbf{I_A}'$ must be zero. In actual practice they will be very small, because the impedance of the transformer to such a current is very high.

If the transformer-primary neutral and generator neutral are connected together, or earthed, $\mathbf{I_A}$ is permitted to flow. Also, if the primary is delta-connected, the zero-sequence components of the current can circulate around the delta, though they do not appear in the lines from the generator. Thus, the effective zero-sequence impedance of a three-phase transformer may be very high, or may be simply the normal leakage impedance, depending on the method of connection.

Fig. 11.12 shows the currents flowing.

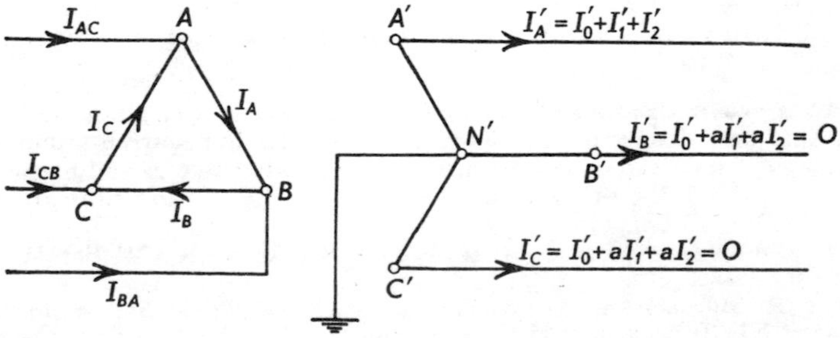

FIG. 11.12

$$\mathbf{I_A} = \mathbf{I_0} + \mathbf{I_1} + \mathbf{I_2},$$
$$\mathbf{I_B} = \mathbf{I_0} + a^2\mathbf{I_1} + a\mathbf{I_2} = 0$$
$$\mathbf{I_C} = \mathbf{I_0} + a\mathbf{I_1} + a^2\mathbf{I_2} = 0$$
$$\mathbf{I_{AC}} = \mathbf{I_A} - \mathbf{I_C} = \mathbf{I_1}(1 - a) + \mathbf{I_2}(1 - a^2)$$
$$\mathbf{I_{BA}} = \mathbf{I_B} - \mathbf{I_A} = \mathbf{I_1}(a^2 - 1) + \mathbf{I_2}(a - 1)$$
$$\mathbf{I_{CB}} = \mathbf{I_C} - \mathbf{I_B} = \mathbf{I_1}(a - a^2) + \mathbf{I_2}(a^2 - a)$$

For the analysis of complex power networks it is simpler and quicker to set up 'model' circuits representing the sequence circuits of the actual system, and to measure the currents flowing under various connection conditions when short-circuits occur, rather than to attempt calculation.*

PROBLEMS

1. An unbalanced delta-connected load is connected to the terminals A, B, C of a 400 V, balanced, three-phase supply, whose phase-sequence is V_{AB}, V_{BC}, V_{CA}. The load consists of:

AB: A non-inductive 10 Ω resistor.
BC: A capacitor of 20 Ω reactance.
CA: An inductor of 10 Ω reactance and 5 Ω resistance.

By drawing a vector diagram to scale, determine the magnitudes of the line currents and the reading given by a wattmeter connected with its current-coil in line A and its pressure-coil between B and C. [S.U.]

[*Ans.* $I_A = 36$ A, $I_B = 25$ A, $I_C = 40$ A, 6,300 W.]

2. Check the results obtained in the previous question by using complex quantities.

3. The voltages between the terminals A, B, C of a three-phase supply, in order of phase-sequence are: $AB = 400$ V, $BC = 380$ V, $CA = 360$ V. An unbalanced delta-connected load is supplied from ABC and consists of:

AB: A 20 Ω resistor.
BC: A 15 Ω inductor in series with a 15 Ω resistor.
CA: A 30 Ω capacitor.

Draw a vector diagram of the line voltages and of the phase and line currents and determine the magnitudes of the line currents and the readings of wattmeters, one with its current-coil in line A and pressure-coil across AB, the other with current-coil in line C and pressure-coil across CB. [S.U.]

[*Ans.* $I_A = 31$ A, $I_B = 39$ A, $I_C = 8{\cdot}5$ A; 12,100 W, 800 W.]

* J. R. Mortlock and M. W. Humphrey Davies, *Power System Analysis*, Chapter XIV (Chapman & Hall, 1952), and C. H. W. Lackey, *Fault Calculations*, Chapter VII (Oliver & Boyd, 1951).

4. A star-connected transformer of phase voltage 100 V (r.m.s.), with line terminals A, B, C and neutral terminal N, supplies balanced voltages to a star-connected load consisting of:

A to X: A 50 Ω resistor.
B to X. A capacitor of 120 Ω reactance.
C to X: A 50 Ω resistor in series with an inductor of 100 Ω reactance.

The transformer voltage phase-sequence is AN, BN, CN. Determine the line currents and the voltage between N and X. [S.U.]

[*Ans.* $I_A = 0{\cdot}72$ A, $I_B = 1{\cdot}74$ A, $I_C = 1{\cdot}785$ A; 134·5 V.]

5. Use Millman's Theorem to calculate the voltage between X and N and the magnitudes of the line currents for the example given on p. 197. (The circuit diagram is given in Fig. 11.3, omitting the neutral connector.)

6. An unbalanced delta-connected load ABC is supplied from a 400 V balanced three-phase source through lines each having an impedance of $(5 + j10)$ Ω. The load impedances are: $AB = (30 + j30)$ Ω, $BC = 40$ Ω, $CA = (30 + j30)$ Ω. Determine the line currents and the voltages between A, B and C.

[*Ans.* 8·75 A, 9·75 A, 9·86 A; 261 V, 248 V, 214 V.]

7. Solve the example given on p. 210 without using symmetrical components.

8. The line-voltages of an unbalanced three-phase system are $\mathbf{V}_{AB} = (200 + j0)$ V, $\mathbf{V}_{BC} = -200\,(1 + j)$ V, $\mathbf{V}_{CA} = j200$ V. (These are, of course, the voltages of a balanced two-phase supply.)

Determine, graphically and by calculation, the symmetrical components.

[*Ans.* $\mathbf{V}_1 = (215{\cdot}4 - j57{\cdot}8)$ V, $\mathbf{V}_2 = (-15{\cdot}4 + j57{\cdot}8)$ V.]

9. A delta-connected, three-phase inductor motor is supplied from the unbalanced source specified in the previous question. The motor impedances, per phase, are $R_1 = 2$ Ω, R_2 (referred to primary) $= 4$ Ω, total X (referred to primary) $= 10$ Ω. The magnetising current may be neglected. Determine the line currents when the motor runs with 5% slip.

[*Ans.* 8·5 A, 14·3 A, 8·2 A.]

10. The motor of problem 9 is re-connected in star and supplied from a single-phase, 415 V source. Determine the current and the voltages between each of the terminals connected to the supply and the free terminal, for a slip of 2%.

[*Ans.* 2 A; 398 V, 414 V.]

11. The positive-, negative- and zero-sequence impedances per phase of a small star-connected alternator are respectively: $\mathbf{Z}_1 = j8$ Ω, $\mathbf{Z}_2 = j1{\cdot}5$ Ω, $\mathbf{Z}_0 = j0{\cdot}5$ Ω, the resistance being negligible.

The excitation is such that the open-circuit voltage per phase (E_1) is 160 V. Determine the short-circuit currents (*a*) when all three line terminals are connected together, (*b*) when one line terminal is connected to the neutral, (*c*) with two line terminals connected together.

Determine also the voltages between each of the open-circuited terminals and the neutral, and the voltages between these terminals for condition (*b*). Determine the voltages between each line terminal and neutral, and between line terminals under condition (*c*).

[*Ans.* 20 A, 48 A, 29·2 A; 50 V, 50 V, 96 V; 25·3 V, 50·6 V, 75·9 V.]

12. The sequence reactances of a 25,000 kVA, 11 kV, three-phase, star-connected alternator are $X_1 = 75\%$, $X_2 = 25\%$, $X_0 = 5\%$, the resistances being negligible. The neutral point is earthed through a 0·5 Ω resistor. The line terminals of the alternator are connected to a three-core cable of 0·5 Ω reactance and 0·25 Ω resistance per phase. Show that the effective sequence impedances for faults at the end of the cable remote from the generator are $\mathbf{Z}_1' = (5{\cdot}17 + j85{\cdot}34)\%$, $\mathbf{Z}_2' = (5{\cdot}17 + j35{\cdot}34)\%$, $\mathbf{Z}_0' = (36{\cdot}2 + j15{\cdot}34)\%$, assuming that the resistance of the earth between the generator and the end of the cable is negligible.

If the alternator excitation is that corresponding to rated voltage on open-circuit, calculate the fault current, as a percentage of the full-load current, when an earth-fault occurs on one core at the remote end of the cable. Calculate also the phase voltages at the generator itself, as percentages of the rated voltage, under this condition.

[*Ans.* 208%, 38·7%, 57%, 69%.]

CHAPTER 12

TRANSIENTS

Effect of self-inductance in direct-current circuits

Self-inductance has no effect in a circuit when the current flowing is steady but only when the current varies. Consider first the effect of self-inductance when a battery is switched on to an inductive coil as illustrated in Fig. 12.1. The inductance of the coil is assumed to be L henrys and the resistance R ohms.

When the current through the coil is changing at a rate di/dt a back e.m.f. is set up of magnitude $L\,di/dt$.

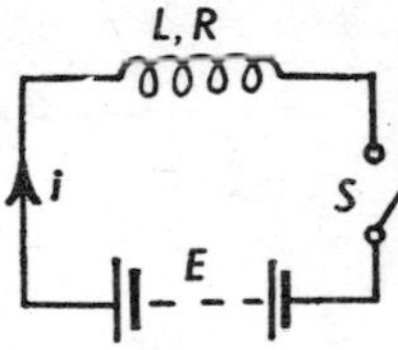

FIG. 12.1

The available e.m.f. for driving current round the circuit is therefore $E - L\,di/dt$.

$$\therefore\quad Ri = E - L.\,di/dt$$

or

$$di/(E/L - Ri/L) = dt.$$

Integrating,

$$\int di/(E/L - Ri/L) = \int dt + \text{a constant}$$

i.e.

$$-(L/R)\ln\{E/L - Ri/L\} = t + \text{a constant.}$$

When $t = 0$, $i = 0$, so the constant $= -(L/R)\ln(E/L)$.

$$\therefore\quad \ln\{E/L - Ri/L\} = -Rt/L + \ln(E/L)$$

$$\textit{i.e.}\quad \ln\{(E - Ri)/E\} = -Rt/L$$

so

$$1 - Ri/E = \exp(-Rt/L)$$

and

$$i = E\{1 - \exp(-Rt/L\}/R \qquad (12.1)$$

The current-time curve therefore has the appearance of that shown in Fig. 12.2.

The quantity L/R is known as the *time constant* of the circuit and is measured in seconds when L is in henrys and R in ohms. L/R can be seen to have the dimensions of time for:

e.m.f. = resistance × current = (self-inductance × current)/time

The current will theoretically only attain its final steady value after infinite time but it is found from the above expression for i that it attains 99% of its final value in a time $4{\cdot}6L/R$, *i.e.* $4{\cdot}6 \times$ time constant. To reach 50% of its final value the current flows for a time ($0{\cdot}693 \times$ time constant) after switching on. This fact enables a quick construction of the required curve to be produced as shown in Fig. 12.3. Point

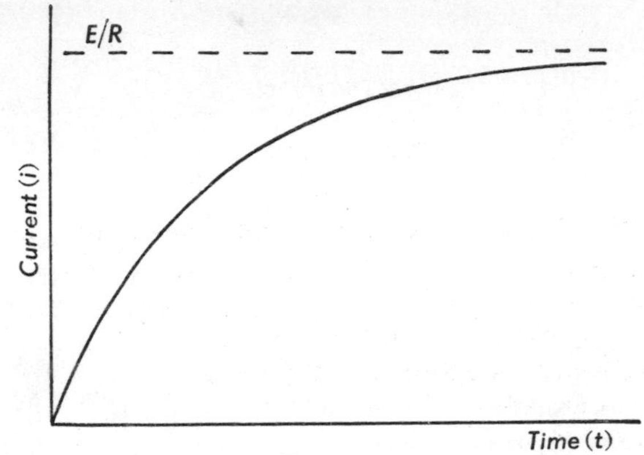

FIG. 12.2

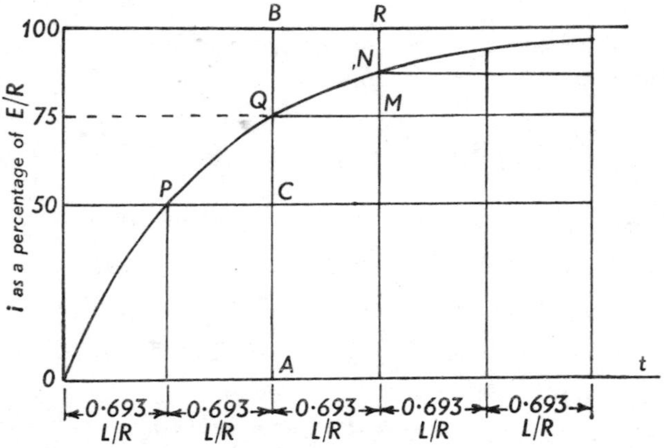

FIG. 12.3

P is the first point on the curve. Then point Q is obtained by drawing the vertical line AB and making $CQ = QB$. Similarly, $MN = NR$, and so on.

Another graphical method for obtaining the current-time curve has been given by Marchant.* This will now be described. For this purpose equation (12.1) is re-considered and can be re-written as

$$di/dt = (E/R - i)/(L/R) \quad . \quad . \quad . \quad . \quad (12.2)$$

Let OB (Fig. 12.4) represent the final steady current which flows in the circuit after the voltage has been applied for a long time. The

* E. W. Marchant, *An Introduction to Electrical Engineering*, Chapter XI (Methuen, 1939).

length OC is made equal to the time constant L/R and fixes the time scale on the diagram. Join BC.

The slope of $BC = BO/OC = (E/R)/(L/R)$.

Referring to equation (12.2) it is seen that since $i = 0$ when the main switch is closed the slope of BC is equal to di/dt when $i = 0$. As soon as current begins to flow through the circuit, therefore, it will increase at a rate corresponding to the slope of BC. Thus, if a short line OD is drawn parallel to BC this will represent the beginning of the required curve.

Next, draw a horizontal line DE cutting the vertical ordinate at F and the vertical through C at E and join B and E.

The slope of $BE = (E/R - i)/(L/R)$ which is equal to the value of di/dt when the current has the value OF. Therefore, if a second short line is drawn parallel to BE from D it will represent the continuation of the current curve. By repeating this process a close approximation may be made to the desired curve as illustrated in Fig. 12.4.

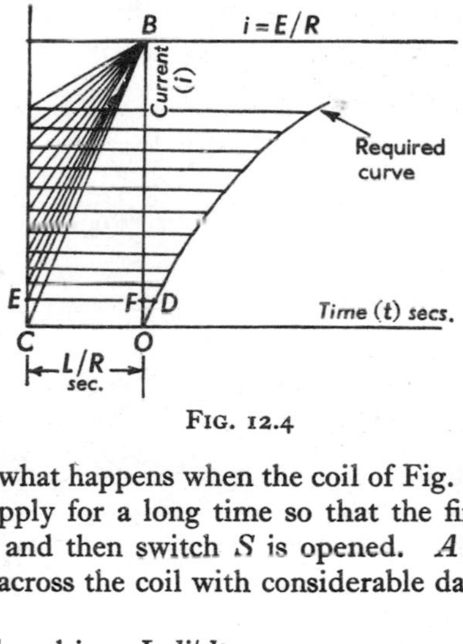

FIG. 12.4

Consider now what happens when the coil of Fig. 12.1 has been connected to the supply for a long time so that the final steady current (E/R) is flowing and then switch S is opened. A very high voltage may be induced across the coil with considerable danger of damage to the insulation.

The e.m.f. induced is $-L\, di/dt$.

If, for example, $L = 15$ H and the current $I = E/R = 10$ A, then if the switch is opened in 0·1 sec. the average rate of decrease of current is $10/0{\cdot}1 = 100$ A/sec. The e.m.f. induced is then $15 \times 100 = 1{,}500$ V.

To protect a coil from damage which may result because of such a large induced e.m.f. it is common to fit a discharge resistor R' (Fig. 12.5) so that when the terminals of the coil are disconnected from the supply they are connected to R'. Consider, for example, that $R = 10\ \Omega$

and $R' = 15\ \Omega$ and that the current flowing through the coil when the battery is disconnected is 10 A. When S is opened and connected to R' the 10 A current will flow through R'. The voltage across R', which is the same as the voltage across the coil, is now $R' \times 10 = 150$ V instead of the previous 1,500 V. It is interesting to calculate the shape of the current-time curve as the current dies away in such a circuit.

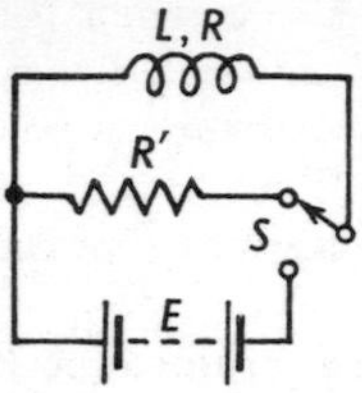

FIG. 12.5

Assume that at the instant of connection of R' the current through the coil is I and that at any time t later the current has fallen to i. Then,

$$L\, di/dt + (R + R')i = 0$$

or $$di/i = -\{(R + R')/L\}\, dt$$

Integrating, $$\ln i = -\{(R + R')/L\}t + \text{a constant.}$$

Now $i = I$ when $t = 0$, so the constant $= \ln I$.

$$\therefore\quad \ln i = -\{(R + R')/L\}t + \ln I$$

so $$i = I \exp[-\{(R + R')/L\}t]$$

Two graphical methods of finding the i/t curve, which correspond to those given already for the rise of current in an inductive circuit, are given below.

The construction for the first method is shown in Fig. 12.6 and will

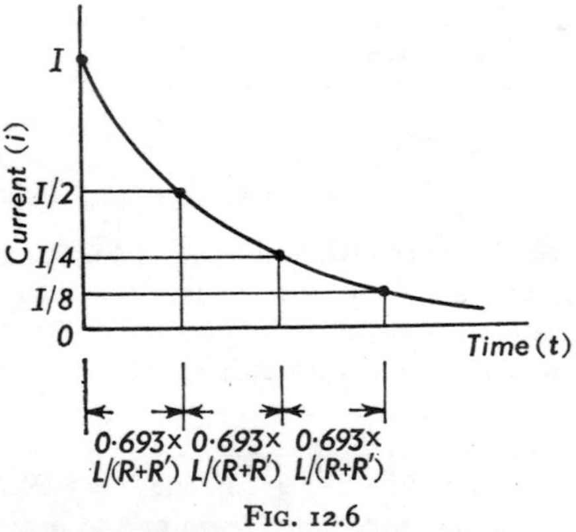

FIG. 12.6

be self-evident after reading how the corresponding curve, for rise of current in an inductive circuit, is obtained.

The second graphical method has again been described by Marchant * and is discussed below.

* E. W. Marchant, *An Introduction to Electrical Engineering*, Chapter XI (Methuen, 1939).

The equation connecting current and time may be written:

$$di/dt = -i/\{L/(R + R')\}$$

To draw the curve let $AB = DC$ (Fig. 12.7) represent the initial value of the current when the circuit is connected to the discharge resistor. Let $BC = L/(R + R')$. Then the slope of the line BD represents the value of di/dt when the current begins to die away. Draw a short line AP parallel to BD; the current will fall to the value PQ after a short time BQ. Draw a line from P parallel to BC, cutting CD at F and join BF. The slope of BF equals $-i\{L/(R + R')\}$, that is, it equals di/dt when the current has fallen to QP. Draw a short line PR parallel to BF; this will represent the slope of the current curve during the next short interval. By continuing this process the complete curve of decay of current with time may be plotted.

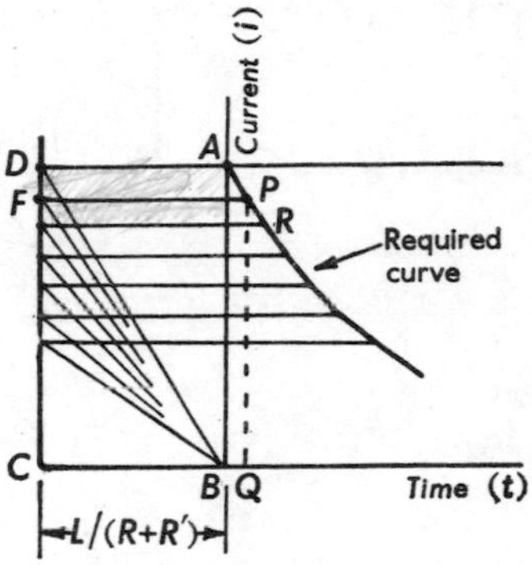

FIG. 12.7

Instead of using a discharge resistor a coil may be protected by connecting a capacitor across its terminals. Current then flows into the capacitor to charge it when the mains switch is opened.

EXAMPLE. A coil of resistance 10 Ω and inductance 0·4 H is connected to a 100 V, d.c. supply.

Calculate (*a*) the rate of change of current at the instant of closing the mains-switch, (*b*) the final steady value of current, (*c*) the time constant of the circuit, (*d*) the time taken for the current to rise to half its final value, (*e*) the energy finally stored in the magnetic field in joules. [S.U.]

Solution.

(*a*) Initial rate of change of current $= E/L = 100/0{\cdot}4 = \underline{250 \text{ A/sec}}$

(*b*) Final steady current $= E/R = 100/10 = \underline{10 \text{ A}}$

(*c*) Time constant $= L/R = 0{\cdot}4/10 = \underline{0{\cdot}04 \text{ sec}}$

(*d*) The current at any instant $i = E\{1 - \exp(-Rt/L)\}/R$

$$\therefore \quad 5 = 10\{1 - \exp(-25t)\}$$

$$\therefore \quad \exp(-25t) = 0{\cdot}5$$

and $\underline{t = 0{\cdot}0277 \text{ sec}}$

(*e*) Energy stored $= LI^2/2$ joules

$= (0{\cdot}4 \times 10^2)/2$ joules

$= \underline{20 \text{ joules.}}$

Charge and discharge of a capacitor through a resistor

When a capacitor of capacitance C is connected in series with a resistor of resistance R and a voltage E is applied across the combination through a switch S (Fig. 12.8) the voltage (v) across the capacitor increases with time from zero according to the law

$$v = E\{1 - \exp(-t/CR)\}$$

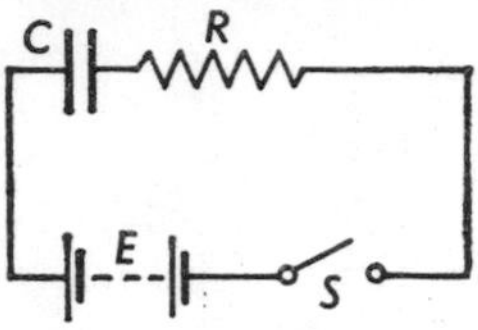

FIG. 12.8

This can be proved as follows.

The displacement current at any instant $i = dq/dt$, where q is the instantaneous charge on the capacitor.

But $$q = Cv$$
so $$i = C\,dv/dt$$
Also, $$i = (E - v)/R$$
$$\therefore \quad (E - v)/R = C\,dv/dt$$
i.e. $$dv/(E - v) = dt/CR$$
Integrating, $$-\ln(E - v) = t/CR + \text{a constant.}$$
But $v = 0$ when $t = 0$, so the constant $= -\ln E$.
$$\therefore \quad -\ln(E - v) = t/CR - \ln E$$
and $$v = E\{1 - \exp(-t/CR)\}$$

The time constant of this circuit is CR and is measured in seconds when C is in farads and R in ohms. CR can be seen to have the dimensions of time for:

$$C = \text{charge/voltage} = (\text{current} \times \text{time})/\text{voltage} = \text{time/resistance}$$

Graphical methods can be employed to obtain the v/t curve in the same way as the i/t curve was plotted for the rise of current in an inductive circuit.

Suppose now that the terminals of the charged capacitor are connected to a resistor of resistance R so that the initial conditions are that $v = E$ when $t = 0$. The current i will now decrease according to the law

$$i = -dq/dt = -C\,dv/dt.$$
Also, $$v = iR$$
$$\therefore \quad v/R = -C\,dv/dt$$
i.e. $$dv/v = -dt/CR$$
Integrating, $$\ln v = -t/CR + \text{a constant.}$$
Since $v = E$ when $t = 0$ the constant $= \ln E$.
Thus, $$\ln v = -t/CR + \ln E$$
and $$v = E\exp(-t/CR).$$

The time t' taken for the capacitor voltage to fall from its initial value E to some lower value V can easily be found as follows:

$$V = E \exp(-t'/CR)$$

so

$$t' \doteq CR \ln (E/V)$$

Thus one method of finding the value of the capacitance of a capacitor is to measure t', E and V and use the formula for t' knowing R.

Simple linear time-base circuits in cathode-ray oscillographs depend for their action on the charging of a capacitor through a resistor, the capacitor being suddenly discharged at some given interval. The X plates of the cathode-ray tube are connected across the capacitor and thus have applied to them a gradually increasing voltage which rapidly falls to zero and then repeats the cycle.

EXAMPLE. A simple neon-tube time base for a cathode-ray oscillograph employs a 300 kΩ resistor and a 0·016 μF capacitor. The striking and extinction voltages of the neon tube are 170 V and 140 V respectively. Calculate the frequency of the time base if the supply voltage is 200 V. [S.U.]

Solution. The capacitor voltage v increases according to the law

$$v = E\{1 - \exp(-t/CR)\}$$

as illustrated in Fig. 12.9.

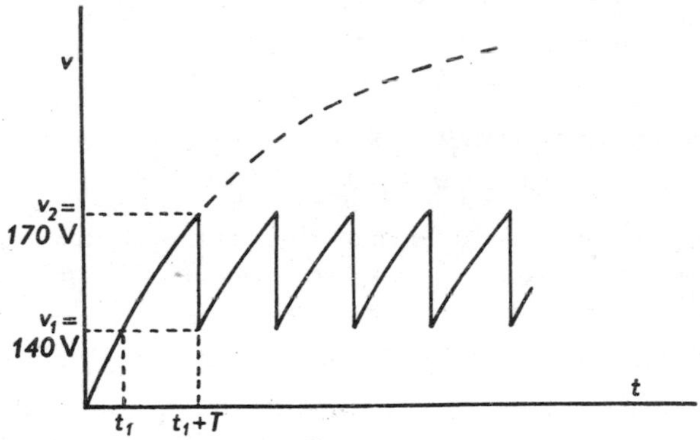

FIG. 12.9

$$\therefore \quad v_1 = E\{1 - \exp(-t_1/CR)\}$$

and

$$v_2 = E[1 - \exp\{-(t_1 + T)/CR\}]$$

From these two equations,

$$T = CR \ln \{(E - v_1)/(E - v_2)\}$$

In this case

$$T = (0{\cdot}016 \times 10^{-6}) \times (300 \times 10^{3}) \ln (60/30) = 1/300 \text{ sec.}$$

Frequency of time base $= 1/T = \underline{300 \text{ c/s}}$.

Discharge of a capacitor through an inductor and resistor in series

Fig. 12.10 shows a capacitor of capacitance C farads initially charged to voltage V_O, the polarity being as indicated. When the switch S is closed the capacitor discharges through the inductor of inductance L henrys and the resistor of resistance R ohms. If q is the instantaneous charge in coulombs on the capacitor, dq/dt will be negative since the capacitor is discharging and therefore if the positive direction of the instantaneous current i is taken in the discharging direction as shown, $i = -dq/dt$.

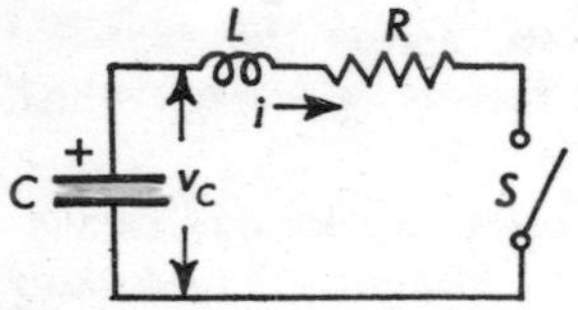

FIG. 12.10

Consider the capacitor as a voltage source supplying current to the rest of the circuit, the instantaneous voltage being v_C,

$$v_C = q/C = L\, di/dt + Ri$$

or

$$-q/C + L\, di/dt + Ri = 0.$$

Differentiating and dividing through by L,

$$-(1/LC)\, dq/dt + d^2i/dt^2 + (R/L)\, di/dt = 0$$

or

$$d^2i/dt^2 + (R/L)\, di/dt + (1/LC)i = 0$$

or in terms of the operator $D = d/dt$

$$\{D^2 + (R/L)D + (1/LC)\}\, i = 0.$$

The solution of this differential equation is of the form, $i = A \exp(mt)$, giving $di/dt = mA \exp(mt)$ and $d^2i/dt^2 = m^2A \exp(mt)$. Substituting these values in the equation,

$$m^2A \exp(mt) + (R/L)mA \exp(mt) + (1/LC)A \exp(mt) = 0.$$

If the assumed solution is a true one, this must be an equality for all values of (mt), so that putting $t = 0$, *i.e.* $\exp(mt) = 1$, in the above,

$$m^2A + (R/L)mA + (1/LC)\, \mathrm{A} = 0$$
$$m^2 + (R/L)m + (1/LC) = 0.$$

This is the 'auxiliary' equation whose solution is

$$m = \tfrac{1}{2}[-(R/L) \pm \sqrt{\{(R/L)^2 - 4(1/LC)\}}]$$
$$= -(R/2L) \pm \sqrt{\{(R/2L)^2 - (1/LC)\}}$$

Thus, there are two possible solutions of the differential equation. If the two values of m are $m_1 = -(R/2L) + \sqrt{\{(R/2L)^2 - (1/LC)\}}$ and $m_2 = -(R/2L) - \sqrt{\{(R/2L)^2 - (1/LC)\}}$, the most general solution of the equation is

$$i = A_1 \exp(m_1 t) + A_2 \exp(m_2 t)$$

where A_1 and A_2 are arbitrary functions whose values depend only on the initial conditions.

Three types of solution are possible:

(*a*) When $R^2 > 4L/C$, m_1 and m_2 are wholly real and negative.

(*b*) When $R^2 < 4L/C$, m_1 and m_2 are complex quantities since the quantity under the square-root sign is negative. Thus $m_1 = -\alpha + j\beta$, $m_2 = -\alpha - j\beta$, say.

(*c*) When $R^2 = 4L/C$ a special case arises because $m_1 = m_2$ and there would appear to be only one solution (see later).

These three cases will now be considered separately.

Case (*a*)

$$i = A_1 \exp(m_1 t) + A_2 \exp(m_2 t).$$

The initial conditions are determined from a consideration of the circuit. At the instant before the switch is closed i is zero and immediately after the switch is closed i must still be zero, because if it were not, the rise of current would be infinitely fast, *i.e.* di/dt and the voltage across the inductor would be infinite, which is manifestly untrue. Thus, at $t = 0$, $i = 0$. (It is convenient though not necessary to measure the time from the instant of closing the switch.)

Using this condition in the above equation:

$$0 = A_1 + A_2 \text{ or } A_1 = -A_2.$$

Also, $di/dt = m_1 A_1 \exp(m_1 t) + m_2 A_2 \exp(m_2 t)$, so that when $t = 0$, $di/dt = m_1 A_1 + m_2 A_2$. The original equation, gives for $t = 0$, $V_o = L\, di/dt$, since $v_C = V_o$ and $i = 0$.

Therefore, $m_1 A_1 + m_2 A_2 = V_o/L$

or $(m_1 - m_2)A_1 = V_o/L$

giving

$$A_1 = V_o/2L \,.\, \sqrt{\{(R/2L)^2 - (1/LC)\}}$$
$$= V_o/\sqrt{\{R^2 - 4L/C\}}.$$

EXAMPLE. A 2·5 μF capacitor, a 2 mH coil and an 80 Ω resistor are connected as in Fig. 12.10. The capacitor is initially charged to a voltage V_o of 100 V. Derive expressions for the current, the capacitor voltage and the charge on the capacitor at a time t after closing the switch. Calculate, also, the maximum value of the current.

Solution.

$$(R/2L) = 2 \times 10^4,\ (R/2L)^2 = 4 \times 10^8.$$
$$(1/LC) = 10^9/5 = 2 \times 10^8$$
$$m = 10^4\{-2 \pm \sqrt{(4-2)}\}$$
$$\therefore\ m_1 = -5{,}858 \text{ and } m_2 = -34{,}142$$
$$A_1 = -A_2 = V_o/L(m_1 - m_2) = 100/(2 \times 10^{-3} \times 28{,}284) = 1{\cdot}77.$$

The complete solution for the current is therefore,

$$\underline{i = 1{\cdot}77\{\exp(-5{,}858t) - \exp(-34{,}142t)\}\ \text{A}.}$$

The curve showing how this current varies with time is plotted in Fig. 12.11. The maximum value of current may be calculated by

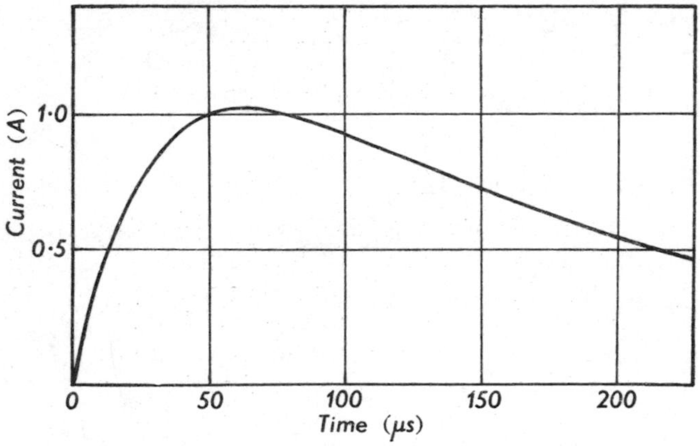

FIG. 12.11

differentiating the above expression for i and equating to zero.

$$di/dt = 1{\cdot}77\{-5{,}858 \exp(-5{,}858t) + 34{,}142 \exp(-34{,}142t)\}$$

The maximum current therefore occurs when

$$\exp(-5{,}858t)/\exp(-34{,}142t) = 34{,}142/5{,}858 = 5{\cdot}82$$

or $$\exp(34{,}142t - 5{,}858t) = 5{\cdot}82$$

i.e. $$28{,}284t = \ln(5{\cdot}82) = 2{\cdot}3026 \log 5{\cdot}82$$

so $$t = 6{\cdot}22 \times 10^{-5}\text{s} = 62{\cdot}2\ \mu\text{s}.$$

The maximum current

$$(i_{\text{max.}}) = 1{\cdot}77\{\exp(-0{\cdot}365) - \exp(-2{\cdot}125)\} = \underline{1{\cdot}02\ \text{A}.}$$

The capacitor voltage, v_C, and the instantaneous charge on the capacitor, q, may be determined from,

$$v_C = q/C = L\, di/dt + Ri$$

$\therefore\quad v_C = 2 \times 1{\cdot}77 \times 10^{-3}\{-5{,}858 \exp(-5{,}858t) + 34{,}142 \exp(-34{,}142t)\} + 80 \times 1{\cdot}77\{\exp(-5{,}858t) - \exp(-34{,}142t)\}$

or $\quad v_C = \underline{120{\cdot}8 \exp(-5{,}858t) - 20{\cdot}8 \exp(-34{,}142t)}.$

[Note that at $t = 0$, $v_C = 100$ V, which is correct.]

Alternatively q (and v_C) may be determined from $q = -\int_0^t i dt + Q_o$, where Q_o is the initial capacitor charge which is $2{\cdot}5 \times 10^{-6} \times 100 = 2{\cdot}5 \times 10^{-4}$ coulombs.

$$\text{Thus, } q = 1{\cdot}77\left[-\exp(-5{,}858t)/5{,}858 + \exp(-34{,}142t)/34{,}142\right]_0^t + 2{\cdot}5 \times 10^{-4}$$

or $\quad q = \underline{10^{-4}\{3{\cdot}02 \exp(-5{,}858t) - 0{\cdot}52 \exp(-34{,}142t)\}}$

These results for v_C and q may also be obtained directly since the original differential equation may be expressed in terms of v_C and q.

Thus, $\quad -q/C + L\, di/dt + Ri = 0$

and since $\quad i = -dq/dt = -C\, dv_C/dt$

$$L\, d^2q/dt^2 + R\, dq/dt + q/C = 0$$

and $\quad LC\, d^2v_C/dt^2 + RC\, dv_C/dt + v_C = 0.$

These equations are of the same form as that for the current, so that the general solution will be the same, but the constants will take different values.

Case (*b*)

If $R^2 < 4L/C$, the roots of the equation are complex; the general solution being

$$i = A_1 \exp(-\alpha + j\beta)t + A_2 \exp(-\alpha - j\beta)t$$

where

$$\alpha = R/2L \quad \text{and} \quad \beta = \sqrt{\{(1/LC) - (R/2L)^2\}}.$$

Thus,

$$i = \exp(-\alpha t)[A_1 \exp(j\beta t) + A_2 \exp(-j\beta t)].$$

Now

$\exp(j\theta) = (\cos\theta + j\sin\theta)$ and $\exp(-j\theta) = (\cos\theta - j\sin\theta)$

so $\quad i = \exp(-\alpha t)[(A_1 + A_2)\cos\beta t + j(A_1 - A_2)\sin\beta t]$

$\quad = \exp(-\alpha t)[B_1 \cos\beta t + B_2 \sin\beta t] = B\exp(-\alpha t)\sin(\beta t + \psi)$

where $B_1 = A_1 + A_2$, $B_2 = j(A_1 - A_2)$, $B = \sqrt{(B_1^2 + B_2^2)}$ and $\tan\psi = B_1/B_2$.

B and ψ are now the arbitrary constants whose values are determined from the initial conditions in a particular case.

EXAMPLE. If, in the example on p. 229 the 80 Ω resistor is replaced by a 40 Ω resistor, derive an expression for the current at a time t after closing the switch.

Solution.

$$\alpha = (R/2L) = 1 \times 10^4, \quad (R/2L)^2 = 1 \times 10^8$$

$$1/LC = 2 \times 10^8$$

$$\beta = 10^4\sqrt{\{2 - 1\}} = 1 \times 10^4$$

$$i = B \exp(-10^4 t) \sin (10^4 t + \psi).$$

As in the previous example, $i = 0$ and $di/dt = V_0/L$ at $t = 0$, so $\psi = 0$

$$di/dt = 10^4 B\{\exp(-10^4 t) \cos (10^4 t) - \exp(-10^4 t) \sin (10^4 t)\}$$

$$\therefore \quad 10^4 B = 5 \times 10^4, \text{ or } B = 5.$$

Thus, $\quad \underline{i = 5 \exp(-10^4 t) \sin (10^4 t) \text{ A.}}$

The equations showing the instantaneous capacitor voltage and charge may be determined, if desired, as in the previous example, either from the current/time equation or by solving the differential equation in voltage or charge.

Case (c)

When $R^2 = 4L/C$, the two roots of the auxiliary equation are equal, *i.e.* $m_1 = m_2$, and it would appear that the differential equation has one solution and one arbitrary constant, whereas the general solution of a second-order differential equation must have two such constants. This difficulty may be resolved by considering the limiting case of the oscillatory type of solution given above. (Case *b*.)

Thus, $\quad i = B \exp(-\alpha t) \sin (\beta t + \psi)$

or $\quad i = B \exp(-\alpha t)\{\sin \beta t \cos \psi + \cos \beta t \sin \psi\}$

When R^2 is slightly smaller than $4L/C$, β is small and the above equation becomes,

$$i = B \exp(-\alpha t)\{(\beta t) \cos \psi + 1 \sin \psi\}$$

$$= \exp(-\alpha t)\{a_1 t + a_2\}$$

where $a_1 = B\beta \cos \psi$ and $a_2 = B \sin \psi$ are the arbitrary constants.

EXAMPLE. Repeat the example on p. 229 for the case where $C = 5\ \mu\text{F}$ instead of $2{\cdot}5\ \mu\text{F}$. Determine, also, the maximum value of the current.

Solution.

$$\alpha = R/2L = 1 \times 10^4.$$

The general solution is therefore,

$$i = \exp(-\alpha t)\{a_1 t + a_2\}$$

As before, the initial conditions at $t = 0$ are $i = 0$ and $di/dt = V_0/L = 5 \times 10^4$, giving, $a_2 = 0$, and since $di/dt = a_1 \exp(-\alpha t) - \alpha a_1 t \exp(-\alpha t)$, $a_1 = 5 \times 10^4$.

Therefore, $i = 5 \times 10^4 t \exp(-\alpha t) = \underline{5 \times 10^4 t \exp(-10^4 t)\ \text{A}}$.

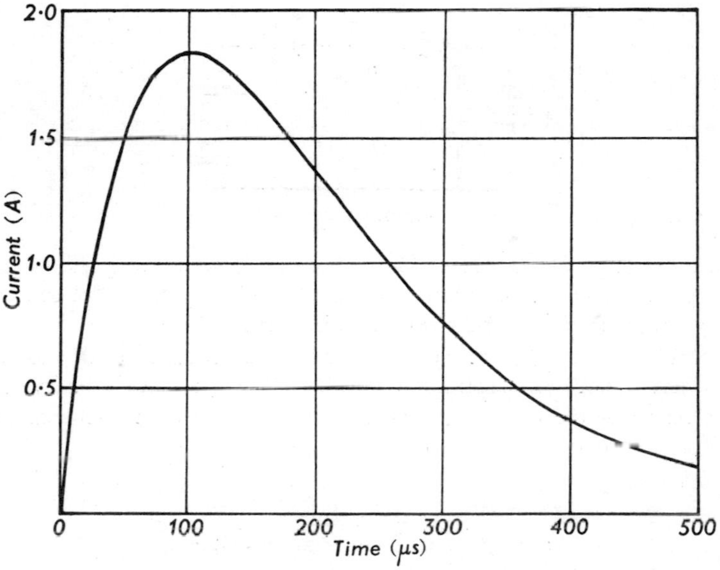

FIG. 12.12

The current-time curve is shown in Fig. 12.12. The time at which the maximum current occurs is given by

$$di/dt = 5 \times 10^4\{\exp(-\alpha t) - \alpha t \exp(-\alpha t)\} = 0$$

or $$t = 1/\alpha = 10^{-4}\ \text{s} = 100\mu\text{s}.$$

Hence, $$i_{\text{max.}} = 5 = 10^4 \exp(-1)/\alpha = 5/e = \underline{1{\cdot}84\ \text{A}}.$$

Charging of a capacitor through an inductor and resistor in series

Consider the circuit of Fig. 12.13.

In this case the current i is taken in the direction of charging so that $i = +Dq$ (the symbols D, D^2, etc., will be used instead of d/dt, d^2/dt^2, etc., in the rest of this chapter).

Since $$v_c = q/C,\ V = Ri + LDi + q/C.$$

Differentiating with respect to time t,

$$0 = RDi + LD^2i + i/C$$

or

$$(LD^2 + RD + 1/C)i = 0.$$

This equation is of exactly the same form as that for the discharge of the capacitor given previously and the types of general solution are the same. The arbitrary constants depend on the initial conditions, at

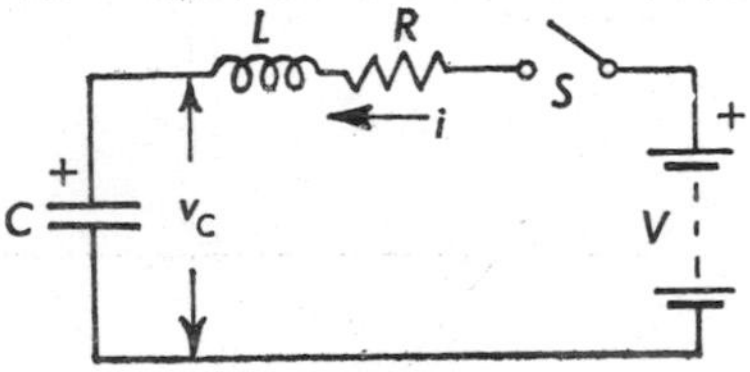

FIG. 12.13

$t = 0$, namely, $i = 0$, $Di = (V - V_o)/L$, where $V_o = Q_o/C$ is the voltage to which the capacitor is charged before closing the switch. Only one example will be given as an illustration.

EXAMPLE. If in Fig. 12.13 $C = 100$ μF, $L = 10$ mH, $R = 8$ Ω, $V = 200$ V and the capacitor is initially charged to 100 V, derive an expression for the current in the circuit at a time t after closing the switch.

Solution.

$$\alpha = R/2L = 400; \; (1/LC) = 10^6.$$

$$\beta = \sqrt{\{(1/LC) - (R/2L)^2\}} = 916{\cdot}5$$

$$\therefore \; i = B \exp(-400t) \sin(916{\cdot}5t + \psi)$$

Since $\quad i = 0$ when $t = 0$, $\psi = 0$.

$$Di = B \exp(-400t)\{-400 \sin 916{\cdot}5t + 916{\cdot}5 \cos(916{\cdot}5t)\}$$

$$(V - V_o)/L = 10{,}000 = 916{\cdot}5B$$

$$\therefore \; B = 10{\cdot}9$$

so $\quad \underline{i = 10{\cdot}9 \exp(-400t) \sin(916{\cdot}5t) \text{ A}.}$

The instantaneous capacitor voltage and charge may be determined in similar ways to those given for the discharge case, though now $q = +\int i\,dt$.

Transients with time-varying applied voltage

In the examples considered above the applied voltage was constant and the resulting differential equations were either quite simple, of first-order, or second-order equations consisting of functions of the dependent variable (current or capacitor voltage or charge) equated to zero. Where the applied voltage varies with time, *e.g.* an alternating voltage, the differential equation is of the general form:

$$(a_n D^n + \ldots a_1 D + a_o)\, i = f(t)$$

where $a_n, \ldots a_1, a_o$ are constants and D^n is the nth differential coefficient of i with respect to time. The complete solution of this nth-order linear equation has two parts, known as the *complementary function* and the *particular integral.* The former is the solution of the equation,

$$(a_n D^n + \ldots + a_1 D + a_o) i = 0,$$

which is

$$i_1 = A_1 \exp(m_1 t) + A_2 \exp(m_2 t) + \ldots A_n \exp(m_n t)$$

where m_1, m_2, etc. are the n roots of the auxiliary equation,

$$a_n m^n + \ldots + a_1 m + a_o = 0.$$

If two of these roots are equal, say $m_1 = m_2$, the complementary function becomes

$$i_1 = (A_1' + A_2' t) \exp(m_1 t) + \ldots + A_n \exp(m_n t)$$

and if three roots are equal, this becomes

$$i_1 = (A_1' + A_2' t + A_3' t^2) \exp(m_1 t) + \ldots + A_n \exp(m_n t).$$

The particular integral is *any* solution of the complete differential equation, say $i_2 = F(t)$ (in general i_2 will be a function of time). Methods of obtaining the particular integral are discussed later. Often its form is evident on inspection.

The complete solution of the differential equation is the sum of the complementary function and the particular integral, *i.e.* $i = (i_1 + i_2)$.

This must be true because $D(i) = D(i_1) + D(i_2)$, $D^2(i) = D^2(i_1) + D^2(i_2)$, etc., so that the left-hand side of the differential equations becomes $(a_n D^n + \ldots + a_1 D + a_o) i_1 + (a_n D^n + \ldots + a_1 D + a_o) i_2$. The first of these functions is, by definition, equal to zero, while the second, also by definition is equal to $f(t)$, so that the equation is completely satisfied.

Only *linear* differential equations, whose coefficients, $a_n \ldots a_1, a_o$, are either constants or functions of the independent variable (time), can be solved in two parts in the foregoing way. Very many important equations of electric circuits have linear equations with constant coefficients.

The auxiliary equation may have real or complex roots, the former giving exponential variation of the dependent variable with time, and the latter oscillatory variation, as illustrated by the second-order differential equations arising from the capacitor charge and discharge examples given above. In these examples the particular integrals are simply, $i_2 = 0$.

Although the determination of the complementary function, as shown above, is a routine matter, it may not be easy to determine the roots of the auxiliary equation if this is of high order. Approximate or trial-and-error methods may have to be used in difficult cases.

Possibly the most obvious way of determining a particular integral is by inspection. Thus, if $(a_2D^2 + a_1D + a_o)y = A + Bt + Ct^2$, the particular integral must have the form,

$$y_2 = A' + B't + C't^2, \text{ giving,}$$
$$Dy_2 = B' + C't \text{ and } D^2y_2 = 2C'.$$

Substituting these in the equation:

$$2a_2C' + a_1B' + 2a_1C't + a_oA' + a_oB't + a_oC't^2 = A + Bt + Ct^2$$

$$\text{or} \quad 2a_2C' + a_1B' + a_oA' = A$$
$$2a_1C' + a_oB' = B$$
$$\text{and } a_oC' = C$$

from which A', B' and C' may be found. Again, if the right-hand side of the differential equation consists of sinusoidal functions of time, the particular integral must also consist of such functions. For example, for the equation $(D^2 + 50D + 2{,}000)y = 3 \sin 2t + 5 \cos 10t$, the particular integral will be of the form:

$$y_2 = A_1 \sin 2t + B_1 \cos 2t + A_2 \sin 10t + B_2 \cos 10t$$
$$Dy_2 = 2A_1 \cos 2t - 2B_1 \sin 2t + 10A_2 \cos 10t - 10B_2 \sin 10t$$
$$D^2y_2 = -4A_1 \sin 2t - 4B_1 \cos 2t - 100A_2 \sin 10t - 100B_2 \cos 10t.$$

Therefore collecting terms and equating,

$$-4A_1 - 4B_1 + 5A_1 = 3$$
$$-4B_1 + 4A_1 + 5B_1 = 0$$
$$\therefore \quad A_1 = 3/17 \text{ and } B_1 = -12/17$$
$$-100A_2 - 20B_2 + 5A_2 = 0$$
$$-100B_2 + 20A_2 + 5B_2 = 5$$
$$\therefore \quad A_2 = 4/377 \text{ and } B_2 = -19/377.$$

Similarly, exponential time functions on the right-hand side of the equation give rise to similar functions in the particular integral.

More formal methods of determining the particular integral are given in mathematical textbooks,* and powerful 'operational' methods which

* H. T. H. Piaggio, *An Elementary Treatise on Differential Equations and their Applications*, Chapter III, p. 33 *et seq.* (G. Bell & Sons, 1940).

give the complete solution of a particular problem are widely used.*

These are beyond the scope of this book. It is desirable that the student should become thoroughly acquainted with the classical methods of solving differential equations before studying the operational techniques.

Transient phenomena in circuits to which alternating voltages are applied are naturally of very great importance and some simple examples are dealt with below.

Inductor-resistor series circuit

Consider a circuit consisting of resistance R ohms in series with inductance L henrys to which a voltage $v = V \sin(\omega t + \theta)$ is applied at $t = 0$. Denoting the instantaneous current by i, the voltage equation after the voltage has been applied is

$$Ri + L\,di/dt = V \sin(\omega t + \theta)$$

or

$$(D + R/L)i = (V/L) \sin(\omega t + \theta).$$

The complementary function is the solution of $(D + R/L)i_1 = 0$ and is $i_1 = A \exp(-Rt/L)$ as shown earlier.

Three methods of determining the particular integral are given below.

(*a*) Regarded as an ordinary a.c. circuit problem, the *steady-state* alternating current, which *must* be a particular integral, can be written down immediately as $i_2 = V \sin(\omega t + \theta - \phi)/\sqrt{(R^2 + \omega^2 L^2)}$, where $\tan \phi = \omega L/R$.

(*b*) In the 'conventional' method the equation is written as

$$i_2 = (V/L) \sin(\omega t + \theta)/\{R/L + D\}$$

or

$$i_2 = (V/L)(R/L - D) \sin(\omega t + \theta)/\{(R/L)^2 - D^2\}.$$

Since the particular integral must consist of functions such as $\sin \omega t$ and $\cos \omega t$ and since $D^2(\sin \omega t) = -\omega^2 \sin \omega t$ and $D^2(\cos \omega t) = -\omega^2 \cos \omega t$, D^2 may be replaced by $-\omega^2$.

Thus, $$i_2 = (V/L)(R/L - D) \sin(\omega t + \theta)/\{(R/L)^2 + \omega^2\}$$

or

$$\begin{aligned} i_2 &= \{V/(R^2 + \omega^2 L^2)\}\{(R - LD) \sin(\omega t + \theta)\} \\ &= \{V/(R^2 + \omega^2 L^2)\}\{R \sin(\omega t + \theta) - \omega L \cos(\omega t + \theta)\} \\ &= \{V/\sqrt{(R^2 + \omega^2 L^2)}\} \sin(\omega t + \theta - \phi) \end{aligned}$$

where $\tan \phi = \omega L/R$.

* H. Tropper, *Electric Circuit Theory*, Chapters VI, VII and VIII (Longmans, Green & Co., 1949); and
H. S. Carslaw and J. C. Jaeger, *Operational Methods in Applied Mathematics* (Oxford Univ. Press, 1949).

(*c*) Since, as shown above, $-\omega^2$ is substituted for D^2, it is reasonable to substitute $j\omega$ for D, since $j^2 = -1$. The applied voltage is represented by the vector $\mathbf{V}$ and the current by $\mathbf{I}_2 = (\mathbf{V}/L)/(R/L + j\omega) = \mathbf{V}/(R + j\omega L)$. The current vector therefore has magnitude of $V/\sqrt{(R^2 + \omega^2 L^2)}$ and *lags* on the voltage by an angle ϕ, where $\tan \phi = \omega L/R$. This particular application is rather trivial but in more complex cases the method is quite valuable (see p. 251).

The complete solution is therefore

$$i = A \exp(-Rt/L) + \{V/\sqrt{(R^2 + \omega^2 L^2)}\} \sin(\omega t + \theta - \phi).$$

The initial condition is $i = 0$ when $t = 0$, therefore

$$A + \{V/\sqrt{(R^2 + \omega^2 L^2)}\} \sin(\theta - \phi) = 0$$

giving the complete solution:

$$i = \{V/\sqrt{(R^2 + \omega^2 L^2)}\}\{\sin(\omega t + \theta - \phi) - \exp(-Rt/L) \sin(\theta - \phi)\}.$$

This is seen to consist of a steady alternating component and an exponentially decaying component. The magnitude of the latter depends on the instantaneous value of the applied voltage when the switch is closed, *i.e.* on the angle θ. If $\theta = 0$, the switch is closed at the instant the applied voltage is zero and rising, the maximum value of the exponential term being

$$V \sin \phi/\sqrt{(R^2 + \omega^2 L^2)} = V\omega L/(R^2 + \omega^2 L^2).$$

If $\theta = \phi$, the switch being closed at the instant when the applied voltage is $V \sin \phi$ there is no transient, the current attaining its steady-state alternating value immediately.

EXAMPLE. A voltage $v = 100 \sin(628t + \theta)$ is applied to an inductor-resistor series circuit having a resistance of 2 Ω and an inductance of 20 mH. Derive an expression for the current at a time t after closing the mains switch. Plot the current-time curve for the case where $\theta = 0$.

Solution.

$$R/L = 100, \quad \tan \phi = 20 \times 10^{-3} \times 628/2 = 6{\cdot}28$$

so that $\phi = 81°$

$$Z = \sqrt{(R^2 + L^2\omega^2)} = 12{\cdot}7\ \Omega$$

$$V/Z = 7{\cdot}87$$

$$\therefore \quad i = 7{\cdot}87\{\sin(628t - 81°) + \sin(81° - \theta) \exp(-100t)\}$$

For $\theta = 0$,

$$i = \underline{7{\cdot}87 \sin(628t - 81°)} + \underline{7{\cdot}68 \exp(-100t)}.$$

The resultant curve is shown in Fig. 12.14, the two components having been drawn separately and then added.

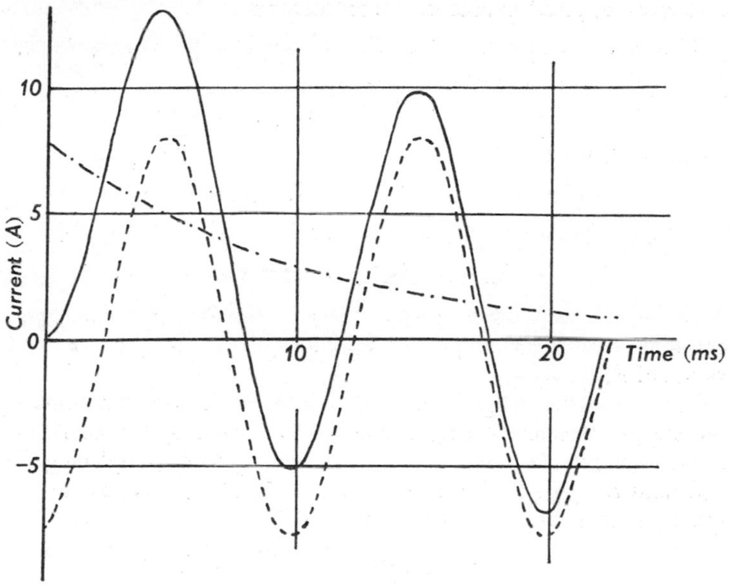

FIG. 12.14

Capacitor-resistor series circuit

In the case of a circuit consisting of a capacitor and resistor in series, to which an alternating voltage is suddenly applied, the voltage equation is

$$V \sin(\omega t + \theta) = Ri + q/C$$

Differentiating with respect to time and remembering that $Dq = i$

$$\omega V \cos(\omega t + \theta) = RDi + i/C = (RD + 1/C)i.$$

This is solved in the same manner as the preceding case, the complete solution being the sum of a steady sinusoidal current and an exponentially decaying current, namely

$$i = \{V/\sqrt{(R^2 + 1/\omega^2 C^2)}\} \sin(\omega t + \theta + \phi) + A \exp(-t/RC)$$

where $\tan \phi = 1/\omega CR$.

A is determined from the initial conditions; if $q = 0$ at $t = 0$, $i_0 = V \sin \theta/R$ (from the original voltage equation) giving

$$V \sin \theta/R = \{V/\sqrt{(R^2 + 1/\omega^2 C^2)}\} \sin(\theta + \phi) + A$$

$$\textit{i.e.} \quad A = -(V/R) \sin \phi \cos(\theta + \phi).$$

If the switch is closed when the voltage is zero, $\theta = 0$,

$$A = -(V/R) \sin \phi \cos \phi = -V(1/\omega C)/(R^2 + 1/\omega^2 C^2).$$

If $\theta = (\pi/2 - \phi)$, $A = 0$ and there is no transient current.

Inductor-capacitor-resistor series circuit

The voltage equation for an inductor-capacitor-resistor series circuit with an alternating applied voltage is

$$LD\,i + Ri + q/C = V \sin(\omega t + \theta),$$

giving on differentiation

$$(LD^2 + RD + 1/C)i = \omega V \cos(\omega t + \theta).$$

The complementary function is the solution of

$$\{D^2 + (R/L)D + 1/LC\}i = 0$$

which has already been given earlier in the chapter, and may be aperiodic, critically-damped or oscillatory depending on the relative values of R, L and C.

The particular integral may either be written down immediately as the steady-state alternating current, or by writing the second of the above equations in vector complex quantity form, replacing D^2 by $-\omega^2$ and D by $j\omega$, and writing $\omega V \cos(\omega t + \theta) = j\omega\mathbf{V}$, where $\mathbf{V}$ is the vector representing $V \sin(\omega t + \theta)$.

$$(-L\omega^2 + Rj\omega + 1/C)\mathbf{I} = j\omega\mathbf{V}$$

$$\mathbf{I} = \mathbf{V}/\{R + j(\omega L - 1/\omega C)\},$$

from which $\qquad i = (V/Z)\sin(\omega t + \theta - \phi)$

where $\qquad Z = \sqrt{\{R^2 + (\omega L - 1/\omega C)^2\}}$

and $\qquad \cos\phi = R/Z$

EXAMPLE. An inductor-capacitor-resistor series circuit has the following constants: $C = 2{\cdot}5\ \mu$F, $L = 2$ mH, $R = 40\ \Omega$. The applied voltage, which is sinusoidal, has a peak value of 100 V and the frequency is 1,000 c/s. The mains switch is closed when the voltage is at half its peak value. The capacitor is initially uncharged. Derive an expression for the current at a time t after closing the switch.

Solution. The complementary function is identical with the general solution of the capacitor-discharge problem given previously:

$$i_1 = B\exp(-10^4 t)\sin(10^4 t + \psi).$$

The applied voltage is represented by $v = 100 \sin(6{,}283t + 30°)$ if the switch is closed at $t = 0$. The particular integral is the steady-state solution.

The reactance of the circuit $X = 6{,}283 \times 2 \times 10^{-3} - 10^6/(6{,}283 \times 2{\cdot}5)$

$$= -51{\cdot}15\ \Omega.$$

The impedance $Z = \sqrt{(40^2 + 51{\cdot}15^2)} = 65\ \Omega$ and $\phi = 50°\ 23'$

$$\therefore\quad i_2 = 1{\cdot}54 \sin(6{,}283t + 80°\ 23')$$

The complete solution is $i = i_1 + i_2$.

At $\quad t = 0,\ i = 0,\ Di = 100 \sin 30°/(2 \times 10^{-3}) = 25{,}000$

$\therefore \quad B \sin \psi = -1{\cdot}54 \sin 80° \ 23' = -1{\cdot}52$

and since $Di = B \exp(-10^4 t)10^4 \cos(10^4 t + \psi) +$
$10^4 B \exp(-10^4 t) \sin(10^4 t + \psi) + (1{\cdot}54 \times 6{,}283) \cos(6{,}283t + 80° \ 23')$

$$10^4 B\{\cos\psi - \sin\psi\} + 1{,}620 = 25{,}000$$

$$\therefore \quad 10^4 B \cos\psi = 23{,}380 - 15{,}200 = 8{,}180$$

Thus, $\quad \tan\psi = -1{\cdot}52 \times 10^4/8{,}180 = -1{\cdot}86$

so $\quad \psi = -61° \ 44'$ and $\sin\psi = -0{\cdot}8808.$

It follows that $B = +1{\cdot}52/0{\cdot}8808 = 1{\cdot}73.$

The complete solution for the current is therefore,

$$\underline{i = 1{\cdot}73 \exp(-10^4 t) \sin(10^4 t - 61° \ 44') + 1{\cdot}54 \sin(6{,}283t + 80° \ 23')}$$

Initial conditions

The complete solution of a transient problem requiring a first-order differential equation may be written:

$$i = f_1(t) + A f_2(t),$$

A being the arbitrary constant, which is determined in a particular case by the initial current i_o at $t = 0$. For an inductor in series with a resistor, the current cannot change instantaneously and is the same immediately after the initiation of the transient as immediately before. A is then determined from $i_o = f_1(0) + A f_2(0)$.

In the case of a capacitor in series with a resistor, the current can change instantaneously but the capacitor charge and voltage cannot as this would require infinite current. An uncharged capacitor acts as a short-circuit initially. Thus, if the capacitor charge is q_o and the instantaneous applied voltage is v_o at the start of the transient, $i_o = (v_o - q_o/C)/R$ and this value is used in the above equation to determine A.

The complete solution for the circuit with inductance, resistance and capacitance in series is of the form $i = f_1(t) + A f_2(t) + B f_3(t)$, the last two terms being the complementary function with arbitrary constants A and B. In this case, i_o at the start of the transient is the same as the current immediately before, so that.

$$i_o = f_1(0) + A f_2(0) + B f_3(0).$$

Also, since the original differential equation is $LDi + Ri + q/C = v$, then $(Di)_{t=0} = (v_o - Ri_o - q_o/C)/L$ and from the complete solution given above,

$$Di = D f_1(t) + A \,.\, D f_2(t) + B \,.\, D f_3(t)$$

so that-

$$D f_1(0) + A\, D f_2(0) + B\, D f_3(0) = (v_o - Ri_o - q_o/C)/L.$$

Thus, two equations are obtained from which the values of A and B can be determined.

Non-sinusoidal applied voltages

The form of the transient component of current, which is the complementary function, is independent of the nature of the applied voltage, as seen above, and is the same whether the voltage is sinusoidal or non-sinusoidal. The arbitrary constants are determined from the initial conditions, which do depend on the form of applied voltage to the extent that this, and the instant of initiation of the transient, determine the initial voltage.

The particular integral is the steady-state solution which is determined by the methods given in Chapter 10.

Repeated transients

One method of solution in the case of a repeated application of a voltage, for instance as represented by Fig. 12.15, would be to analyze

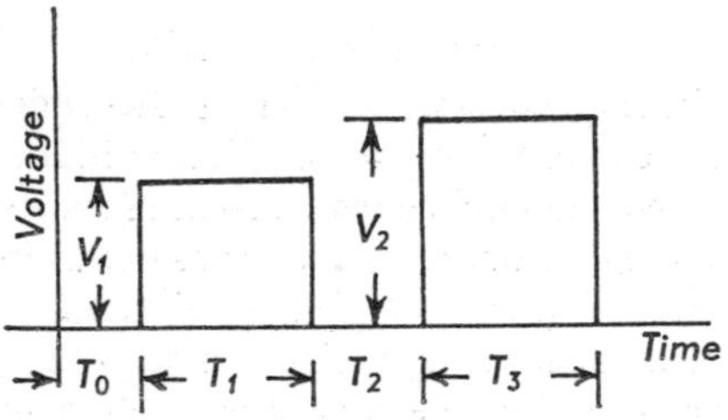

FIG. 12.15

the applied voltage into Fourier components. This involves a considerable amount of work, and with simple wave-shapes such as the rectangular one illustrated it may be easier to adopt the procedure outlined below which may also be applied when the voltage pulses are not of equal duration or magnitude.

If the voltage pulses of Fig. 12.15 are applied to a series L, C, R circuit, for example, at time $t = T_o$, the voltage V_1 is suddenly applied giving the equation

$$\{LD + R + 1/DC\}i = V_1$$

This differential equation is solved in the usual way, giving, for example, an oscillatory complementary function or transient term

$$i = B \exp\{\alpha(t - T_o)\} \sin \{\beta(t - T_o) + \psi\}.$$

The particular integral is zero, and the initial current is zero, so that $B \sin \psi = 0$. Also $(Di)_{t=T_o} = \beta B \cos \psi - \alpha B \sin \psi = V_1/L$, so that

B and ψ may be determined and inserted in the above equation. The instantaneous current i_1 and the capacitor charge q_1 are then calculated for $t = T_o + T_1$. At this time it is assumed that a voltage of $-V_1$ is suddenly applied and the new equation is thus,

$$(LD + R + 1/DC)i = -V_1.$$

This equation is solved, the initial conditions being as worked out, giving a new transient which lasts for time T_2, when the instantaneous conditions are again calculated. At $t = T_o + T_1 + T_2$, the voltage $+ V_2$ is suddenly applied and the equation is again solved.

Transients in parallel and series-parallel circuits

If a voltage is suddenly applied to circuits connected in parallel the transient currents in each circuit are independent, just as the steady-state currents are, and the total current at any instant is the algebraic sum of the individual currents at that instant.

For series-parallel circuits the general circuit laws and theorems may be applied, because these are valid for instantaneous values of voltage and current as well as for steady values. Simultaneous differential equations are obtained, which are reduced by elimination to one equation which is solved in the usual way.

EXAMPLE. A steady voltage of 100 V is applied to the circuit of Fig. 12.16. The capacitor is initially uncharged. Derive expressions for the currents i_1 and i_2 at time t after closing the switch.

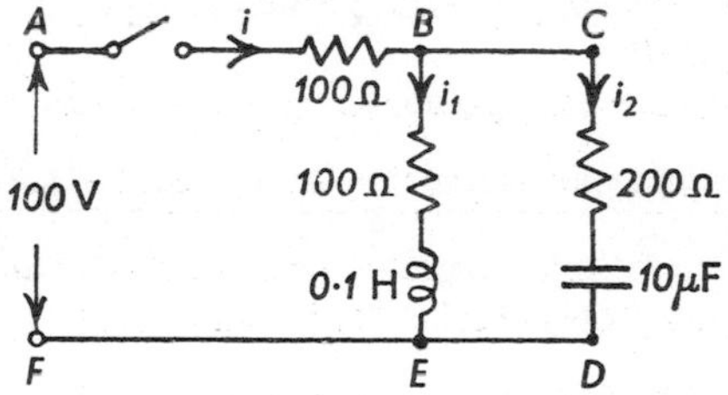

FIG. 12.16

Solution. The equations are

$$i = i_1 + i_2 \quad . \quad . \quad . \quad . \quad . \quad . \quad (12.3)$$

Mesh ABEF,

$$100i + 100i_1 + 0{\cdot}1Di_1 = 100$$

and using equation (12.3)

$$100i_2 + 200i_1 + 0{\cdot}1Di_1 = 100 \quad . \quad . \quad . \quad (12{\cdot}4)$$

Mesh ACDF,

$$100i + 200i_2 + 10^5q = 100$$

and using equation (12.3)

$$100i_1 + 300i_2 + 10^5 q = 100$$

which differentiated gives

$$100Di_1 + 300Di_2 + 10^5 i_2 = 0 \quad . \quad . \quad . \quad (12.5)$$

From (12.4) $$i_2 = 1 - 2i_1 - 0{\cdot}001Di_1. \quad . \quad . \quad . \quad (12.6)$$

and $$Di_2 = -2Di_1 - 0{\cdot}001D^2i_1$$

and eliminating i_2 from (12.5) gives

$$100Di_1 - 600Di_1 - 0{\cdot}3D^2i_1 + 10^5 - 2 \times 10^5 i_1 - 100Di_1 = 0$$

or $$0{\cdot}3D^2i_1 + 600Di_1 + 2 \times 10^5 i_1 = 10^5$$

The solution of this is determined from the complementary function and particular integral in the usual way. The latter is $i_1 = 0{\cdot}5$ A, since when the capacitor is fully charged $i_2 = 0$ and $i_1 = 100/200 = 0{\cdot}5$ A. The auxiliary equation is

$$0{\cdot}3m^2 + 600m + 2 \times 10^5 = 0$$

$$\therefore \quad m = \{-600 \pm \sqrt{(120{,}000)}\}/0{\cdot}6$$

$$= -1{,}575 \text{ or } -424$$

Thus, $$i_1 = A\exp(-1{,}575t) + B\exp(-424t) + 0{\cdot}5$$

When $$t = 0,\ i_1 = 0, \text{ so } A + B + 0{\cdot}5 = 0.$$

Also, when $t = 0$, $i_2 = i = 100/300 = (1/3)$ A, so that the voltage across $BE = 100 - 100/3 = (200/3)$ V and $(Di_1)_{t=0} = 200/(3 \times 0{\cdot}1) = -1{,}575\ A - 424\ B$.

It follows that $A = 0{\cdot}395$ and $B = -0{\cdot}105$ and

$$\underline{i_1 = \{-0{\cdot}395\exp(-1{,}575t) - 0{\cdot}105\exp(-424t) + 0{\cdot}5\} \text{ A}}$$

i_2 may then be determined directly, without solving another differential equation, from equation (12.6). It is found that

$$\underline{i_2 = \{0{\cdot}168\exp(-1{,}575t) + 0{\cdot}1653\exp(-424t)\} \text{ A}}$$

If the voltage applied to the circuit of Fig. 12.16 is a function of time (*e.g.* an alternating voltage), of instantaneous value v, instead of the constant voltage, equation (12.4) becomes

$$100i_2 + 200i_1 + 0{\cdot}1Di_1 = v$$

giving $$i_2 = (v - 200i_1 - 0{\cdot}1Di_1)/100$$

and differentiating, $Di_2 = (Dv - 200Di_1 - 0{\cdot}1D^2i_1)/100$

Similarly, equation (12.5) becomes

$$100Di_1 + 300Di_2 + 10^5 i_2 = Dv.$$

Eliminating i_2 as before yields the equation

$$0{\cdot}3D^2i_1 + 600Di_1 + 2 \times 10^5 i_1 = 10^3 v + 2Dv.$$

The complementary function of this equation is the same as that of the previous case,

$$i_1' = A\exp(-1{,}575t) + B\exp(-424t)$$

The particular integral, $i_1'' = f(t)$, depends on the way in which v varies with time. If it is a sinusoidal alternating voltage $v = V\sin(\omega t + \theta)$, the steady-state alternating current through the inductor is calculated using the complex-quantity technique say, giving

$$i_1'' = I_1 \sin(\omega t + \theta - \phi), \text{ say.}$$

The complete solution is then

$$i_1 = A\exp(-1{,}575t) + B\exp(-424t) + I_1\sin(\omega t + \theta - \phi).$$

A and B are determined from the initial conditions, $i_1 = 0$ at $t = 0$, and $(Di_1)_{t=0} = \{V\sin\theta - 100(i_2)_0\}/0{\cdot}1$, where $(i_2)_0 = V\sin\theta/300$.

Transients in more complex circuits, yielding differential equations of higher order than the second, are beyond the scope of this book and are preferably treated by operational methods (*e.g.* Laplace transforms) in which the initial conditions are incorporated from the start, so that the complete solution is obtained. However, higher-order equations can be solved by the complementary-function/particular-integral method as indicated by the following example:

In a circuit of the form of Fig. 12.16, the branch AB consists of an inductor of L henrys in series with a resistor of R ohms, branch BE has an inductor of L_1 henrys and resistance R_1 ohms, branch CD has a resistor of resistance R_2 ohms in series with a capacitor of value C farads and the applied voltage is V.

The particular integral is determined as the steady-state solution. The circuit equations are

$$i = i_1 + i_2$$

$$(R + LD)i + (R_1 + L_1D)i_1 = v$$

or $$\{(R + R_1) + (L + L_1)D\}i_1 + (R + LD)i_2 = v$$

or $$i_2 = [v - \{(R + R_1) + (L + L_1)D\}i_1]/(R + LD)$$

and $$(R + LD)i + (R_2 + 1/DC)i_2 = v$$

which, differentiated, *i.e.* multiplied by D, gives

$$(RD + LD^2)(i_1 + i_2) + (R_2D + 1/C)i_2 = Dv$$

or $$(RD + LD^2)i_1 + \{(R + R_2)D + LD^2 + 1/C\}i_2 = Dv$$

Substituting for i_2 and simplifying yields

$$[LL_1D^3 + \{L(R_1 + R_2) + L_1(R + R_2)\}D^2 + \{RR_1 + R_1R_2 + R_2R + (L + L_1)/C\}D + (R + R_1)/C]i = (R_2D + 1/C)v$$

In the manipulation the operators such as $(R + LD)$ are treated as coefficients in algebraic equations. The validity of this procedure is given in mathematical texts.*

The auxiliary equation is a cubic which may have three real roots, or one real and two conjugate complex roots, say α, β, γ, so that the complete solution is

$$i_1 = A\exp(\alpha t) + B\exp(\beta t) + C\exp(\gamma t) + (\text{the particular integral}).$$

Three initial conditions are required for the determination of A, B and C.

At $t = 0$, $i_1 = 0$, and since the total current i must also be zero at $t = 0$, due to the presence of inductor L, $i_2 = 0$ at $t = 0$.

From the original equations, putting $i = i_1 = i_2 = 0$,

$$LD(i_1 + i_2) + L_1Di_1 = v$$

$$LD(i_1 + i_2) = v, \text{ since } (1/DC)i_2 = 0,$$

if the capacitor is initially uncharged.

Therefore, $L_1Di_1 = 0$ or $Di_1 = 0$. This is the second condition. Also, $Di_2 = v/L$.

Differentiating the original equations yields

$$\{(R + R_1)D + (L + L_1)D^2\}i_1 + (RD + LD^2)i_2 = Dv$$

giving

$$(L + L_1)D^2i_1 + Rv/L + LD^2i_2 = Dv$$

and

$$(RD + LD^2)i_1 + \{(R + R_2)D + LD^2 + 1/C\}i_2 = Dv$$

giving

$$LD^2i_1 + (R + R_2)v/L + LD^2i_2 = Dv$$

Thus, $L_1D^2i_1 = R_2v/L$ or $D^2i_1 = R_2v/LL_1$, which is the third condition.

Transients in circuits with mutual inductance

Two methods of determining the steady-state alternating currents in circuits with mutual inductance are given in Chapter 8, the basic mutual inductance method and the transformer method. Both these are also applicable to transient problems. The transformer concept is particularly valuable when the coupling is very nearly perfect, as in an iron-cored transformer, since it enables a reasonable result to be obtained in spite of the variable mutual inductance. Both methods are illustrated below.

* See, for example, H. T. H. Piaggio, *An Elementary Treatise on Differential Equations and their Applications*, Chapter III, pp. 30–2 (G. Bell & Sons, 1940).

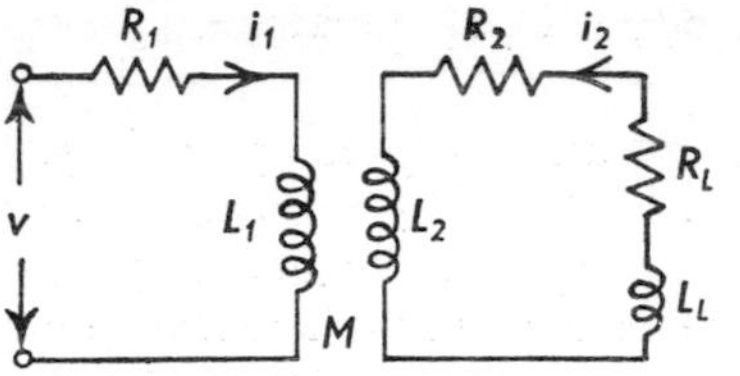

FIG. 12.17

Consider the circuit of Fig. 12.17. The voltage v is suddenly applied to the primary, giving

$$v = (R_1 + L_1D)i_1 + MDi_2$$

and $$0 = \{(R_2 + R_L) + (L_2 + L_L)D\}i_2 + MDi_1$$

or $$i_2 = -MDi_1/(R + LD)$$

where $$R = (R_2 + R_L) \text{ and } L = (L_2 + L_L)$$

Substituting for i_2 in the first equation, $v = (R_1 + L_1Di_1) - M^2D^2i_1/(R + LD)$

$$\therefore \quad (R + LD)v = (R_1 + L_1D)(R + LD)i_1 - M^2D^2i_1$$
$$= \{R_1R + (R_1L + RL_1)D + (L_1L - M^2)D^2\}i_1$$

This is a perfectly straightforward second-order differential equation which may be solved by the normal method of particular integral and complementary function. However, the initial conditions are not quite so obvious as in a circuit without mutual inductance. For this circuit the roots of the auxiliary equation are

$$m = [-(R_1L + RL_1) \pm \sqrt{\{(R_1L + RL_1)^2 - 4R_1R(L_1L - M^2)\}}]/2(L_1L - M^2).$$

The term under the square-root sign may be re-arranged to $\{(R_1L - RL_1)^2 + 4R_1RM\}$ which is always positive. The roots are therefore real and the transient current is of exponential form, and not oscillatory.

It has been stated previously that, in a circuit with self-inductance, the current cannot change instantaneously and this is true, but the more fundamental axiom is that the *flux-linkage* of a circuit cannot change instantaneously. (This is known as the constant flux-linkage theorem.) This means that, in the case of the circuit of Fig. 12.17, neither the primary flux linkage, $(L_1i_1 + Mi_2)$, nor the secondary flux linkage, $(Mi_1 + Li_2)$, can change instantaneously. Thus, if i_1' and i_2' are the current *changes* between the time immediately *before* the initiation of the transient and immediately after, then $(L_1i_1' + Mi_2') = 0$ and $(Mi_1' + Li_2') = 0$, whence $i_1'(M^2 - L_1L) = 0$. Therefore, $i_1' = 0$, *unless* $M^2 = L_1L$, *i.e.* unless the coupling is perfect and $L_L = 0$, so that $L = L_2$ and $M^2 = L_1L_2$. Likewise $i_2' = 0$ unless $M^2 = L_1L_2$ and $L_L = 0$.

EXAMPLE. In the circuit of Fig. 12.17, $R_1 = 20\ \Omega$, $R = R_2 + R_L = 100\ \Omega$, $L_1 = 2$ H, $L = L_2 + L_L = 4$ H and $M = 2$ H. A sinusoidal voltage of peak value 100 V and frequency 50 c/s is suddenly applied to the primary at the instant when it is a maximum. Derive expressions for the currents i_1 and i_2 at any time t after the voltage is applied. How would the solution be obtained to this problem if the reactor L_L was replaced by a capacitor?

Solution. $v = 100 \cos(314t)$ and the differential equation is

$$(4D^2 + 280D + 2{,}000)i_1 = (100 + 4D)(100 \cos 314t)$$

or $$(D^2 + 70D + 500)i_1 = 2{,}500 \cos 314t - 31{,}400 \sin 314t.$$

The auxiliary equation is

$$m^2 + 70m + 500 = 0, \text{ giving } m = -61{\cdot}9 \text{ or } -8{\cdot}1$$

The complementary function $i_1' = A \exp(-61{\cdot}9t) + B \exp(-8{\cdot}1t)$. To obtain the particular integral, put $\mathbf{V} = 100 + j0$,

$$Dv = 100j\omega$$
$$D = j314,\ D^2 = -98{,}696$$
$$\therefore\ (-98{,}196 + j21{,}990)\mathbf{I} = 2{,}500 + j31{,}400$$
$$\mathbf{I} = (1 + j12{\cdot}57)/(-39{\cdot}3 + j8{\cdot}8) = 0{\cdot}044 - j0{\cdot}283$$

so $$i_1'' = 0{\cdot}287 \cos(314t - 81^\circ\ 3').$$

The complete solution is

$$\underline{i_1 = A \exp(-61{\cdot}9t) + B \exp(-8{\cdot}1t) + 0{\cdot}287 \cos(314t - 81^\circ\ 3')}$$

At $t = 0$, $i_1 = 0$, $\therefore\ A + B + 0{\cdot}0446 = 0$.

From the first equation,

$$MDi_2 = v - (R_1 + L_1D)i_1$$

and from the second

$$(R + LD)i_2 = -MDi_1$$

and eliminating Di_2 from these,

$$i_2 = -Lv/MR + LR_1i_1/MR + (L_1L - M^2)Di_1/MR$$
$$= -2 \cos 314t + 0{\cdot}4i_1 + 0{\cdot}02Di_1$$
$$= \underline{-2 \cos 314t - 0{\cdot}838A \exp(-61{\cdot}9t) + 0{\cdot}238B \exp(-8{\cdot}1t)}$$
$$\underline{+ 0{\cdot}1146 \cos(314t - 81^\circ\ 3') - 1{\cdot}81 \sin(314t - 81^\circ\ 3')}$$

and since $i_2 = 0$ at $t = 0$,

$$-0{\cdot}838A + 0{\cdot}238B - 0{\cdot}2232 = 0.$$

From the two equations involving A and B, A is found to be $-0{\cdot}2176$ and B is found to be $0{\cdot}173$.

If the reactor L_L is replaced by a capacitor C, the voltage equations are

$$v = (R_1 + L_1D)i_1 + MDi_2$$

and
$$0 = \{R + L_2D + 1/DC\}i_2 + MDi_1$$

from which, eliminating i_2, the result is the third-order differential equation,

$$\{(L_1L_2 - M^2)D^3 + (L_1R + R_1L_2)D^2 + (R_1R + L_1/C)D + R_1/C\}i_1 = (L_2D^2 + RD + 1/C)v$$

Consider now the transformer under transient conditions. When the coupling of a mutual inductance is very high, and particularly in the case of a transformer with a laminated-iron core, it may be more convenient to deal with the transient problem in a different way from that given above. It may also be permissible to make certain approximations which lead to simplification of the differential equations and make it possible to deal with the problem of a variation in the coefficient of mutual inductance due to variation in the permeance of an iron core.

Consider the circuit shown in Fig. 12.18, in which the coils are assumed to be wound in the same direction on the iron core, so that a

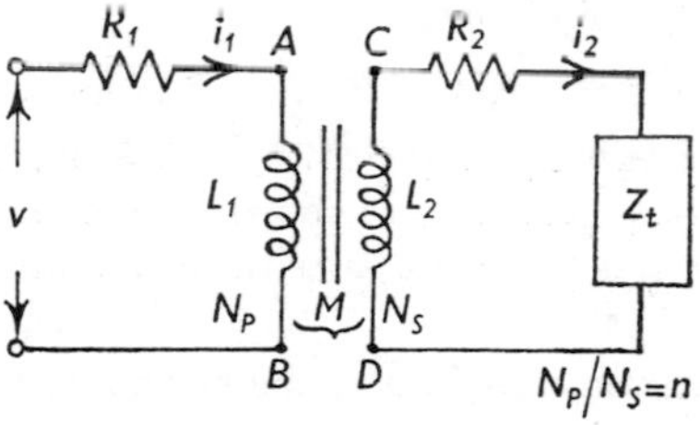

FIG. 12.18

direct current flowing from A to B produces the same direction of core flux as one flowing from C to D. It is convenient in this case to take the directions of the currents as shown, rather than as in the previous examples, giving a negative mutual inductance ($-M$). The parameters of the transformer, R_1, L_1, R_2 and L_2 are as shown and the secondary load has an 'operational' impedance Z_t. This means, for example, that for a resistor in series with an inductor $Z_t = (R + LD)$.

Then
$$v = (R_1 + L_1D)i_1 - MDi_2$$

and
$$0 = (R_2 + DL_2 + Z_t)i_2 - MDi_1$$

Let $L_1 = L_1' + l_1$ and $L_2 = L_2' + l_2$, where $L_1'L_2' = M^2$ and l_1 and l_2 are the 'leakage' inductances (see Chapter 8). Then $L_1'/L_2' =$

$(N_p/N_s)^2 = n^2$, where N_p and N_s are the numbers of primary and secondary turns respectively.

Also, let $i_1' = \{\sqrt{(L_2'/L_1')}\}i_2 = i_2/n$

Then $\quad v = \{R_1 + L_1'D + l_1D)\}i_1 - \{\sqrt{(L_1'L_2')}\sqrt{(L_1'/L_2')}\}Di_1'$

or $\quad v = (R_1 + l_1D)i_1 + L_1'D(i_1 - i_1')$.

This equation indicates that an equivalent circuit as shown in Fig. 12.19 can be drawn.

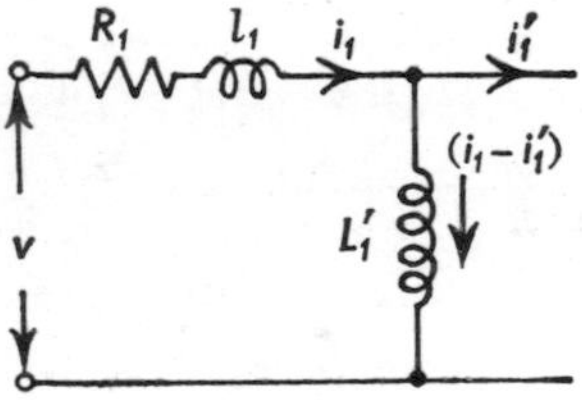

FIG. 12.19

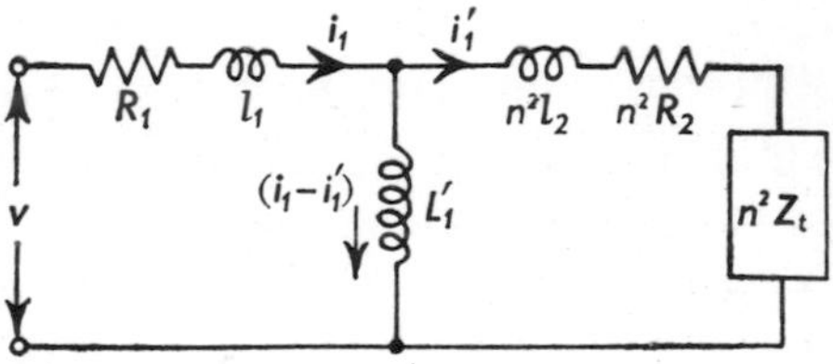

FIG. 12.20

From the secondary-circuit equation,

$$0 = (R_2 + l_2D + Z_t)i_2 + L_2'Di_2 - \sqrt{(L_1'L_2')}Di_1$$

or $0 = \sqrt{(L_1'/L_2')}(R_2 + l_2D + Z_t)i_1' + \sqrt{(L_1'L_2')}Di_1' - \sqrt{(L_1'L_2')}Di_1$

Multiplying by $\sqrt{(L_1'/L_2')} = n$

$$0 = n^2(R_2 + l_2D + Z_t)i_1' - L_1'D(i_1 - i_1').$$

This gives the secondary equivalent circuit (referred to the primary) so that the whole arrangement is as shown in Fig. 12.20.

A similar circuit can be obtained with all quantities referred to the secondary.

EXAMPLE. In a certain transformer the constants are (see Figs. 12.18 and 12.19):

$v = 100 \sin 314t$ volts, $R_1 = 0{\cdot}8\ \Omega$, $R_2 = 0{\cdot}2\ \Omega$, $l_1 = 0{\cdot}002$ H, $l_2 = 0{\cdot}001$ H, $L_1' = 1$ H, $M^2/L_1L_2 = (0{\cdot}994)^2$,
$n = 2$ and $Z_t = 5\ \Omega$ (pure resistance).

Determine the current i_1 as a function of the time t after applying the voltage.

Solution.

$$v = (R_1 + l_1D)i_1 + L_1'D(i_1 - i_1')$$

$$\therefore \quad 100 \sin 314t = (0{\cdot}8 + 0{\cdot}002D)i_1 + 1D(i_1 - i_1')$$

Also, $\quad 0 = n^2(R_2 + l_2D + Z_t)i_1' - L_1'D(i_1 - i_1')$

$$\therefore \quad 0 = 4(5{\cdot}2 + 0{\cdot}001D)i_1' - 1D(i_1 - i_1')$$

or $\quad Di_1 = (20{\cdot}8 + 1{\cdot}004D)i_1'$.

Eliminating i_1' from these equations

$$(0{\cdot}006D^2 + 21{\cdot}645D + 16{\cdot}64)i_1 = 100(20{\cdot}8 + 1{\cdot}004D)\sin 314t$$

To solve the auxiliary equation, $0{\cdot}006m^2 + 21{\cdot}645m + 16{\cdot}64 = 0$, requires care because one root is large and the other very small. Consider the equation $a(m+\alpha)(m+\beta) = 0$ where $\alpha \gg \beta$

$$am^2 + a(\alpha+\beta)m + a\alpha\beta = 0$$

Then, equating the first two terms to zero, $m = -(\alpha+\beta)$ which is very nearly $-\alpha$ and equating the second and third terms to zero, $m = -\alpha\beta/\alpha + \beta \simeq -\beta$.

Thus, in the above equation, $m = -3{,}607$ or $-0{\cdot}77$ and the complementary function is

$$i = A\exp(-3{,}607t) + B\exp(-0{\cdot}77t).$$

The particular integral is obtained by replacing D by $j\omega = j314$

$$\{0{\cdot}006 \times 314^2 + 21{\cdot}645 \times j314 + 16{\cdot}64\}\mathbf{I} = 100\{20{\cdot}8 + j1{\cdot}004 \times 314\}$$

$$\therefore \quad \mathbf{I} = 4{\cdot}58 - j0{\cdot}695$$

so

$$i = 4{\cdot}63 \sin(314t - 8^\circ\ 39')$$

The complete solution is therefore

$$i_1 = A\exp(-3{,}607t) + B\exp(-0{\cdot}77t) + 4{\cdot}63\sin(314t - 8^\circ\ 39').$$

At $t = 0$, $i_1 = 0$, so that $A + B = 0{\cdot}7$.

From the original equations,

$$(0{\cdot}8 + 1{\cdot}002D)i_1 - Di_1' = 100\sin 314t$$

and

$$20{\cdot}8i_1' - Di_1 + 1{\cdot}004Di_1' = 0$$

or

$$20{\cdot}7i_1' - 0{\cdot}995Di_1 + Di_1' = 0$$

Eliminating Di_1' from these equations

$$20{\cdot}7i_1' = -100\sin 314t + 0{\cdot}8i_1 + 0{\cdot}007Di_1$$

or

$$20{\cdot}7i_1' = -100\sin 314t - 24{\cdot}45A\exp(-3{,}607t) + 0{\cdot}8B\exp(-0{\cdot}77t + 3{\cdot}71\sin(314t - 8^\circ\ 39') + 10{\cdot}2\cos(314t - 8^\circ\ 39')$$

At $t = 0$, $i_1' = 0$

$$\therefore \quad -24{\cdot}45A + 0{\cdot}8B - 0{\cdot}41 + 10{\cdot}05 = 0$$

$$\textit{i.e.} \quad 30{\cdot}6A - B = 12{\cdot}05.$$

From the two equations involving A and B,

$$A = 0{\cdot}403 \text{ and } B = 0{\cdot}30.$$

Thus, the complete solution is

$$\underline{i_1 = 0{\cdot}403\exp(-3{,}607t) + 0{\cdot}30\exp(-0{\cdot}77t) + 4{\cdot}63\sin(314t - 8^\circ\ 39').}$$

Approximate solution

An approximate solution may be found on the assumption that the current $(i_1 - i_1')$ through the 1 H shunt inductor is small compared with i_1 and i_1' and is slow to rise to its final value. The first stage is therefore to neglect this shunt current and assume $i_1 = i_1'$, so that

$$(21 \cdot 6 + 0 \cdot 006D)i_1 = 100 \sin 314t$$

The solution of this equation, putting $i_1 = 0$ at $t = 0$, is

$$i_1' = 0 \cdot 402 \exp(-3{,}600t) + 4 \cdot 61 \sin (314t - 5°).$$

Then, considering the primary circuit, assuming that i_1' is as above,

$$(0 \cdot 8 + 0 \cdot 002D)i_1 + 1D(i_1 - i_1') = 100 \sin 314t$$

Writing $(i_1 - i_1') = i$, so that $i_1 = (i + i_1')$

$$(0 \cdot 8 + 0 \cdot 002D)(i + i_1') + Di = 100 \sin 314t$$

or

$$(0 \cdot 8 + 1 \cdot 002D)i = 100 \sin 314t - (0 \cdot 8 + 0 \cdot 002D)i_1'.$$

Assuming that i_1' has reached its steady-state value of $4 \cdot 61 \sin (314t - 5°)$, before i is of appreciable magnitude, the equation becomes:

$$(0 \cdot 8 + 1 \cdot 002D)i = 100 \sin 314t - 3 \cdot 69 \sin (314t - 5°) - 2 \cdot 9 \cos (314t - 5°).$$

The complementary function is

$$i = B \exp(-0 \cdot 795t).$$

Neglecting the 5° phase angle, and putting $D = j314$, the particular integral is given by,

$$\mathbf{I} = \{(100 - 3 \cdot 69) - j2 \cdot 9\}/(0 \cdot 8 + j315)$$

or

$$\mathbf{I} = 0 \cdot 01 - j0 \cdot 304$$

i.e.

$$i = 0 \cdot 304 \sin (314t - 88° \, 7').$$

The complete solution is therefore:

$$i = B \exp(-0 \cdot 795t) + 0 \cdot 304 \sin (314t - 88° \, 7')$$

and since $i = 0$ at $t = 0$,

$$B = 0 \cdot 304 \sin 88° \, 7' = 0 \cdot 304$$

$$\therefore \quad i = 0 \cdot 304 \sin (314t - 88° \, 7') + 0 \cdot 304 \exp(-0 \cdot 795t)$$

and since $i_1 = (i + i_1')$,

$$\underline{i_1 = 0 \cdot 402 \exp(-3{,}600t) + 0 \cdot 304 \exp(-0 \cdot 795t) + 4 \cdot 68 \sin (314t - 12° \, 8')}.$$

This compares reasonably well with the more accurate solution.

PROBLEMS

1. A coil having a resistance R and inductance L is connected across a d.c. voltage E. Prove that the current at a time t after switching on is $(1 - a)E/R$, where $\ln(a) = -Rt/L$. If the circuit is then broken show that the current after a further time t is $a(1 - a)E/R$. [S.U.]

2. A series circuit consisting of a 2,500 Ω resistor and a 4 μF capacitor is connected to a 300 V d.c. supply. A glow discharge tube is connected across the capacitor and is triggered to strike every 20 ms. The capacitor is discharged completely in a negligibly short time when the tube strikes. Determine the voltage across the capacitor when the tube strikes and find the r.m.s. value of the charging current. [*Ans.* 260 V, 60 mA.]

3. A coil having a self-inductance of 5 H and a resistance of 4 Ω is connected to a battery of voltage 8 V. Plot a curve showing the rate of increase of current through the coil after switching on and calculate how long it takes before the current reaches 1·9 A.
What is the time-constant of this circuit?
[*Ans.* 3·74 sec, 1·25 sec.]

4. A circuit consisting of a 20 Ω resistor in series with a 0·2 H inductor is supplied from 200 V, r.m.s., 50 c/s, a.c. mains. Deduce equations showing how the current varies with time if the supply is suddenly switched on: (*a*) at the instant when the voltage is zero, (*b*) at the instant when the voltage is a maximum. [S.U.]
[*Ans.* (*a*) $\{4{\cdot}11e^{-100t} + 4{\cdot}32\sin(314t - 72°\,16')\}$ A,
(*b*) $\{-1{\cdot}245e^{-100t} + 4{\cdot}32\cos(314t - 72°\,16')\}$ A.]

5. A circuit consisting of a 20 Ω resistor, a 20 mH inductor and a 100 μF capacitor in series is connected to a 200 V, d.c. supply. The capacitor is initially uncharged. Determine the equation relating the instantaneous current to the time, and find the maximum instantaneous current. [S.U.] [*Ans.* $\{20e^{-500t}\sin 500t\}$ A, 6·44 A.]

6. A resistor and inductor in series are supplied with an alternating voltage $v = 100\sin 1{,}500t$, the *steady-state* current being 5 A, r.m.s. at a power-factor of 0·6. If the supply is switched on at the instant when the voltage is zero, find the expression for the instantaneous current at time t. [S.U.] [*Ans.* $\{5{\cdot}656e^{-1{,}130t} + 7{\cdot}07\sin(1{,}500t - 53°\,8')\}$ A.]

7. A 40 Ω resistor and a 50 μF capacitor are connected in series and supplied with an alternating voltage $v = 283\sin 314t$. The supply is switched on at the instant when the voltage is zero. Determine the expression for the instantaneous current at time t. [S.U.]
[*Ans.* $\{-3{\cdot}18e^{-500t} + 3{\cdot}76\sin(314t + 57°\,50')\}$ A.]

8. A d.c. voltage of 100 V is suddenly applied to a circuit consisting of a 100 Ω resistor, a 0·1 H inductor and a 10 μF capacitor in series. The capacitor is initially uncharged. Obtain the equation which shows how the capacitor voltage varies with time. [S.U.]
[*Ans.* $\{100 - 115{\cdot}3e^{-500t}\sin(866t + 60°)\}$ V.]

9. The voltage $v = 200\sin 314t$ is suddenly applied at $t = 0$ to a circuit consisting of a 10 Ω resistor in series with a 0·1 H inductor. Deduce an equation showing how the current varies with time. [S.U.]
[*Ans.* $\{5{\cdot}78e^{-100t} + 6{\cdot}06\sin(314t - 72°\,20')\}$ A.]

10. A 20 Ω resistor, a 0·01 H inductor and a 100 μF capacitor are connected in series. A d.c. voltage of 100 V is suddenly applied to the circuit. Obtain the equation showing how the current through the circuit varies with time. Find the maximum current and the time at which it occurs. [S.U.] [*Ans.* $\{10{,}000te^{-1{,}000t}\}$ A; 3·67 A; 0·001 sec.]

11. A resonant L, C, R circuit has the following constants: $C = 0{\cdot}003$ μF, $L = 0{\cdot}001$ H, $R = 10$ Ω. The capacitor is charged and allowed to discharge through the circuit. Find the number of oscillations which occur up to the point where the amplitude of oscillation is reduced to 10% of the initial amplitude. [*Ans.* 43.]

12. A coil of resistance 10 Ω and self-inductance 10 mH is coupled to a second coil of self-inductance 5 mH and resistance 10 Ω. The coefficient of mutual inductance is 5 mH. The second coil is short-circuited and the first is then connected to a 200 V d.c. supply. Show that the instantaneous current in the first coil is given by

$$i = [20 + (179 \times 10^5) \exp(-0{\cdot}76t) - (199 \times 10^5) \exp(-5{\cdot}24t)] \text{ A}$$

where t is in millisecs.

13. A 100 μF capacitor is shunted by a 1,000 Ω resistor, the combination being connected in series with another 1,000 Ω resistor. With the capacitor initially uncharged, the circuit is connected to a 100 V d.c. supply. Show that the instantaneous current through the capacitor is given by

$$i_1 = \{0{\cdot}1 \exp(-t/20)\} \text{ A},$$

and the total current by:

$$i_2 = 0{\cdot}05\{1 - \exp(-t/20)\} \text{ A},$$

t being measured in seconds.

14. A circuit consisting of a 20 Ω resistor, a 2·5 μF capacitor and a 2 mH inductor, connected in series, is supplied at its resonant frequency from a source of 10 V peak. If the supply is switched on at the instant when the voltage is a maximum, show that the current is given by

$$i = [0{\cdot}5 \cos(14{,}142t) + 0{\cdot}535 \exp(-5{,}000t) \sin(13{,}200t - 69^\circ\ 18')\text{A}]$$

where t is in seconds.

CHAPTER 13

THERMIONIC-VALVE CIRCUITS

Equivalent circuit of a triode valve

It will be assumed that the reader is familiar with the constructions and characteristics of diode, triode, tetrode and pentode valves, so these will not be discussed. It will also be assumed that the reader knows how to obtain the amplification factor (μ), the mutual conductance (g_m) and the anode slope resistance (r_a) of a triode from the valve characteristics. These three quantities are defined below in terms of changes in anode voltage (V_a), anode current (I_a) and grid voltage (V_g).

Amplification factor

$$\mu = -(\partial V_a/\partial V_g)_{Ia \text{ constant}}$$

Mutual conductance

$$g_m = (\partial I_a/\partial V_g)_{Va \text{ constant}}$$

Anode slope resistance

$$r_a = (\partial V_a/\partial I_a)_{Vg \text{ constant}}$$

The anode current of a triode depends on the anode and grid voltages, *i.e.* $I_a = f(V_a, V_g)$

$$\therefore \quad \delta I_a = (\partial I_a/\partial V_g)_{Va}\, \delta V_g + (\partial I_a/\partial V_a)_{Vg}\, \delta V_a$$

$$= g_m\, \delta V_g + \delta V_a/r_a$$

If $\quad \delta I_a = 0$, I_a is constant and

$$0 = g_m\, \delta V_g + \delta V_a/r_a$$

$$\therefore \quad g_m r_a = -(\delta V_a/\delta V_g)_{Ia} = \mu.$$

The above expression for δI_a may be written as

$$\delta V_a = r_a\, \delta I_a - g_m r_a\, \delta V_g$$

$$i.e. \quad \delta V_a = r_a\, \delta I_a - \mu\, \delta V_g$$

Thus the valve (Fig. 13.1 (*a*)) can be replaced by the equivalent circuit shown in Fig. 13.1 (*b*).

It is important to note that no steady quantities are indicated on the diagram. The equivalent circuit is concerned only with *changes* about the operating point on the valve characteristic. D.C. voltages are necessary to operate the valve and to arrange for it to work at the correct operating point but they do not enter into the equivalent circuit. It should also be noted that the equivalent circuit has been derived without any mention of the external anode circuit, thus the circuit is valid for any type of load, whether it be a resistor, an impedor or a second valve. The only restriction on the use of the equivalent circuit is that μ, r_a and g_m must remain reasonably constant over the operating range of the

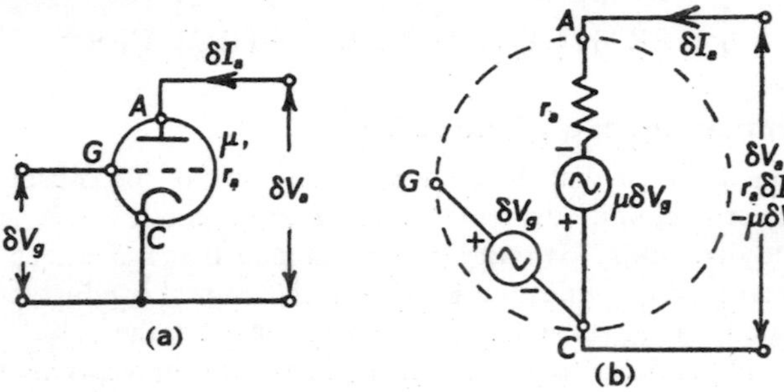

FIG. 13.1

valve characteristics. It is very important to observe that the positive side of the $\mu\ \delta V_g$ generator is *always* connected to C and δV_g is the *drop* in voltage from G to C, *i.e.* G is connected to the positive side of generator δV_g.

To draw the equivalent circuit for an arrangement containing valves the following rules should be observed.

(*a*) Draw the circuit diagram, such as Fig. 13.1 (*a*) and mark the points A, G and C.

(*b*) Replace the valve by the resistance r_a and generator $\mu\ \delta V_g$, again marking points A, G and C on the second diagram, as in Fig. 13.1 (*b*).

(*c*) Transfer all the other elements of the original circuit to the equivalent circuit. In doing this the relative positions of the various elements should be the same on the two diagrams.

(*d*) Replace all direct voltages by short-circuits because d.c. sources act as short-circuits to changing currents.

As an example consider a simple triode amplifier with resistive load (Fig. 13.2 (*a*)).

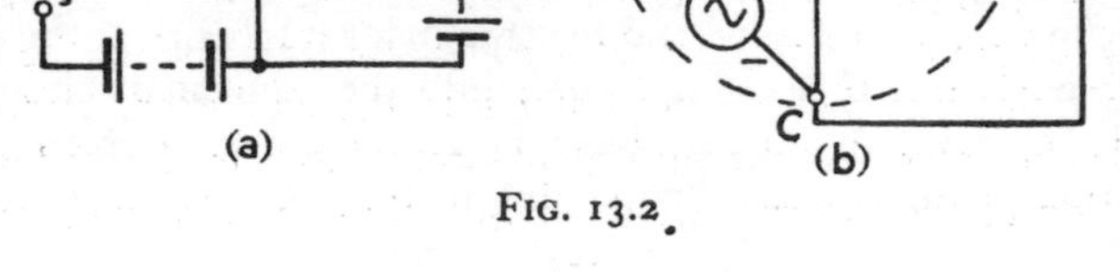

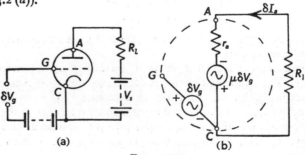

FIG. 13.2.

Applying the above rules the equivalent circuit is found to be that shown in Fig. 13.2 (*b*).

The voltage across R_l, the output voltage of the amplifier, is therefore, $\mu\,\delta V_g\,.\,R_l/(r_a + R_l)$ and so the gain A is $\mu R_l/(r_a + R_l)$. Thus, when $R_l \gg r_a$, $A \rightarrow \mu$. The power output $= R_l(\delta I_a)^2 = R_l(\mu\,\delta V_g)^2/(r_a + R_l)^2$. The maximum power output is obtained when $R_l = r_a$ and is $\mu^2(\delta V_g)^2/4r_a$.

EXAMPLE. The circuit illustrated in Fig. 13.3 may be used as a d.c. voltmeter with a high input impedance. Draw the equivalent circuit

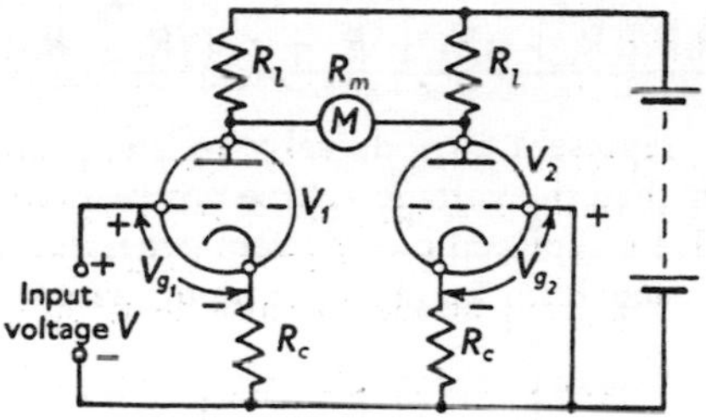

FIG. 13.3

of the arrangement and then determine the current through the meter M, which has a resistance R_m. The amplification factor and anode slope resistance of each valve is μ and r_a respectively.

Solution. The equivalent circuit is shown in Fig. 13.4. Let the currents flowing be as illustrated.

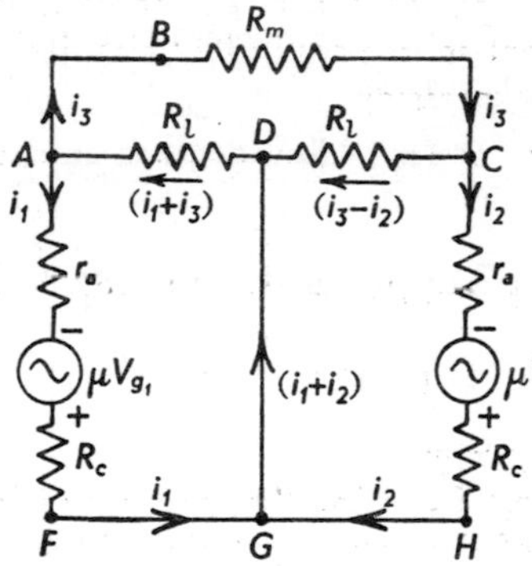

FIG. 13.4

For mesh ABCA,

$$R_m i_3 + R_l(i_3 - i_2) + R_l(i_1 + i_3) = 0$$

For mesh ADGFA,

$$r_a i_1 - \mu V_{g1} + R_c i_1 + R_l(i_1 + i_3) = 0$$

For mesh CHGDC,

$$r_a i_2 - \mu V_{g2} + R_c i_2 - R_l(i_3 - i_2) = 0$$

It should also be noted that V_{g1} is the voltage drop from grid to cathode of valve V_1; it is *not* the input voltage.

$$V_{g1} = V - R_c i_1$$

Similarly, $$V_{g2} = -R_c i_2.$$

Eliminating V_{g1}, V_{g2}, i_1 and i_2 from the above equations it is found that the current through the meter

$$i_3 = \underline{-\mu R_l V/[(R_l + \mu R_c + R_c + r_a)(2R_l + R_m) - 2R_l^2]}$$

It is possible to represent a triode valve by a current-source equivalent circuit, rather than the voltage-source representation, discussed so far. Here the valve is replaced by a current generator which supplies a current $g_m \delta V_g$ flowing from anode to cathode within the valve, and

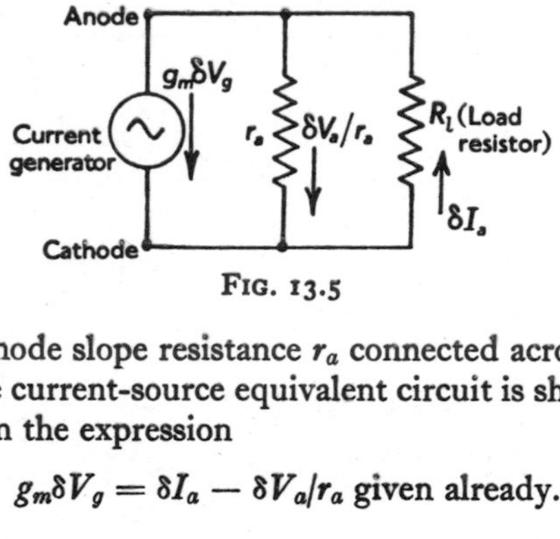

FIG. 13.5

which has the anode slope resistance r_a connected across the generator terminals. The current-source equivalent circuit is shown in Fig. 13.5 and follows from the expression

$$g_m \delta V_g = \delta I_a - \delta V_a / r_a \text{ given already.}$$

Load lines

The voltage (V_a) between the anode and cathode of the valve in Fig. 13.2 (*a*) is given by

$$V_a = V_s - R_l I_a$$

where I_a is the anode current.

If I_a is plotted against V_a, using the same set of axes as for the static characteristic curves of the valve, a straight line, called the *load line*, results (Fig. 13.6 (*a*)). The line passes through the point $V_a = V_s$ when $I_a = 0$ and its slope depends on R_l as shown. If R_l is fixed and the supply voltage V_s varies a family of curves similar to those shown in Fig. 13.6 (*b*) is obtained.

Once the load line is drawn it is only necessary to know one of the three quantities I_a, V_a or V_g in order to determine the other two. The

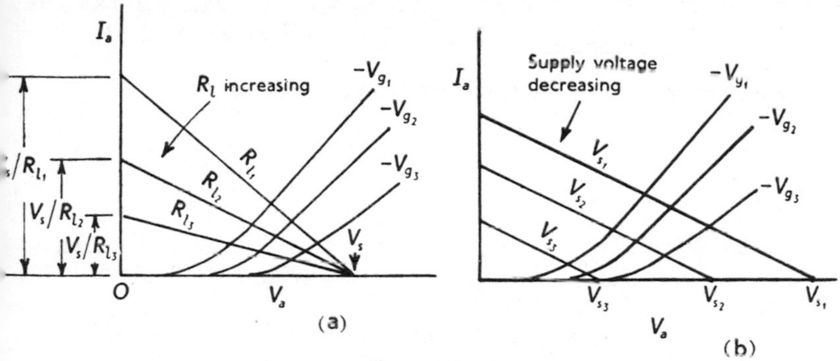

FIG. 13.6

load line also gives by inspection such information as the anode-current variation for a given grid-voltage swing.

EXAMPLE. A certain diode has a static I_a/V_a characteristic represented by the following figures:

I_a(mA)	0·52	1·17	1·90	2·78	3·85	5·15	6·50
V_a(V)	25	50	75	100	125	150	175

The diode is connected in series with a resistor of 30,000 Ω and a battery of 300 V. A resistor of 60,000 Ω is placed between the anode and cathode of the valve. Find the current through the diode. [S.U.]

Solution. Let the voltage across the valve be V_a and the current through it I_a mA.

Then $$V_a = 300 - 30(V_a/60 + I_a)$$

i.e. $$V_a = 200 - 20I_a.$$

This is the equation of the load line.

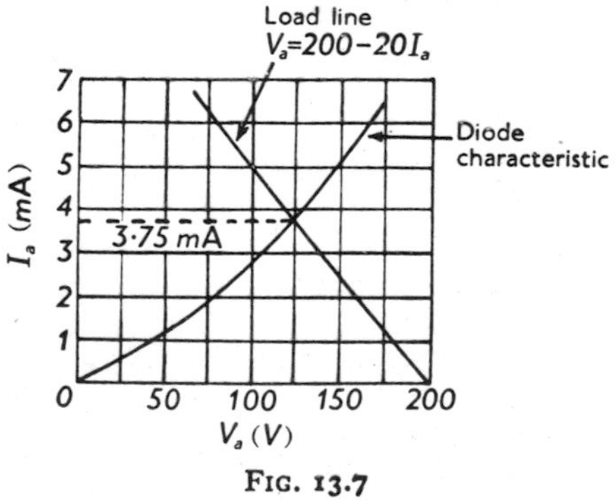

FIG. 13.7

At the point of intersection of the I_a/V_a curve and the load line (Fig. 13.7) $\underline{I_a = 3{\cdot}75 \text{ mA}}$ which is the current through the diode.

Rectification. Single-phase half-wave rectifier

Consider Fig. 13.8 which shows a high-vacuum diode connected in series with a resistive load R_l across the secondary of a transformer

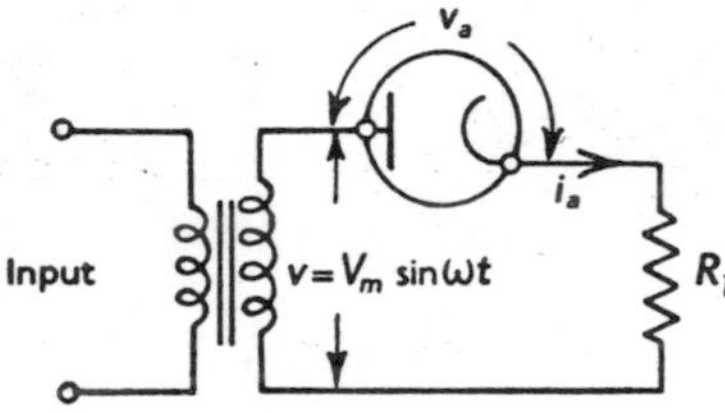

FIG. 13.8

which will be assumed perfect. The currents and voltages shown represent instantaneous values.

Thus,
$$v_a = v - i_a R_l \quad . \quad . \quad . \quad . \quad . \qquad (13.1)$$
which is the equation of the load line.

If this line is plotted along with the static characteristic of the diode, the current flowing in the circuit can be found, for any given value of v.

When a sinusoidal voltage is applied at the input terminals of Fig. 13.8, the load current takes the form of half sine waves, separated by periods of 180° where the current is zero.

During conduction,
$$v_a = i_a r_a \quad . \quad . \quad . \quad . \quad . \quad . \qquad (13.2)$$
where r_a is the reciprocal of the slope of the static anode-current/anode voltage characteristic of the diode. This characteristic will be assumed to be a straight line through the origin so that r_a is taken as constant.

From (13.1) and (13.2),
$$v = v_a + i_a R_l = i_a(R_l + r_a) = V_m \sin \omega t \quad . \qquad (13.3)$$

Thus, $i_a = \{V_m/(R_l + r_a)\} \sin \omega t = I_m \sin \omega t = I_m \sin \theta$ when θ lies between 0 and π

and $i_a = 0$ when θ lies between π and 2π (13.4)

where
$$I_m = V_m/(R_l + r_a) \quad . \quad . \quad . \quad . \quad . \quad . \quad . \qquad (13.5)$$

The mean current ($I_{\text{d.c.}}$) through R_l
$$= \frac{1}{2\pi}\left[\int_0^{\pi} I_m \sin \theta \, d\theta + \int_{\pi}^{2\pi} 0 \, d\theta\right]$$
$$\textit{i.e.} \quad I_{\text{d.c.}} = I_m/\pi \quad . \quad . \quad . \quad . \quad . \qquad (13.6)$$

The r.m.s. current ($I_{r.m.s.}$) through R_l

$$= \left[\frac{1}{2\pi}\int_0^{\pi} (I_m \sin\theta)^2\, d\theta\right]^{\frac{1}{2}}$$

$$i.e.\quad I_{r.m.s.} = I_m/2 \quad . \quad . \quad . \quad . \quad (13.7)$$

It should be noted that this is not the same as the r.m.s. value of a sinusoidal current.

The total power (P) supplied to the anode circuit of the rectifier

$$= \frac{1}{2\pi}\int_0^{2\pi} (vi_a)\, d\theta = \frac{1}{2\pi}\int_0^{2\pi} i_a^2(R_l + r_a)\, d\theta$$

$$i.e.\quad P = (I_{r.m.s.})^2(R_l + r_a) \quad . \quad . \quad . \quad (13.8)$$

If the mean power supplied to the load ($P_{d.c.}$) is defined as

$\{I_{d.c.} \times$ d.c. voltage across the load $(V_{d.c.})\}$

$$P_{d.c.} = (I_{d.c.})^2(R_l) = (V_{d.c.})(I_{d.c.}) \quad . \quad . \quad (13.9)$$

Conversion efficiency of rectifier (η) $= (P_{d.c.}/P) \times 100\%$

$$i.e.\quad \eta = \left(\frac{I_{d.c.}}{I_{r.m.s.}}\right)^2 \times \frac{100}{(1 + r_a/R_l)}\% \quad . \quad . \quad (13.10)$$

Substituting (13.6) and (13.7) in (13.10):

$$\eta = 40{\cdot}6/(1 + r_a/R_l)\% \quad . \quad . \quad . \quad . \quad (13.11)$$

The theoretical maximum efficiency of the circuit is 40·6%. It should be noted that the overall efficiency of the arrangement considering the total power supplied will be much less than this figure.

The mean power $P_{d.c.}$

$$= (I_m/\pi)^2 R_l = \{V_m/(R_l + r_a)\}^2(R_l/\pi^2) = kR_l/(R_l + r_a)^2$$

where $\quad k = (V_m/\pi)^2$

The maximum value of $P_{d.c.}$ is obtained when $dP_{d.c.}/dR_l = 0$

i.e. when $r_a = R_l$.

Under this condition the value of η is 20·3%.

To calculate the regulation of the system, *i.e.* the variation of mean output voltage as a function of current, a relation between $I_{d.c.}$ and $V_{d.c.}$ is required. This can be obtained as follows

$$V_{d.c.} = I_{d.c.}R_l = V_m R_l/\pi(R_l + r_a)$$

$$\therefore\quad V_{d.c.} = (V_m/\pi) - I_{d.c.}r_a \quad . \quad . \quad . \quad . \quad (13.12)$$

When $I_{d.c.} = 0$, $V_{d.c.}$ has its maximum value of V_m/π. As $I_{d.c.}$ increases $V_{d.c.}$ falls linearly depending on the value of r_a. The regulation is poor.

Equation (13.11) can be modified to give η in terms of $I_{d.c.}$. The result is

$$\eta = 40{\cdot}6\{1 - (\pi r_a I_{d.c.}/V_m)\}\% \quad . \quad . \quad . \quad (13.13)$$

Ripple factor

Ripple factor is defined as the ratio of the r.m.s. value of the alternating components of a waveform to the mean value.

For any wave-shape the instantaneous alternating current component is $i_1 = i_a - I_{d.c.}$. Thus, the r.m.s. value ($I'_{r.m.s.}$) of i_1

$$= \sqrt{\frac{1}{2\pi}\int_0^{2\pi} (i_a - I_{d.c.})^2 \, d\theta}$$

$$\therefore \quad I'_{r.m.s.} = \sqrt{\frac{1}{2\pi}\int_0^{2\pi} (i_a^2 - 2i_a I_{d.c.} + I_{d.c.}^2) \, d\theta}$$

$$= \sqrt{I_{r.m.s.}^2 - 2I_{d.c.}^2 + I_{d.c.}^2} = \sqrt{I_{r.m.s.}^2 - I_{d.c.}^2}$$

Thus, the ripple factor $(r.f) = \sqrt{I_{r.m.s.}^2 - I_{d.c.}^2}/(I_{d.c.})$.

$$= \sqrt{(I_{r.m.s.}/I_{d.c.})^2 - 1} \quad . \quad . \quad . \quad (13.14)$$

For the single-phase, half-wave rectifier circuit, using (13.6) and (13.7),

$$r.f. = \sqrt{1{\cdot}57^2 - 1} = 1{\cdot}21 \quad . \quad . \quad . \quad (13.15)$$

Single-phase full-wave rectifier

Consider Fig. 13.9 (*a*) which shows a full-wave rectifier circuit employing two high-vacuum diodes. On the half-cycle when A is positive, valve V_1 conducts. Diode V_2 conducts during the next half-cycle when B is positive. The current through R_l thus takes the form shown in Fig. 13.9 (*b*). It will be assumed that the valves are identical. If the maximum value of the voltage from either end of the transformer secondary winding to the centre tap is V_m, it is evident from Fig. 13.9 (*b*) that $I_{d.c.}$ is now twice its previous value where only one half-cycle was used.

Thus, $\quad I_{d.c.} = 2I_m/\pi \quad . \quad . \quad . \quad . \quad . \quad . \quad . \quad (13.16)$

Also, $\quad I_{r.m.s.} = I_m/\sqrt{2} \quad . \quad . \quad . \quad . \quad . \quad (13.17)$

where, as before, $\quad I_m = V_m/(r_a + R_l) \quad . \quad . \quad . \quad (13.18)$

The mean power output

$$P_{d.c.} = (I_{d.c.})^2 R_l$$

$$= 4V_m^2 R_l/\pi^2(r_a + R_l)^2 \quad . \quad . \quad . \quad (13.19)$$

i.e. the mean power output is four times that of the half-wave circuit.

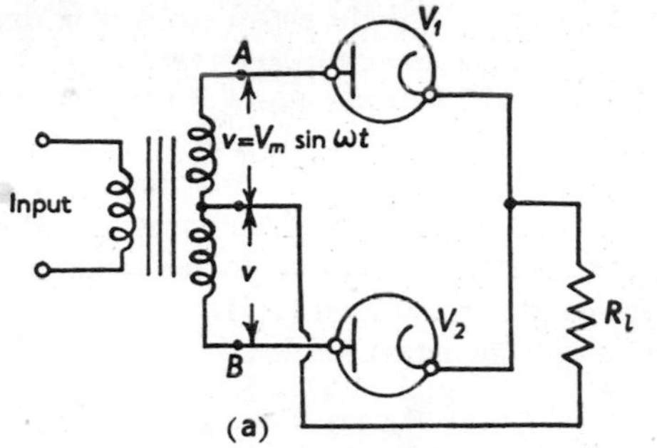

FIG. 13.9 (a)

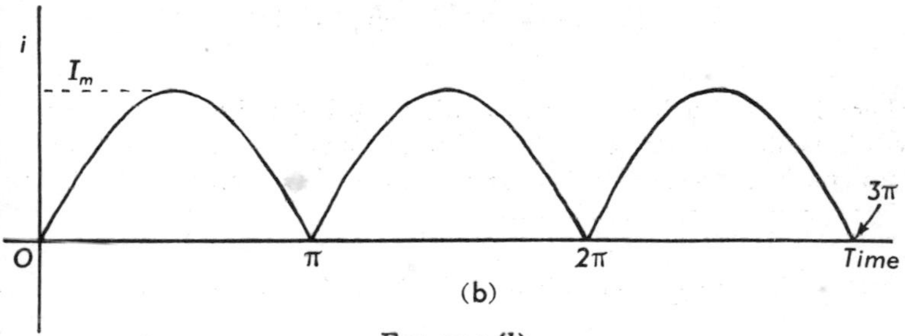

FIG. 13.9 (b)

The input power P is again

$$(I_{\text{r.m.s.}})^2(r_a + R_l) \quad . \quad . \quad . \quad . \quad (13.20)$$

$$\therefore \quad \eta = (P_{\text{d.c.}}/P) \times 100\% = 81{\cdot}2/(1 + r_a/R_l)\% \quad (13.21)$$

Thus, η is twice the value obtained for the half-wave case.

Here, $I_{\text{r.m.s.}}/I_{\text{d.c.}} = 1{\cdot}11$

so the ripple factor $(r.f)$

$$= \sqrt{1{\cdot}11^2 - 1} = 0{\cdot}482 \quad . \quad . \quad . \quad . \quad (13.22)$$

The mean output voltage

$$V_{\text{d.c.}} = 2V_m/\pi - I_{\text{d.c.}}r_a \quad . \quad . \quad . \quad . \quad (13.23)$$

Thus, in addition to better efficiency and a smaller ripple factor the full-wave circuit has the advantage over the half-wave arrangement of improved regulation.

Rectifier circuits with gas diodes

The single-phase half-wave and full-wave rectifier circuits already described may use gas valves instead of high-vacuum valves. Conduction in a gas diode does not begin until the anode/cathode voltage is equal to the striking value and the valve stops conducting when the voltage across it falls below the extinction value. During conduction the voltage drop across the valve is approximately constant. Current now flows through the valve for less than π.

Only a half-wave circuit employing a gas diode will be considered. It will be assumed that the voltage drop across the diode when it is conducting (V_c) is small compared with the maximum value of the secondary voltage of the transformer (V_m).

The instantaneous voltage across the load

$$= V_m \sin\theta - V_c$$

The mean load voltage

$$V_{\text{d.c.}} = \frac{1}{2\pi}\int_{\theta_s}^{\theta_e} (V_m \sin\theta - V_c)\, d\theta$$

where θ_s is the angle at which the diode strikes and θ_e is the angle at which conduction stops. When V_c/V_m is small, however, θ_s is nearly zero and θ_e is almost π and no great error will be introduced by using these limits of 0 and π.

$$\therefore \quad V_{\text{d.c.}} \simeq \frac{1}{2\pi}\int_0^{\pi} (V_m \sin\theta - V_c)\, d\theta = (V_m/\pi) - (V_c/2) \quad (13.24)$$

Thus, a gas diode gives a slightly smaller value of $V_{\text{d.c.}}$ than the maximum possible value attainable with a high-vacuum valve; but $V_{\text{d.c.}}$ does not now depend on the load current so the gas diode may produce a higher output voltage in practice.

The input power to the circuit

$$P = \frac{1}{2\pi}\int_{\theta_s}^{\theta_e} \frac{(V_m \sin\theta)(V_m \sin\theta - V_c)}{R_l}\, d\theta$$

$$\therefore \quad P \simeq \frac{1}{2\pi}\int_0^{\pi} \frac{(V_m \sin\theta)(V_m \sin\theta - V_c)}{R_l}\, d\theta$$

$$\simeq V_m^2(1 - 4V_c/\pi V_m)/4R_l \quad . \quad . \quad . \quad (13.25)$$

The mean power supplied to the load

$$P_{\text{d.c.}} = (V_{\text{d.c.}})^2/R_l = V_m^2(1 - \pi V_c/2V_m)^2/\pi^2 R_l \quad . \quad . \quad . \quad (13.26)$$

$\therefore$ the efficiency $\eta = P_{\text{d.c.}}/P$

$$= 4(1 - \pi V_c/2V_m)^2/\pi^2(1 - 4V_c/\pi V_m)$$

$$= 4(1 - \pi V_c/V_m + \pi^2 V_c^2/4V_m^2)/\pi^2(1 - 4V_c/\pi V_m) \quad . \quad (13.27)$$

But V_c/V_m is small, so dividing the numerator by the denominator of this last expression and neglecting powers of V_c/V_m greater than the first it is found that

$$\eta \simeq 4\{1 - (\pi - 4/\pi)V_c/V_m\}/\pi^2$$
$$\simeq 40{\cdot}6(1 - 1{\cdot}87\, V_c/V_m)\% \quad . \quad . \quad . \quad (13.28)$$

Thus, a gas diode also gives a slightly smaller value of η than the maximum possible value attainable with a high-vacuum valve but again η is independent of the load current in the present case. It can also be shown that the *r.f.* with a gas diode is slightly greater than the corresponding value calculated for the high-vacuum valve.

Effect of interelectrode capacitances of a triode when the valve is used as an amplifier

Consider the simple amplifier stage of Fig. 13.10 (*a*) with a load impedance Z_l. The equivalent circuit is illustrated in Fig. 13.10 (*b*).

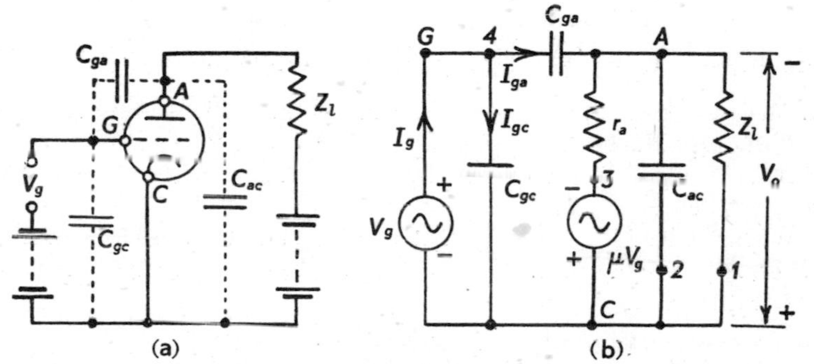

FIG. 13.10

Millman's Theorem can be employed to find the output voltage V_o. For this purpose points 1, 2, 3 and 4 are chosen.

$$\therefore \quad \mathbf{V}_o = \mathbf{V}_{14} = (\mu \mathbf{V}_g Y_a - \mathbf{V}_g \mathbf{Y}_{ga})/(Y_a + \mathbf{Y}_l + \mathbf{Y}_{ga} + \mathbf{Y}_{ac})$$

where $\quad Y_a = 1/r_a$, $\mathbf{Y}_l = 1/Z_l$, $\mathbf{Y}_{ga} = j\omega C_{ga}$ and $\mathbf{Y}_{ac} = j\omega C_{ac}$

The gain, $\mathbf{A} = -\mathbf{V}_o/\mathbf{V}_g = (\mathbf{Y}_{ga} - g_m)/(Y_a + \mathbf{Y}_l + \mathbf{Y}_{ga} + \mathbf{Y}_{ac})$

since $\quad g_m = \mu/r_a = \mu Y_a$

Thus, in general, **A** is complex.

If $\mathbf{Y}_{ga} = \mathbf{Y}_{ac} = 0$, $\mathbf{A} = -g_m/(Y_a + \mathbf{Y}_l) = -\mu \mathbf{Z}_l/(r_a + \mathbf{Z}_l)$ as shown previously.

For the whole audio-frequency range $\mathbf{Y}_{ga}$ can generally be neglected in comparison with g_m and, unless r_a is high, $(\mathbf{Y}_{ga} + \mathbf{Y}_{ac})$ will also be negligible compared with Y_a. Frequently, therefore, the simple expression for the gain will be sufficiently accurate. For frequencies above the audible range the complete expression for **A** must be used and if r_a is greater than about 10,000 Ω the formula to be used is

$$\mathbf{A} = -g_m/(Y_a + \mathbf{Y}_l + \mathbf{Y}_{ga} + \mathbf{Y}_{ac}).$$

Input admittance of a triode

Referring to Fig. 13.10 (*b*), the input admittance $\mathbf{Y}_g = \mathbf{I}_g/\mathbf{V}_g$.

But $\mathbf{I}_g = \mathbf{I}_{gc} + \mathbf{I}_{ga}$

$= \mathbf{V}_g\mathbf{Y}_{gc} + \mathbf{Y}_{ga}(\mathbf{V}_g + \mathbf{V}_o)$

where $\mathbf{Y}_{gc} = j\omega C_{gc}$

Also $\mathbf{V}_o = -\mathbf{A}\mathbf{V}_g$

so $\mathbf{I}_g = \{\mathbf{Y}_{gc} + \mathbf{Y}_{ga}(1 - \mathbf{A})\}\mathbf{V}_g$

$$\therefore \quad \mathbf{Y}_g = \mathbf{Y}_{gc} + (1 - \mathbf{A})\mathbf{Y}_{ga} = j\omega\{C_{gc} + (1 - \mathbf{A})C_{ga}\}$$

For a purely resistive load

$$A = -\mu R_l/(r_a + R_l)$$

and then $\mathbf{Y}_g = j\omega[C_{gc} + \{1 + \mu R_l/(r_a + R_l)\}C_{ga}]$

so that the input admittance is the same as that which would result if a pure capacitance $C_g = [C_{gc} + \{1 + \mu R_l/(r_a + R_l)\}C_{ga}]$ was connected from grid to cathode of the valve. If $C_{ga} = C_{gc} = 2\mu\mu$F and $A = 50$ then $C_g = 104\ \mu\mu$F.

When the load is not purely resistive, but takes the form of an impedance, **A** is complex of the form $a_1 + ja_2$. $\mathbf{Y}_g$ then consists of resistive and reactive components:

$$\mathbf{Y}_g = a_2\omega C_{ga} + j\omega\{C_{gc} + (1 - a_1)C_{ga}\}$$

The input circuit to the grid of the valve can therefore be considered as a resistor in parallel with a capacitor.

EXAMPLE. Calculate the gain, the input capacitance and the input resistance of a triode amplifier when the load is a coil having an inductance of 25 mH and a resistance of 3,000 Ω, and the frequency is 12,000 c/s. The amplification factor of the valve is 20 and the anode slope resistance is 8,000 Ω. The interelectrode capacitances are $C_{ga} = 3{\cdot}4\ \mu\mu$F, $C_{gc} = 3{\cdot}4\ \mu\mu$F and $C_{ac} = 3{\cdot}6\ \mu\mu$F.

Solution.

The gain $= (\mathbf{Y}_{ga} - g_m)/(Y_a + \mathbf{Y}_l + \mathbf{Y}_{ga} + \mathbf{Y}_{ac})$

Here, since $\omega = 2\pi \times 12{,}000$,

$\mathbf{Y}_{ac} = j\omega C_{ac} = j2{\cdot}71 \times 10^{-7}$ mho, $\mathbf{Y}_{ga} = j\omega C_{ga} = j2{\cdot}56 \times 10^{-7}$ mho,

$Y_a = 1/r_a = 1{\cdot}25 \times 10^{-4}$ mho, $g_m = 25 \times 10^{-4}$ mho,

$\mathbf{Y}_l = 1/(R_l + j\omega L) = 1/(3{,}000 + j1{,}885) = (2{\cdot}391 - j1{\cdot}502)10^{-4}$ mho.

$$\therefore \text{ the gain } (\mathbf{A}) = \frac{(2{\cdot}56 \times 10^{-7}) - (25 \times 10^{-4})}{(1{\cdot}25 + 2{\cdot}391 - j1{\cdot}502)10^{-4} + (j2{\cdot}56 + j2{\cdot}71)10^{-7}}$$
$$= -5{\cdot}87 - j2{\cdot}43 = 6{\cdot}35\underline{|202{\cdot}5^\circ} = \underline{6{\cdot}35\underline{|-157{\cdot}5^\circ}}$$

The input admittance

$$= \mathbf{Y}_g = \mathbf{Y}_{gc} + (1 - \mathbf{A})\mathbf{Y}_{ga}$$

Here $\quad \mathbf{Y}_{gc} = 2{\cdot}56 \times 10^{-7}$ mho.

$$\therefore \quad \mathbf{Y}_g = j2{\cdot}56 \times 10^{-7} + (6{\cdot}87 + j2{\cdot}43)(j2{\cdot}56 \times 10^{-7})$$
$$= (-6{\cdot}22 + j20{\cdot}15)10^{-7} \text{ mho.}$$

If the input circuit is supposed to consist of a resistor R and a capacitor C in parallel,

$$R = 1/(-6{\cdot}22 \times 10^{-7})\ \Omega = \underline{-1{\cdot}608\ \text{M}\Omega}$$

and $\quad C = (20{\cdot}15 \times 10^{-7})/(2\pi \times 12{,}000)\ \text{F} = \underline{26{\cdot}7\ \mu\mu\text{F}}$

Resistor-capacitor coupled amplifier

If a larger voltage gain is required than is obtainable from a single amplifier stage two or more stages must be cascaded. The output voltage from the first stage forms the input voltage for the second, and so on, and the resultant gain is the product of the individual gains of the various stages. One of the simplest and commonest methods of coupling is called the resistor-capacitor (R-C) coupling. Two stages of such an amplifier are shown in Fig. 13.11.

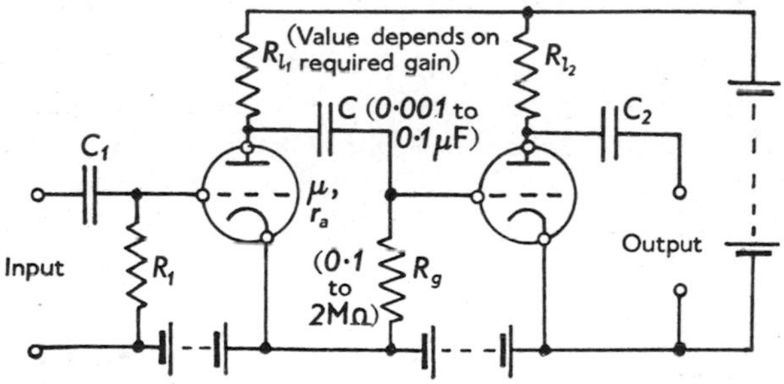

FIG. 13.11

The capacitors C_1, C and C_2 (blocking or coupling capacitors) prevent direct voltages present in one stage from being transmitted to the next stage. R_g and R_1 are called grid leaks and they provide d.c. paths for the grid-bias voltages as well as preventing the grid from 'floating'.

The equivalent circuit of one stage of such an amplifier is shown in Fig. 13.12. C_g is the input capacitance to the next stage. R_g in the equivalent circuit represents the combination of R_g in Fig. 13.11 and

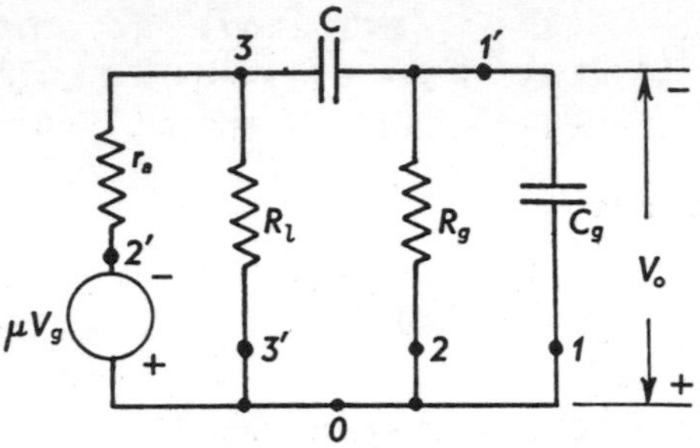

FIG. 13.12

the resistive component of the input impedance of the next stage. Millman's Theorem can be used to find the output voltage $\mathbf{V}_o$. For this purpose points 1, 2 and 3 are chosen.

Then $\mathbf{V}_o = \mathbf{V}_{o3}\mathbf{Y}_C/(\mathbf{Y}_C + Y_{Rg} + \mathbf{Y}_{Cg})$ . . . (13.29)

where $\mathbf{Y}_C = j\omega C$, $Y_{Rg} = 1/R_g$ and $\mathbf{Y}_{Cg} = j\omega C_g$.

Before $\mathbf{V}_o$ can be calculated it is necessary to know $\mathbf{V}_{o3}$. This can be found by applying Millman's Theorem again employing points 1′, 2′ and 3′ (Fig. 13.12).

Then $\mathbf{V}_{o3} = (\mu\mathbf{V}_g Y_a + \mathbf{V}_o\mathbf{Y}_C)/(Y_a + Y_l + \mathbf{Y}_C)$. (13.30)

where $Y_a = 1/r_a$ and $Y_l = 1/R_l$

Thus, from (13.29) and (13.30), the gain

$$\mathbf{A} = -\mathbf{V}_o/\mathbf{V}_g = -\mu Y_a\mathbf{Y}_C/\{(\mathbf{Y}_C + Y_{Rg} + \mathbf{Y}_{Cg})(Y_l + Y_a) + \mathbf{Y}_C(Y_{Rg} + \mathbf{Y}_{Cg})\} \quad (13.31)$$

It is well known that the gain of an R-C coupled amplifier falls off at both low and high frequencies and that over a range of frequencies is almost constant. The gain at intermediate, low and high frequencies will now be investigated using as a starting point the above expression for **A**.

Intermediate frequencies:

At intermediate frequencies $\mathbf{Y}_{Cg}$ is small and $\mathbf{Y}_C$ is large. The above expression for **A** therefore reduces to

$$\mathbf{A} = A_i = -\mu Y_a/(Y_a + Y_l + Y_{Rg})$$

i.e. A_i is independent of frequency and the phase change through the amplifier is constant at 180°.

Low frequencies:

At low frequencies $\mathbf{Y}_{Cg}$ is negligible. The original expression for **A** therefore becomes:

$$\mathbf{A} = \mathbf{A}_l = -\mu Y_a \mathbf{Y}_C / \{(\mathbf{Y}_C + Y_{Rg})(Y_a + Y_l) + \mathbf{Y}_C Y_{Rg}\}$$
$$= -\mu Y_a \mathbf{Y}_C / \{\mathbf{Y}_C(Y_a + Y_l + Y_{Rg}) + Y_{Rg}(Y_a + Y_l)\}$$
$$\therefore \quad \frac{\mathbf{A}_l}{A_i} = \frac{1}{1 + \{Y_{Rg}(Y_a + Y_l)/\mathbf{Y}_C(Y_a + Y_l + Y_{Rg})\}}$$
$$= \frac{1}{1 + \{Y_{Rg}(Y_a + Y_l)/j2\pi fC(Y_a + Y_l + Y_{Rg})\}}$$

Following Terman * this can be written as

$$\frac{\mathbf{A}_l}{A_i} = \frac{1}{1 - j(f_1/f)}$$

where $$f_1 = Y_{Rg}(Y_a + Y_l)/2\pi C(Y_a + Y_l + Y_{Rg})$$

Assuming the load is still a pure resistance it is seen that f_1 is a real number. Thus,

$$A_l/A_i = 1/\sqrt{\{1 + (f_1/f)^2\}}$$

If follows that f_1 represents the frequency at the low-frequency end of the response curve where the gain falls to $1\sqrt{2}$ of its value at intermediate frequencies. It will also be observed that as f approaches zero so does A_l and the larger the value of C the smaller the value of f_1 and the greater A_l. Thus, large values of C give better response curves at low frequencies. The relative phase shift through the amplifier is ϕ_1 where $\tan \phi_1 = f_1/f$, so as $f \to 0$, $\phi_1 \to 90°$.

High frequencies:

At high frequencies $\mathbf{Y}_C$ is large so the original expression for **A** reduces to

$$\mathbf{A} = \mathbf{A}_h = -\mu Y_a/(Y_a + Y_l + Y_{Rg} + \mathbf{Y}_{Cg})$$
$$\therefore \quad \mathbf{A}_h/A_i = 1/\{1 + \mathbf{Y}_{Cg}/(Y_a + Y_l + Y_{Rg})\}$$
$$= 1/\{1 + j2\pi fC_g/(Y_a + Y_l + Y_{Rg})\}.$$

Again following Terman * the ratio $\mathbf{A}_h/A_i$ can be written in the form

$$\mathbf{A}_h/A_i = 1/\{1 + j(f/f_2)\}$$

where $$f_2 = (Y_a + Y_l + Y_{Rg})/2\pi C_g.$$

With a purely resistive load, f_2 is a real number.

Thus, $$A_h/A_i = 1/\sqrt{\{1 + (f/f_2)^2\}}$$

Therefore, f_2 represents the frequency at the high-frequency end of the response curve where the gain falls to $1/\sqrt{2}$ of its value at intermediate frequencies. For very large values of f, A_h will fall to zero.

* F. E. Terman, " Universal Amplification Charts ", *Electronics*, 10, p. 34 (June, 1937).

If C_g is large, f_2 is small and the gain will be small. Thus, large values of C_g give poor response curves at high frequencies. The effects of the other component values on the response curve can also be seen from the expression for $\mathbf{A}_l$ and $\mathbf{A}_h$. For example, large values of R_l (small values of Y_l) give low values of f_2 and therefore poor gain at the high-frequency end of the response curve. The relative phase shift ϕ_2 is now given by $\tan \phi_2 = -f/f_2$ so that when $f \gg f_2$, ϕ_2 approaches $-90°$.

EXAMPLE. The first stage of a resistor-capacitor coupled amplifier employs a triode with $\mu = 20$ and $r_a = 7{,}700\ \Omega$. The other constants of the amplifier are $R_l = 50{,}000\ \Omega$, $C = 0{\cdot}01\ \mu\text{F}$, $R_g = 500{,}000\ \Omega$, $C_g = 200\ \mu\mu\text{F}$. Calculate A_i, f_1 and f_2 and determine the frequency range over which the gain is greater than 14.

Solution.

$$A_i = -\mu Y_a/(Y_a + Y_l + Y_{Rg})$$

Here, $Y_a = 1{\cdot}3 \times 10^{-4}$ mho, $Y_l = 0{\cdot}2 \times 10^{-4}$ mho and $Y_{Rg} = 0{\cdot}02 \times 10^{-4}$ mho.

$$\therefore\ A_i = -(20 \times 1{\cdot}3 \times 10^{-4})/(1{\cdot}3 + 0{\cdot}2 + 0{\cdot}02)10^{-4}$$

$$= \underline{-17{\cdot}1}$$

$$f_1 = \frac{Y_{Rg}(Y_a + Y_l)}{2\pi C(Y_a + Y_l + Y_{Rg})}$$

$$= \frac{0{\cdot}02 \times 10^{-4}(1{\cdot}3 + 0{\cdot}2)10^{-4}}{2\pi \times 0{\cdot}01 \times 10^{-6}(1{\cdot}3 + 0{\cdot}2 + 0{\cdot}02)10^{-4}}$$

i.e. $\underline{f_1 = 31\ \text{c/s}}$.

$$f_2 = (Y_a + Y_l + Y_{Rg})/2\pi C_g$$

$$= (1{\cdot}3 + 0{\cdot}2 + 0{\cdot}02)10^{-4}/(2\pi \times 200 \times 10^{-12})$$

i.e. $\underline{f_2 = 121{,}000\ \text{c/s}}$.

The minimum gain ratio prescribed $= 14/17{\cdot}1 = 0{\cdot}8187$. If f_l is the low frequency where the gain drops to 14 and f_h is the corresponding high frequency,

$$1/\sqrt{\{1 + (f_1/f_l)^2\}} = 0{\cdot}8187 = 1/\sqrt{\{1 + (f_h/f_2)^2\}}$$

From these expressions it is found that

$$\underline{f_l = 44\ \text{c/s}} \text{ and } \underline{f_h = 84{,}960\ \text{c/s}}.$$

Choke-capacitor coupled amplifier

The choke-capacitor coupled amplifier is shown in Fig. 13.13 and the only variation from the circuit of Fig. 13.11 is that the previous load resistor is replaced by a choke of high inductance. If the choke has a low resistance, then for given valve operating conditions, a lower supply voltage is required than in the case when the load is purely resistive.

C_1 represents the distributed capacitance of L.

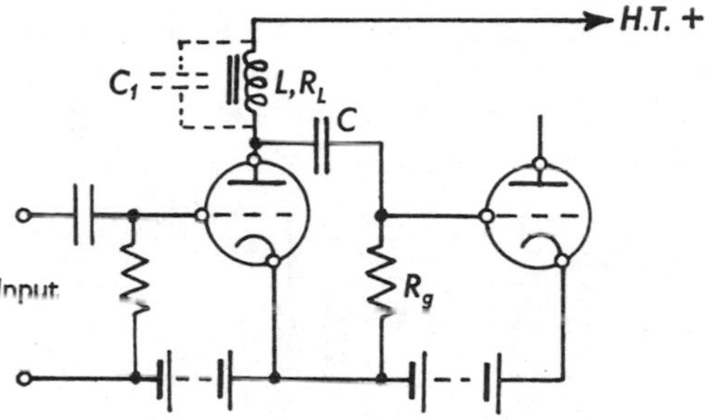

FIG. 13.13

It is evident that the calculations made for the *R-C* coupled amplifier apply in this case provided $\mathbf{Y}_l$, which was previously $1/R_l$, is replaced by

$$j\omega C_1 + 1/(R_L + j\omega L)$$

The frequency-response characteristics of the amplifier can be investigated in the same manner as for the *R-C* coupled circuit. The necessary analysis will be left to the reader. The frequency response is found to be inferior to that obtained with the *R-C* coupled circuit; at low frequencies the gain falls off more rapidly because the reactance of L decreases while that of C increases and at high frequencies the gain drops off more quickly because of the shunting effect of C_1 as well as C_g. The circuit is not extensively used.

Transformer-coupled amplifiers

A two-stage transformer-coupled amplifier is illustrated in Fig. 13.14. A coupling capacitor is not needed because the transformer itself blocks

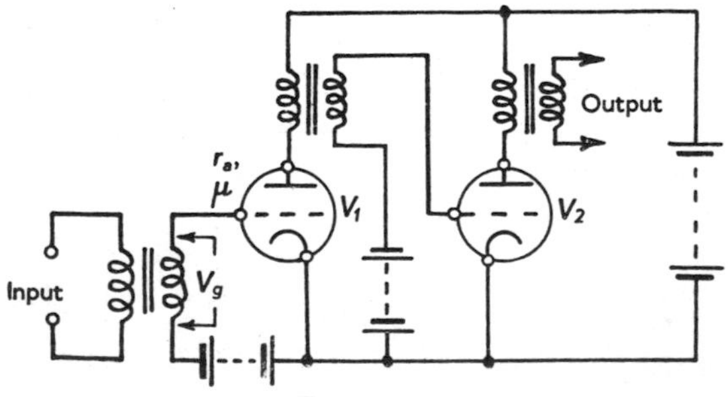

FIG. 13.14

the d.c. component of the anode voltage of V_1, preventing it from appearing in the secondary circuit. A grid resistor is not necessary either because the secondary winding provides a low-resistance path for removing charges on the grid of V_2.

An approximate expression for the gain **A** of one stage will be determined first at frequencies for which the equivalent circuit is as shown in Fig. 13.15. Thus, the output impedance is taken as infinite, the

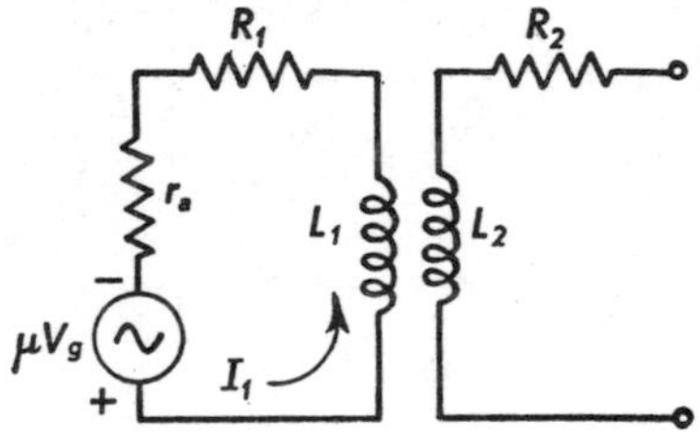

FIG. 13.15

stray capacitances and the admittance of the second valve being regarded as negligible.

R_1 and L_1 are the resistance and self-inductance of the primary winding of the transformer, respectively, while R_2 and L_2 are the corresponding quantities for the secondary winding.

The current $\mathbf{I}_1 = \mu\mathbf{V}_g/(r_a + R_1 + j\omega L_1)$

Voltage across $L_1 = j\omega L_1\mathbf{I}_1$

Voltage across $L_2 = \pm nj\omega L_1\mathbf{I}_1$ where $n = \dfrac{\text{number of secondary turns}}{\text{number of primary turns}}$

Thus, gain

$$\mathbf{A} = (\text{voltage across } L_1)/\mathbf{V}_g = \pm n\mu j\omega L_1/(r_a + R_1 + j\omega L_1)$$

i.e. $\mathbf{A} = \pm n\mu/\{1 - j(r_a + R_1)/\omega L_1\}$

The magnitude of **A**

$$= A = \pm n\mu/\{1 + (r_a + R_1)^2/(\omega L_1)^2\}^{\frac{1}{2}}$$

If A is plotted against frequency ($\omega/2\pi$) a curve such as that shown in Fig. 13.16 is obtained, the gain falling rapidly at low frequencies. The gain falls to $n\mu/\sqrt{2}$ when $\omega L_1 = r_a + R_1$. In fact, for good response $(r_a + R_1)$ must be small compared with ωL_1. This result should be compared with the performance of a single-stage amplifier having a coil as a load. If the coil has an inductance L and resistance R the gain **A** is $\mu(R + j\omega L)/(r_a + R + j\omega L)$. If $R \ll \omega L$, $\mathbf{A} \simeq \mu j\omega L/(r_a + j\omega L)$.

If $\omega L \ll r_a$, $\mathbf{A} \simeq \mu j\omega L/r_a$ and is directly proportional to frequency giving serious frequency distortion.

If $\omega L \gg r_a$, $A \simeq \mu$. At very low frequencies ωL is small so the gain falls off rapidly.

Returning now to the transformer-coupled amplifier it is evident that valves with low r_a values should be employed. Further, R_1 should

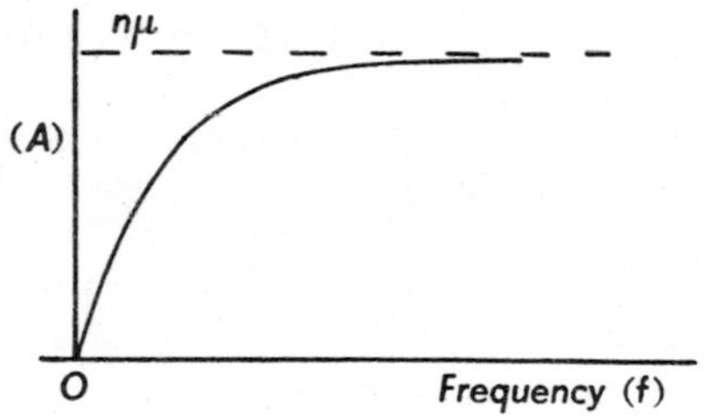

FIG. 13.16

be small and L_1 large. If L_1 is made too big, however, distributed capacitances produce severe frequency distortion at the high-frequency end of the response curve. High-permeability materials should be used for the core of L_1.

At higher frequencies (>about 3,000 c/s), the output impedance is not infinite, as assumed so far. Leakage inductances of the windings and winding, interwinding, interelectrode and stray capacitances must be taken into account. The equivalent circuit is now that illustrated in Fig. 13.17. Here C represents the total effective capacitance shunt-

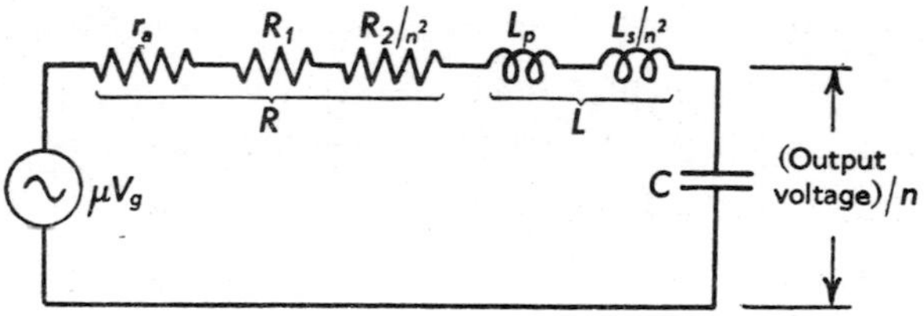

FIG. 13.17

ing the primary circuit. L and R represent the total effective leakage inductance and resistance referred to the primary winding.

Thus, $\mathbf{A} = \pm jn\mu/\omega C\{R + j(\omega L - 1/\omega C)\}$

and $A = n\mu/\omega C\{R^2 + (\omega L - 1/\omega C)^2\}^{\frac{1}{2}}$

At low frequencies for which ωL is small and $1/\omega C$ is large, $A \simeq \mu n$. At high frequencies for which ωL is large and $1/\omega C$ is small, A tends to zero rapidly. Between these two extremes A reaches a maximum when $dA/d\omega = 0$, *i.e.* when $1/\omega C = \{2(\omega L)^2 + R^2\}/2\omega L$.

If $R \ll \omega L$, A reaches its maximum value A_{max} when $\omega L = 1/\omega C$, which is the condition for series resonance in the circuit.

It is found that at this frequency, $f = 1/2\pi\sqrt{LC}$,

$$A_{max} = n\mu/\omega CR = n\mu(L/C)^{\frac{1}{2}}/R.$$

R-C coupled amplifiers are preferred to transformer-coupled ones when the object is merely to achieve large voltage gain. Pentode valves in *R-C* coupled amplifiers are capable of providing greater gain than triodes and step-up transformers. It might appear that any desired stage gain could be obtained with a transformer-coupled amplifier if a sufficiently large value of n was used. If n is made large by using a small number of primary turns, L_1 is small and the low-frequency response is poor. On the other hand if the secondary has a large number of turns both leakage inductance and inter-winding capacitance are high and the resonant peak in the response curve appears at a relatively low frequency. For these reasons n is usually not more than 3. Other disadvantages of transformer coupling are that the transformer is fairly expensive and bulky. Transformers, however, permit impedance matching and are frequently used in power amplifiers.

EXAMPLE. A transformer-coupled amplifier has the following constants:

$$\mu = 9,\ r_a = 9{,}000\ \Omega,\ n = 3,\ L_1 = 60\ \text{H},\ L = 0{\cdot}5\ \text{H},$$
$$R_1 = 3{,}000\ \Omega,\ C = 1{,}200\ \mu\mu\text{F},\ R = 14{,}000\ \Omega$$

Investigate the frequency-response characteristics of the arrangement.

Solution. Over the normal range of frequencies the gain $= n\mu = \underline{27}$

The gain falls to $(1/\sqrt{2})27$ at the frequency $f = (r_a + R_1)/2\pi L_1$

i.e. $f = 12{,}000/(2\pi \times 60)$ c/s $= \underline{31{\cdot}8 \text{ c/s}}$

$A_{max} = n\mu(L/C)^{\frac{1}{2}}/R = 27(5 \times 10^9/12)^{\frac{1}{2}}14{,}000 = \underline{39{\cdot}3}$

A_{max} is obtained when $f = 1/2\pi\sqrt{LC} = \underline{6{,}500 \text{ c/s.}}$

Other values of A at other frequencies could be calculated from the equations developed but the above information alone enables the approximate shape of the response curve to be sketched.

The peak in the response curve can be reduced by loading the secondary of the transformer with a resistor R_2, which is equivalent to shunting C of Fig. 13.17 with a resistor R_2/n^2. The gain at normal frequencies is then somewhat less than $n\,\mu$.

Feedback in amplifiers

Feedback in an amplifier is achieved by combining part of the output voltage with the input signal. In this way distortion is reduced, noise may be reduced, and stability is improved. There are two types of feedback, *positive* and *negative*, depending on whether the effect of the portion of the output voltage fed back to the input increases or decreases the effective signal input.

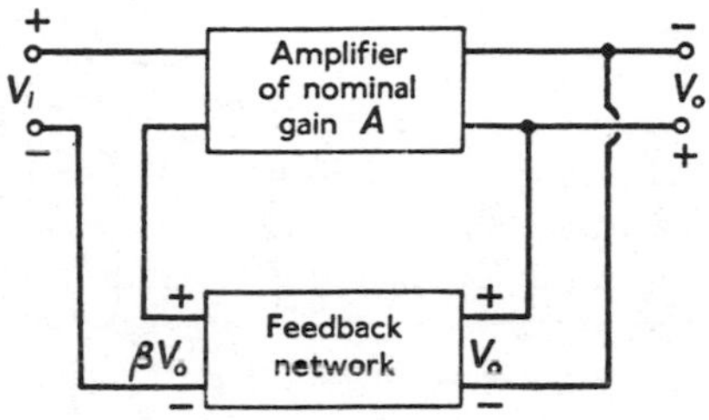

FIG. 13.18

Consider Fig. 13.18, which shows an amplifier of nominal gain A, to which negative feedback is applied. A fraction βV_o of the output voltage V_o is fed back to the input and subtracts from V_i.

Thus, $$A = -V_o/(V_i - \beta V_o)$$
or $$V_o/V_i = -A/(1 - A\beta).$$

The gain of the amplifier with feedback (A_f) is therefore $A/(1 - A\beta)$ where A is the gain without feedback.

If $A\beta \gg 1$, $A_f \simeq 1/\beta$, so that the gain depends only on the feedback network and not on the valve. It is evident that if β is not a function of frequency, negative feedback allows reductions of frequency and phase distortions to be obtained. When $A\beta \gg 1$, however, $|A_f| \simeq |A/A\beta|$, which is $\ll |A|$, so the advantages of negative feedback can only be gained by accepting reduced overall gain of the amplifier.

Consider now the effects of feedback on amplitude distortion. Suppose the valve generates a harmonic voltage V_h so that without feedback V_h is present at the output of the amplifier. With negative feedback a voltage v_h appears at the output where

$$V_h + A\beta v_h = v_h$$
so $$v_h = V_h/(1 - A\beta)$$

Since $|1 - A\beta|$ is normally considerably greater than unity, amplitude distortion is reduced by the presence of negative feedback. Similarly, noise produced in an amplifier is multiplied by $1/(1 - A\beta)$ when feedback is used and so it would appear that the amplifier output noise would be considerably reduced if $|1 - A\beta| \gg 1$. It should be remembered, however, that the use of negative feedback gives reduced gain so for a given output the gain must be increased; if this is done by incorporating an extra stage further noise will be introduced.

Two typical feedback networks are illustrated in Fig. 13.19.

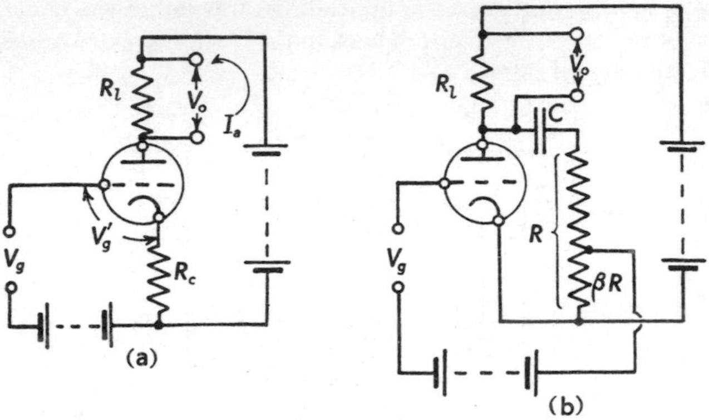

FIG. 13.19

In Fig. 13.19 (*a*) $V_g' = V_g - I_aR_C = V_g - V_oR_C/R_l$.
Thus, the feedback factor $\beta = R_C/R_l$.

If β is large, the gain $A_f \simeq 1/\beta \simeq R_l/R_C$.

$\therefore \quad V_o = R_lV_g/R_C$, *i.e.* V_o is proportional to R_l.

Since $I_a = V_o/R_l = V_g/R_C$, I_a is independent of Z_l with the above assumptions.

The equivalent circuit of the arrangement is shown in Fig. 13.20. From this the complete expression for I_a can be found as follows:

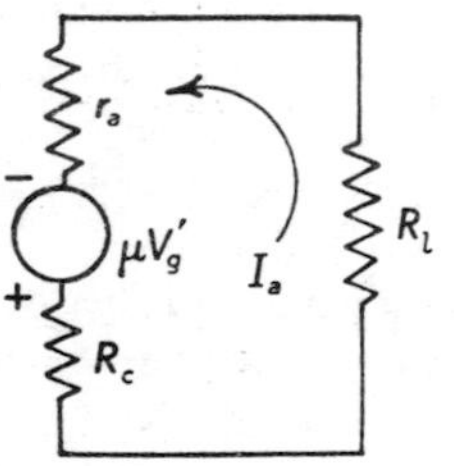

FIG. 13.20

$$I_a(R_C + R_l + r_a) = \mu V_g' = \mu(V_g - I_aR_C)$$

$$\therefore \quad I_a = \mu V_g/\{r_a + R_C(\mu + 1) + R_l\}$$

In the arrangement of Fig. 13.19 (*b*), R is large in comparison with R_l so that its shunting effect can be neglected. Further, C has a negligible reactance compared with R at the frequencies used. The purpose of C is to block the direct anode voltage from the grid circuit.

If β is large, $V_o \simeq V_g/\beta$ which is independent of R_l.

Now the gain with feedback $(A_f) = A/(1 - A\beta)$

where $\quad A = -\mu R_l/(r_a + R_l)$

$$\therefore \quad A_f = -\mu R_l/\{r_a + R_l(1 + \mu\beta)\}$$

$$= -\{\mu/(1 + \mu\beta)\}R_l/\{r_a/(1 + \mu\beta) + R_l\}.$$

This is the gain which would be given by an amplifier with a resisitive load R_l, without feedback, if the valve used had an amplification factor of $\mu/(1 + \mu\beta)$ and an anode slope resistance of $r_a/(1 + \mu\beta)$. In this way a high-impedance valve can be matched to a load of low impedance.

The examples given above employ negative feedback where $|1 - A\beta| > 1$. If $|1 - A\beta| < 1$ positive feedback is obtained and $A_f > A$. Positive feedback results in reduced stability of an amplifier. Nyquist has given a criterion for the stability of feedback amplifiers but a discussion of this topic is beyond the scope of this book. The reader who wishes to obtain further information about the criterion should refer to Nyquist's original paper * or consult, for example, the book by Bode.†

The cathode follower

The cathode-follower circuit is illustrated in Fig. 13.21 (*a*) and can be regarded as an amplifier with negative voltage feedback and with a feedback ratio of unity. The equivalent circuit is that of Fig. 13.21 (*b*).

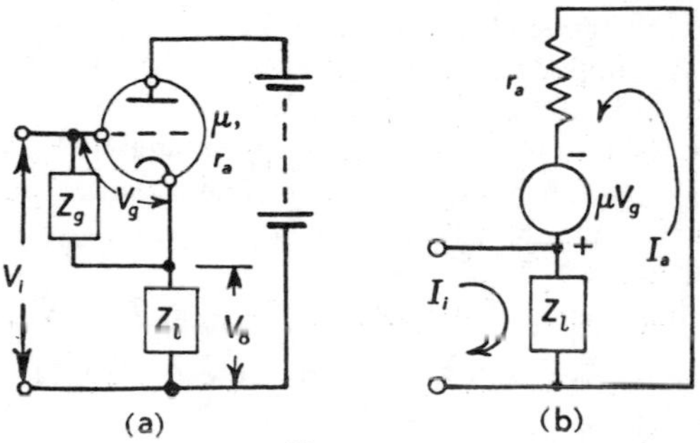

FIG. 13.21

From the equivalent circuit,

$$\mu\mathbf{V}_g = (\mathbf{I}_a + \mathbf{I}_i)\mathbf{Z}_l + r_a\mathbf{I}_a \quad (13.32)$$

The output voltage $\mathbf{V}_o = (\mathbf{I}_i + \mathbf{I}_a)\mathbf{Z}_l$ . . . . . . (13.33)

Also, $\mathbf{V}_g = \mathbf{I}_i\mathbf{Z}_g$ . . . . (13.34)

and $\mathbf{V}_i = \mathbf{I}_i(\mathbf{Z}_g + \mathbf{Z}_l) + \mathbf{I}_a\mathbf{Z}_l$ . . . (13.35)

From (13.32) and (13.34),

$$\mathbf{I}_i = \mathbf{I}_a(\mathbf{Z}_l + r_a)/(\mu\mathbf{Z}_g - \mathbf{Z}_l) \quad (13.36)$$

Substituting (13.36) in (13.35) gives

$$\mathbf{V}_i = \mathbf{I}_a[\{(\mathbf{Z}_l + r_a)(\mathbf{Z}_g + \mathbf{Z}_l) + \mathbf{Z}_l(\mu\mathbf{Z}_g - \mathbf{Z}_l)\}/(\mu\mathbf{Z}_g - \mathbf{Z}_l)] \quad (13.37)$$

* H. Nyquist, "Regeneration Theory", *Bell System Tech. J.*, **11**, p. 126 (1932).

† H. W. Bode, *Network Analysis and Feedback Amplifier Design* (Van Nostrand, 1945).

Substituting (13.36) in (13.33) gives

$$\mathbf{V}_o = \mathbf{I}_a\{(\mu\mathbf{Z}_g\mathbf{Z}_l + r_a\mathbf{Z}_l)/(\mu\mathbf{Z}_g - \mathbf{Z}_l)\} \quad . \quad . \quad (13.38)$$

Dividing (13.37) and (13.38),

$$\mathbf{V}_i/\mathbf{V}_o = \{(\mathbf{Z}_l + r_a)(\mathbf{Z}_g + \mathbf{Z}_l) + \mathbf{Z}_l(\mu\mathbf{Z}_g - \mathbf{Z}_l)\}/\{\mathbf{Z}_l(\mu\mathbf{Z}_g + r_a)\} \quad . \quad . \quad (13.39)$$

$$\therefore \quad \mathbf{V}_o = [\mathbf{V}_i\mathbf{Z}_l(\mu\mathbf{Z}_g + r_a)/\{r_a + (1 + \mu)\mathbf{Z}_g\}]/[\mathbf{Z}_l + \mathbf{Z}_g r_a/\{r_a + (1+ \mu)\mathbf{Z}_g\}] \quad . \quad (13.40)$$

Thus, the valve acts as a generator of voltage.

$$\mathbf{V}_i(\mu\mathbf{Z}_g + r_a)/\{r_a + (1 + \mu)\mathbf{Z}_g\}$$

and of impedance $\quad \mathbf{Z}_g r_a/\{r_a + (1 + \mu)\mathbf{Z}_g\}$

feeding a load $\mathbf{Z}_l$.

If μ is large, the generator voltage $\simeq V_i$.

The generator impedance is $1/\{1/\mathbf{Z}_g + (1 + \mu)/r_a\}$, *i.e.* it is the combination of $\mathbf{Z}_g$ and $r_a/(1 + \mu)$ in parallel.

If μ is large the output impedance is approximately $r_a/(1 + \mu)$ which equals $1/(1/r_a + g_m)$ or $1/g_m(1 + 1/\mu)$. Thus, the output impedance is approximately equal to $1/g_m$ if μ is large. *e.g.* if $g_m = 4m$A/V, the output impedance is 250 Ω.

The input impedance of the cathode follower $\mathbf{Z}_i = \mathbf{V}_i/\mathbf{I}_i$

$$= \{(\mathbf{Z}_l + r_a)(\mathbf{Z}_g + \mathbf{Z}_l) + \mathbf{Z}_l(\mu\mathbf{Z}_g - \mathbf{Z}_l)\}/(\mathbf{Z}_l + r_a)$$

from (13.37) and (13.36).

$$\therefore \quad \mathbf{Z}_i = \mathbf{Z}_g\{1 + \mu + r_a/\mathbf{Z}_l + r_a/\mathbf{Z}_g\}/\{1 + r_a/\mathbf{Z}_l\}$$
$$= \mathbf{Z}_g\{1 + (\mu + r_a/\mathbf{Z}_g)/(1+r_a/\mathbf{Z}_l)\}$$
$$\simeq \mathbf{Z}_g\{1 + \mu/(1 + r_a/\mathbf{Z}_l)\} \text{ if } \mu \gg (r_a/Z_g)$$

If $\quad Z_l = r_a, \ \mathbf{Z}_i \simeq \mathbf{Z}_g(1 + \mu/2)$.

For example, if $\mu = 60$ and $Z_g = 0{\cdot}5$ MΩ, $Z_i = 15{\cdot}5$ MΩ.

Thus, the cathode-follower stage has a high input impedance and a low output impedance so is used when a load of low impedance is to be connected to a source of high impedance, but it gives no gain since $V_o \simeq V_i$. Since the output voltage across Z_l is approximately equal to the input voltage, the alternating voltage between the grid and cathode of the valve is very small, *i.e.* the cathode voltage *follows* the grid voltage.

Power amplifiers

Consider the circuit of Fig. 13.22 (*a*) where a triode supplies power to a resistive load R_l. The equivalent circuit is illustrated in Fig. 13.22 (*b*). The arrangement is known as a *simple series-fed amplifier.*

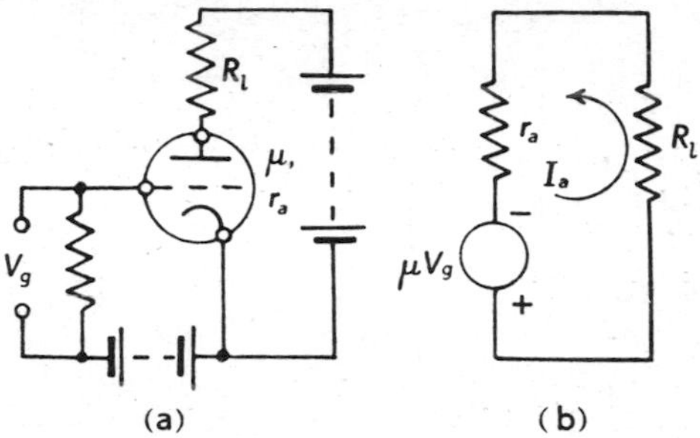

FIG. 13.22

The power supplied to the load is $P = I_a^2 R_l = \{\mu V_g/(r_a + R_l)\}^2 R_l$. If μ, r_a and V_g are constant P is found to reach its maximum value P_{max} when $R_l = r_a$.

Thus, $$P_{\text{max}} = \mu^2 V_g^2/4r_a = \mu g_m V_g^2/r_a$$

To get an idea of how critical the condition that $R_l = r_a$ is for maximum power, consider the ratio P/P_{max} which equals $(4R_l/r_a)/(1 + R_l/r_a)^2$. If P/P_{max} is plotted against R_l/r_a the resulting curve is found to be fairly flat in the region where $R_l/r_a = 1$. In fact, over the range R_l/r_a from 0·5 to 2, $P/P_{\text{max}} > 0{\cdot}88$.

The power P can be calculated easily if the load line is drawn on the valve characteristics as demonstrated below with the aid of Fig. 13.23.

$$P = (E_m/\sqrt{2})(I_m/\sqrt{2})$$

for purely resistive load.

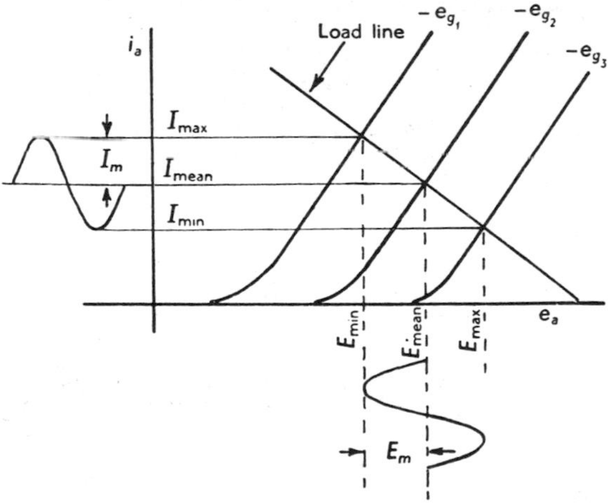

FIG. 13.23

Thus, $$P = (E_{max} - E_{min})(I_{max} - I_{min})/8$$

from Fig. 13.23. The values E_{max}, E_{min}, I_{max} and I_{min} can be read off from Fig. 13.23 when the load line has been drawn. Harmonic components of current can be determined if distortion is not negligible but this topic cannot be dealt with here.

With the series-fed arrangement of Fig. 13.22 the steady anode current flows through R_l and gives a power wastage. This disadvantage can be overcome by using the *parallel-fed* or *shunt-fed* system of Fig. 13.24 (*a*) or a transformer as in Fig. 13.24 (*b*).

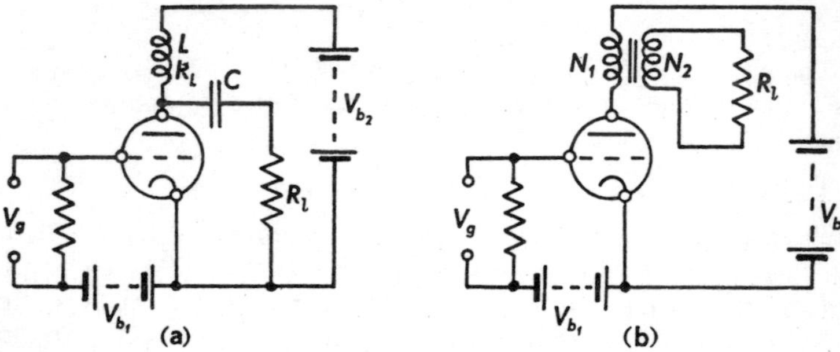

FIG. 13.24

In Fig. 13.24 (*a*) the reactance of *C* is small compared with R_l and *L* is of such a value that alternating currents do not pass through it but go through R_l. The load lines and static valve characteristics for this arrangement are shown in Fig. 13.25. Since the resistance of *L* is small, load line PVb_2 is nearly vertical. The remainder of the diagram is

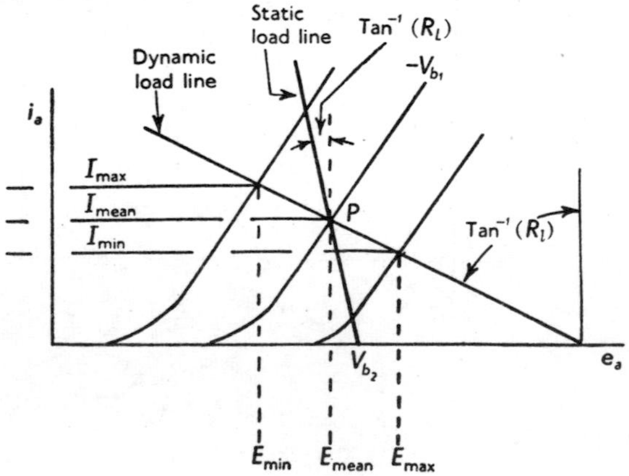

FIG. 13.25

self-explanatory if it is remembered that on a.c. the dynamic load line has a slope determined by R_l. The power can be determined as before.

With the arrangement of Fig. 13.24 (*b*) a low-resistance load may be matched to the valve. For an ideal transformer, the effective resistance presented to the valve is $R_l' = (N_1/N_2)^2 R_l$. Thus, if $R_l = 12\ \Omega$ and $N_1/N_2 = 15$, $R_l' = 2{,}700\ \Omega$ which is of the same order as the internal resistance of a power triode.

Let us reconsider the problem of calculating the power output of an amplifier with a resistive load but now let $I_{\min}$ be fixed to avoid distortion which might arise from the lower curved portions of the valve characteristics (see Fig. 13.26). Assume also that the grid is never

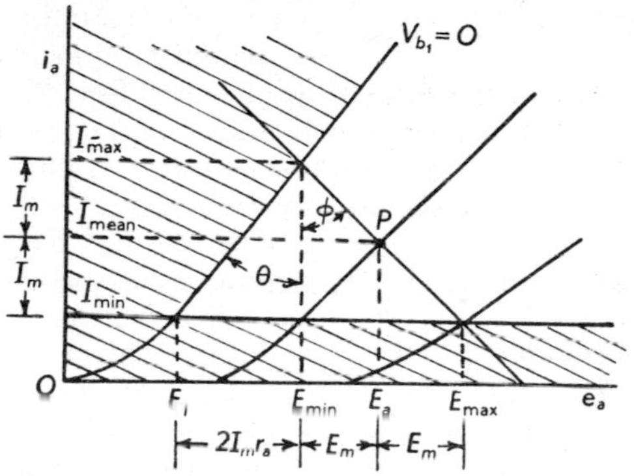

FIG. 13.26

driven positive. Under these conditions it will be shown that the power output is slightly less than the previously calculated value. The valve may now be operated anywhere except in the shaded area of Fig. 13.26. Assume that above $I_{\min}$ the characteristics are linear and so $\tan\theta = r_a$. Also, $\tan\phi = R_l = E_m/I_m$.

From Fig. 13.26,

$$E_a = E_1 + 2I_m r_a + E_m = E_1 + 2I_m r_a + R_l I_m$$

$$\therefore \quad I_m = (E_a - E_1)/(R_l + 2r_a)$$

Power $$P = (I_m/\sqrt{2})^2 R_l = (E_a - E_1)^2 R_l / 2(R_l + 2r_a)^2.$$

The power is a maximum ($P_{\max}$) when $R_l = 2r_a$.

Under this condition $P_{\max} = (E_a - E_1)^2/16r_a$.

The ratio $P/P_{\max} = 8r_a R_l/(R_l + 2r_a)^2$ so that $P/P_{\max} > 0{\cdot}88$ over the range R_l/r_a from 1 to 4.

The maximum value of the grid-voltage swing E_g to give the conditions for maximum undistorted power output can be found as follows: From the equivalent circuit,

$$I_m = \mu E_g/(r_a + R_l)$$

But $$I_m = (E_a - E_1)/(R_l + 2r_a)$$
and $$R_l = 2r_a$$
$$\therefore \quad E_g = 3(E_a - E_1)/4\mu$$

E_1 can be obtained from the characteristics of Fig. 13.26 when I_{min} is fixed.

It follows from the above expressions that

$$P_{max} = \mu^2 E_g^2/9r_a = 2\mu^2(E_g/\sqrt{2})^2/9r_a$$

which is slightly less than P_{max} calculated previously.

It has been shown above how the power output of an amplifier can be evaluated. This power is, of course, converted from the H.T. supply voltage and the ratio $\dfrac{\text{(a.c. power output of load)}}{\text{d.c. power input to anode circuit}}$ is termed the anode-circuit efficiency of the amplifier. The above analyses can be extended to show that the theoretical maximum efficiency of a shunt-fed or transformer-fed arrangement is 50%, but for the series-fed circuit the corresponding figure is 25%. Under conditions of maximum power output these figures become 25% and 12·5% respectively and in practice the efficiencies are less than these figures.

Push–pull amplifiers

Two valves can be connected in parallel to obtain twice the power output of a single valve with the same amount of distortion. A better arrangement is to connect the two valves in *push–pull* because a good deal of distortion caused by non-linear valve characteristics can be

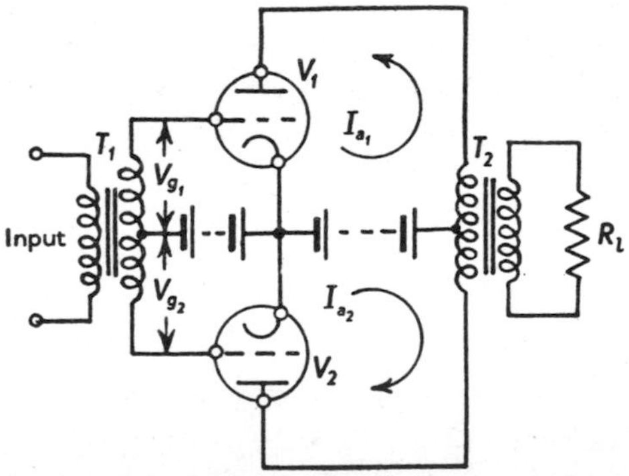

FIG. 13.27

removed. The circuit arrangement of a push–pull amplifier is shown in Fig. 13.27 where a transformer with a centre-tapped secondary provides two voltages for the valve grids which are equal in magnitude and 180° out of phase.

The anode current of valve V_1 can be represented as

$$I_{a1} = a_o + a_1 V_{g1} + a_2 V_{g1}^2 + a_3 V_{g1}^3 + \ldots$$

If $V_{g1} = V \cos \omega t$, then I_{a1} can be written as

$$I_{a1} = A_o + A_1 \cos \omega t + A_2 \cos 2\omega t + A_3 \cos 3\omega t + \ldots$$

where the A's are functions of a's and V.

If the valves are identical, then since $V_{g2} = -V_{g1}$,

$$I_{a2} = A_o - A_1 \cos \omega t + A_2 \cos 2\omega t - A_3 \cos 3\omega t + \ldots$$

The currents I_{a1} and I_{a2} are flowing in opposite directions through the primary of transformer T_2 so the output does not contain even harmonics. The third harmonic therefore provides the chief source of distortion. Even harmonics will appear, of course, if the two valves have characteristics which are not the same. The equivalent circuit of the class-A push–pull amplifier is shown in Fig. 13.28 (*a*). Since

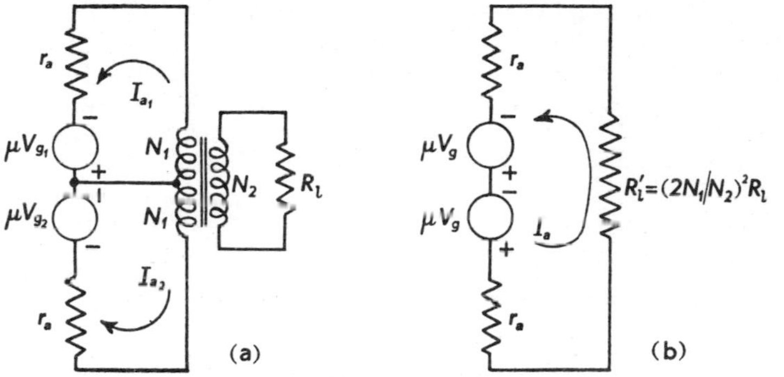

FIG. 13.28

the fundamental current through the common link is zero the circuit can be re-drawn as in Fig. 13.28 (*b*).

From Fig. 13.28 (*b*),

$$I_a = 2\mu V_g/(2r_a + R_l') = \mu V_g/(r_a + R_l'/2)$$

The power output

$$P = I_a^2 R_l' = 2\{\mu V_g/(r_a + R_l'/2)\}^2 R_l'/2$$

which is twice the power which would be obtained from each valve operating into a load of $R_l'/2$.

It is also seen that

$$P = [(\mu V_g)^2/\{(r_a/2) + (R_l'/4)\}^2] R_l'/4$$

Thus, a Class-A push–pull amplifier can be replaced by a single generator of μV_g and internal resistance $r_a/2$ working into a load resistance $R_l'/4$. A set of static characteristics can, in fact, be drawn for the composite valve starting with the static anode-current/anode-voltage characteristics. Space limitations do not permit of further discussion of push–pull amplifiers, however, and for additional information the reader should consult other texts.*

Difference amplifier

A number of circuits have been used for obtaining the difference between two given voltages. Only one of these, which is extensively used as a d.c. amplifier and is shown in Fig. 13.29 will be considered.

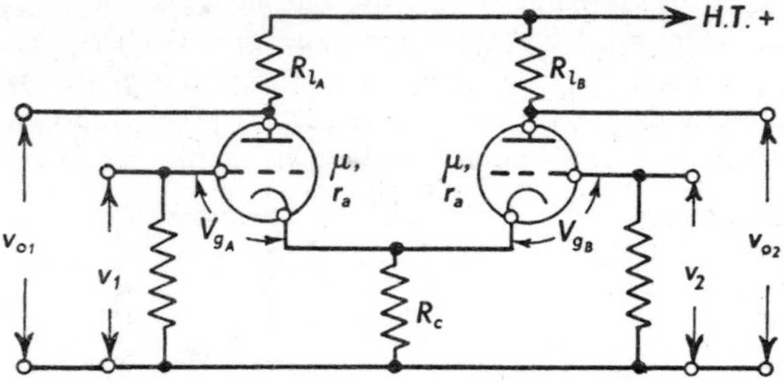

FIG. 13.29

Assuming the valves are identical the equivalent circuit of the amplifier is as shown in Fig. 13.30.

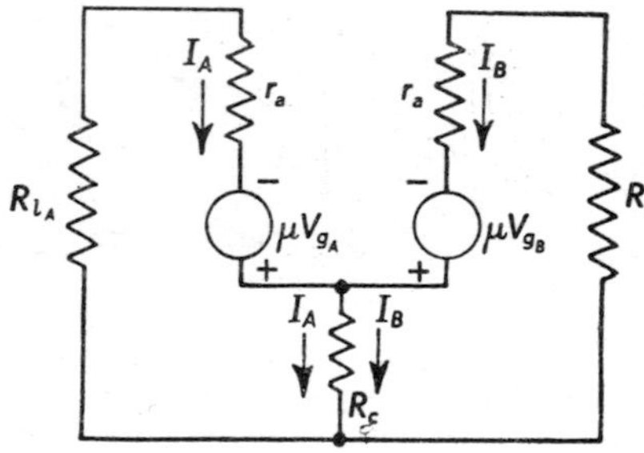

FIG. 13.30

For the I_A mesh,

$$I_A(R_{lA} + r_a + R_C) + R_C I_B = \mu V_{gA} \quad . \quad . \quad (13.41)$$

For the I_B mesh,

$$I_A R_C + I_B(r_a + R_{lB} + R_C) = \mu V_{gB} \quad . \quad . \quad (13.42)$$

* See, for example, E. Williams, *Thermionic Valve Circuits*, 3rd Edition (Pitman, 1952) and J. Millman and S. Seely, *Electronics*, 2nd Edition (McGraw-Hill, 1951).

Also $$V_{gA} = v_1 - R_C(I_A + I_B) \quad . \quad . \quad . \quad . \quad (13.43)$$

and $$V_{gB} = v_2 - R_C(I_A + I_B) \quad . \quad . \quad . \quad . \quad (13.44)$$

The output voltages v_{o1} and v_{o2} are

$$v_{o1} = -R_{lA}I_A \quad . \quad . \quad . \quad . \quad . \quad (13.45)$$

$$v_{o2} = -R_{lB}I_B \quad . \quad . \quad . \quad . \quad . \quad (13.46)$$

Substituting (13.43) in (13.41) and (13.44) in (13.42) and solving the two resultant equations for I_A and I_B it is found that

$$I_A = \frac{\mu\left[\left\{\frac{r_a + R_{lB}}{(\mu + 1)} + R_C\right\}v_1 - R_C v_2\right]}{(R_{lA} + r_a)(R_{lB} + r_a)/(\mu + 1) + R_C(R_{lA} + R_{lB} + 2r_a)} \quad (13.47)$$

and

$$I_B = \frac{-\mu\left[R_C v_1 - \left\{\frac{r_a + R_{lA}}{(\mu + 1)} + R_C\right\}v_2\right]}{(R_{lA} + r_a)(R_{lB} + r_a)/(\mu + 1) + R_C(R_{lA} + R_{lB} + 2r_a)} \quad (13.48)$$

Thus, if $(R_{lA} + r_a)/(\mu + 1)$ and $(R_{lB} + r_a)/(\mu + 1)$ are made much less than R_C, then from (13.45) and (13.47),

$$v_{o1} = -kR_{lA}(v_1 - v_2) \quad . \quad . \quad . \quad . \quad (13.49)$$

where $$k = \mu/(R_{lA} + R_{lB} + 2r_a) \quad . \quad . \quad (13.50)$$

Similarly from (13.46) and (13.48),

$$v_{o2} = +kR_{lB}(v_1 - v_2) \quad . \quad . \quad . \quad . \quad (13.51)$$

Both output voltages are therefore given as the amplified difference between the two input voltages.

Summing amplifiers

Several circuits exist for adding voltages. An arrangement for the addition of voltages in the cathode circuit of a chain of identical valves is shown in Fig. 13.31 (*a*).

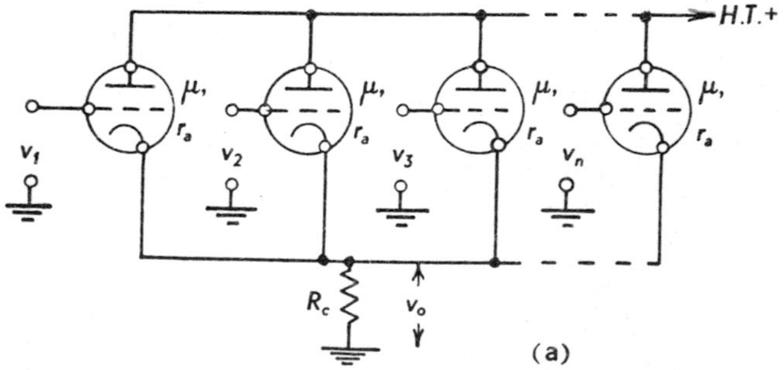

FIG. 13.31 (*a*)

The equivalent circuit of the arrangement is shown in Fig. 13.31 (*b*).

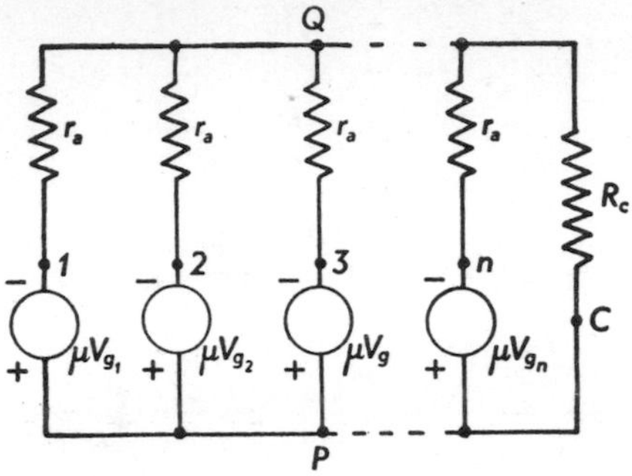

(b)

FIG. 13.31 (*b*)

The output voltage v_o across R_C can be found by applying Millman's Theorem between points P and Q. For this purpose points 1, 2, 3 . . . n and C are chosen. Then

$$v_o = (\mu V_{g1} Y_a + \mu V_{g2} Y_a + \mu V_{g3} Y_a + \dots + \mu V_{gn} Y_a)/(Y_C + nY_a)$$

where $Y_a = 1/r_a$ and $Y_C = 1/R_C$

$$\therefore \quad v_o = \mu Y_a\{V_{g1} + V_{g2} + V_{g3} + \dots + V_{gn}\}/(Y_C + nY_a)$$

But, $V_{g1} = v_1 - v_o$

$V_{g2} = v_2 - v_o$

$V_{g3} = v_3 - v_o$

. . . .

$V_{gn} = v_n - v_o$

$$\therefore \quad v_o = \mu Y_a\{v_1 + v_2 + v_3 + \dots + v_n - nv_o\}/(Y_C + nY_a)$$

or

$$v_o = \mu R_C\{v_1 + v_2 + v_3 + \dots + v_n\}/\{n(\mu + 1)R_C + r_a\}.$$

This adding circuit requires one valve for each voltage source. Another arrangement, which employs only one valve, is shown in Fig. 13.32.

Applying Kirchhoff's first law at P,

$$\frac{(v_1 - v_g)}{R_1} + \frac{(v_2 - v_g)}{R_2} + \frac{(v_3 - v_g)}{R_3} + \dots + \frac{(v_n - v_g)}{R_n} + \frac{(v_o - v_g)}{R_a} = \frac{v_g}{R_b}$$

i.e.

$$\frac{v_1}{R_1} + \frac{v_2}{R_2} + \frac{v_3}{R_3} + \dots + \frac{v_n}{R_n} = v_g\left\{\frac{1}{R_b} + \frac{1}{R_a} + \left(\frac{1}{R_1} + \frac{1}{R_2} + \frac{1}{R_3} + \dots + \frac{1}{R_n}\right)\right\} - \frac{v_o}{R_a}$$

Let $$R_1 = R_2 = R_3 = \ldots = R_n = R_a = R$$

$$\therefore \quad \frac{1}{R}(v_1 + v_2 + v_3 + \ldots + v_n) = v_g\left\{\frac{1}{R_b} + \frac{(n+1)}{R}\right\} - \frac{v_o}{R}$$

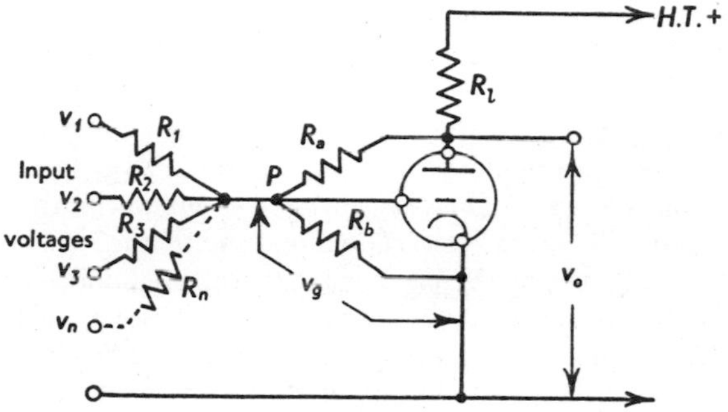

FIG. 13.32

If $R_b \gg R$,

$$(v_1 + v_2 + v_3 + \ldots + v_n)/R = \{v_g(n+1)/R\} - v_o/R$$

If the gain of *the valve itself* is A, then $v_g = v_o/A$

so $$(v_1 + v_2 + v_3 + \ldots + v_n) = v_o\{(n+1)/A - 1\}$$

A will be large, particularly if the valve is a pentode. Thus,

$$(v_1 + v_2 + v_3 + \ldots + v_n) \simeq -v_o.$$

Valve oscillators

It has been shown in Chapter 12 that the current i at any instant in an LCR oscillating circuit is given by the differential equation

$$d^2i/dt^2 + (R/L)(di/dt) + i/LC = 0$$

The form of the current wave during the decrease or increase of amplitude depends on whether α^2 is greater than, equal to or less than $1/LC$, where $\alpha = R/2L$. If $\alpha^2 > 1/LC$ an aperiodic discharge results and a limiting condition of this case results when $\alpha^2 = 1/LC$. When $\alpha^2 < \frac{1}{LC}$, the solution of the differential equation represents a sinusoidal oscillation, in which the rate of rise or fall of amplitude depends on the value of R, and in which the frequency of oscillation $(\omega/2\pi)$ is given by

$$\omega^2 = (1/LC) - (R^2/4L^2).$$

The amplitude of oscillation will decrease or increase with time depending on whether R is positive or negative. If R is zero the amplitude of oscillation will remain unchanged with time.

It is seen from the above expression for ω^2 that when $R^2/4L^2$ is small compared with $1/LC$ the frequency $f = 1/2\pi\sqrt{LC}$. With $R = 0$, the potential energy stored in the capacitor is converted into an equal amount of magnetic or kinetic energy every cycle, *i.e.* $CV^2/2 = LI^2/2$ where V and I are the maximum values of voltage and current respectively. This is so because $CV^2/2 = C(I/\omega C)^2/2 = LI^2(1/\omega^2 LC)/2 = LI^2/2$.

Valve oscillators employ some form of maintaining system and the effect of this is equivalent to reducing the circuit resistance to zero. The maintaining system takes the form of a shunt circuit across the tuned elements. Thomas * has shown that the frequency of oscillation is affected only slightly by the presence of the maintaining system. For this purpose he considers the LCR tuned circuit to be shunted by an impedance $\mathbf{Z}_a$ having two components R_a and X_a. The whole arrangement is then equivalent to a simple series circuit having a resistance of

$$R + \frac{R_a}{(1 - \omega C X_a)^2 + (R_a)^2\omega^2 C^2}$$

and a reactance of

$$\omega L + \frac{X_a(1 - \omega C X_a) - (R_a)^2\omega C}{1 - (\omega C X_a)^2 + (R_a)^2\omega^2 C^2}$$

Thus, if R_a is negative the resistance of the equivalent circuit is less than the original resistance R. If then $R_a = R\{(1 - \omega C X_a)^2 + (R_a)^2\omega^2 C^2\}$ the effective resistance is zero and this is the limiting condition for the commencement of self oscillation. No power is then dissipated in the circuit and the oscillation frequency is given by equating to zero the reactive components.

Consider the special case of the above maintaining system where $X_a = 0$. Then the condition for maintenance of oscillation is given by $R_a = R\{1 + \omega^2 C^2 (R_a)^2\}$ or $R_a \simeq (\omega^2 L^2/R)$. Under these conditions the reactance of the circuit is

$$\omega L - \{(R_a)^2\omega C\}/\{1 + (R_a)^2\omega^2 C^2\} \simeq (\omega L - 1/\omega C)$$

As stated already, therefore, the frequency of oscillation is only slightly affected by the presence of R_a. It will be seen that if $\mathbf{Z}_a$ contains a reactive part then both the frequency of oscillation and the value of R_a necessary to start oscillation are changed.

Valve oscillators in which the frequency depends primarily on the constants of a tuned circuit, may be divided into two types, namely dynatron and feedback types. In the first type the oscillator relies on the fact that under certain conditions the anode-current/anode-voltage characteristic of a valve may have a negative slope over part of its range.

* H. A. Thomas, *Theory and Design of Valve Oscillators* (Chapman & Hall, 1941).

In the second type of oscillator some form of coupling is provided between the grid and anode circuits of the valve. In the first type it is evident how the negative-resistance component of the required maintaining system is introduced. In the second type this is not so apparent and to gain an understanding of the mechanism of oscillation it is preferable to regard the device as an amplifier with part of the output energy fed back into the input circuit. It will be seen later, however, that circuits of the second type do all reduce to the equivalent form discussed above where an impedance shunts the tuned circuit.

The fundamental differential equation for the current

$$d^2i/dt^2 + (R/L)(di/dt) + i/LC = 0$$

is sometimes written in the form $\{D^2 + (R/L)D + 1/LC\}i = 0$ as used in Chapter 12 where $D = d/dt$.

If this form is used then the maintenance condition for oscillation is evidently given by equating the D term to zero and the frequency of oscillation is given by putting ω^2 equal to the term which does not contain D or D^2.

The differential equation may also be written in the form

$$Ri + L\,di/dt + \frac{1}{C}\int i\,dt = 0$$

or

$$(R + LD + 1/DC)i = 0.$$

If this is compared with the expression

$$(R + j\omega L + 1/j\omega C)i = 0$$

it will be seen that D and $j\omega$ are equivalent. The frequency of oscillation corresponds to equating the imaginary terms to zero and the maintenance condition corresponds to equating the real terms to zero.

To determine the frequency of oscillation and the condition for maintenance of oscillation it is obviously only necessary to form the differential equation for current; it is unnecessary to solve it.

The dynatron oscillator

The phenomenon of secondary emission causes the anode-current/anode-voltage characteristic of a tetrode to have a negative-resistance portion. The dynatron oscillator makes use of this fact. A tetrode is operated under such conditions, the screen grid being maintained at a high positive potential for this purpose. A tuned circuit is placed in the anode lead of the valve as shown by the typical arrangement of Fig. 13.33 (*a*).

The equivalent circuit of the arrangement is given in Fig. 13.33 (*b*). Let the currents circulate as shown.

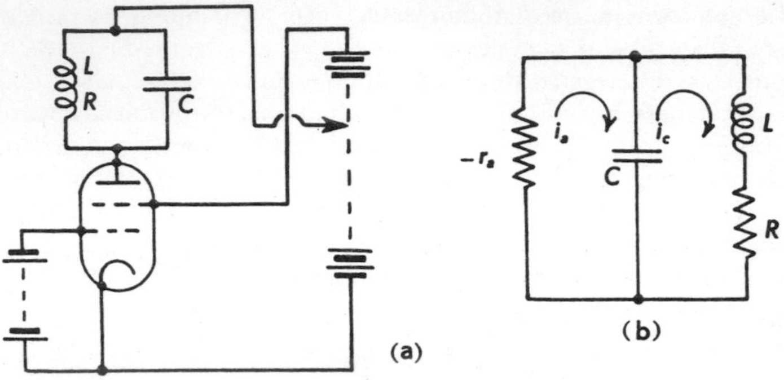

FIG. 13.33

For the i_a loop,

$$(-r_a + 1/DC)i_a - (1/DC)i_C = 0 \quad . \quad . \quad (13.52)$$

For the i_C loop,

$$(LD + R + 1/DC)i_C - (1/DC)i_a = 0 \quad . \quad . \quad (13.53)$$

Eliminating i_a from these equations,

$$i_C\{D^2 + (R/L - 1/r_aC)D + (r_a - R)/r_aL\}\,C = 0$$

The limiting condition for maintenance of oscillation is therefore given by $(R/L - 1/r_aC) = 0$ *i.e.* $r_a = L/CR$.

The frequency of oscillation $(\omega/2\pi)$ is given by

$$\omega = \sqrt{(r_a - R)/r_aLC} = \sqrt{(1 - R/r_a)/LC}$$

Since r_a is large compared with R, $\omega \simeq \sqrt{(1/LC)}$, as expected.

Feedback types of oscillator

Tuned-Anode Oscillator. A typical circuit of a tuned-anode oscillator is shown in Fig. 13.34 (*a*)

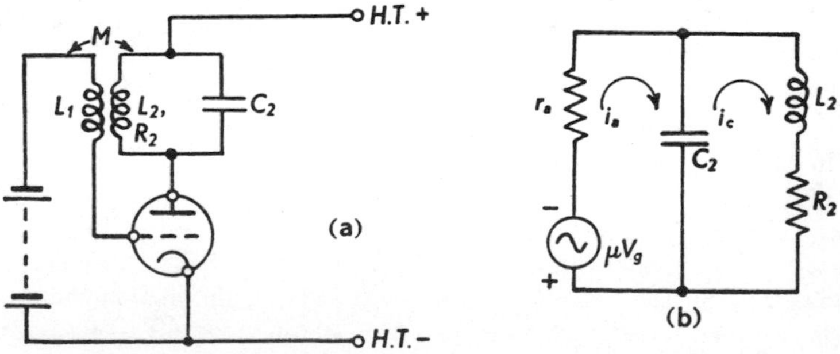

FIG. 13.34

[*Note.* r_a is positive now.]

and its equivalent circuit is shown in Fig. 13.34 (*b*).

Let the currents circulate as shown.

For the i_a loop,

$$i_a\{r_a + 1/DC_2\} - i_C(1/DC_2) = -\mu V_g = \mu M D i_C \,. \quad (13.54)$$

For the i_C loop,

$$i_C\{DL_2 + 1/DC_2 + R_2\} - i_a(1/DC_2) = 0 \quad (13.55)$$

If i_a is eliminated from these equations, the following results:

$$i_C\{r_a L_2 C_2 D^2 + D(r_a R_2 C_2 + L_2 - \mu M) + r_a + R_2\} = 0$$

The condition for maintenance of oscillation is, therefore,

$$M = (L_2 + r_a R_2 C_2)/\mu$$

The angular frequency

$$\omega = \sqrt{(r_a + R_2)/r_a L_2 C_2}$$

Since $r_a \gg R_2$,

$$\omega = \sqrt{(1 + R_2/r_a)/L_2 C_2} \simeq \sqrt{1/L_2 C_2} \text{ as expected.}$$

It should be pointed out that conventional self-excited oscillators generally operate as Class-C devices although Class-A ones are possible. The theory given therefore must be recognized as a limited solution of the oscillator problem.

Tuned-grid oscillator. A typical circuit of a tuned-grid oscillator is shown in Fig. 13.35 (*a*) and its equivalent circuits are shown in Fig. 13.35 (*b*) and (*c*).

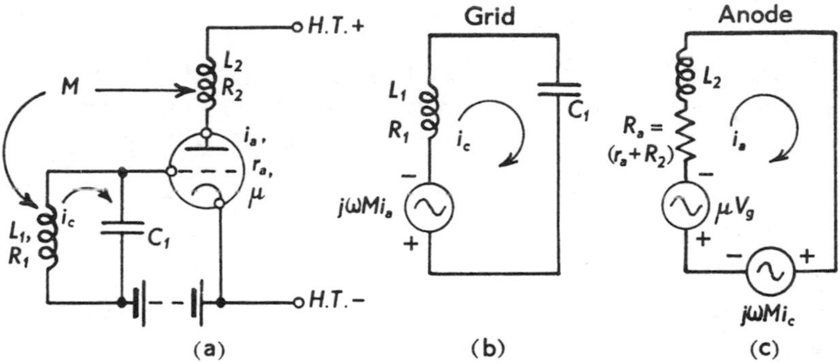

FIG. 13.35

For the i_C loop,

$$(R_1 + DL_1 + 1/DC_1)i_C = -MDi_a \quad . \quad . \quad (13.56)$$

For the i_a loop,

$$(R_a + DL_2)i_a + \mu V_g = -MDi_C \quad . \quad . \quad . \quad (13.57)$$

Also, $$V_g = +i_C/DC_1 \quad . \quad . \quad . \quad . \quad . \quad (13.58)$$

From (13.56), $$i_a = -(R_1 + DL_1 + 1/DC_1)i_C/MD \quad . \quad . \quad (13.59)$$

Substituting (13.59) in (13.57) and using (13.58),

$$i_C\{R_aR_1 + R_aDL_1 + R_a/DC_1 + DL_2R_1 + D^2L_1L_2 + L_2/C_1 - MD\mu/DC_1 - M^2D^2\} = 0$$

This equation cannot be put into the usual form so it is necessary to write $j\omega$ instead of D. Then,

$$R_aR_1 + j\omega L_1R_a - jR_a/\omega C_1 + j\omega L_2R_1 - \omega^2L_1L_2 + L_2/C_1 - \mu M/C_1 + \omega^2M^2 = 0$$

Equating the imaginary parts of this equation gives the frequency of oscillation

$$R_1\omega L_2 + \omega L_1R_a - R_a/\omega C_1 = 0$$

$$\therefore \quad \omega = \sqrt{1/L_1C_1\{R_1L_2/L_1R_a + 1\}} \simeq \sqrt{1/L_1C_1} \text{ since } R_1 \ll R_a$$

Equating the real parts of the above equation gives the maintenance condition

$$R_1R_a - \omega^2L_1L_2 + L_2/C_1 + \omega^2M^2 - \mu M/C_1 = 0$$

Assuming $$\omega^2 = 1/L_1C_1$$

$$\mu M\{1 - M/\mu L_1\}/C_1 = R_1R_a$$

Now $M < L_1$ and μ is large so $(1 - M/\mu L_1) \simeq 1$

$\therefore$ the condition for maintenance is

$$\mu M/C_1 \simeq R_aR_1$$

$$i.e. \quad M \simeq R_aR_1C_1/\mu \simeq R_1C_1/g_m \text{ since } R_a \simeq r_a.$$

The Hartley oscillator. The Hartley oscillator circuit in its simplest form is shown in Fig. 13.36 (*a*). This arrangement is called the series-fed circuit and is not very satisfactory except for battery-operated

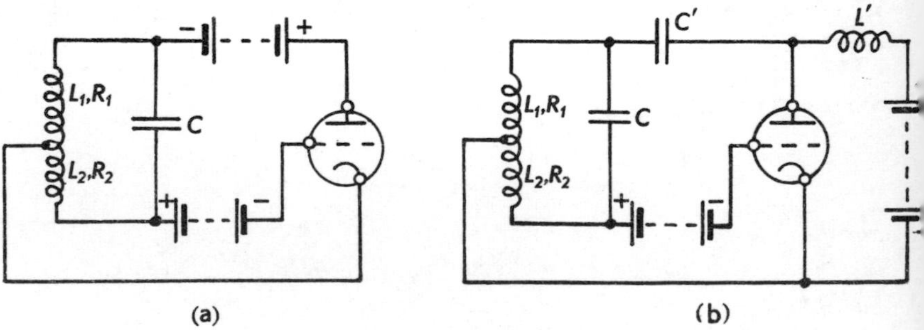

FIG. 13.36

oscillators as any capacitance between the cathode of the valve and the anode-voltage supply is shunted across L_1. A better form of circuit, the parallel-fed arrangement is shown in Fig. 13.36 (*b*).

The choke L' has a large reactance at the oscillation frequency and the capacitor C' has a small reactance at the oscillation frequency. These two components do not enter into the equivalent circuit, therefore, and the equivalent circuit is the same for both the series-fed and parallel-fed arrangements (Fig. 13.37).

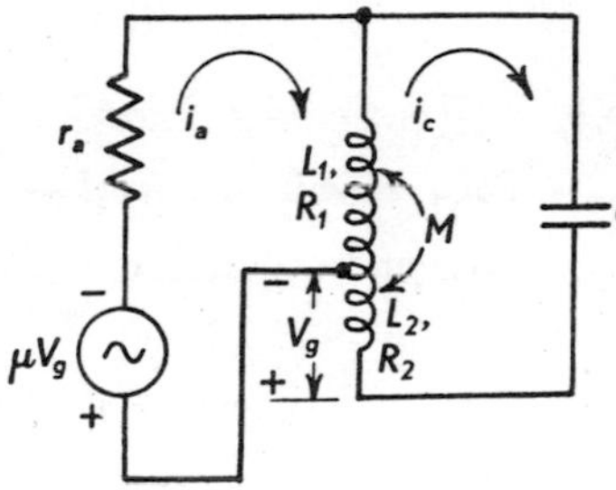

FIG. 13.37

An approximate analysis of the circuit can quickly be made if R_1 and R_2 are assumed to be zero. With this assumption the reactance of the tuned circuit considered as a closed loop is

$$j\omega L_1 + j\omega L_2 + 2j\omega M + 1/j\omega C$$

If the reactance is equated to zero,

$$\omega = 1/\sqrt{C(L_1 + L_2 + 2M)}$$

and this gives the frequency of oscillation.

The tuned circuit presents two parallel branches to the generator μV_g and at the oscillation frequency, given by the above expression, the sum of the reactances of these branches is zero, *i.e.* the reactances are equal and opposite. The currents through the two branches, supplied by the generator, are therefore also equal and opposite, so i_a is zero and the voltage across the top section of the coil is μV_g since there is no voltage drop across r_a. But the voltage across the bottom section of the coil is V_g.

$$\therefore \quad (j\omega L_1 + j\omega M)i_C/(j\omega L_2 + j\omega M)i_C = \mu$$

or

$$\mu = (L_1 + M)/(L_2 + M).$$

This is the condition for maintenance of oscillation.

A complete analysis, including R_1 and R_2, will now be made.

For the i_a loop,

$$i_a(r_a + R_1 + j\omega L_1) + \mu V_g = i_C\{R_1 + j\omega(L_1 + M)\}. \quad (13.60)$$

For the i_C loop,

$$i_a(R_1 + j\omega L_1) = i_C\left(R_1 + j\omega L_1 + j\omega M + \frac{1}{j\omega C}\right) + V_g \quad (13.61)$$

Also, $$V_g = (R_2 + j\omega L_2)i_C + j\omega M(i_C - i_a) \quad . \quad . \quad (13.62)$$

Substituting (13.62) in (13.60) and (13.61) gives

$$\begin{aligned} &i_a(r_a + R_1 + j\omega L_1 - j\omega\mu M) \\ &\quad = i_C\{R_1 - \mu R_2 + j\omega(L_1 + M) - j\omega\mu(L_2 + M)\} \quad (13.63) \end{aligned}$$

and

$$\begin{aligned} &i_a(R_1 + j\omega L_1 + j\omega M) \\ &\quad = i_C(R_1 + R_2 + j\omega L_1 + j\omega L_2 + 2j\omega M + 1/j\omega C) \quad (13.64) \end{aligned}$$

Dividing (13.63) and (13.64) and equating the imaginary parts gives

$$\omega^2 = \frac{1 + R_1/r_a}{C[(L_1 + L_2 + 2M) + \{(R_1L_2 + R_2L_1)(1 + \mu)\}/r_a]}$$

When R_1 and R_2 are small,

$$\omega^2 \simeq 1/C(L_1 + L_2 + 2M) \text{ as shown already.}$$

Dividing (13.63) and (13.64) and equating the real parts gives

$$\begin{aligned} &(r_a + R_1)(R_1 + R_2) - \omega^2(L_1 - \mu M)(L_1 + L_2 + 2M) + (L_1 - \mu M)/C \\ &\quad = R_1(R_1 - \mu R_2) - \omega^2(L_1 + M)(L_1 + M - \mu L_2 - \mu M). \end{aligned}$$

If ω^2 is assumed to be $1/C(L_1 + L_2 + 2M)$ this condition of maintenance reduces to

$$(L_1 + M) = \mu(L_2 + M) - \{r_a(R_1 + R_2) + R_1R_2(1 + \mu)\}/\omega^2(L_1 + M)$$

and if R_1 and R_2 are small,

$$(L_1 + M) \simeq \mu(L_2 + M) \text{ as shown already.}$$

The Colpitts oscillator. The Colpitts oscillator circuit is shown in Fig. 13.38 (*a*) and its equivalent circuit in Fig. 13.38 (*b*).

Coil L' and resistor R' are included to provide paths in the anode and grid circuits so that direct voltages can be applied to the valve. These elements do not enter into the equivalent circuit because L' is of large reactance and R' of large resistance. In the Hartley circuit such elements were unnecessary because the tapped coil provided the d.c. paths.

An approximate analysis of the circuit can quickly be made, as it was in the case of the Hartley circuit, if $R = 0$. The reactance of the tuned circuit considered as a closed loop is now

$$j\omega L + 1/j\omega C_2 + 1/j\omega C_1.$$

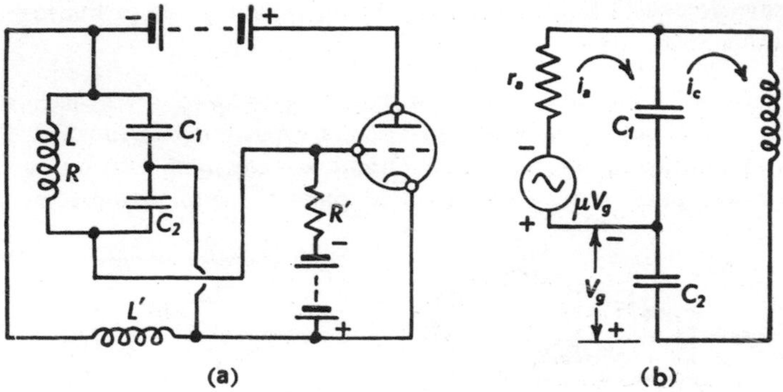

FIG. 13.38

If this is equated to zero,

$$\omega^2 = (1/C_1 + 1/C_2)/L$$

which gives the frequency of oscillation.

Under this condition the voltage across C_1 is μV_g. The voltage across $C_2 = V_g$. Thus the condition for maintenance of oscillation, when $R = 0$, is that

$$\mu = C_2/C_1.$$

A complete analysis, including R, will now be made.

For the i_a loop,

$$i_a(r_a + 1/j\omega C_1) + \mu V_g = i_C/j\omega C_1 \quad . \quad . \quad . \quad (13.65)$$

For the i_C loop,

$$i_a/j\omega C_1 = i_C(R + j\omega L + 1/j\omega C_1 + 1/j\omega C_2) \quad . \quad (13.66)$$

Also, $$V_g = i_C/j\omega C_2 \quad . \quad . \quad . \quad . \quad . \quad . \quad . \quad . \quad . \quad (13.67)$$

Substituting (13.67) in (13.65) gives

$$i_a(r_a + 1/j\omega C_1) = i_C(1/j\omega C_1 - \mu/j\omega C_2) \quad . \quad (13.68)$$

Dividing (13.66) and (13.68) and equating the imaginary parts gives

$$\omega^2 = \{1/C_2 + (1 + R/r_a)/C_1\}/L.$$

When $R = 0$ this reduces to the approximate formula given already. Dividing (13.66) and (13.68) and equating the real parts gives

$$(1 + \mu)/\omega^2 C_1 C_2 = r_a R + L/C_1.$$

If ω^2 is assumed to be $(1/C_2 + 1/C_1)/L$ this condition of maintenance reduces to

$$C_2/C_1 = \mu - r_a R(C_1 + C_2)/L.$$

When $R = 0$ this also reduces to the expression given earlier for the maintenance condition.

Oscillator relying on valve grid-anode capacitance. An oscillator arrangement relying on valve grid-anode capacitance is illustrated in Fig. 13.39 (*a*) and its equivalent circuit is shown in Fig. 13.39 (*b*). The capacitance C may be provided by a capacitor external to the

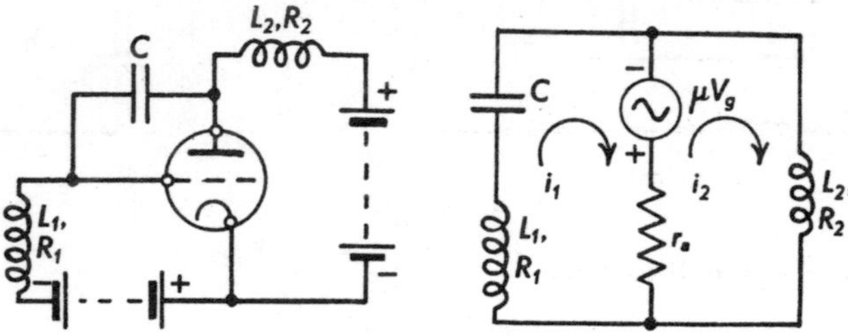

FIG. 13.39

valve or it may simply be the grid-anode interelectrode capacitance. There is no mutual inductance between L_1 and L_2 in this circuit.

A preliminary approximate analysis of the circuit can be made as was done in the cases of the Hartley and Colpitts arrangements. Proceeding in exactly the same way by neglecting R_1 and R_2 the frequency of oscillation is given by

$$\omega^2 = 1/C(L_1 + L_2)$$

and the maintenance condition is

$$\mu = L_2/L_1.$$

A complete analysis, including R_1 and R_2, will now be made.

For the i_1 loop,

$$i_1(r_a + R_1 + j\omega L_1 + 1/j\omega C) - \mu V_g = i_2 r_a \quad . \quad (13.69)$$

For the i_2 loop,

$$i_2(r_a + R_2 + j\omega L_2) + \mu V_g = r_a i_1 \quad . \quad . \quad . \quad (13.70)$$

Also,
$$V_g = -(R_1 + j\omega L_1)i_1 \quad . \quad . \quad . \quad . \quad (13.71)$$

Substituting (13.71) in (13.69) and (13.70) gives

$$i_1\{r_a + (R_1 + j\omega L_1)(\mu + 1) + 1/j\omega C\} = i_2 r_a \quad . \quad (13.72)$$

and
$$i_1(r_a + \mu R_1 + \mu j\omega L_1) = i_2(r_a + R_2 + j\omega L_2) \quad . \quad . \quad (13.73)$$

Dividing (13.72) and (13.73) and equating the imaginary parts gives

$$\omega^2 = \frac{1 + R_2/r_a}{C[L_1 + L_2 + \{(R_1 L_2 + R_2 L_1)(\mu + 1)/r_a\}]}$$

When R_1 and $R_2 = 0$ this reduces to the approximate formula for ω^2 given already.

Dividing (13.72) and (13.73) and equating the real parts gives

$$r_a(R_1 + R_2) + R_1R_2(\mu + 1) + L_2/C = \omega^2 L_1 L_2(\mu + 1)$$

If ω^2 is assumed to be $1/C(L_1 + L_2)$ this condition of maintenance reduces to

$$L_1 = L_2/\mu + [\{r_a(R_1 + R_2) + R_1R_2(1 + \mu)\}\{(L_1 + L_2)C\}/\mu L_2]$$

When $R_1 = R_2 = 0$ this also reduces to the expression $L_1 = L_2/\mu$ given earlier for the maintenance condition.

Frequency stability

For all the oscillator circuits considered so far it has been found that the frequency of oscillation is nearly equal to the resonant frequency of the tuned circuit itself. As a first step towards keeping the frequency of oscillation constant therefore the resonant frequency of the tuned circuit should be maintained constant. Factors which cause this resonant frequency to change include ageing of components and variations of component values with temperature. Even if the tuned circuit resonant frequency is maintained constant a stable oscillation frequency is not ensured because, as seen already, the frequency actually generated differs from the tuned circuit resonant frequency by a small amount which depends on the resistance of the tuned circuit and the valve constants (and therefore on electrode voltages). Many methods have been suggested for improving the stability of valve oscillators but a discussion of these is beyond the scope of this book. The reader can find further information on the subject in publications by Terman,* Thomas,† Llewellyn ‡ and Kusunose and Ishikawa.§

Crystal oscillators

The frequency of an oscillator can be made very stable by using a piezo-electric crystal to replace the normal tuned circuit. The literature on crystal oscillators and related piezo-electric phenomena is very extensive.|| It is impossible in the limited space available to describe the properties of piezo-electric crystals; in fact, the equivalent electrical

* F. E. Terman, *Radio Engineers' Handbook*, (McGraw-Hill, 1943).

† H. A. Thomas, *Theory and Design of Valve Oscillators*, (Chapman & Hall, 1941).

‡ F. B. Llewellyn, "Constant Frequency Oscillators", *Proc. I.R.E.*, **19**, p. 2063 (1931).

§ Y. Kusunose and S. Ishikawa, "Frequency Stabilization of Radio Transmitters", *Proc. I.R.E.*, **20**, p. 310 (1932).

|| See, for example, the book *Piezoelectricity*, by W. G. Cady (McGraw-Hill, 1946), which has 36 chapters; it gives 57 book references and 602 periodical references.

circuit of a crystal will also be used without any discussion of why the crystal behaves in the same way as a series LCR circuit with a resonant frequency equal to that of the natural frequency of mechanical vibrations. For information on these topics the reader might consult the books by Terman * and Williams.†

Only one crystal oscillator will be discussed. It is shown in Fig. 13.40 (*a*) and its equivalent circuit in Fig. 13.40 (*b*). The circuit is

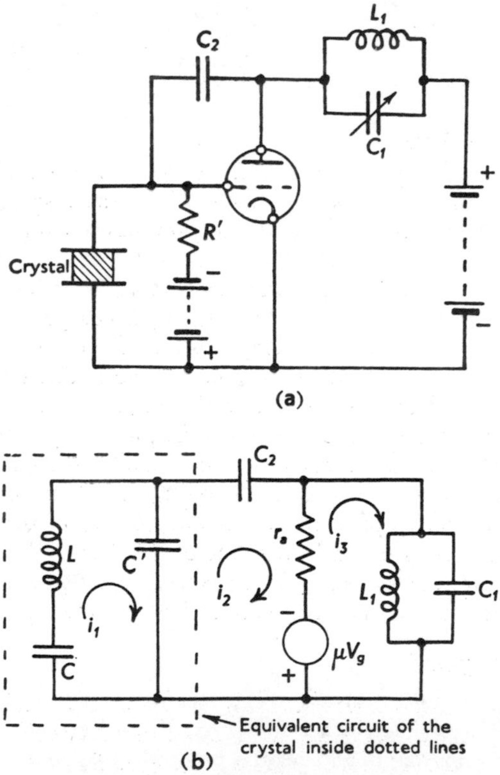

FIG. 13.40

equivalent to a tuned-anode/tuned-grid arrangement, the crystal acting as the tuned-grid portion. C_2, which supplements the anode-grid interelectrode capacitance of the valve, is included to facilitate making the frequency of oscillation insensitive to circuit adjustments and to the electrode voltages of the valve.

* F. E. Terman, *Radio Engineers' Handbook* (McGraw-Hill, 1943).
† E. Williams, *Thermionic Valve Circuits*, 3rd Edition (Pitman, 1952).

The circuit will be analyzed assuming the crystal equivalent circuit contains no resistance and that the resistance of coil L_1 is negligible.

For the i_1 mesh,

$$i_1(j\omega L + 1/j\omega C + 1/j\omega C') = i_2/j\omega C' \quad . \quad . \quad (13.74)$$

For the i_2 mesh,

$$i_2(r_a + 1/j\omega C' + 1/j\omega C_2) - \mu V_g = i_3 r_a + i_1/j\omega C' \quad . \quad (13.75)$$

For the i_3 mesh,

$$i_3\{r_a + j\omega L_1/(1 - \omega^2 L_1 C_1)\} = i_2 r_a - \mu V_g \quad . \quad . \quad (13.76)$$

Also,
$$V_g = -i_1(j\omega L + 1/j\omega C) \quad . \quad . \quad . \quad (13.77)$$

Substituting (13.77) in (13.75) and (13.76) gives

$$i_1(j\omega\mu L + \mu/j\omega C - 1/j\omega C') + i_2(1/j\omega C' + 1/j\omega C_2 + r_a) = i_3 r_a \quad . \quad . \quad (13.78)$$

and

$$i_1(j\omega\mu L + \mu/j\omega C) + i_2 r_a = i_3\{r_a + j\omega L_1/(1 - \omega^2 L_1 C_1)\} \quad (13.79)$$

Eliminating i_3 from (13.78) and (13.79) gives

$$i_1\left\{\frac{\mu L_1/C - L_1/C' - \mu\omega^2 L L_1}{1 - \omega^2 L_1 C_1} - \frac{r_a}{j\omega C'}\right\}$$
$$= i_2\left\{\frac{L_1/C' + L_1/C_2}{1 - \omega^2 L_1 C_1} + r_a\left(\frac{1}{j\omega C'} + \frac{1}{j\omega C_2} + \frac{j\omega L_1}{1 - \omega^2 L_1 C_1}\right)\right\} (13.80)$$

Dividing (13.80) by (13.74), cross-multiplying and equating the imaginary parts gives

$$\omega^2 = \frac{1}{LC}\left\{\frac{1 + (1 + C'/C_2 + C/C_2)/\mu}{1 + (1 + C'/C_2)/\mu}\right\}$$

Dividing (13.80) by (13.74), cross-multiplying and equating the real parts gives:

$$-r_a/(\omega C')^2 =$$
$$r_a(j\omega L + 1/j\omega C + 1/j\omega C')\{j\omega L_1/(1 - \omega^2 L_1 C_1) + 1/j\omega C' + 1/j\omega C_2\}$$

If ω^2 is taken as $1/LC$ this condition for maintenance of oscillation reduces to

$$L_1 C_1 = LC - L_1 C_2.$$

It will be seen that the oscillation frequency is fixed primarily by the constants of the crystal.

A general theorem for valve oscillators

A general theorem for all valve oscillators states that

$$\mathbf{Z} + r_a/(1 + \mu\mathbf{N}) = 0$$

where $\mathbf{Z}$ is the vector impedance of the whole external circuit connected between the anode and cathode of the valve, $\mathbf{N}$ is the complex ratio $\mathbf{V}_g/\mathbf{V}_a$ of the grid and anode voltage vectors and r_a and μ are the anode-slope resistance and amplification factor of the valve respectively.

Proof. Fig. 13.41 shows the equivalent circuit of the valve. From this,

$$\mathbf{V}_a = r_a\mathbf{I}_a - \mu\mathbf{V}_g$$

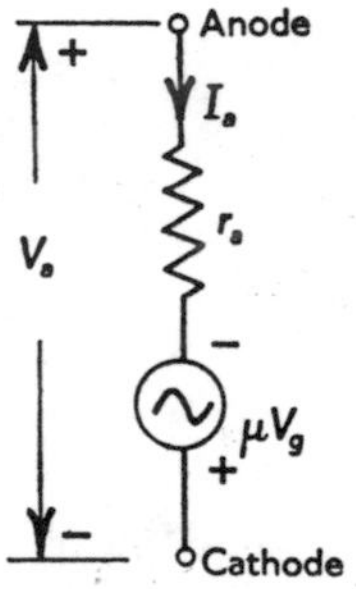

FIG. 13.41

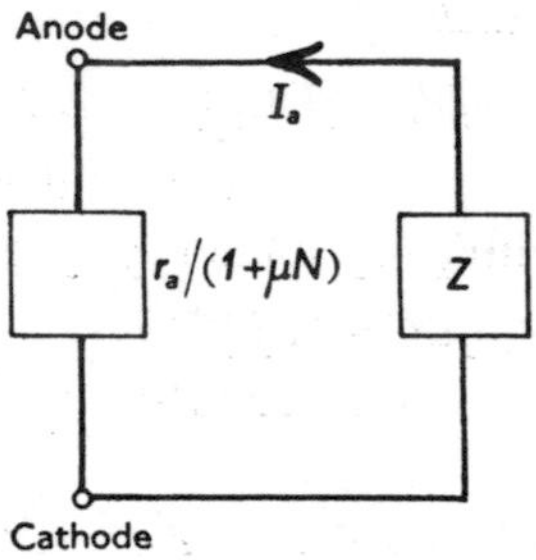

FIG. 13.42

If the coupling between the grid and anode circuits is such as to maintain $\mathbf{V}_g = \mathbf{N}\mathbf{V}_a$, where $\mathbf{N}$ may be complex, then,

$$\mathbf{V}_a = -\mu\mathbf{N}\mathbf{V}_a + r_a\mathbf{I}_a$$

or

$$\mathbf{V}_a/\mathbf{I}_a = r_a/(1 + \mu\mathbf{N})$$

i.e. the valve behaves as an impedance of $r_a/(1 + \mu\mathbf{N})$. The oscillator circuit can now be re-drawn as in Fig. 13.42. Thus,

$$\{\mathbf{Z} + r_a/(1 + \mu\mathbf{N})\}\mathbf{I}_a = 0.$$

If $\mathbf{I}_a$ is not zero,

$$\mathbf{Z} + r_a/(1 + \mu\mathbf{N}) = 0.$$

This theorem will now be used to find the condition for maintenance and the frequency of oscillation for a tuned-anode oscillator circuit. For this purpose re-consider Fig. 13.34 (*a*).

$$\mathbf{Z} = \{(R_2 + j\omega L_2)/j\omega C_2\}/\{R_2 + j\omega L_2 + 1/j\omega C_2\}$$

Now, referring to Fig. 13.43,

$$\mathbf{V}_g = -j\omega M\mathbf{I}_L$$

$$= -j\omega M\mathbf{V}_a/(R_2 + j\omega L_2)$$

$$\therefore \quad \mathbf{N} = -j\omega M/(R_2 + j\omega L_2).$$

Substituting the values of $\mathbf{Z}$ and $\mathbf{N}$ in the expression $\mathbf{Z} + r_a/(1 + \mu\mathbf{N}) = 0$ gives

$$\frac{(R_2 + j\omega L_2)/j\omega C_2}{R_2 + j\omega L_2 + 1/j\omega C_2} + \frac{r_a}{1 - \mu j\omega M/(R_2 + j\omega L_2)} = 0$$

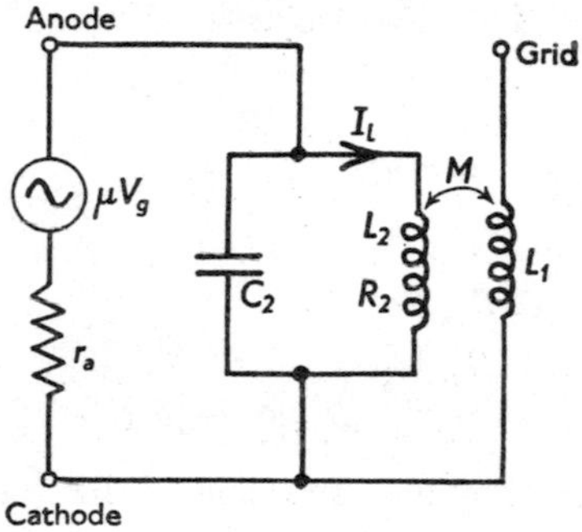

FIG. 13.43

If the real and imaginary parts of this expression are separately equated it is found that

$$M = (L_2 + r_a R_2 C_2)/\mu$$

and

$$\omega = \sqrt{\{(r_a + R_2)/r_a L_2 C_2\}} \text{ as before.}$$

Resistor-capacitor oscillators

Resistor-capacitor oscillators are essentially positive feedback amplifiers where the feedback is applied through a resistor-capacitor network which is frequency selective.* There are two common types of feedback network, namely the Wien-bridge network and the ladder network. In the first arrangement the network produces zero phase shift at some particular frequency. So, in association with a two-valve amplifier giving 360° phase shift, oscillations can be produced at this frequency provided the amplifier gain is greater than the attenuation of the network. In the ladder network a phase shift of 180° can be obtained at some specific frequency so a further phase shift of 180° is necessary in the amplifier (say by using one valve only) if the system is to oscillate.

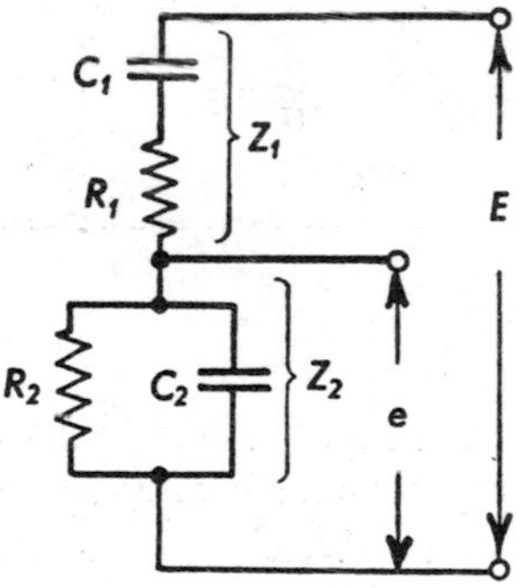

FIG. 13.44

The feedback network used in the Wien-bridge type of oscillator is illustrated in Fig. 13.44. For this circuit,

$$e = \mathbf{Z}_2\mathbf{E}/(\mathbf{Z}_1 + \mathbf{Z}_2).$$

In general $\mathbf{Z}_2/(\mathbf{Z}_1 + \mathbf{Z}_2)$ is a complex quantity of the form $a + jb$. $\boldsymbol{e}$ will be in phase with $\mathbf{E}$ at the frequency where $b = 0$ and then $e = aE$.

* A good account of such oscillators is given by T. P. Flanagan, "Resistor-Capacitor Oscillator Design", *Marconi Instrumentation*, 3, p. 82 (May 1952).

Now $$\mathbf{Z}_1 = R_1 + 1/j\omega C_1$$
and $$\mathbf{Z}_2 = R_2/(1 + jR_2\omega C_2)$$
so $$e = \frac{R_2\mathbf{E}}{(R_2 + R_1 + R_2C_2/C_1) + j(R_1R_2\omega C_2 - 1/\omega C_1)}$$
Thus, $b = 0$ when $R_1R_2\omega C_2 = 1/\omega C_1$

i.e. when $\omega^2 = 1/C_1C_2R_1R_2$.

When $b = 0$, $$a = R_2/(R_2 + R_1 + R_2C_2/C_1)$$ $$= 1/(1 + R_1/R_2 + C_2/C_1)$$

Thus, if the associated amplifier has a gain A, the condition for oscillation is

$$A \geqslant 1 + R_1/R_2 + C_2/C_1$$

A very successful oscillator using the Wien-bridge network has been described by Terman *et al.** and is shown in Fig. 13.45.

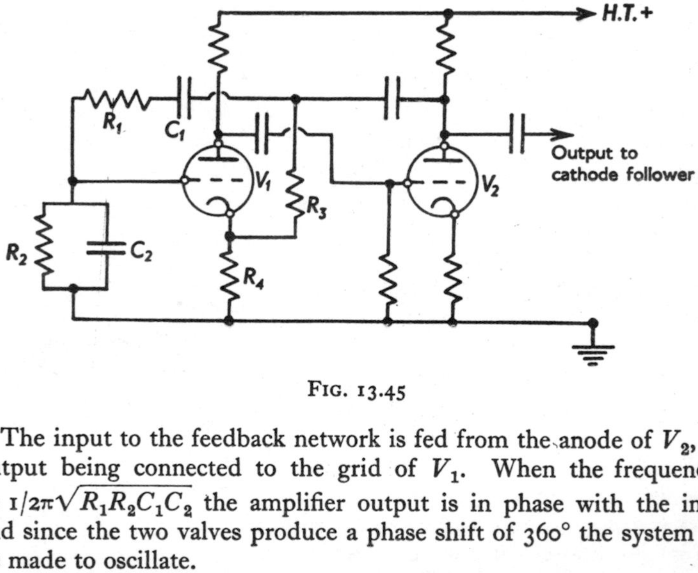

FIG. 13.45

The input to the feedback network is fed from the anode of V_2, the output being connected to the grid of V_1. When the frequency $f = 1/2\pi\sqrt{R_1R_2C_1C_2}$ the amplifier output is in phase with the input and since the two valves produce a phase shift of 360° the system can be made to oscillate.

Resistors R_3 and R_4 form a negative-feedback circuit the feedback ratio β being $R_4/(R_3 + R_4)$.

If the gain of an amplifier without feedback is A_o then the gain with feedback, $A_f = A_o/(1 + \beta A_o) \simeq 1/\beta$ if $\beta A_o \gg 1$. Thus, for sustained oscillation, $(R_3 + R_4)/R_4 \geqslant 1 + R_1/R_2 + C_2/C_1$.

* F. E. Terman, R. R. Buss, W. R. Hewlett and F. C. Cahill, "Some Applications of Negative Feedback with Particular Reference to Laboratory Equipment", *Proc. I.R.E.*, **27**, p. 649 (1939).

If $R_1 = R_2 = R$ and $C_1 = C_2 = C$, $f = 1/2\pi CR$ and the required amplifier gain is 3.

R_4 is frequently a low-wattage lamp because it then acts as an amplitude stabilizer. If the amplitude increases, the temperature of R_4 and therefore its resistance, will increase and the value of β will rise so reducing the amplifier gain. A thermistor used instead of R_3 (because of its negative temperature coefficient) can be employed to give the same effect.

It should be noted that the frequency of oscillation is proportional to $1/C$ and not to $1/\sqrt{C}$ as in LC oscillators. Thus, a given variable capacitor will give a larger frequency variation in one sweep of its range with the RC oscillator than with an LC type. The RC oscillator, however, requires two ganged capacitors. At very low audio frequencies simple feedback oscillators, such as the Hartley arrangement, are impracticable because of the difficulty of constructing large inductors with low losses. RC oscillators work well, however, at both low and high audio frequencies.

For fixed-frequency work Whale * has pointed out that the frequency stability of the Wien-bridge type of RC oscillator is improved by making C_2/C_1 and R_1/R_2 as large as possible consistent with maintaining oscillations.

A ladder phase-shift network for use in an RC oscillator may take the form of Fig. 13.46 (*a*), where phase-advancing sections are used, or the form of Fig. 13.46 (*b*) where phase-retarding sections are employed.

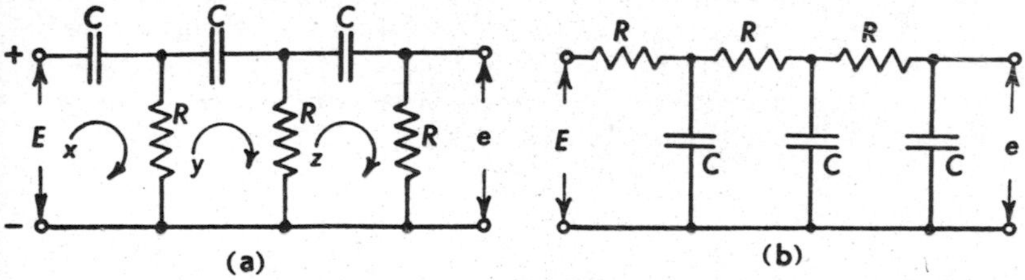

FIG. 13.46

In each case there is one frequency where the total phase-shift through the network is 180°.

Consider first Fig. 13.46 (*a*) and let currents x, y and z circulate as illustrated.

For the x loop,

$$(R + 1/j\omega C)x - Ry = E \quad . \quad . \quad . \quad . \quad (13.81)$$

For the y loop,

$$(2R + 1/j\omega C)y - Rx - Rz = 0 \quad . \quad . \quad (13.82)$$

* H. A. Whale, " Optimum Conditions for an R.C. Oscillator ", *Electronics*, **21**, p. 178 (February 1948).

For the z loop,

$$(2R + 1/j\omega C)z - Ry = 0 \quad . \quad . \quad . \quad (13.83)$$

From (13.83) $$y = (2R + 1/j\omega C)z/R \quad . \quad . \quad . \quad . \quad (13.84)$$

From (13.81) and (13.84),

$$x = \{E + (2R + 1/j\omega C)z\}/(R + 1/j\omega C) \; . \quad . \quad (13.85)$$

Substituting (13.84) and (13.85) in (13.82) gives

$$z(R^3 + 6R^2/j\omega C - 5R/\omega^2C^2 - 1/j\omega^3C^3) = ER^2 \, . \quad (13.86)$$

There is no j term when $6R^2/\omega C = 1/\omega^3C^3$,

i.e. when $\omega^2 = 1/6R^2C^2$

or when $f = 1/2\pi RC\sqrt{6}$

since the frequency $f = \omega/2\pi$.

At this frequency, $z(-29R^3) = ER^2$

so $e = Rz = -E/29$

Thus, the attenuation ratio of the network is 29 and the total phase-shift is 180° when $f = 1/2\pi RC\sqrt{6}$.

If a similar analysis is carried out for the network of Fig. 13.46 (*b*) it is found that the frequency f at which the network produces 180° phase shift is $\sqrt{6}/2\pi CR$ and the attenuation ratio of the network is again 29.

An oscillator can be constructed from only one valve and one of the networks of Fig. 13.46 provided the gain of the amplifier is greater than 29. Such an oscillator is particularly useful for fixed-frequency work but the arrangement can be used to give a range of frequencies by ganging the capacitors.* The ladder phase-shift networks discussed above were first fully described by Ginzton and Hollingsworth.†

PROBLEMS

1. A triode valve has characteristics for $V_g = 0$ and $V_g = -1$ V respectively given by the following figures:

V_a (V)	50	100	150
I_a (mA)	5	10	15

V_a (V)	50	100	150
I_a (mA)	0	5	10

* See, W. C. Vaughan, "Phase-Shift Oscillator", *Wireless Engr.*, **26**, p. 391 (1949).

† See E. L. Ginzton and L. M. Hollingsworth, "Phase-Shift Oscillators", *Proc. I.R.E.*, **29**, p. 43 (1941).

Determine the mutual conductance, anode-slope resistance and amplification factor.

If the valve is used as a simple amplifier with a load resistor of 10,000 Ω, an anode-supply voltage of 100 V and a grid bias of −1 V, draw the load line on the characteristics and find the voltage across the load.

[*Ans.* 5 mA/V, 10 kΩ, 50, 25 V.]

2. Some anode-current/anode-voltage characteristics of a certain pentode valve are given by the following figures, the screen voltage being held constant at 250 V:

V_a (V)	20	50	100	150	200	300	400	At
I_a (mA)	30	40	45	48	50	52	53	$V_g = -12$ V

V_a (V)	20	50	100	150	200	300	400	At
I_a (mA)	25	33	38	39	40	41·3	43	$V_g = -15$ V

Plot the characteristics and find the approximate values of μ, g_m and r_a over the normal operating range. [*Ans.* 246, 3·33 mA/V, 77 kΩ.]

3. A triode valve has an amplification factor of 20 and an anode-slope resistance of 8 kΩ. It is used as an amplifier with a resistive load of 20 kΩ and the input signal is 1 V. Calculate the output voltage using (*a*) the constant-voltage-source equivalent circuit, (*b*) the constant-current-source equivalent circuit. [*Ans.* 14·3 V.]

4. A certain triode when used as an amplifier with a resistive load of 50 kΩ gives a gain of 30. When the load resistance is changed to 85 kΩ the gain increases to 34. Find the anode-slope resistance, the mutual conductance and the amplification factor of the valve.

[*Ans.* 20 kΩ, 2·1 mA/V, 42.]

5. A high-vacuum diode whose internal resistance is 250 Ω is to supply power to a 1,000 Ω load from a 325 V, r.m.s. source. Evaluate (*a*) the peak load current, (*b*) the mean load current, (*c*) the alternating load current (r.m.s.), (*d*) the total input power to the anode circuit, (*e*) the rectification efficiency, (*f*) the percentage regulation from no-load to full-load. [S.U.]

[*Ans.* (*a*) 368 mA, (*b*) 117 mA, (*c*) 184 mA, (*d*) 42·3 W, (*e*) 32·5%, (*f*) 20%.]

6. The striking and extinction voltages of a gas-filled diode may both be taken as 10 V. The diode is used in a half-wave rectifier circuit to supply power to a 1,000 Ω load from a 300 V r.m.s. source. Find (*a*) the mean load voltage, (*b*) the d.c. power supplied to the load, (*c*) the input power to the anode circuit, (*d*) the rectification efficiency, (*e*) the ripple factor. [S.U.] [*Ans.* (*a*) 130 V, (*b*) 16·9 W, (*c*) 43·7 W, (*d*) 38·7%, (*e*) 1·225.]

7. A full-wave single-phase rectifier circuit contains a double-diode valve, the internal resistance of each element of which may be assumed constant at 500 Ω. The r.m.s. secondary voltage of the transformer from the centre tap to each anode is 300 V. The load has a resistance of 2,000 Ω. Calculate (*a*) the mean load current, (*b*) the r.m.s. alternating load current, (*c*) the d.c. output power, (*d*) the input power to the anode circuit, (*e*) the rectification efficiency, (*f*) the ripple factor, (*g*) the regulation from no-load to the given load. [S.U.]

[*Ans.* (*a*) 108 mA, (*b*) 120 mA, (*c*) 23·3 W, (*d*) 36 W, (*e*) 64·8%, (*f*) 0·482, (*g*) 54 V.]

8. Calculate the voltage gain V_o/V_i of the amplifier arrangement illustrated.

$$\left[Ans. \quad \frac{-(g_m - 1/R_2)(1/R_1)}{(g_m - 1/R_2)1/R_2 + (1/R_1 + 1/R_2 + 1/R_3)(1/R_2 + 1/r_a + 1/R_l)} \right].$$

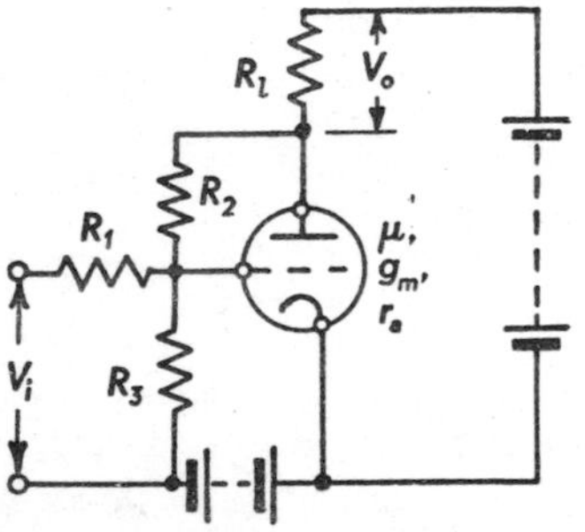

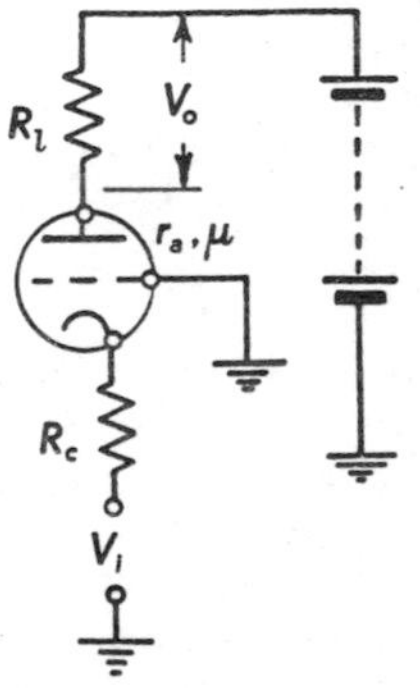

9. Determine the voltage gain V_o/V_i of the grounded-grid-amplifier arrangement shown.

[*Ans.* $R_l/\{R_c + (r_a + R_l)/(\mu + 1)\}$.]

10. A triode amplifier operating at a frequency of 10,000 c/s has a resistive load of 90 kΩ. Calculate the voltage gain. The valve has an amplification factor of 60 and an anode-slope resistance of 40 kΩ. The interelectrode capacitances are C_{ga} = 3 μμF, C_{gc} = 3 μμF and C_{ac} = 3·6 μμF.

Find the gain of this stage when it forms the first section of a two-stage amplifier. The two stages are identical. It may be assumed that the arrangement is such that the 90 kΩ load of the first stage is shunted by a capacitance of 200 μμF, but this assumption should be justified. [S.U.]

[*Ans.* 41·6, 39·1$\underline{|160{\cdot}2^\circ}$.]

11. In a certain stage of a resistor-capacitor coupled amplifier the anode load consists of a 2,000 Ω resistor in series with a 70 μH inductor. The stage employs a tetrode having a mutual conductance of 10 mA/V. The effective capacitance shunting the load may be taken as equivalent to a 40 μμF capacitor from the valve anode to earth. Find the voltage amplification and phase-shift of the stage at a frequency of 3 Mc/s. What reduction in gain results if the inductor in the anode circuit is removed? [*Ans.* 15·9, 123·4°, 4·8.]

12. A transformer-coupled amplifier has the following constants: Amplification factor of valve = 10; Anode-slope resistance of valve = 10,000 Ω; Ratio of secondary to primary turns of transformer = 3; Effective leakage inductance of transformer referred to primary = 0·5 H; Total effective shunt capacitance of transformer referred to primary = 1,500 μμF; Total effective resistance of transformer referred to primary

= 15,000 Ω; Resistance of primary winding of transformer = 4,000 Ω; Inductance of primary winding of transformer = 75 H.

Investigate the frequency-response characteristics of the amplifier. [S.U.]

13. In a certain transformer-coupled amplifier stage the triode valve employed has an amplification factor of 20 and an anode-slope resistance of 10 kΩ. The turns ratio of the transformer is 3 and the inductance of the primary winding is 30 H. The secondary load is a 0·5 MΩ resistor. Determine the amplification of the stage at 100 c/s and 5,000 c/s. Neglect the resistance, self-capacitance and leakage of the transformer.

[*Ans.* 46·6, 50·8.]

14. The output stage of an audio-frequency amplifier uses a triode valve which has an anode-slope resistance of 5,000 Ω and an amplification factor of 20. The output transformer has a turns ratio of 25 : 1. Calculate the signal voltage which must be applied to the grid of the valve in order to deliver one watt of power to a 15 Ω loudspeaker.

[*Ans.* 7·42$V_{r.m.s.}$]

15. A triode valve with an amplification factor of 20 and an anode-slope resistance of 8,000 Ω is used as an amplifier and arranged to give maximum power output. An input voltage of 1 $V_{r.m.s.}$ is applied. Determine (*a*) the amplified output voltage, (*b*) the power output.

Draw a curve of power output against load-resistor value as the resistance of the load varies from zero to 15,000 Ω. [*Ans.* 10 V, 1/80 W.]

16. The figures given below refer to a 25 W triode valve which delivers power to a resistive load by means of a choke-capacitor coupling:

V_a (V)	24	60	100	150	180
I_a (mA)	10	30	68	120	154

$V_g = 0$

V_a (V)	123	150	200	250
I_a (mA)	10	25	66	120

$V_g = -10{\cdot}7$ V

V_a (V)	220	250	300	350
I_a (mA)	10	27	67	119

$V_g = -21$ V

V_a (V)	312	350	400
I_a (mA)	10	29	68

$V_g = -32$ V

The h.t. supply voltage is 300 V. Determine the approximate resistance of the load for maximum undistorted power output. Calculate this maximum value of power and the efficiency.

[*Ans.* 1·95 kΩ, 4 W, 16%.]

17. Two power triodes, each having characteristics given by the following figures, operate in Class-A push–pull. Draw the composite characteristics, if the quiescent point is at $V_a = 200$ V, $V_g = -20$ V, and the composite load line for an anode-to-anode load of 5 kΩ.

Calculate the power output of this amplifier when the peak input to each valve is 20 V.

V_a (V)	0	40	80	120
I_a (mA)	0	13	32	52

$V_g = 0$

V_a (V)	0	40	80	120	160	200	240
I_a (mA)	0	0	0	5	15	30	47

$V_g = -20$ V

V_a (V)	0	40	80	120	160	200	240	280	320
I_a (mA)	0	0	0	0	0	3	9	19	33

$V_g = -40$ V

[*Ans.* ≃ 1·53 W.]

18. Show that the output impedance of a cathode-follower stage, which employs a valve with a mutual conductance of 5 mA/V is about 200 Ω.

19. An amplifier employing a pentode with an amplification factor of 1,000 and a mutual conductance of 5 mA/V has a 200 kΩ load resistor. Find the voltage amplification (*a*) without feedback, (*b*) with 5% negative voltage feedback.

Calculate also the effective constants of the valve when feedback is used.

[*Ans.* 500, 19·2, $\mu' = 19{\cdot}6$, $r_a' = 3{\cdot}92$ kΩ, $g_m' = 5$ mA/V.]

20. A certain amplifier has a gain of 500 without feedback. Calculate the input voltage necessary with 5% negative feedback to give an output voltage of 1 V. [*Ans.* 0·052 V.]

21. An amplifier having a gain of 10,000 without feedback and negligible phase-shift has 1/1,000 of the output voltage fed back in anti-phase to the input. Evaluate the reduction in harmonic distortion which will result from the application of the feedback. [*Ans.* 91%.]

22. A low frequency amplifier has a gain of 60 dB. The input circuit is of 600 Ω resistive impedance and the output is arranged for a load of 10 Ω. What will be the current through the load when an alternating voltage of 1 V is applied at the input?

Express the gain of the amplifier in nepers.

[*Ans.* 12·9 A, 6·9 nepers.]

{For definitions of decibels and nepers see Appendix 3.}

23. If the anode loads of the difference-amplifier circuit of Fig. 13·29 are equal, of valve R_l, show that the two output voltages are of equal magnitude but of opposite polarity and that appreciable gain is provided by the arrangement.

Prove also that the difference between the two output voltages is $-\mu R_l(v_1 - v_2)/(R_l + r_a)$.

24. If the anode loads of the circuit of Fig. 13.29 are equal and one grid is grounded (say $v_2 = 0$) show that the arrangement can then be used as a paraphase amplifier to produce push–pull signals from a single source of voltage.

25. Show how a difference amplifier, an ordinary amplifier of high gain and a squaring circuit may be used to give the square root of a given input voltage.

26. Explain how a difference amplifier, an ordinary amplifier of high gain and a multiplying circuit may be employed to provide the ratio of two given input voltages.

27. A screen-grid valve has a negative anode-slope resistance r_a of 75,000 Ω with suitable anode and screen voltages, and it is to be used with a coil L of 140 μH inductance and a capacitor C of 560 μμF capacitance to form a dynatron oscillator. Find the maximum coil resistance R to permit oscillation and the corresponding frequency. [S.U.]

[*Ans.* 3·33 Ω, 568 kc/s.]

28. Evaluate the mutual inductance necessary to maintain oscillation in a tuned-anode oscillator in which the valve is specified by $r_a = 5$ kΩ, $g_m = 6$ mA/V and the tuned circuit by $L = 150$ μH, C = 200 μμF, $Q = 120$. The tuning capacitor may be assumed loss-free.

[*Ans.* 5·25 μH.]

29. A triode with a mutual conductance of 1·4 mA/V is to be used as an oscillator. The tuned-grid circuit may be taken to have an equivalent series resistance of 30 Ω and a total capacitance of 120 μμF. Determine the minimum value of mutual inductance between the anode coil and the grid coil which will maintain oscillation. [*Ans.* 2·6 μH.]

30. In a certain Hartley oscillator the inductance of each coil is 18 mH and the capacitor has a capacitance of 0·1 μF. Determine the frequency of oscillation if there is no mutual inductance between the coils. Neglect losses.

Find also the coefficient of coupling which will reduce the frequency to 2 kc/s. [*Ans.* 2·65 kc/s, 0·76.]

31. In a particular Wien-bridge type of oscillator the frequency-selective network employs 120 kΩ resistors and 0·001 μF capacitors. Find the frequency of oscillation. [S.U.] [*Ans.* 1,326 c/s.]

32. A three-section ladder phase-shift oscillator has three similar phase-advancing sections, each consisting of a 100 kΩ resistor and a 0·0005 μF capacitor. Evaluate the frequency of oscillation and show that the attenuation ratio of the network is 29. Repeat the calculation for a similar oscillator having three phase-retarding sections showing again that the attenuation ratio is 29.

If a fourth similar section is added to the original network determine the new frequency of oscillation and the attenuation ratio of the arrangement. [S.U.] [*Ans.* 1,300 c/s, 7,800 c/s, 2,663 c/s, 18·39.]

CHAPTER 14

TRANSISTOR CIRCUITS

It will be assumed that the reader is familiar with the constructions and characteristics of the various transistors which are available. The first transistors developed were the point-contact ones, but these have been largely superseded by the junction types.

Current in transistors is carried by positive carriers called *holes* as well as by electrons. A hole has a positive charge equal to the negative charge of an electron. The semiconductor material used for a transistor is originally very carefully purified and then a controlled amount of impurity is added which gives an excess of holes over electrons or vice-versa. Materials in which the majority carriers are electrons are known as *n*-type, but if the holes predominate the material is called *p*-type.

Junction transistors can be of *p–n–p* or *n–p–n* forms. The majority of transistors available at present are of the *p–n–p* type, which has a thin region of *n*-type semiconducting material sandwiched between two thicker layers of *p*-type material as illustrated in Fig. 14.1 (*a*). An *n–p–n* type is shown in Fig. 14.1 (*b*). The central layer of the sandwich

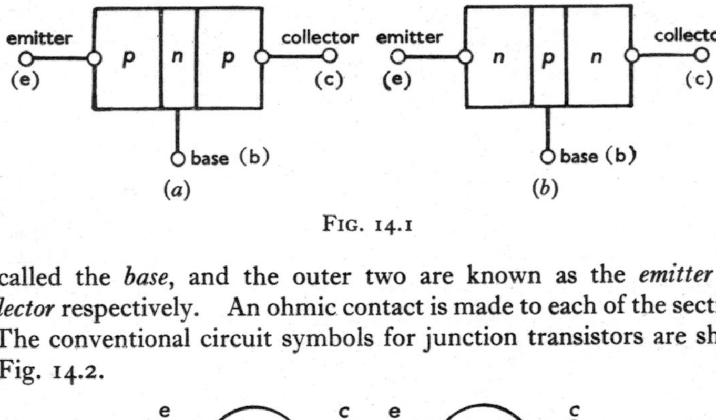

FIG. 14.1

is called the *base*, and the outer two are known as the *emitter* and *collector* respectively. An ohmic contact is made to each of the sections.

The conventional circuit symbols for junction transistors are shown in Fig. 14.2.

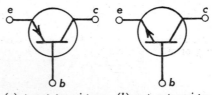

(*a*) *p–n–p transistor* (*b*) *n–p–n transistor*

FIG. 14.2

Consider the n–p–n transistor of Fig. 14.3. The electrons from the emitter flow to the base, and the collector absorbs electrons from the base. Electrons exist in the base only as minority carriers. Electrons reaching the collector are mainly derived from the emitter by diffusion through the base. A small number of the electrons which flow from the emitter to the base recombine with holes in the base instead of being

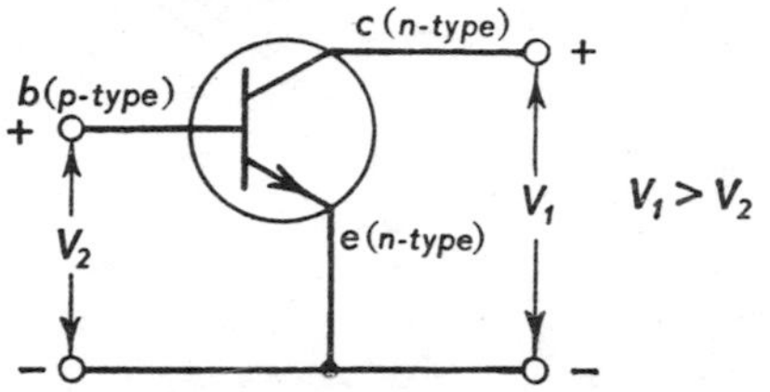

FIG. 14.3

removed by the collector. Base current flows to make good this loss of charge in the base. Altering the base current changes the voltage across the emitter junction, and thus controls the collector–emitter current.

In the p–n–p transistor (Fig. 14.4) holes flow from the emitter to the base. Holes diffuse from the emitter through the base to the collector, while a few holes from the emitter recombine with electrons in the base.

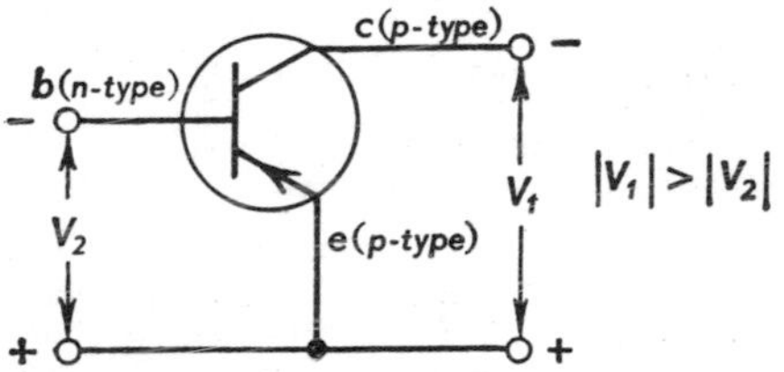

FIG. 14.4

The emitter is analogous to the cathode of the triode valve; the base is analogous to the grid; and the collector corresponds to the anode. In fact, the transistor, which is a current-controlled device, may be regarded as the dual of the valve, which is a voltage-controlled device. Since the transistor has three terminals, its performance can be analysed in terms of three currents and three voltages, one pair for each electrode. For small-signal applications, the analysis of a circuit containing a transistor is generally accomplished by representing the transistor by a four-terminal equivalent network. A study of the latter requires a knowledge of only four variables, namely a current and voltage at each pair of terminals, so that it is evident that the original six transistor variables are not mutually independent.

One of the three transistor terminals is selected as a common point in the four-terminal network. Thus, there are three basic circuits depending on this choice, namely the *common-base*, *common-emitter* and *common-collector* arrangements as illustrated in Fig. 14.5. These are

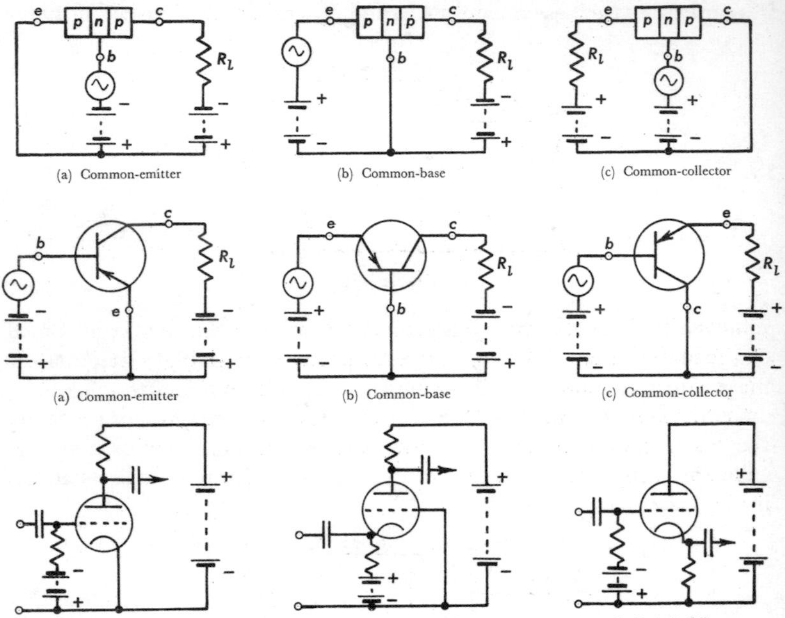

(a) Common-emitter (b) Common-base (c) Common-collector

(a) Common-emitter (b) Common-base (c) Common-collector

(a) Grounded-cathode (b) Grounded-grid (c) Cathode-follower

Notes. If an *n–p–n* transistor is employed the bias voltage polarities must be reversed. The emitter is negative with respect to the base if the emitter semiconductor is *n*-type and positive with respect to the base if the emitter semiconductor is *p*-type. The collector bias always has opposite polarity to the emitter bias.

FIG. 14.5

analogous to the grounded-grid, grounded-cathode and cathode-follower valve circuits respectively.

The common-base equivalent circuits

The anode current I_a of a triode depends on the anode and grid voltages V_a and V_g respectively, *i.e.*

$$I_a = f(V_a, V_g) \quad . \quad . \quad . \quad . \quad . \quad . \quad . \quad . \quad . \quad (14.1)$$

$$\therefore \quad \delta I_a = (\partial I_a/\partial V_g)_{V_a}\delta V_g + (\partial I_a/\partial V_a)_{V_g}\delta V_a \quad . \quad (14.2)$$

$$= g_m\,\delta V_g + \delta V_a/r_a \quad . \quad . \quad . \quad . \quad . \quad . \quad (14.3)$$

where the mutual conductance $g_m = (\partial I_a/\partial V_g)_{V_a \text{ constant}}$ and the anode slope resistance $r_a = (\partial V_a/\partial I_a)_{V_g \text{ constant}}$ may be obtained from the valve characteristics. The equivalent circuit of the triode was derived from the expression for δI_a (see Chapter 13).

The transistor may be treated in a similar way, but it must be remembered that it is a current-controlled device. Considering the common-base connection first, the emitter and collector voltages, V_e and V_c, measured with respect to the base, are functions of the independent variables I_e and I_c, the emitter and collector currents,

i.e. $$V_e = f_1(I_e, I_c) \qquad (14.4)$$

and $$V_c = f_2(I_e, I_c) \qquad (14.5)$$

For small-signal variations, *i.e.* for small changes of the currents from their quiescent values, the voltage variations are given by:

$$\delta V_e = (\partial V_e/\partial I_e)_{I_c}\delta I_e + (\partial V_e/\partial I_c)_{I_e}\delta I_c \qquad (14.6)$$

and $$\delta V_c = (\partial V_c/\partial I_e)_{I_c}\delta I_e + (\partial V_c/\partial I_c)_{I_e}\delta I_c \qquad (14.7)$$

If δV_e, δV_c, δI_e and δI_c are written as v_e, v_c, i_e and i_c respectively, these equations become:

$$v_e = r_{11}i_e + r_{12}i_c \qquad (14.8)$$

and $$v_c = r_{21}i_e + r_{22}i_c \qquad (14.9)$$

where the coefficients r_{11}, r_{12}, r_{21} and r_{22}, which have the dimensions of resistance, are defined as:

$$r_{11} = (\partial V_e/\partial I_e)_{I_c \text{ constant}} \qquad (14.10)$$

$$r_{12} = (\partial V_e/\partial I_c)_{I_e \text{ constant}} \qquad (14.11)$$

$$r_{21} = (\partial V_c/\partial I_e)_{I_c \text{ constant}} \qquad (14.12)$$

and $$r_{22} = (\partial V_c/\partial I_c)_{I_e \text{ constant}} \qquad (14.13)$$

In deriving the equivalent circuit of the triode only *changes* about the operating point on the valve characteristics were considered. Further, the only restriction on the use of the equivalent circuit was that the quantities μ, r_a and g_m should remain reasonably constant over the operating range on the valve characteristics. In just the same way here, if the changes are small, the transistor characteristics may be assumed to be linear over the operating range and the coefficients r_{11}, r_{12}, r_{21} and r_{22} become constants which may be obtained from the characteristic curves. At low frequencies it may be assumed that the coefficients are purely resistive, but this approximation is not valid at the higher frequencies, as will be discussed later. The parameters will evidently vary if the operating point is changed, as in the case of valve parameters. Characteristics of transistors, like those of valves, show production spreads which may be fairly large.

It is possible to draw several equivalent circuits which satisfy equations (14.8) and (14.9). One such four-terminal network is illustrated in

Fig. 14.6 (*b*). This corresponds to Fig. 14.6 (*a*), which is a redrawn version of the common-base arrangement of Fig. 14.5 (*b*). It is assumed that the electrodes are biased * to their recommended d.c. values and only small changes (v_e, v_c, i_e and i_c) about the operating point are being considered. It is evident from Fig. 14.6 (*b*) that the i_e mesh satisfies equation (14.8) and the i_c mesh satisfies equation (14.9). Two other commonly used equivalent circuits are shown in Figs. 14.6 (*c*) and 14.6 (*d*). It should be noted that the four-terminal networks in

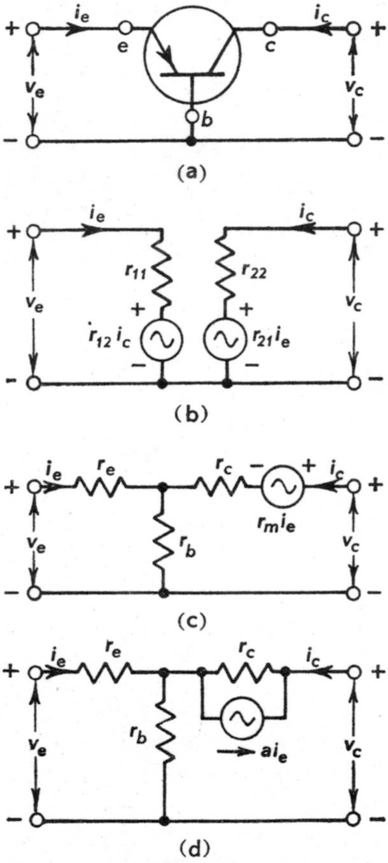

FIG. 14.6

* Methods of obtaining current bias and stabilising the operating point will not be discussed, but are described in many books, *e.g.*:

J. D. Ryder, *Engineering Electronics*, (McGraw-Hill, 1957).
L. M. Krugman, *Fundamentals of Transistors*, Second Revised Edition (Rider & Chapman & Hall, 1958).
Mullard Reference Manual on Transistor Circuits, First Edition (1960).

this case are active, not passive, so *four* independent parameters are needed to specify their performances, *i.e.* $r_{12} \neq r_{21}$ here. In Fig. 14.6 (*c*) the four parameters are r_e, r_b, r_c and r_m. The relationship between these parameters and r_{11}, r_{12}, r_{21} and r_{22} will be shown later. They are known as the emitter, base, collector and mutual or transfer resistances of the transistor, respectively. In Fig. 14.6 (*d*) the parameters are r_e, r_c, r_b and another quantity a to be discussed below.

For the two meshes of Fig. 14.6 (*c*) the following equations hold:

$$v_e = (r_e + r_b)i_e + r_b i_c \quad . \quad . \quad . \quad . \quad . \quad (14.14)$$

$$v_c = (r_b + r_m)i_e + (r_b + r_c)i_c \quad . \quad . \quad (14.15)$$

For Fig. 14.6 (*d*) the corresponding equations are:

$$v_e = (r_e + r_b)i_e + r_b i_c \quad . \quad . \quad . \quad . \quad . \quad (14.16)$$

$$v_c = (ar_c + r_b)i_e + (r_b + r_c)i_c \quad . \quad . \quad (14.17)$$

From equations (14.8) and (14.9), which hold for Fig. 14.6 (*b*), and (14.14) and (14.15) it follows that:

$$r_{11} = r_e + r_b \quad . \quad . \quad . \quad . \quad . \quad . \quad (14.18)$$

$$r_{12} = r_b \quad . \quad . \quad . \quad . \quad . \quad . \quad . \quad . \quad (14.19)$$

$$r_{21} = r_b + r_m \quad . \quad . \quad . \quad . \quad . \quad . \quad (14.20)$$

and

$$r_{22} = r_b + r_c \quad . \quad . \quad . \quad . \quad . \quad . \quad (14.21)$$

Thus,

$$r_e = r_{11} - r_{12} \quad . \quad . \quad . \quad . \quad . \quad . \quad (14.22)$$

$$r_b = r_{12} \quad . \quad . \quad . \quad . \quad . \quad . \quad . \quad (14.23)$$

$$r_c = r_{22} - r_{12} \quad . \quad . \quad . \quad . \quad . \quad . \quad (14.24)$$

and

$$r_m = r_{21} - r_{12} \quad . \quad . \quad . \quad . \quad . \quad . \quad (14.25)$$

From equations (14.9) and (14.17):

$$ar_c + r_b = r_{21} \quad . \quad . \quad . \quad . \quad . \quad . \quad (14.26)$$

Thus, using equation (14.20):

$$ar_c + r_b = r_b + r_m$$

i.e.

$$a = r_m/r_c \quad . \quad . \quad . \quad . \quad . \quad . \quad (14.27)$$

Parameter a can also be shown to be approximately equal to the current amplification factor α which is defined as $-(\partial i_c/\partial i_e)_{V_c \text{ constant}}$, *i.e.* α is the ratio of a change in collector current to a change in emitter current with the collector voltage held constant.

From equation (14.9):

$$\alpha = r_{21}/r_{22} \quad . \quad . \quad . \quad . \quad . \quad . \quad (14.28)$$

Thus, using (14.26) and (14.21):

$$\alpha = (ar_c + r_b)/(r_b + r_c) \quad . \quad . \quad . \quad . \quad (14.29)$$

i.e.

$$a = \alpha + (\alpha - 1)r_b/r_c \quad . \quad . \quad . \quad . \quad (14.30)$$

For a typical junction transistor r_b is of the order of a few hundred ohms and r_c of the order of 1 MΩ. Thus, the term $(\alpha - 1)r_b/r_c$ can be neglected and

$$a \simeq \alpha \quad . \quad . \quad . \quad . \quad . \quad . \quad (14.31)$$

Note: α is defined for the common-base circuit and is always less than but near to unity.

The common-emitter equivalent circuits

The common-emitter arrangement and three equivalent circuits corresponding to those of Fig. 14.6 are illustrated in Fig. 14.7. The same internal transistor parameters r_b, r_e, r_c and r_m introduced in Fig. 14.6 (*c*) are, of course, also used in Fig. 14.7 (*c*) with different inter-

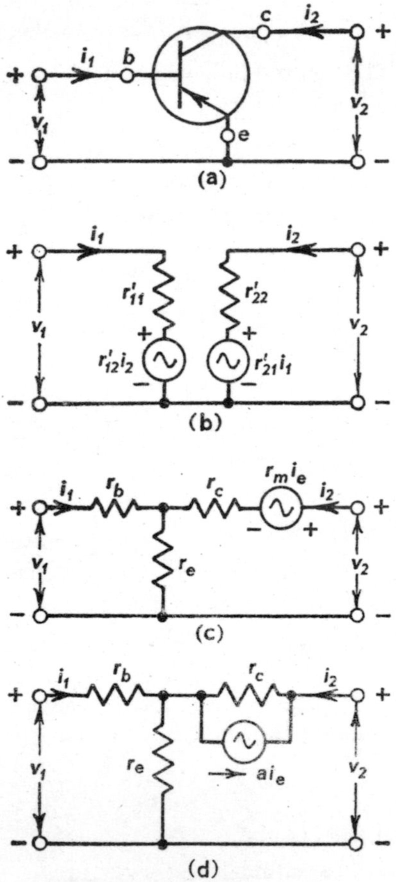

FIG. 14.7

connection. These parameters depend only on the transistor and not on the method of connection, a major advantage in their use, as in the case of μ, g_m and r_a for a triode. New parameters must be employed in Fig. 14.7 (*b*), however, but these are related to those used in Fig. 14.6 (*b*), as shown below.

The circuit equations are now:

For Fig. 14.7 (*b*):

$$v_1 = r'_{11}i_1 + r'_{12}i_2 \quad \text{(14.32)}$$

$$v_2 = r'_{21}i_1 + r'_{22}i_2 \quad \text{(14.33)}$$

For Fig. 14.7 (*c*):

$$v_1 = (r_b + r_e)i_1 + r_e i_2 \quad \text{(14.34)}$$

$$v_2 = r_e i_1 + (r_e + r_c)i_2 + r_m i_e \quad \text{(14.35)}$$

But $i_e = -(i_1 + i_2)$ which is clear from Fig. 14.7 (*a*) so equation (14.35) becomes:

$$v_2 = (r_e - r_m)i_1 + (r_e + r_c - r_m)i_2 \quad \text{(14.36)}$$

For Fig. 14.7 (*d*):

$$v_1 = (r_b + r_e)i_1 + r_e i_2 \quad \text{(14.37)}$$

$$v_2 = ar_c i_e + r_e i_1 + (r_e + r_c)i_2 \quad \text{(14.38)}$$

From equations (14.32), (14.34), (14.18) and (14.22):

$$r'_{11} = r_b + r_e = r_{11} \quad \text{(14.39)}$$

and

$$r'_{12} = r_e = r_{11} - r_{12} \quad \text{(14.40)}$$

From equations (14.33), (14.36), (14.22), (14.24) and (14.25):

$$r'_{21} = r_e - r_m = r_{11} - r_{21} \quad \text{(14.41)}$$

and

$$r'_{22} = (r_e + r_c - r_m) = r_{11} + r_{22} - r_{12} - r_{21} \quad \text{(14.42)}$$

Equations (14.39) to (14.42) express the parameters of the common-emitter equivalent circuit of Fig. 14.7 (*b*) in terms of those of the common-base circuit of Fig. 14.6 (*b*).

Equation (14.36) may be written as:

$$v_2 = (r_e - r_m)i_1 + \{r_e + r_c(1 - a)\}i_2 \quad \text{(14.43)}$$

This equation and equation (14.34) may be represented by the equivalent circuit of Fig. 14.8, which gives the generator voltage in terms of the input current i_1 rather than i_e.

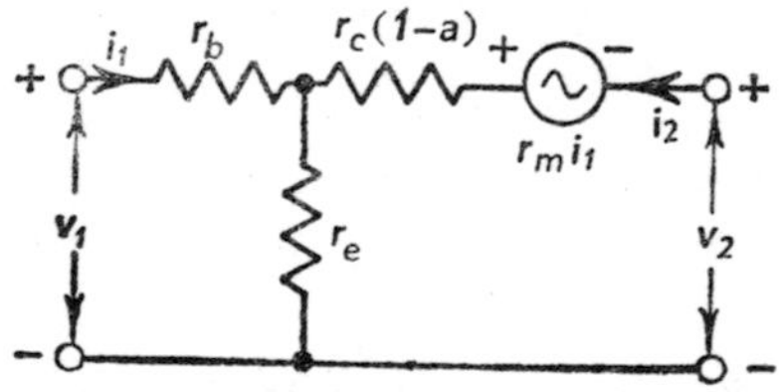

FIG. 14.8

Replacing the voltage generator $r_m i_1$ of Fig. 14.8 by its equivalent current source the equivalent circuit of Fig. 14.9 results.

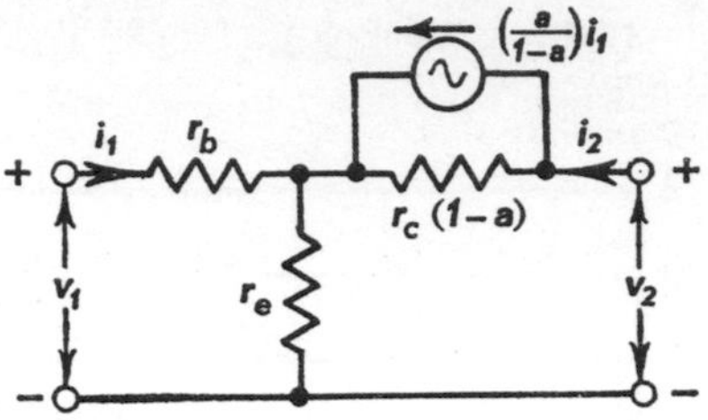

FIG. 14.9

EXAMPLE. The output characteristics of the OC71 p–n–p transistor for common-base and common-emitter connections are illustrated in Figs. 14.10 and 14.11 respectively. Determine, from these curves, the values of $\alpha = -(\partial i_c/\partial i_e)_{V_{cb}}$ and $\alpha' = (\partial i_c/\partial i_b)_{V_{ce}}$.

Show how α' may be expressed in terms of α, and vice-versa.

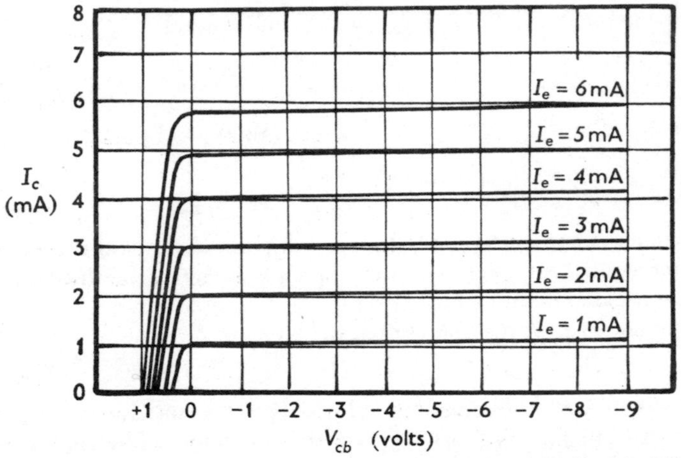

[*By courtesy of Mullard Ltd.**]

FIG. 14.10

Solution. Consider first Fig. 14.10.

With the collector-base voltage constant at -4 V a change in I_e from 1 mA to 5 mA gives a change in collector current from $-1{\cdot}03$ to $-4{\cdot}95$ mA.

* Taken from *Simple Transistor Measurements*, published by Mullard Educational Service.

Thus, $$\alpha = -\left\{\frac{-(4{\cdot}95 - 1{\cdot}03)}{(5 - 1)}\right\} = \underline{0{\cdot}98}$$

Consider now Fig. 14.11 and a constant value of collector-emitter voltage of -4 V. A change of I_b from -20 μA to -80 μA gives a change of collector current from $-1{\cdot}1$ to $-4{\cdot}5$ mA.

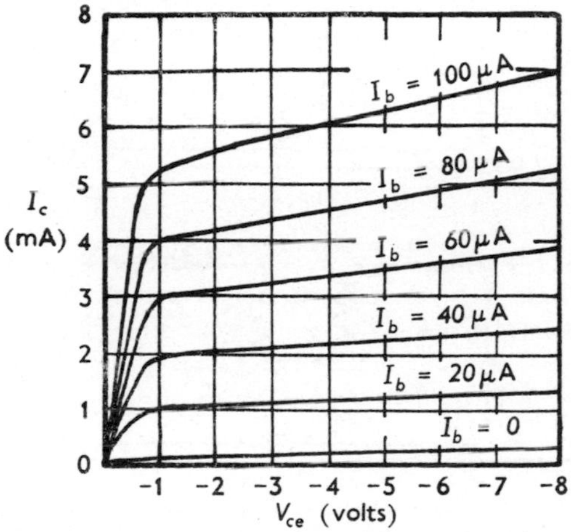

[*By courtesy of Mullard Ltd.**]

FIG. 14.11

Thus, $$\alpha' = \frac{-(4{\cdot}5 - 1{\cdot}1)\,.\,10^{-3}}{-(80 - 20)\,.\,10^{-6}} \simeq \underline{57}$$

$$\alpha' = (\partial i_c/\partial i_b)$$

But $$\partial i_b = -(\partial i_e + \partial i_c)$$

so $$\alpha' = -\partial i_c/(\partial i_e + \partial i_c)$$

$$= -(\partial i_c/\partial i_e)/(\partial i_e/\partial i_e + \partial i_c/\partial i_e)$$

i.e. $$\underline{\alpha' = \alpha/(1 - \alpha)}$$

Note that a change in α from say 0·99 to 0·985 causes α' to change from 99 to 66.

From the expression for α' it is seen that:

$$\underline{\alpha = \alpha'/(1 + \alpha')}$$

This equation can also be obtained directly from the definition of α, substituting $-(\partial i_b + \partial i_c)$ for ∂i_e and dividing each term in the numerator and denominator by ∂i_b.

* Taken from *Simple Transistor Measurements*, published by Mullard Educational Service.

The common-collector equivalent circuits

The common-collector arrangement and three equivalent circuits, corresponding to those of Figs. 14.6 and 14.7, are illustrated in Fig. 14.12.

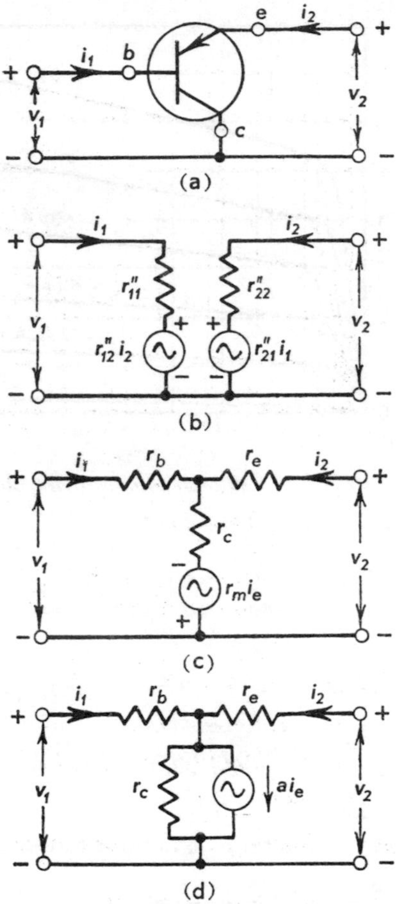

FIG. 14.12

The circuit equations are now:

For Fig. 14.12 (*b*):

$$v_1 = r''_{11}i_1 + r''_{12}i_2 \quad . \quad . \quad . \quad . \quad (14.44)$$

$$v_2 = r''_{21}i_1 + r''_{22}i_2 \quad . \quad . \quad . \quad . \quad (14.45)$$

For Fig. 14.12 (*c*):

$$v_1 = (r_b + r_c)i_1 + r_c i_2 - r_m i_e \quad . \quad . \quad . \quad (14.46)$$

$$v_2 = r_c i_1 + (r_e + r_c)i_2 - r_m i_e \quad . \quad . \quad . \quad (14.47)$$

But $i_e = i_2$, as may be seen from Fig. 14.12 (*a*), so equations (14.46) and (14.47) become:

$$v_1 = (r_b + r_c)i_1 + (r_c - r_m)i_2 \quad . \quad . \quad . \quad (14.48)$$

$$v_2 = r_c i_1 + (r_e + r_c - r_m)i_2 \quad . \quad . \quad . \quad (14.49)$$

For Fig. 14.12 (*d*):

$$v_1 = (r_b + r_c)i_1 + r_c i_2 - a i_e r_c \quad . \quad . \quad . \quad (14.50)$$

$$v_2 = r_c i_1 + (r_e + r_c)i_2 - a i_e r_c \quad . \quad . \quad . \quad (14.51)$$

From equations (14.44), (14.48), (14.23), (14.24) and (14.25):

$$r''_{11} = r_b + r_c = r_{22} \quad . \quad . \quad . \quad . \quad . \quad (14.52)$$

and $$r''_{12} = r_c - r_m = r_{22} - r_{21} \quad . \quad . \quad . \quad (14.53)$$

From equations (14.45), (14.49), (14.22), (14.24) and (14.25):

$$r''_{21} = r_c = r_{22} - r_{12} \quad . \quad . \quad . \quad . \quad . \quad . \quad . \quad . \quad (14.54)$$

and $$r''_{22} = r_e + r_c - r_m = r_{11} + r_{22} - r_{12} - r_{21} \quad . \quad (14.55)$$

Equations (14.52) to (14.54) express the parameters to the common-collector equivalent circuit of Fig. 14.12 (*b*) in terms of those of the common-base circuit of Fig. 14.6 (*b*).

Equations (14.48) and (14.49) may be represented by the equivalent circuit of Fig. 14.13, which gives the generator voltage in terms of the input current i_1 rather than i_e.

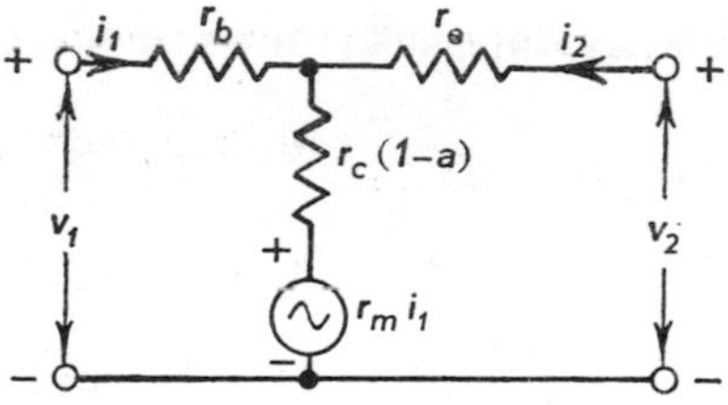

FIG. 14.13

The common-base amplifier

A simplified circuit diagram of a single-stage common-base amplifier is shown in Fig. 14.14 (*a*) (note that methods of applying bias are not illustrated) and the equivalent circuit to be used for the amplifier analysis is that of Fig. 14.14 (*b*), which is merely Fig. 14.6 (*c*) with the source and load added.

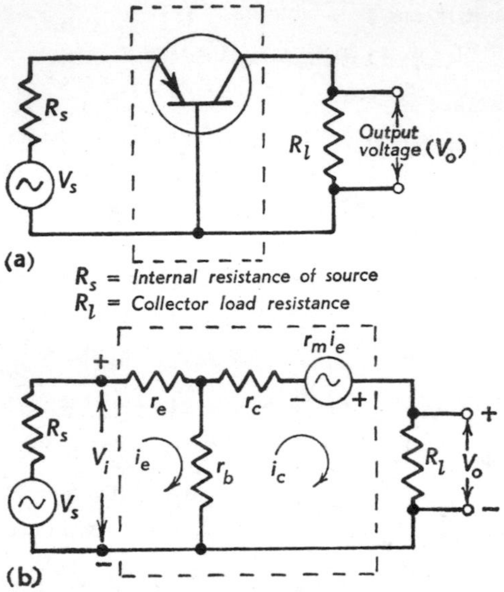

FIG. 14.14

Let the currents in the two loops be i_e and i_c as shown. Kirchhoff's second law applied to these two meshes gives:

$$V_s = (r_e + r_b + R_s)i_e - r_b i_c \quad . \quad . \quad . \quad . \quad (14.56)$$

or

$$V_i = (r_e + r_b)i_e - r_b i_c \quad . \quad . \quad . \quad . \quad . \quad . \quad (14.57)$$

and

$$0 = -(r_m + r_b)i_e + (r_b + r_c + R_l)i_c \quad . \quad . \quad (14.58)$$

Using Cramer's Rule (see Appendix 1) on equations (14.57) and (14.58):

$$i_e = \begin{vmatrix} V_i & -r_b \\ 0 & (r_b + r_c + R_l) \end{vmatrix} \Big/ D = V_i(r_b + r_c + R_l)/D \quad (14.59)$$

and

$$i_c = \begin{vmatrix} (r_e + r_b) & V_i \\ -(r_m + r_b) & 0 \end{vmatrix} \Big/ D = V_i(r_m + r_b)/D. \quad . \quad . \quad (14.60)$$

where the determinant $D = \begin{vmatrix} (r_e + r_b) & -r_b \\ -(r_m + r_b) & (r_b + r_c + R_l) \end{vmatrix} \quad . \quad (14.61)$

If the voltage gain (A_v) is defined as V_o/V_i, then:

$$A_v = i_c R_l / V_i = (r_m + r_b)R_l / D$$

$$= \frac{(r_m + r_b)R_l}{(r_e + r_b)(r_b + r_c + R_l) - r_b(r_m + r_b)}$$

$$= \frac{(r_m + r_b)R_l}{r_b(r_c + R_l + r_e - r_m) + r_e(r_c + R_l)} \quad (14.62)$$

The current gain A_i is i_c/i_e.

$$\therefore \quad A_i = (r_m + r_b)/(r_b + r_c + R_l) \quad . \quad . \quad (14.63)$$

The input resistance $R_i = V_i/i_e$

$$\therefore \quad R_i = D/(r_b + r_c + R_l)$$

$$= \frac{r_b(r_c + R_l + r_e - r_m) + r_e(r_c + R_l)}{r_b + r_c + R_l} \quad (14.64)$$

The power gain

$$A_p = i_c^2 R_l / i_e^2 R_i = (A_i)^2 R_l / R_i$$

$$= \frac{(r_m + r_b)^2 R_l}{(r_b + r_c + R_l)[r_b(r_c + R_l + r_e - r_m) + r_e(r_c + R_l)]} \quad (14.65)$$

To obtain the output impedance consider Fig. 14.15.

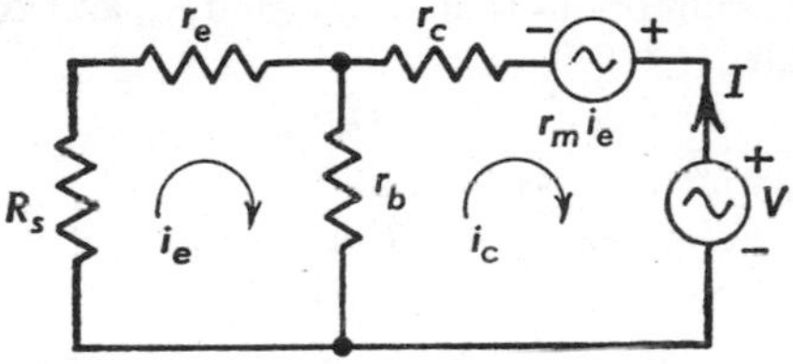

FIG. 14.15

Kirchhoff's second law applied to the two meshes gives:

$$(R_s + r_e + r_b)i_e = r_b i_c \quad . \quad . \quad . \quad . \quad . \quad . \quad (14.66)$$

$$(r_b + r_m)i_e = i_c(r_b + r_c) + V \quad . \quad . \quad (14.67)$$

From equations (14.66) and (14.67) the output impedance

$$R_0 = V/I = -V/i_c$$

$$= r_c - \frac{r_b(r_m - R_s - r_e)}{R_s + r_e + r_b} \quad . \quad . \quad . \quad (14.68)$$

A typical junction transistor may have the following parameters:

$$r_{11} = 820\ \Omega, \qquad r_{12} = 800\ \Omega,$$

$$r_{21} = 1{\cdot}98\ \text{M}\Omega, \ r_{22} = 2\ \text{M}\Omega.$$

So

$$r_e = r_{11} - r_{12} = 20\ \Omega$$

$$r_b = r_{12} = 800\ \Omega$$

$$r_c = r_{22} - r_{12} \simeq 2\ \text{M}\Omega$$

$$r_m = r_{21} - r_{12} \simeq 1{\cdot}98\ \text{M}\Omega$$

$$a = r_m/r_c \simeq 0{\cdot}99$$

Since r_b is small in comparison with r_m and $r_e \ll r_c$ equation (14.62) may be written:

$$A_v = \frac{r_m R_l}{(r_e + r_b)(r_c + R_l) - r_b r_m}$$

$$= \frac{aR_l}{\{(r_e + r_b)(r_c + R_l)/r_c\} - ar_b} \qquad (14.69)$$

If, in addition, $R_l \ll r_c$, which is probable since r_c is of the megohm order and R_l will be small to give a wide frequency response (*i.e.* good bandwidth) and reduce the effects of shunting capacitances, equation (14.69) further reduces to:

$$A_v = aR_l/\{r_e + r_b(1 - a)\} \quad . \quad . \quad . \quad (14.70)$$

Now $a \simeq \alpha$ and $\alpha < 1$ so A_v is always positive, *i.e.* there is no phase-reversal in the common-base amplifier. The circuit gives reasonable voltage amplifications.

With the same assumptions that $r_b \ll r_c$ and r_m, and $R_l \ll r_c$, equation (14.63) shows that

$$A_i \simeq r_m/r_c \quad . \quad . \quad . \quad . \quad . \quad (14.71)$$

i.e. $A_i \simeq a \simeq \alpha$, which is less than unity.

Similarly, expression (14.64) for R_i reduces to:

$$R_i \simeq r_e + r_b(1 - a) \quad . \quad . \quad . \quad . \quad (14.72)$$

Since $(1 - a)$ is usually in the range 0·01–0·05, $R_i \simeq r_e$ and is very low. The arrangement also provides high output impedance.

The common-emitter amplifier

The equivalent circuit of the single-stage common-emitter amplifier, corresponding to Fig. 14.14 (*b*) is shown in Fig. 14.16.

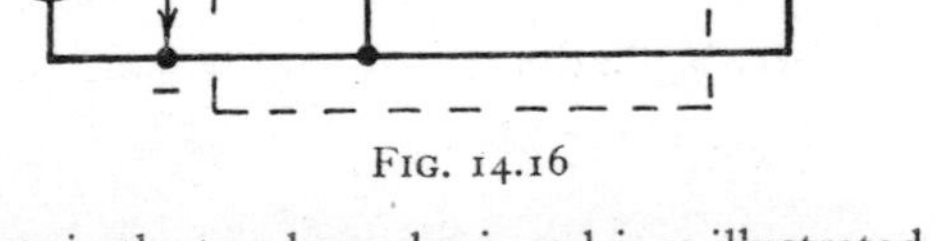

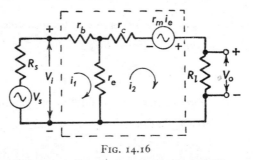

FIG. 14.16

Let the currents in the two loops be i_1 and i_2 as illustrated. Kirchhoff's second law applied to these two meshes gives:

$$V_i = (r_b + r_e)i_1 - r_e i_2 \quad . \quad . \quad . \quad . \quad . \quad . \quad . \quad (14.73)$$

and $$0 = (r_m - r_e)i_1 + (r_e + r_c - r_m + R_l)i_2 \quad . \quad (14.74)$$

because $$i_e = i_2 - i_1 \quad . \quad . \quad . \quad . \quad . \quad . \quad . \quad . \quad (14.75)$$

Using Cramer's Rule on equations (14.73) and (14.74):

$$i_1 = \begin{vmatrix} V_i & -r_e \\ 0 & (r_e + r_c - r_m + R_l) \end{vmatrix} \Big/ D$$

$$= V_i(r_e + r_c - r_m + R_l)/D \quad (14.76)$$

and $$i_2 = \begin{vmatrix} (r_b + r_e) & V_i \\ (r_m - r_e) & 0 \end{vmatrix} \Big/ D = -V_i(r_m - r_e)/D \quad . \quad . \quad . \quad . \quad (14.77)$$

where the determinant $$D = \begin{vmatrix} (r_b + r_e) & -r_e \\ (r_m - r_e) & (r_e + r_c - r_m + R_l) \end{vmatrix} \quad (14.78)$$

The voltage gain $A_v = V_o/V_i = i_2R_l/V_i$

$$= \frac{R_l}{r_b + \{(r_b + r_e)(r_c + R_l)/(r_e - r_m)\}} \cdot \quad (14.79)$$

The current gain $A_i = i_2/i_1$ so

$$A_i = \frac{(r_e - r_m)}{(r_e + r_c - r_m + R_l)} = \frac{1}{1 + (r_c + R_l)/(r_e - r_m)} \quad (14.80)$$

The input resistance $R_i = V_i/i_1 = r_b + \dfrac{r_e(r_c + R_l)}{r_c + r_e - r_m + R_l}$ (14.81)

The output resistance may be determined by a similar calculation to that for the common-base amplifier. It is found that:

$$R_o = (r_c - r_m) + \frac{r_e(r_b + r_m + R_s)}{r_b + r_e + R_s} \quad . \quad . \quad (14.82)$$

With the previous approximations the voltage gain for the common-emitter amplifier becomes:

$$A_v \simeq \frac{R_l(r_e - r_m)}{r_er_c + r_b(r_c - r_m)} \simeq \frac{-R_lr_m}{r_er_c + r_b(r_c - r_m)} \cdot \quad (14.83)$$

i.e. $$A_v \simeq -aR_l/\{r_e + r_b(1 - a)\} \quad . \quad . \quad . \quad (14.84)$$

The negative sign indicates a phase-reversal. Large voltage gains are possible with large values of R_l but at the expense of bandwidth.

Similarly, for the same amplifier it follows from equation (14.80), when $r_e \ll R_l \ll r_c$ or r_m, that:

$$A_i \simeq -r_m/(r_c - r_m) \simeq -a/(1 - a) \quad . \quad . \quad (14.85)$$

Thus, the circuit will provide a large current gain.

This amplifier has higher input and lower output resistances than the common-base arrangement and cascading of stages is possible without the use of matching transformers. This amplifier is consequently used extensively.

EXAMPLE. A junction transistor whose parameters are $r_{11} = 820\ \Omega$, $r_{12} = 800\ \Omega$, $r_{21} = 1{\cdot}98\ \text{M}\Omega$ and $r_{22} = 2\ \text{M}\Omega$ is used in a single-stage, common-emitter amplifier, with a load resistance of $430\ \Omega$.

Calculate the voltage gain, the current gain and the input resistance.

Solution

$$r_e = r_{11} - r_{12} = 20\ \Omega \qquad r_b = r_{12} = 800\ \Omega$$

$$r_c = r_{22} - r_{12} \simeq 2\ \text{M}\Omega \qquad r_m = r_{21} - r_{12} \simeq 1{\cdot}98\ \text{M}\Omega$$

$$A_v = \frac{R_l}{r_b + \{(r_b + r_e)(r_c + R_l)/(r_e - r_m)\}}$$

$$\simeq \frac{430}{800 - \{(820)(2 \times 10^6 + 430)/(1{\cdot}98 \times 10^6 - 20)\}}$$

$$\simeq \underline{-15{\cdot}2}$$

i.e. *a* 180° *phase change has been introduced.*

$$A_i = \frac{1}{1 + (r_c + R_l)/(r_e - r_m)}$$

$$\simeq \frac{1}{1 - (2 \times 10^6 + 430)/(1{\cdot}98 \times 10^6 - 20)}$$

$$\simeq \underline{-99}$$

$$R_i = r_b + \frac{r_e(r_c + R_l)}{(r_c + r_e - r_m + R_l)}$$

$$\simeq 800 + \frac{20(2 \times 10^6 + 430)}{(2 \times 10^6 + 20 - 1{\cdot}98 \times 10^6 + 430)}$$

$$\simeq \underline{2{,}755\ \Omega}$$

The common-collector amplifier

The equivalent circuit of the single-stage common-collector amplifier, corresponding to Fig. 14.14 (*b*), is shown in Fig. 14.17.

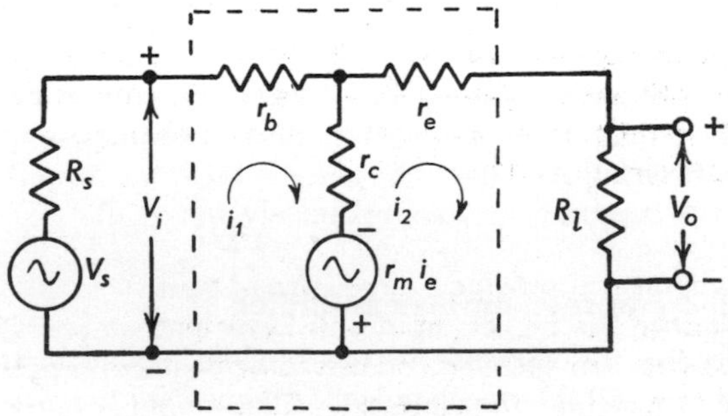

FIG. 14.17

Let the currents in the two loops be i_1 and i_2 as illustrated. Kirchhoff's second law applied to these two meshes gives:

$$V_i = (r_b + r_c)i_1 + (r_m - r_c)i_2 \quad . \quad . \quad . \quad . \quad (14.86)$$

and

$$0 = -r_c i_1 + (r_e + r_c - r_m + R_l)i_2 \quad . \quad . \quad (14.87)$$

because

$$i_e = -i_2 \quad . \quad . \quad . \quad . \quad . \quad . \quad . \quad . \quad . \quad . \quad (14.88)$$

Using Cramer's Rule on equations (14.86) and (14.87):

$$i_1 = \begin{vmatrix} V_i & (r_m - r_c) \\ 0 & (r_e + r_c - r_m + R_l) \end{vmatrix} \Big/ D$$

$$= V_i(r_e + r_c - r_m + R_l)/D \quad . \quad . \quad (14.89)$$

and $i_2 = \begin{vmatrix} (r_b + r_c) & V_i \\ -r_c & 0 \end{vmatrix} \Big/ D = V_i r_c D \quad . \quad . \quad . \quad . \quad . \quad . \quad . \quad (14.90)$

where the determinant $D = \begin{vmatrix} (r_b + r_c) & (r_m - r_c) \\ -r_c & (r_e + r_c - r_m + R_l) \end{vmatrix}$ (14.91)

The voltage gain

$$A_v = V_o/V_i = i_2 R_l/V_i$$

$$= \frac{r_c R_l}{r_b(r_c - r_m + r_e + R_l) + r_c(r_e + R_l)} \quad . \quad (14.92)$$

The current gain

$$A_i = i_2/i_1 = \frac{r_c}{r_e + r_c - r_m + R_l} \quad . \quad . \quad . \quad . \quad (14.93)$$

The input resistance

$$R_i = V_i/i_1 = r_b + \frac{r_c(r_e - R_l)}{r_e + r_c - r_m + R_l} \quad . \quad . \quad (14.94)$$

The output resistance may be determined by a similar calculation to that for the common-base amplifier. It is found that:

$$R_o = \frac{(r_c - r_m)(r_b + R_s)}{r_b + r_c + R_s} + r_e \quad . \quad . \quad . \quad (14.95)$$

Studies of equations (14.92) to (14.95) using the same approximations as before show that the voltage gain is slightly less than unity and there is no phase-reversal, the input resistance is high, the output resistance is low and the current gain is approximately $1/(1 - a)$.

R–C-coupled common-emitter amplifier

To determine the response of the R–C-coupled common-emitter amplifier at low and intermediate audio-frequencies the circuit of Fig. 14.18 is analysed.

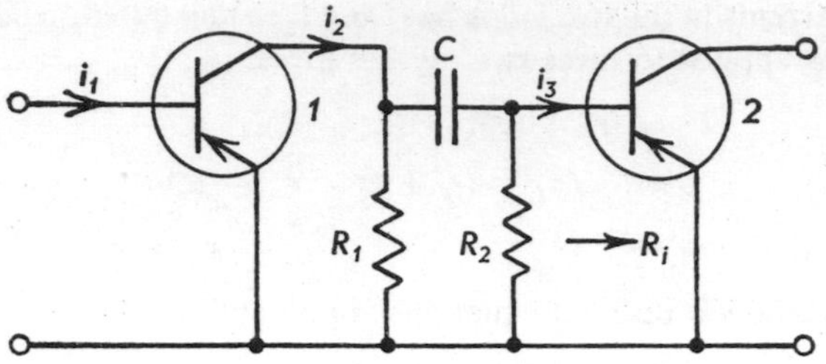

FIG. 14.18

The current gain of a common-emitter stage is given by equation (14.80) as:

$$A_i = \frac{(r_e - r_m)}{(r_e + r_c - r_m + R_l)} = \frac{1}{1 + (r_c + R_l)/(r_e - r_m)}$$

If $r_e \ll r_m$,

$$|A_i| \simeq r_m/(r_c - r_m + R_l) \simeq \frac{ar_c}{r_c(1 - a) + R_l} \quad . \quad (14.96)$$

Thus, for the circuit of Fig. 14.18:

$$i_2 \simeq \frac{i_1 ar_c}{r_c(1 - a) + R_l} \quad . \quad . \quad . \quad . \quad (14.97)$$

In this expression R_l is the total a.c. load of transistor 1.

If $R_2 \gg R_i$, the input resistance of the second transistor stage, then in the mid-frequency band, where the reactance of C may be neglected, $R_l \simeq R_1R_i/(R_1 + R_i)$. Now $i_3 \simeq i_2R_1/(R_1 + R_i)$, so the overall current gain, at these intermediate frequencies, Ai_i is:

$$Ai_i = i_3/i_1 \simeq \left\{\frac{ar_c}{r_c(1 - a) + R_l}\right\} \cdot \left\{\frac{R_1}{R_1 + R_i}\right\} \quad (14.98)$$

At low frequencies the reactance of C is large, so:

$$i_2 \simeq \frac{i_1 ar_c}{r_c(1 - a) + R_1/(1 + j\omega CR_1)} \quad . \quad . \quad (14.99)$$

The overall current gain now, $\mathbf{A}i_l$, is therefore:

$$\mathbf{A}i_l = i_3/i_1 \simeq \left\{\frac{ar_c}{r_c(1 - a) + R_1/(1 + j\omega CR_1)}\right\}\left\{\frac{R_1}{R_1 + 1/j\omega C}\right\} \quad (14.100)$$

which can be reduced to:

$$\mathbf{A}i_l \simeq \frac{a}{(1 - a)\left[1 - \frac{j}{\omega C}\left\{\frac{1}{R_1} + \frac{1}{r_c(1 - a)}\right\}\right]} \quad (14.101)$$

As in the case of the corresponding expression for the valve amplifier, this may be written as:

$$\mathbf{A}i_l \simeq \left(\frac{a}{1-a}\right)\left\{\frac{1}{1-j(f_1/f)}\right\} \quad . \quad . \quad (14.102)$$

where

$$f_1 = \frac{1}{2\pi C}\left\{\frac{1}{R_1} + \frac{1}{r_c(1-a)}\right\} \quad . \quad . \quad . \quad (14.103)$$

As with the valve amplifier, f_1 represents the frequency at the low-frequency end of the response curve where the gain falls to $1/\sqrt{2}$ of its value at intermediate frequencies (see equation (14.85)).

High-frequency effects

So far, no account has been taken of the capacitances of the junctions or charge diffusion times. At frequencies above the audio range,

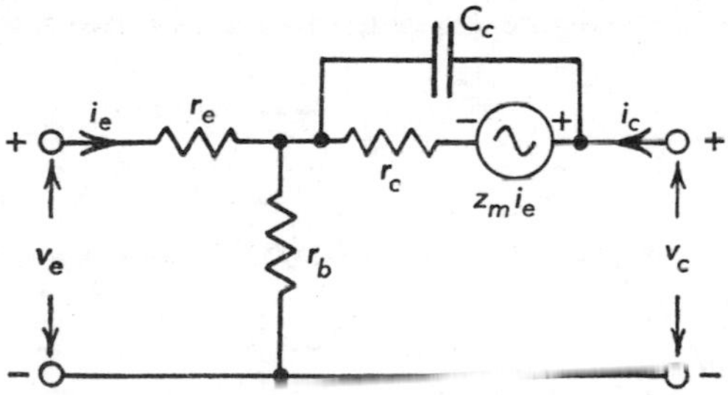

FIG. 14.19

however, the effects of these become increasingly important and must be taken into consideration. In drawing the high-frequency equivalent circuit it is usual to assume that the collector-base capacitance C_c is shunted across the collector resistance r_c of the low-frequency equivalent circuit. The emitter-base junction has a similar capacitance, but this may be ignored, since it is in shunt with the low resistance r_e, even though it may have a value of 100–150 μμF. The collector capacitance, usually between 5 and 20 μμF, depending on the type of transistor, is in shunt with the high resistance r_c, and may reduce the high-frequency response and output impedance considerably, possibly being effective at frequencies down to 1 kc/s. The precise value of C_c also depends on the collector voltage. This is so because as the collector voltage varies the spacing of the charges of opposite polarity changes. Also, both r_c and C_c fall with increasing frequency.

An approximate high-frequency equivalent circuit for the common-base arrangement is illustrated in Fig. 14.19. In this case $\mathbf{z_m}$ is used instead of r_m because of the complex nature of α at high frequencies as discussed below. Similar circuits for the other transistor arrangements may be derived from Fig. 14.19, *e.g.* Figs. 14.8 and 14.9 for the common-emitter arrangement become Figs. 14.20 and 14.21.

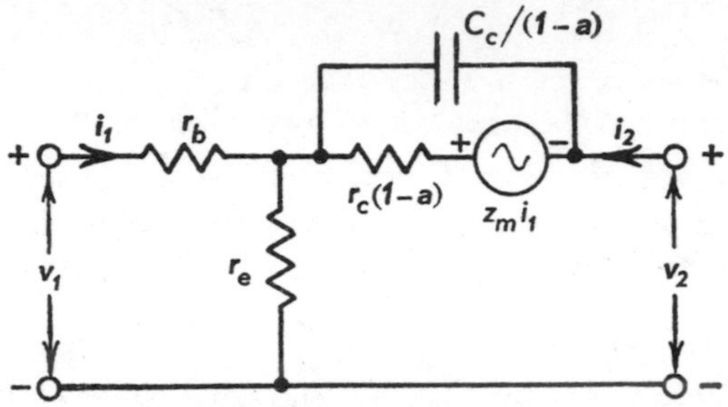

FIG. 14.20

A phase-angle may now be associated with a as discussed below.

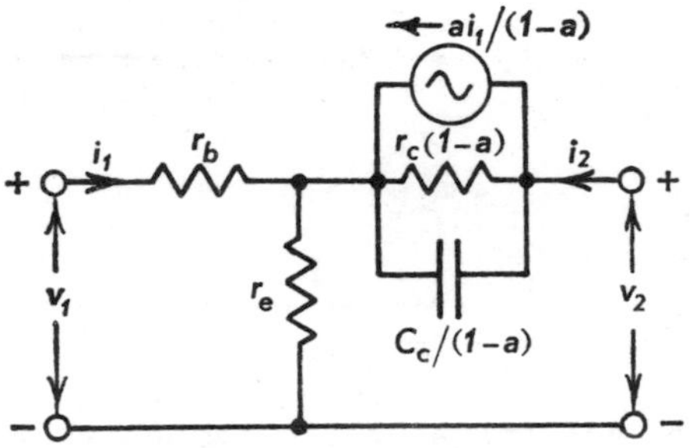

FIG. 14.21

At high frequencies some of the carriers emitted into the base do not reach the collector before the applied voltage reverses polarity. Owing to this, α varies with frequency, and at the higher frequencies there may be a phase-angle associated with α too. It is found * that $\boldsymbol{\alpha}$ varies with frequency according to the following expression:

$$\boldsymbol{\alpha} = \alpha_0 \left\{ \frac{1}{1 + j(f/f\alpha)} \right\} \quad . \quad . \quad . \quad . \quad (14.104)$$

where α_0 is the low-frequency value of α and $f\alpha$, called the alpha cut-off frequency, is that frequency where $\alpha = \alpha_0/\sqrt{2}$. The expression for $\boldsymbol{\alpha}$ should be compared with the expression for $\mathbf{A}_h/A_i$ of a valve amplifier given on p. 269.

* R. L. Pritchard, " Frequency Variations of Current-Amplification Factor for Junction Transistors ", *Proc. I.R.E.*, **40**, p. 1476 (1952). D. E. Thomas, " Transistor Amplifier Cut-off Frequency ", *ibid.*, **40**, p. 1481 (1952).

A good description of high-frequency effects in junction transistors has been given by Terman * and a calculation to determine the high-frequency response of an R–C coupled common-emitter amplifier by Ryder.†

EXAMPLE. A transistor has a current amplification factor of 0·96 at low frequencies, and the alpha cut-off frequency is 5 Mc/s. Determine the current amplification factor at 10 Mc/s.

Solution

$$\alpha = \frac{\alpha_0}{\sqrt{1 + (f/f\alpha)^2}}$$

$$= \frac{0{\cdot}96}{\sqrt{1 + (10/5)^2}}$$

$$= \underline{0{\cdot}43}$$

EXAMPLE. For the transistor in the previous example calculate the frequency at which the current amplification factor falls to 0·6.

Solution.

Since $$\alpha = \frac{\alpha_0}{\sqrt{1 + (f/f\alpha)^2}}$$

$$f = f\alpha\sqrt{(\alpha_0/\alpha)^2 - 1}$$

$$\therefore\ f = (5\sqrt{(0{\cdot}96/0{\cdot}6)^2} - 1)\ \text{Mc/s}$$

$$= \underline{6{\cdot}25\ \text{Mc/s.}}$$

Transistor oscillators

Transistor oscillators are, in general, of the same basic types as the valve oscillators discussed in Chapter 13. For example, the Colpitts oscillator is essentially as illustrated in Fig. 14.22, and its equivalent circuit is shown in Fig. 14.23.

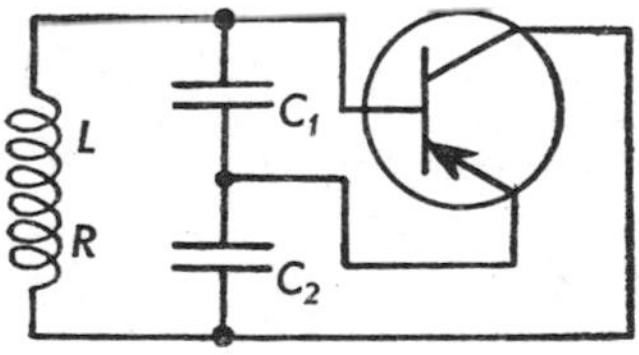

FIG. 14.22

* F. E. Terman, *Electronic and Radio Engineering*, 4th Edition, Chapter 21 (McGraw-Hill, 1955).

† J. D. Ryder, *Electronic Fundamentals and Applications*, 2nd Edition, Chapter 10 (Pitman, 1960).

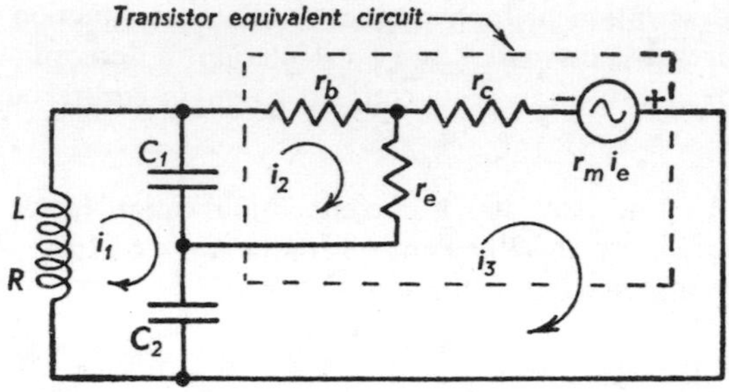

FIG. 14.23

In analysing this circuit it will be assumed that the resistance R of the coil is negligible and $C_1C_2/(C_1 + C_2)$ will be denoted by C.

For the i_1 loop:

$$\left(j\omega L + \frac{1}{j\omega C}\right)i_1 - \frac{1}{j\omega C_1}i_2 - \frac{1}{j\omega C_2}i_3 = 0 \quad (14.105)$$

For the i_2 loop:

$$\left(r_b + r_e + \frac{1}{j\omega C_1}\right)i_2 - \frac{1}{j\omega C_1}i_1 - r_e i_3 = 0. \quad (14.106)$$

For the i_3 loop:

$$\left(r_e + r_c + \frac{1}{j\omega C_2}\right)i_3 - r_e i_2 - \frac{1}{j\omega C_2}i_1 - r_m i_e = 0 \quad (14.107)$$

Also,

$$i_e = i_3 - i_2 \quad . \quad . \quad . \quad . \quad . \quad (14.108)$$

Substituting (14.108) in (14.107) and then eliminating i_1 and i_2 from the resulting equation using (14.105) and (14.106) gives an expression involving only current i_3, which could also be obtained by using Cramer's Rule, of course.

Equating the imaginary parts of this expression gives:

$$\left(\omega L - \frac{1}{\omega C}\right)\left\{(r_b + r_e)r_c + r_b(r_e - r_m) - \frac{1}{\omega^2 C_1 C_2}\right\}$$
$$- \frac{1}{\omega^3}\left(\frac{1}{C_1^2 C_2} + \frac{1}{C_2^2 C_1}\right) = 0 \quad (14.109)$$

If $(r_b + r_e)r_c + r_b(r_e - r_m)$ is written as k, equation (14.109) becomes:

$$\left(\omega L - \frac{1}{\omega C}\right)\left(k - \frac{1}{\omega^2 C_1 C_2}\right) - \frac{1}{\omega^3}\left(\frac{1}{C_1^2 C_2} + \frac{1}{C_2^2 C_1}\right) = 0 \quad (14.110)$$

$$\therefore \quad \omega^2 = \frac{1}{LC} + \frac{1}{kC_1C_2} \quad . \quad . \quad . \quad (14.111)$$

The frequency of oscillation $f = \omega/2\pi$,

i.e.

$$f = \frac{1}{2\pi}\sqrt{\frac{1}{LC} + \frac{1}{kC_1C_2}} \quad . \quad . \quad . \quad . \quad (14.112)$$

Thus, to keep f constant it is necessary to have a constant value of k, *i.e.* constant transistor parameters, but the parameters are temperature dependent.

The term k is approximately $(r_b + r_e)r_c - r_b r_m$ since $r_e \ll r_m$,

i.e.
$$k \simeq (r_b + r_e)r_c - a r_b r_c \quad . \quad . \quad . \quad (14.113)$$
or
$$k \simeq r_c\{r_b(1 - a) + r_e\} \quad . \quad . \quad . \quad (14.114)$$
If $r_b(1 - a)$ is small compared with r_e,
$$k \simeq r_c r_e \quad . \quad . \quad . \quad . \quad . \quad . \quad (14.115)$$
which shows that changes of r_c and r_e have the largest effect on the frequency stability.

Equating the real parts of the expression which results from equations (14.105) to (14.108):

$$\frac{(r_c + r_e - r_m)}{\omega^2 C_1^2} + \frac{(2r_e - r_m)}{\omega^2 C_1 C_2} + \frac{(r_b + r_e)}{\omega^2 C_2^2} + \left(\omega L - \frac{1}{\omega C}\right)\left\{\frac{(r_c + r_e - r_m)}{\omega C_1} + \frac{(r_b + r_e)}{\omega C_2}\right\} = 0 \quad (14.116)$$

This is the condition for maintenance of oscillations.

If ω^2 is assumed to be $\frac{1}{LC}$ and $r_e \ll r_m$ this condition of maintenance reduces to:

$$\frac{C_1}{C_2} = \frac{r_m \pm \sqrt{r_m^2 - 4(r_c - r_m)(r_b + r_e)}}{2(r_b + r_e)} \quad (14.117)$$

Normally, $r_m^2 \gg 4(r_c - r_m)(r_b + r_e)$, so the condition for maintenance of oscillation becomes:

$$\frac{C_1}{C_2} \geqslant \frac{r_m}{(r_b + r_e)} \quad . \quad . \quad . \quad . \quad (14.118)$$

Transistor feedback oscillators can be designed as equivalents for all the known types of valve oscillator (several of which were discussed in Chapter 13) and in appearance look very similar to their valve counterparts. Tuned-collector, Hartley, Colpitts and crystal-controlled circuits are some examples of transistor devices frequently described in books.* The design of *R–C* phase-shift oscillators is similar for transistors and valves, but three factors must be borne in mind:†

(*a*) The *R–C* phase-shifting network feeds into the input of the transistor and this is of low impedance.

* See, for example:
L. M. Krugman, *Fundamentals of Transistors*, Second Revised Edition (Rider and Chapman and Hall, 1958).
R. B. Hurley, *Junction Transistor Electronics* (Wiley, 1958).
W. D. Bevitt, *Transistors Handbook* (Prentice-Hall, 1956).
J. D. Ryder, *Engineering Electronics*, Chapter 12 (McGraw-Hill, 1957).

† *Mullard Reference Manual on Transistor Circuits*, First Edition (1960).

(*b*) The internal phase-shift of the transistor adds to or subtracts from the phase-shift of the network.

(*c*) The current amplification factor of the transistor has to be considerably greater than the attenuation produced by any ladder network used.

Complete circuit diagrams of some transistor *R–C* oscillators of the Wien-bridge type and employing ladder networks have been given elsewhere.*

A point-contact transistor is capable of operation in a negative-resistance oscillator. Although this has rather limited application, the analysis is frequently given,† as it is instructive (as in the case of the dynatron negative-resistance oscillator described in Chapter 13).

Hybrid or 'h' parameters

In deriving the equivalent circuit of the transistor the common-base connection was first considered and equations (14.8) and (14.9) were used. These equations introduced the parameters r_{11}, r_{12}, r_{21} and r_{22}, which correspond with the Z parameters in equation (7.14). The equations give the two voltages v_e and v_c in terms of the r parameters and the currents i_e and i_c (see Fig. 14.24).

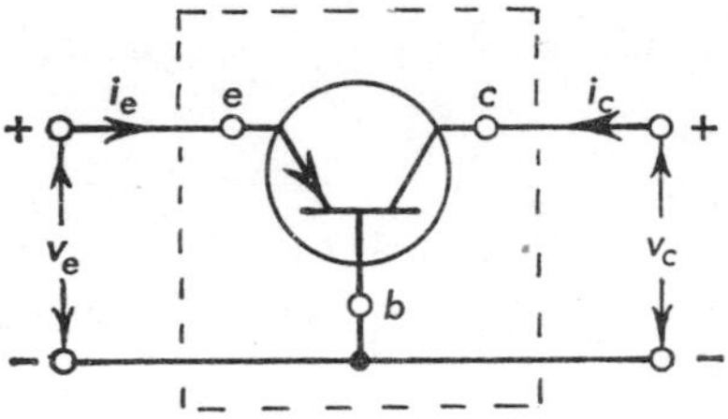

FIG. 14.24

h parameters are now frequently used and are easily measured directly and are specified in manufacturers' data sheets. It is therefore important to be able to convert the previous *r* parameters to the *h* ones, or vice-versa.

Equations (14.8) and (14.9) can be rearranged to give the voltage v_e and current i_c of Fig. 14.24 in terms of i_e and v_c. The *h* parameters are then defined by these equations as follows:

$$v_e = h_{11}i_e + h_{12}v_c \quad . \quad . \quad . \quad . \quad . \quad (14.119)$$

$$i_c = h_{21}i_e + h_{22}v_c \quad . \quad . \quad . \quad . \quad . \quad (14.120)$$

* *Mullard Reference Manual on Transistor Circuits*, First Edition (1960).

† See, for example:

L. M. Krugman, *Fundamentals of Transistors*, Second Revised Edition (Rider and Chapman and Hall, 1958).

J. D. Ryder, *Electronic Fundamentals and Applications*, 2nd Edition (Pitman, 1960).

where $h_{11} = (\partial V_e/\partial I_e)_{V_c \text{ constant}}$ . . . (14.121)

$h_{12} = (\partial V_e/\partial V_c)_{I_e \text{ constant}}$ . . . (14.122)

$h_{21} = (\partial I_c/\partial I_e)_{V_c \text{ constant}}$ . . . (14.123)

and $h_{22} = (\partial I_c/\partial V_c)_{I_e \text{ constant}}$ . . . (14.124)

It will also be seen that:

$h_{11} = (v_e/i_e)$ when $v_c = 0$,

$h_{12} = (v_e/v_c)$ when $i_e = 0$,

$h_{21} = (i_c/i_e)$ when $v_c = 0$,

and $h_{22} = (i_c/v_c)$ when $i_e = 0$.

Thus (compare page 126),

h_{11} = the input impedance with the output terminals short-circuited to a.c. (*e.g.* a large capacitance may be connected across the output terminals).

h_{12} = the reverse voltage transfer with the input terminals open-circuited to a.c. (*e.g.* by the inclusion of a large series resistance or inductance).

h_{21} = the current amplification factor with the output terminals short-circuited to a.c.

and h_{22} = the output admittance with the input terminals open-circuited to a.c.

Note that h_{11} and h_{22} have the dimensions of impedance and admittance respectively, but h_{12} and h_{21} are ratios or pure numbers (hence the term hybrid system and the use of h).

Similar parameters may be defined for common-emitter and common-collector arrangements; these are frequently distinguished by single and double dashes respectively (*e.g.* h'_{11} and h''_{11}) or by the use of e and c subscripts (*e.g.* h_{11e} and h_{11c}).

The relationships between the h and r parameters can easily be determined as follows:

From equation (14.8), $r_{11} = v_e/i_e$ with $i_c = 0$. Under this condition:

$$v_e = h_{11}i_e + h_{12}v_c$$

and $$0 = h_{21}i_e + h_{22}v_c$$

Thus, $$r_{11} = v_e/i_e = (h_{11}h_{22} - h_{12}h_{21})/h_{22}. \quad . \quad (14.125)$$

Similarly, $r_{21} = v_c/i_e$ when $i_c = 0$.

Then, $$0 = h_{21}i_e + h_{22}v_c$$

$$\therefore \quad r_{21} = -h_{21}/h_{22} \quad . \quad . \quad . \quad . \quad . \quad . \quad . \quad . \quad (14.126)$$

Also, $r_{12} = v_e/i_c$ with $i_e = 0$.

Then, $$v_e = h_{12}v_c$$

and $\qquad i_c = h_{22}v_c$

so $\qquad r_{12} = h_{12}/h_{22}$ . . . . (14.127)

Finally, $\qquad r_{22} = v_c/i_c$ with $i_e = 0$.

Then $\qquad i_c = h_{22}v_c$

i.e. $\qquad r_{22} = 1/h_{22}$ . . . . (14.128)

From equation (14.28):

$$\alpha = r_{21}/r_{22} = -h_{21} \quad (14.129)$$

It follows that:

$$r_e = r_{11} - r_{12} = h_{11} - h_{12}(1 + h_{21})/h_{22} \quad (14.130)$$

$$r_b = r_{12} = h_{12}/h_{22} \quad (14.131)$$

$$r_c = r_{22} - r_{12} = (1 - h_{12})/h_{22} \simeq 1/h_{22} \quad (14.132)$$

and
$$r_m = r_{21} - r_{12} = -(h_{21} + h_{12})/h_{22} \quad (14.133)$$

Rearranging these equations:

$$h_{11} = r_e + (1 - \alpha)r_b \quad (14.134)$$

$$h_{21} = -\alpha \quad (14.135)$$

$$h_{22} \simeq 1/r_c \quad (14.136)$$

$$h_{12} = r_b/r_c \quad (14.137)$$

EXAMPLE. The hybrid parameters of a certain transistor are:

$$h_{11} = 35\ \Omega$$

$$h_{21} = -0{\cdot}976$$

$$h_{22} = 1{\cdot}0\ \mu\text{mho}$$

$$h_{12} = 7 \times 10^{-4}$$

Calculate the values of r_{11}, r_{12}, r_{21}, r_{22}, α, r_e, r_b, r_c and r_m.

Solution

$r_{11} = (h_{11}h_{22} - h_{12}h_{21})/h_{22} =$
$(35 \times 1 \times 10^{-6} + 7 \times 10^{-4} \times 0{\cdot}976)/(1 \times 10^{-6}) = \underline{718{\cdot}2\ \Omega}$

$r_{12} = h_{12}/h_{22} = (7 \times 10^{-4})/(1 \times 10^{-6}) = \underline{700\ \Omega}$

$r_{21} = -h_{21}/h_{22} = \{0{\cdot}976/(1 \times 10^{-6})\}\ \Omega = \underline{976\ \text{k}\Omega}$

$r_{22} = 1/h_{22} = \underline{1\ \text{M}\Omega}$

$\alpha = -h_{21} = \underline{0{\cdot}976}$

$r_e = r_{11} - r_{12} = \underline{18{\cdot}2\ \Omega}$

$r_b = r_{12} = \underline{700\ \Omega}$

$r_c = r_{22} - r_{12} \simeq r_{22} \simeq \underline{1\ \text{M}\Omega}$

$r_m = r_{21} - r_{12} = \underline{975{\cdot}3\ \text{k}\Omega}$

Measurement of h parameters is described by Terman.* A discussion about the advisability of measuring hybrid parameters rather than r parameters has been given by Knight *et al.*†

Most transistors are now specified by their common-base or common-emitter h parameters, and these can be converted to other commonly used parameters, as already illustrated. A good deal of calculation is involved and, as there are several types of parameters for each of the three circuit configurations, many conversions are possible. The use of Jacobians ‡ reduces the complexity to a simple operation involving two tables.

PROBLEMS

1. A junction transistor has the following constants:

$$r_{11} = 550\ \Omega,\ r_{12} = 500\ \Omega,\ r_{21} = 1{\cdot}9\ \text{M}\Omega \text{ and } r_{22} = 2\ \text{M}\Omega.$$

Determine, from first principles, the input resistance of a common-base amplifier stage using this transistor, as the load resistance varies from zero to infinity.

If the resistance of the source at the input of the amplifier is zero, find the output resistance of the arrangement.

Calculate, also, the maximum possible voltage gain. [S.U.]

[*Ans.* 75–550 Ω, $2{\cdot}72 \times 10^5$ Ω, 3,454.]

2. Derive the expressions for the output resistances of the common-emitter and common-collector amplifier stages which are given on pp. 325 and 327.

3. The characteristics of a junction transistor are given in the following table:

Collector Voltage V_{ce} (volts)	Collector Current (I_c) in mA.		
	$I_b = 0$	$I_b = 40\ \mu\text{A}$	$I_b = 80\ \mu\text{A}$
1	0·2	1·90	3·7
4	0·3	2·05	4·0
7	0·4	2·20	4·3

The transistor is connected in a common-emitter stage with a collector load of 1,500 Ω, a supply voltage of 6 V and a d.c. bias of 40 μA. Plot

* F. E. Terman, *Electronic and Radio Engineering* (McGraw-Hill, 1955).

† G. Knight, R. A. Johnson and R. B. Holt, "Measurement of the Small-Signal Parameters of Transistors", *Proc. I.R.E.*, **41**, p. 983 (1953).

‡ T. R. Nisbet and W. W. Happ, "Jacobians—A New Computational Tool", *Electronic Industries*, **17**, p. 69 (November, 1958).

the characteristics, draw the appropriate load line and calculate the power dissipated in the transistor.

What will be the total voltage swing at the collector for an a.c. input signal current of 40 μA peak in the base? [S.U.]

[*Ans.* 6 mW, ≃ 4·9 V.]

4. Show that the arrangement illustrated, which is frequently used as a transistor equivalent circuit, does not, in general, satisfy the reciprocity condition.

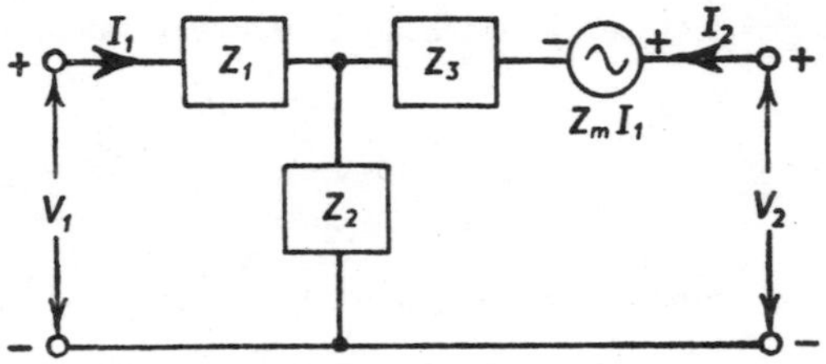

Determine the condition that must be satisfied for reciprocity to apply.

[*Ans.* $Z_m = 0$.]

5. Compute the input resistance, output resistance, current gain and power gain for a common-base transistor amplifier having $r_e = 25\ \Omega$, $r_b = 500\ \Omega$, $r_c = 500\ \text{k}\Omega$, $a = 0{\cdot}96$, $R_l = 25\ \text{k}\Omega$ and $R_s = 100\ \Omega$.

[*Ans.* 67·9 Ω, 116 kΩ, 0·914, 307.]

6. Show that the output resistance R_0 for the common-base amplifier, given by equation (14.68), may be put into the form:

$$R_0 = r_{22} - r_{12} \cdot r_{21}/(R_s + r_{11})$$

Hence, using the junction transistor whose characteristics are given in Problem 1, plot a curve of R_0 against R_s. If R_s varies from zero to infinity, what are the limits of R_0? [*Ans.* 270 kΩ and 2 MΩ.]

7. Show that the input resistance R_i for the common-base amplifier, given by equation (14.64), may be put into the form:

$$R_i = r_{11} - r_{12} \cdot r_{21}/(R_l + r_{22})$$

Hence, using the junction transistor, whose characteristics are given in Problem 1, plot a curve of R_i against R_l.

Plot a similar curve for a transistor which has parameters $r_e = 25\ \Omega$, $r_b = 300\ \Omega$ and $\alpha = 0{\cdot}98$ and prove that R_i must lie between 31 Ω and 325 Ω.

8. Derive the following expressions for the common-base transistor amplifier:

$$A_v = \frac{-h_{21}}{h_{11}h_{22} - h_{12}h_{21} + h_{11}/R_l}$$

$$A_i = h_{21}/(h_{22}R_l + 1)$$

and

$$R_i = \frac{(h_{11}h_{22} - h_{12}h_{21}) + h_{11}/R_l}{h_{22} + 1/R_l}$$

9. Prove the following expressions relating the common-emitter h parameters to the common-base h parameters:

$$h'_{11} = (1 + \alpha')h_{11}$$
$$h'_{12} = h'_{22}r_e$$
$$h'_{21} = \alpha'$$
$$h'_{22} = (1 + \alpha')h_{22}$$

10. Prove the following expressions relating the common-collector h parameters to the common-emitter h parameters:

$$h''_{11} = h'_{11}$$
$$h''_{12} = 1/(1 + h'_{12})$$
$$h''_{21} = -(1 + h'_{21})$$
$$h''_{22} = h'_{22}$$

11. The essential parts of a Hartley transistor oscillator are as illustrated.

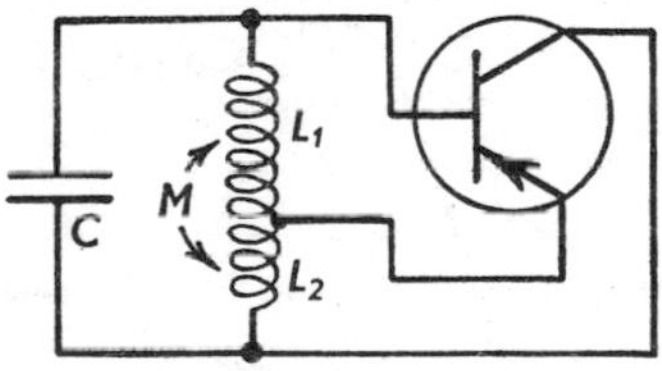

Show that the frequency of oscillation (f) is given by:

$$f = \frac{1}{2\pi}\sqrt{\frac{1}{C(L_1 + L_2 + 2M) - (L_1L_2 - M^2)/k}}$$

where $k = (r_b + r_e)r_c + r_b(r_e - r_m)$. Prove, also, that for maintenance of oscillations the oscillator requires that:

$$(L_2 + M)/(L_1 + M) \geqslant r_m/(r_b + r_e)$$

12. The hybrid parameters for a common-base transistor amplifier circuit are: $h_{11} = 20\ \Omega$, $h_{21} = -0{\cdot}975$, $h_{12} = 8 \times 10^{-4}$ and $h_{22} = 2{\cdot}0$ µmhos. The load resistance is 10 kΩ and the source resistance is 500 Ω. Evaluate the voltage gain, current gain, input resistance and output resistance. [*Ans.* 346, 0·956, 27·7 Ω, 286 kΩ.]

13. The hybrid parameters for a common-emitter transistor amplifier circuit are $h'_{11} = 800\Omega$, $h'_{21} = 47$, $h'_{12} = 5{\cdot}4 \times 10^{-4}$ and $h'_{22} = 80$ µmhos. The load resistance is 20 kΩ. Calculate the voltage gain.

[*Ans.* 598.]

14. Show that the output resistance R_0 for the common-base amplifier given by equation (14.68), may be put into the form:

$$R_0 = \frac{1}{h_{22} - h_{12}h_{21}/(h_{11} + R_s)}$$

CHAPTER 15

COMMUNICATION CIRCUITS

Series resonance

If a constant voltage V of variable frequency is applied to an LCR series circuit the current flowing varies with frequency as illustrated in Fig. 15.1.

I/f curves of this type are called ***resonance curves*** and they reach a maximum value at the ***resonant frequency*** f_r as discussed in Chapter 3.

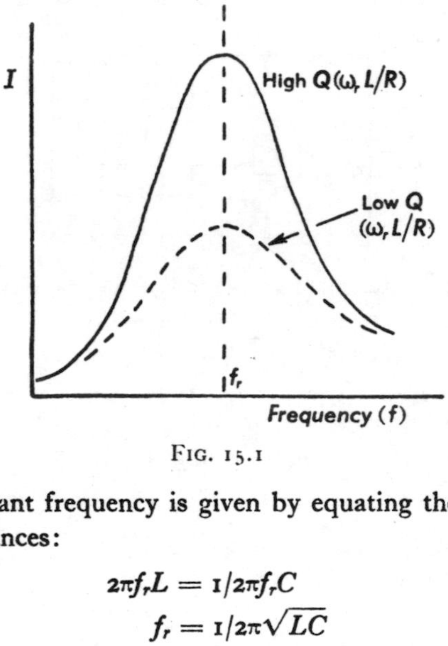

FIG. 15.1

Thus, the resonant frequency is given by equating the inductive and capacitive reactances:

i.e. $$2\pi f_r L = 1/2\pi f_r C$$

or $$f_r = 1/2\pi\sqrt{LC}$$

The shape of the I/f curve for a given circuit can be determined from the expression

$$I = V/\sqrt{R^2 + \omega L - 1/\omega C)^2}$$

where $\omega = 2\pi f$.
It follows from this expression that $I = 0$ when $\omega = 0$ or $\omega = \infty$.

At resonance the current is V/R and the series impedance is a pure resistance R. Thus, the current at resonance is in phase with the applied voltage.

The shape of the resonance curve in the vicinity of resonance depends on the quantity $\omega_r L/R$ which is called the *Q value* of the circuit. [R is the *total* resistance of the circuit.] If Q is reasonably high, the resonance curve may be taken as symmetrical about f_r.

Since at resonance $I = V/R$, the voltage across L or C at resonance $= \omega_r LI = \omega_r LV/R = QV$ *i.e.* the voltage across L or C at resonance is Q times the supply voltage. Thus, a series resonant circuit may develop high voltages across L or C even for small supply voltages, as pointed out in Chapter 3. For this reason Q is sometimes called the *voltage magnification factor.*

Q is a measure of the selectivity of the circuit as is shown by the following analysis.

Consider points A and B on the I/f curve (Fig. 15.2) where the current is $1/\sqrt{2}$ times the maximum value I_r. Thus, these points

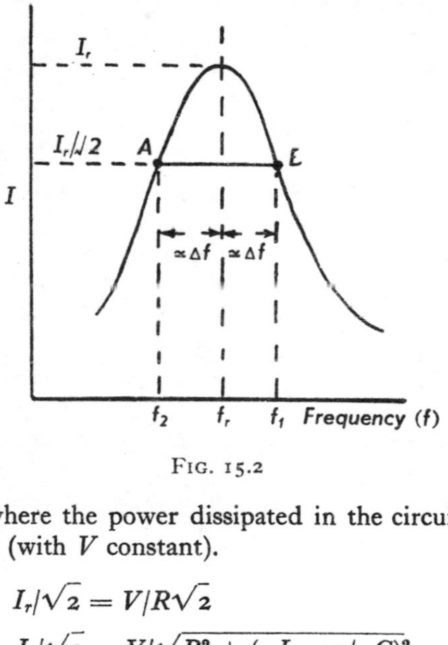

FIG. 15.2

correspond to where the power dissipated in the circuit is 50% of its maximum value (with V constant).

Now $\quad I_r/\sqrt{2} = V/R\sqrt{2}$

and $\quad I_r/\sqrt{2} = V/\sqrt{R^2 + (\omega L - 1/\omega C)^2}$

$$\therefore \quad R = \pm(\omega L - 1/\omega C) = \pm(2\pi fL - 1/2\pi fC).$$

Thus, $\quad R = +(2\pi f_1 L - 1/2\pi f_1 C)$

and $\quad R = -(2\pi f_2 L - 1/2\pi f_2 C)$

where $\quad f_1 = f_r + \Delta f$ and $f_2 = f_r - \Delta f$.

$$\therefore \quad R/f_2 = 2\pi f_1 L/f_2 - 1/2\pi f_1 f_2 C$$

and $\quad R/f_1 = -2\pi f_2 L/f_1 - 1/2\pi f_1 f_2 C$

Thus, $R(1/f_2 + 1/f_1) = 2\pi L(f_1/f_2 - f_2/f_1)$

i.e. $R = 2\pi L(f_1 - f_2) \simeq 2\pi L(2\Delta f)$

Therefore, $f_r/2\Delta f = 2\pi f_r/2\pi(2\Delta f) \simeq 2\pi f_r L/R = Q.$

It should be noted that Q is also given by

$$\underline{1/\omega_r CR} \text{ and } \underline{\sqrt{(L/C)}/R}.$$

Q can be interpreted in yet another way by proceeding as follows:

$$Q = 2\pi f_r L/R = 2\pi(LI_r^2/2)/(RI_r^2/2f_r).$$

Now $LI_r^2/2$ is the maximum energy stored in the magnetic field of the coil and $(RI_r^2/2f_r)$ is the energy dissipated in the circuit during one cycle of the applied voltage.

$$\therefore \quad Q = \frac{2\pi \text{ (maximum energy stored in the circuit)}}{\text{energy dissipated in the circuit during one cycle}}.$$

The maximum voltages across L and C do not occur at the same frequency nor at the resonant frequency.

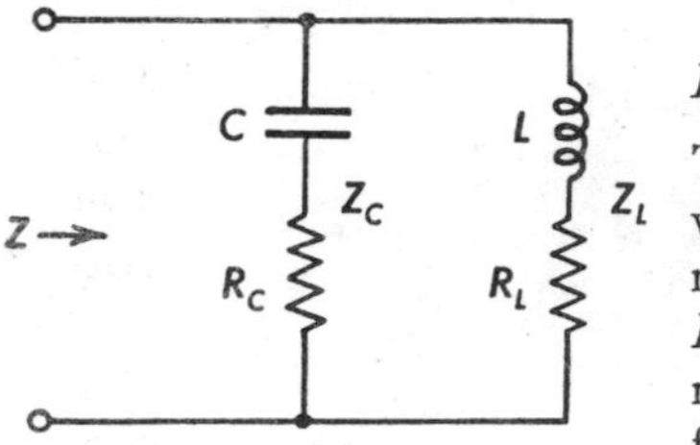

(a)

FIG. 15.3 (*a*)

The voltage across C is

$$I/\omega C = V/\omega C\sqrt{R^2 + (\omega L - 1/\omega C)^2}.$$

Thus, this voltage is a maximum when $\omega\{^2R^2 + (\omega L - 1/\omega C)^2\}$ is a minimum, *i.e.* when $\omega^2 = 1/LC - R^2/2L^2 = \omega_r^2 - R^2/2L^2$. The maximum voltage across C occurs therefore at a frequency below the resonant frequency, provided $R \neq 0$. Similarly, the voltage across L is found to reach its maximum value at a frequency above the resonant frequency.

Parallel resonance

Consider the parallel circuit of Fig. 15.3 (*a*). The resulting impedance Z varies with frequency as shown in Fig. 15.3 (*b*).

The impedance

$$\mathbf{Z} = \mathbf{Z}_C\mathbf{Z}_L/(\mathbf{Z}_C + \mathbf{Z}_L) = \frac{(R_C + 1/j\omega C)(R_L + j\omega L)}{R_C + R_L + j(\omega L - 1/\omega C)}$$

$$\text{i.e.} \quad \mathbf{Z} = \frac{R_C R_L + L/C - j(R_L/\omega C - \omega L R_C)}{R_C + R_L + j(\omega L - 1/\omega C)}$$

At resonance the impedance is a pure resistance so

$$\frac{-R_L/\omega C + \omega L R_C}{R_C R_L + L/C} = \frac{\omega L - 1/\omega C}{R_C + R_L} \text{ where } \omega = \omega_r \text{ now}$$

$$\text{i.e.} \quad \omega_r = [(R_L^2 C - L)/LC(CR_C^2 - L)]^{\frac{1}{2}}$$

When $R_L = R_C = 0$, $f_r = 1/2\pi\sqrt{LC}$ and when R_L and R_C are small $f_r \simeq 1/2\pi\sqrt{LC}$.

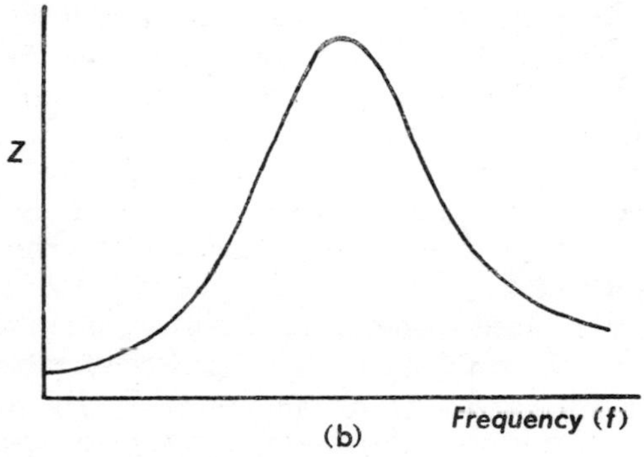

FIG. 15.3 (b)

If R_C is very small,

$$\mathbf{Z} = \frac{(1/j\omega C)/(R_L + j\omega L)}{R_L + j(\omega L - 1/\omega C)} = \frac{(1/j\omega C)/(R_L + j\omega L)}{\mathbf{Z}_1}$$

$$i.e. \quad \mathbf{Z} \simeq (L/C)/\mathbf{Z}_1.$$

Assuming at resonance $Z_1 = R_L$, $Z \simeq L/CR_L$, which is a pure resistance, often called the *dynamic resistance.*

Thus, the parallel-circuit impedance at resonance

$$\simeq (\omega_r L)^2/R_L \simeq \omega_r LQ \simeq Q/\omega_r C$$

The series circuit of Fig. 15.4 (*a*) can be replaced at any frequency by the shunt arrangement of Fig. 15.4 (*b*).

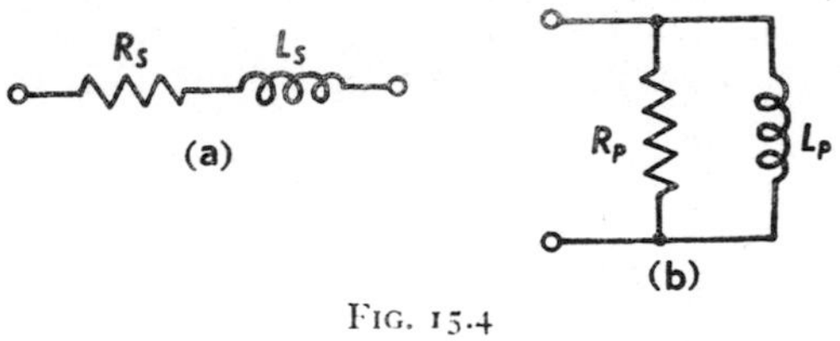

FIG. 15.4

where $\qquad (R_S + j\omega L_S) = R_P j\omega L_P/(R_P + j\omega L_P).$

Cross-multiplying and collecting real and imaginary parts of this expression gives two equations from which

$$L_P = (R_S^2 + \omega^2 L_S^2)/\omega^2 L_S$$

and

$$R_P = (R_S^2 + \omega^2 L_S^2)/R_S$$

$$\therefore \quad R_P/\omega L_P = \omega L_S/R_S = Q.$$

Thus, Q is given in terms of the shunt components.

Tuned amplifiers

Parallel resonant circuits can be used as anode-load impedances in amplifiers where only voltages of a single frequency are encountered. At resonance the circuit has a high impedance ($\simeq L/CR$) and so gives good gain equal to $(\mu L/CR)/(r_a + L/CR)$. Such amplifiers are called *tuned-anode* types. For large gain, $L/CR \gg r_a$. It may be shown,* however, that for a given tuned circuit the selectivity of the amplifier increases with r_a and for high selectivity $r_a \gg L/CR$. If both good gain and selectivity are required then a pentode is normally used. Then, even though r_a is large compared with L/CR, large amplification can still be obtained.

The output of a tuned-anode amplifier can be fed to the grid circuit of a second stage by employing resistor-capacitor coupling but at high frequencies tuned-transformer coupling is used. By using a transformer with tuned primary and secondary windings, band-pass response characteristics can then be obtained, as discussed in Chapter 8. For some further information on tuned amplifiers the reader may consult the book by Williams.*

EXAMPLE. A triode valve with an amplification factor of 50 and an anode slope resistance of 30,000 Ω has for its anode load a parallel resonant circuit, of 'Q' = 45, which contains a resistor R of 15,000 Ω. The circuit resonates at 20 kc/s. A second coil L_2 is magnetically coupled to the resonant-circuit coil L, the mutual inductance M between the coils being 1 mH. Determine the voltage between the terminals of L_2 when a voltage of 1 V at a frequency of 20·5 kc/s is applied between the grid and cathode of the valve. [S.U.]

Solution. Let L, C and R be the three shunt elements of the parallel resonant circuit. Then the impedance $\mathbf{Z}$ of the combination is given by

$$1/\mathbf{Z} = j\omega C + 1/R + 1/j\omega L$$

Let $\omega_r^2 LC = 1$ and $Q = R/\omega_r L$.

Then $1/\mathbf{Z} = \{R(1 - \omega^2/\omega_r^2) + j\omega R/\omega_r Q\}/(Rj\omega R/\omega_r Q)$

$$\therefore \quad \mathbf{Z} = R/\{1 + jQ(\omega/\omega_r - \omega_r/\omega)\}$$

When ω is near to ω_r let $\omega = \omega_r + \Delta\omega$

Then $$\mathbf{Z} = R/\{1 + 2jQ\Delta\omega/\omega_r\}$$

The voltage across $L = \mathbf{v}_L = -\mu \mathbf{Z} v_g/(\mathbf{Z} + r_a)$

Thus, the voltage across $L_2 = (\mathbf{v}_L/j\omega L)j\omega M = \mathbf{v}_L M/L = \mathbf{v}_o$

$$\therefore \quad \mathbf{v}_o = -\mu \mathbf{Z} v_g M/L(\mathbf{Z} + r_a)$$

$$= -50 M v_g \Big/ \left[L\left\{1 + \frac{30{,}000}{15{,}000}(1 + 2j\,.\,45\,.\,\Delta\omega/\omega_r)\right\}\right]$$

* E. Williams, *Thermionic Valve Circuits*, 3rd Edition, Chapter 4 (Pitman, 1952).

Now $\Delta\omega/\omega_r = 500/20{,}000$, $v_g = 1\,\text{V}$, $M = 1$ mH and

$$L = R/\omega_r Q = 15{,}000/(2\pi \times 20{,}000 \times 45)$$

$$\therefore \quad v_o = 3{\cdot}485\ \text{V}.$$

Transmission-line Theory

The voltage **V** and current **I** at any distance x along a uniform transmission line will be found for the case where a sinusoidal voltage $\mathbf{V}_s$ is applied to the line input.

Let R and L be the resistance and inductance respectively of both conductors of the line per unit length and let G and C be the leakage conductance and leakage capacitance between the line conductors per unit length. Since the line is regarded as uniform, R, L, G and C are constants throughout the length.

Consider the short section of line of Fig. 15.5 between x and $(x + dx)$. Wherever G and C are 'lumped' in the elementary length dx, only a second-order difference appears in the differential equation for the voltage, so they will be considered at the end of the element as in Fig. 15.5.

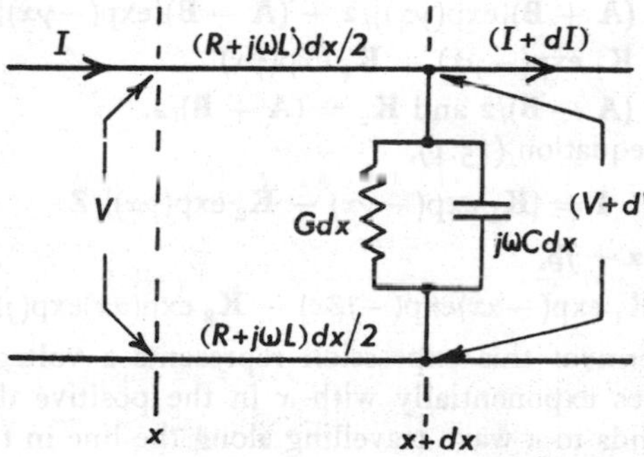

FIG. 15.5

Then

$$-d\mathbf{V} = (R + j\omega L)dx \,.\, \mathbf{I} \quad . \quad . \quad . \quad (15{\cdot}1)$$

and

$$-d\mathbf{I} = (G + j\omega C)dx \,.\, \mathbf{V} \quad . \quad . \quad . \quad (15{\cdot}2)$$

Differentiating (15.1) and using (15.2),

$$d^2\mathbf{V}/dx^2 = (R + j\omega L)(G + j\omega C)\mathbf{V} = \gamma^2\mathbf{V} \quad . \quad (15{\cdot}3)$$

where

$$\gamma = \sqrt{(R + j\omega L)(G + j\omega C)} = \alpha + j\beta \quad . \quad . \quad (15{\cdot}4)$$

and is called the *propagation constant* of the line.

Similarly,

$$d^2\mathbf{I}/dx^2 = \gamma^2\mathbf{I} \quad . \quad . \quad . \quad . \quad (15{\cdot}5)$$

The general solution of equation (15.5) is

$$\mathbf{I} = \mathbf{M} \cosh \gamma x + \mathbf{N} \sinh \gamma x \quad . \quad . \quad . \quad (15{\cdot}6)$$

and, similarly, from (15.3):

$$\mathbf{V} = \mathbf{A} \cosh \gamma x + \mathbf{B} \sinh \gamma x \quad . \quad . \quad . \quad (15.7)$$

Substituting (15.6) in (15.2) and using (15.7),

$$\mathbf{A} \cosh \gamma x + \mathbf{B} \sinh \gamma x = -\mathbf{Z}_o(\mathbf{M} \sinh \gamma x + \mathbf{N} \cosh \gamma x) \quad (15.8)$$

where

$$\mathbf{Z}_o = \sqrt{(R + j\omega L)/(G + j\omega C)} \quad . \quad . \quad . \quad (15.9)$$

Similarly, substituting (15.7) in (15.1) and using (15.6),

$$\mathbf{A} \sinh \gamma x + \mathbf{B} \cosh \gamma x = -\mathbf{Z}_o(\mathbf{M} \cosh \gamma x + \mathbf{N} \sinh \gamma x) \quad (15.10)$$

Multiplying (15.8) by $\cosh \gamma x$ and (15.10) by $\sinh \gamma x$ and subtracting gives

$$\mathbf{N} = -\mathbf{A}/\mathbf{Z}_o \quad . \quad . \quad . \quad . \quad . \quad . \quad (15.11)$$

Multiplying (15.10) by $\cosh \gamma x$ and (15.8) by $\sinh \gamma x$ and subtracting gives

$$\mathbf{M} = -\mathbf{B}/\mathbf{Z}_o \quad . \quad . \quad . \quad . \quad . \quad . \quad (15.12)$$

Thus,

$$\mathbf{I} = -(\mathbf{B}/\mathbf{Z}_o) \cosh \gamma x - (\mathbf{A}/\mathbf{Z}_o) \sinh \gamma x \quad . \quad (15.13)$$

Equations (15.7) and (15.13) give the general solution to the problem.

Equation (15.7) can be written in the form

$$\mathbf{V} = (\mathbf{A} + \mathbf{B})\{\exp(\gamma x)\}/2 + (\mathbf{A} - \mathbf{B})\{\exp(-\gamma x)\}/2$$
$$= \mathbf{K}_1 \exp(-\gamma x) + \mathbf{K}_2 \exp(\gamma x)$$

where $\mathbf{K}_1 = (\mathbf{A} - \mathbf{B})/2$ and $\mathbf{K}_2 = (\mathbf{A} + \mathbf{B})/2$.

Thus, from equation (15.1),

$$\mathbf{I} = \{\mathbf{K}_1 \exp(-\gamma x) - \mathbf{K}_2 \exp(\gamma x)\}/\mathbf{Z}_o$$

Writing, $\gamma = \alpha + j\beta$,

$$\mathbf{V} = \mathbf{K}_1 \exp(-\alpha x)\exp(-j\beta x) + \mathbf{K}_2 \exp(\alpha x)\exp(j\beta x).$$

The first term of this expression represents a voltage component which decreases exponentially with x in the positive direction of x. This corresponds to a wave travelling along the line in the forward or positive-x direction. The second term, however, represents the voltage component of a wave travelling in the reverse, or backward direction.

For an infinite line where $V = I = 0$ when $x = \infty$, K_2 must be zero, *i.e.* the backward wave does not exist. Thus, there is no reflection from the end of the line. An infinite line represents the behaviour of a finite line which is terminated in such a way that there is no reflected wave. Such a line is called a *correctly terminated line* and the load *matches* the line.

When an impedance $\mathbf{Z}_l$ terminates the line (x is then equal to l the line length) then since $\mathbf{Z}_l = V/I$,

$$\mathbf{Z}_l = \mathbf{Z}_o\{\mathbf{K}_1 \exp(-\gamma l) + \mathbf{K}_2 \exp(\gamma l)\}/\{\mathbf{K}_1 \exp(-\gamma l) - \mathbf{K}_2 \exp(\gamma l)\}$$
$$\therefore \quad \{\mathbf{K}_2 \exp(\gamma l)\}/\{\mathbf{K}_1 \exp(-\gamma l)\} = (\mathbf{Z}_l - \mathbf{Z}_o)/(\mathbf{Z}_l + \mathbf{Z}_o)$$

This expression gives the ratio at the end of the line of the backward to the forward voltage wave components and is called the *voltage reflection coefficient* and is normally denoted by $\boldsymbol{\rho} = \rho \exp(j\phi)$.

For a loss-less line the quantity $(1 - \rho)/(1 + \rho)$ is referred to as the voltage-standing-wave ratio (V.S.W.R.). This term arises because there are fixed points on the line where the voltages of the two waves add instantaneously and others where they subtract. A stationary composite wave, called a *standing wave*, will therefore exist.

[*Note.* Sometimes V.S.W.R. is defined as a quantity greater than unity, *i.e.* as $(1 + \rho)/(1 - \rho)$.]

Solution for an infinite line

For the infinite line, when $x = 0$, $\mathbf{V} = \mathbf{V}_S$ and when $x = \infty$, $\mathbf{V} = 0$.

$\therefore$ equation (15.7) gives

$$\mathbf{V}_S = \mathbf{A} \text{ and } \mathbf{A} = -B$$

so

$$\mathbf{V} = \mathbf{V}_S\{\exp(-\gamma x)\} \quad . \quad . \quad . \quad . \quad (15.14)$$

Also, from (15.13), $\mathbf{I} = (\mathbf{V}_S/\mathbf{Z}_o)\{\exp(-\gamma x)\} = \mathbf{V}/\mathbf{Z}_o$ . . . (15.15)

Thus, at any point on an infinite line $\mathbf{Z}_o = \mathbf{V}/\mathbf{I}$, so the line appears as an impedance $\mathbf{Z}_o$, wherever it is cut. It follows that if a finite line is terminated by $\mathbf{Z}_o$ it behaves as an infinite line. $\mathbf{Z}_o$ is called the *characteristic impedance* of the line.

Equation (15.14) gives

$$\mathbf{V} = \mathbf{V}_S\exp\{-(\alpha + j\beta)x\} = \mathbf{V}_S\exp(-\alpha x)\{\cos \beta x - j \sin \beta x\} \quad (15.16)$$

i.e.

$$\mathbf{V} = \mathbf{V}_S\exp(-\alpha x) \quad . \quad . \quad . \quad . \quad . \quad . \quad (15.17)$$

The amplitude of the applied voltage is reduced by the factor $\exp(-\alpha x)$ at point x. α is known as the *attenuation constant* of the line.

Equation (15.16) shows that $\mathbf{V}$ consists of a voltage $\mathbf{V}_S \exp(-\alpha x) \cos \beta x$ in phase with $\mathbf{V}_S$ and a voltage $\mathbf{V}_S \exp(-\alpha x) \sin \beta x$ lagging 90° behind $\mathbf{V}_S$, *i.e.* $\mathbf{V}$ lags $\mathbf{V}_S$ by an angle βx. β is known as the *phase constant* of the line. It is evident that at some distance λ along the line (called a *wave-length*), given by $\beta\lambda = 2\pi$, $\mathbf{V}$ is again in phase with $\mathbf{V}_S$.

Solutions for a finite line

(*a*) *Receiving end short-circuited*

For the finite line where the receiving end is short-circuited, when $x = 0$, $\mathbf{V} = \mathbf{V}_s$ and when $x = l$, the length of the line, $\mathbf{V} = 0$.

$\therefore$ from (15.7)

$$\mathbf{V}_S = \mathbf{A} \text{ and } \mathbf{B} = -\mathbf{V}_1 \coth \gamma l$$

$\therefore$ (15.7) becomes

$$\mathbf{V} = \mathbf{V}_S \sinh \gamma(l - x)/\sinh \gamma l \quad . \quad . \quad . \quad (15.18)$$

and (15.13) gives

$$\mathbf{I} = \mathbf{V}_S \cosh \gamma(l - x)/\mathbf{Z}_o \sinh \gamma l \quad . \quad . \quad (15.19)$$

From (15.18) and (15.19),

$$\mathbf{V}/\mathbf{I} = \mathbf{Z}_o \tanh \gamma(l - x) \quad . \quad . \quad (15.20)$$

Thus, the input impedance of the line,

$$\mathbf{Z}_{is} = \mathbf{Z}_o \tanh \gamma l \quad . \quad . \quad . \quad (15.21)$$

(b) *Receiving end open-circuited*

For the finite line where the receiving end is open-circuited, when $x = 0$, $\mathbf{V} = \mathbf{V}_S$ and when $x = l$, $\mathbf{I} = 0$.

$\therefore$ from (15.17),

$$\mathbf{A} = \mathbf{V}_S$$

and from (15.13):

$$\mathbf{B} = -\mathbf{A} \tanh \gamma l = -\mathbf{V}_S \tanh \gamma l$$

$\therefore$ (15.7) becomes

$$\mathbf{V} = \mathbf{V}_S \cosh \gamma(l - x)/\cosh \gamma l \quad . \quad . \quad . \quad (15.22)$$

and (15.13) gives

$$\mathbf{I} = \mathbf{V}_S \sinh \gamma(l - x)/\mathbf{Z}_o \cosh \gamma l \quad . \quad . \quad . \quad (15.23)$$

From (15.22) and (15.23);

$$\mathbf{V}/\mathbf{I} = \mathbf{Z}_o \coth \gamma(l - x) \quad . \quad . \quad . \quad (15.24)$$

Thus, the input impedance of the open-circuited line

$$\mathbf{Z}_{io} = \mathbf{Z}_o \coth \gamma l \quad . \quad . \quad . \quad . \quad (15.25)$$

From (15.21) and (15.25):

$$(\mathbf{Z}_{is})(\mathbf{Z}_{io}) = \mathbf{Z}_o^2 \quad . \quad . \quad . \quad . \quad . \quad (15.26)$$

indicating a method of measuring $\mathbf{Z}_o$.

(c) *Line terminated by an impedance Z_r.*

For the finite line terminated by an impedance $\mathbf{Z}_r$, when $x = 0$, $\mathbf{V} = \mathbf{V}_S$ and when $x = l$, $\mathbf{V}/\mathbf{I} = \mathbf{Z}_r$.

$\therefore$ from (15.7) and (15.13),

$$\mathbf{A} = \mathbf{V}_S$$

and

$$\mathbf{B} = -\mathbf{V}_S(\mathbf{Z}_o \cosh \gamma l + \mathbf{Z}_r \sinh \gamma l)/(\mathbf{Z}_r \cosh \gamma l + \mathbf{Z}_o \sinh \gamma l) \quad (15.27)$$

so (15.7) becomes

$$\mathbf{V} = \mathbf{V}_S[\mathbf{Z}_r \cosh \gamma(l - x) + \mathbf{Z}_o \sinh \gamma(l - x)]/[\mathbf{Z}_r \cosh \gamma l + \mathbf{Z}_o \sinh \gamma l] \quad (15.28)$$

and (15.13) gives

$$\mathbf{I} = \mathbf{V}_S[\mathbf{Z}_r \sinh \gamma(l - x) + \mathbf{Z}_o \cosh \gamma(l - x)]/\mathbf{Z}_o(\mathbf{Z}_r \cosh \gamma l + \mathbf{Z}_o \sinh \gamma l) \quad (15.29)$$

$$\therefore \quad \mathbf{V}/\mathbf{I} = \mathbf{Z}_o[\mathbf{Z}_r \cosh \gamma(l-x) + \mathbf{Z}_o \sinh \gamma(l-x)]/[\mathbf{Z}_r \sinh \gamma(l-x) + \mathbf{Z}_o \cosh \gamma(l-x)] \quad (15.30)$$

Thus, the input impedance of this line is

$$\mathbf{Z}_i = \mathbf{Z}_o(\mathbf{Z}_r \cosh \gamma l + \mathbf{Z}_o \sinh \gamma l)/[\mathbf{Z}_r \sinh \gamma l + \mathbf{Z}_o \cosh \gamma l] \quad (15.31)$$

EXAMPLE. A transmission line, of length 5 m, is tested at a frequency of 20 Mc/s. When the far end of the line is short-circuited the impedance measured at the sending end is 4·61 Ω resistive and when the far end is open-circuited the impedance becomes 1,390 Ω resistive. Evaluate the characteristic impedance of the line, the attenuation constant in dB/m, the velocity of propagation and the permittivity of the dielectric. [S.U.]

Solution. The line must be half a wavelength long. In free space the wavelength corresponding to 20 Mc/s is 15 m so that if ε is the permittivity of the dielectric,

$$5 = 7{\cdot}5/\sqrt{\varepsilon}$$
$$\therefore \quad \underline{\varepsilon = 2{\cdot}25}$$

For a short-circuited line of length l the input impedance

$$Z_{is} = Z_o \tanh \gamma l$$

For an open-circuited line of length l the input impedance

$$Z_{os} = Z_o \coth \gamma l$$
$$\therefore \quad Z_{is} \,.\, Z_{os} = Z_o^2 = 4{\cdot}61 \times 1{,}390$$
$$\therefore \quad \underline{Z_o = 80\ \Omega.}$$

Also, $\tanh \gamma l = \sqrt{Z_{is}/Z_{os}} = \sqrt{4{\cdot}61/1{,}390} = 0{\cdot}05758.$

$\therefore$ the attenuation constant $= 0{\cdot}05758/5$ nepers/m

$$= \underline{0{\cdot}1 \text{ dB/m.}}$$

The velocity of propagation = (velocity of electromagnetic waves in free space)/$\sqrt{\varepsilon}$

$$= \underline{2 \times 10^8 \text{ m/sec.}}$$

Solutions for high frequencies

When the frequency of V_S is very high the constants R and G are small compared with ωL and ωC.

Thus, $\gamma = \alpha + j\beta = \sqrt{(R + j\omega L)(G + j\omega C)} \simeq j\omega\sqrt{LC}$ (15.32)

i.e. $\alpha \simeq 0$ and $\beta \simeq \omega\sqrt{LC}$ . . . (15.33)

Therefore, $\mathbf{Z}_o = \sqrt{(R + j\omega L)/(G + j\omega C)} \simeq \sqrt{L/C}$. (15.34)

The above approximations can be used to explain satisfactorily many of the uses of transmission lines in electronic circuits but for some applications a better approximation for α is necessary. This can be obtained as follows:

$$\gamma = \alpha + j\beta = \sqrt{j\omega L(1 + R/j\omega L)j\omega C(1 + G/j\omega C)}$$

$$\simeq j\omega\sqrt{LC}(1 + R/2j\omega L + G/2j\omega C) \qquad (15.35)$$

$$\left.\begin{aligned} \therefore \quad \alpha &\simeq (R/2)\sqrt{C/L} + (G/2)\sqrt{L/C} \simeq R/2Z_o + GZ_o/2 \\ \text{and} \quad \beta &\simeq \omega\sqrt{LC} \text{ as before.} \end{aligned}\right\} \qquad (15.36)$$

Further, in many cases,

$$G \ll RC/L \text{ so } \alpha \simeq R/2Z_o \quad . \quad . \quad . \quad (15.37)$$

Quarter-wavelength lines

For the quarter-wavelength line, $l = \lambda/4 = \pi/2\beta$.

$\therefore$ using the approximations of (14.33),

$$\gamma l = j\beta l = j\beta(\pi/2\beta) = j\pi/2.$$

Equation (15.31) gives

$$Z_i = Z_o^2/Z_r \quad . \quad . \quad . \quad . \quad . \quad . \quad (15.38)$$

Thus, if the line is open-circuited at the receiving end, *i.e.* $Z_r = \infty$, $Z_i = 0$ and the line behaves in the same way as a series tuned circuit. If, on the other hand, the line is short-circuited at the receiving end so that $Z_r = 0$, $Z_i = \infty$ and the line acts like a parallel tuned circuit. These same results are obtained if l is any odd multiple of $\lambda/4$.

Half-wavelength lines

For the half-wavelength line, $l = \lambda/2 = \pi/\beta$.

Then $\gamma l = j\pi$ and (15.31) gives

$$Z_i = Z_r.$$

Thus, the line acts as a 1:1 transformer and is like a series or parallel tuned circuit depending on whether the receiving end is short-circuited or open-circuited.

Resonant transmission lines can evidently serve as interstage coupling devices for valve amplifiers in place of the normally-used parallel-resonant circuits. At high frequencies resonant lines have the advantage of giving greater impedance and greater selectivity, as shown below, than are obtainable with a parallel tuned circuit.

Impedance of resonant lines

The above equations indicate that the impedance of a short-circuited quarter-wave line or an open-circuited half-wave line is infinite. In practice, however, Z_i is large but finite because $\alpha \neq 0$. Using the better approximation for α given in (15.37), $\mathbf{Z}_i$ may be evaluated in the following manner:

The input impedance of a finite short-circuited line is from (15.21),

$$\mathbf{Z}_{is} = \mathbf{Z}_o \tanh(\alpha + j\beta l)$$

If $l = n\lambda/4$, where n is an *odd* integer, $\beta l = n\pi/2$.

$$\therefore \quad \mathbf{Z}_{is} = \mathbf{Z}_o/\tanh \alpha l$$

[*Note.* The same result is obtained for the input impedance of a finite open-circuited line where $l = n\lambda/2$, n being *any* integer.]

If α is small, $\qquad \mathbf{Z}_{is} \simeq \mathbf{Z}_o/\alpha l$

But $\alpha \simeq R/2\mathbf{Z}_o$ and $l = n\lambda/4$ so $\mathbf{Z}_{is} = 8\mathbf{Z}_o^2/Rn\lambda$, so if R is small, $\mathbf{Z}_{is}$ is large.

Selectivity of resonant lines

Consider a short-circuited quarter-wave line, then its input impedance, which will now be denoted by $\mathbf{Z}_R$, at resonance is $\mathbf{Z}_R = \mathbf{Z}_o/\alpha l$ and in general its impedance $\mathbf{Z} = \mathbf{Z}_o \tanh(\alpha + j\beta)l$. But $\beta = 2\pi/\lambda = 2\pi f_R/c = \omega_R/c$ where c is the velocity of electromagnetic waves.

When the frequency is such that ω_R becomes $\omega_R + \delta\omega$

$$\beta = (\omega_R + \delta\omega)/c = 2\pi/\lambda + \delta\omega/c$$

$$\therefore \quad \beta l = (2\pi/\lambda + \delta\omega/c)l = \pi/2 + (\delta\omega)l/c$$

Thus, $\qquad \mathbf{Z} = \mathbf{Z}_o \tanh(\alpha l + j\pi/2 + j(\delta\omega)l/c)$

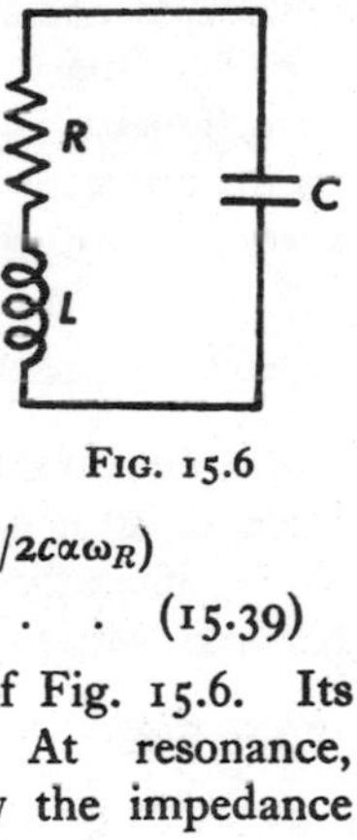

FIG. 15.6

Since αl and $(\delta\omega)l/c$ are small,

$$\mathbf{Z} \simeq \mathbf{Z}_o/(\alpha l + j(\delta\omega)l/c) \simeq \mathbf{Z}_o/\alpha l(1 + 2j\omega_R\delta\omega/2c\alpha\omega_R)$$

$$\text{i.e.} \quad \mathbf{Z} \simeq \mathbf{Z}_R\{1 - j2(\omega_R/2c\alpha)\delta\omega/\omega_R\} \quad . \quad . \quad (15.39)$$

Now, consider the simple parallel-tuned circuit of Fig. 15.6. Its impedance $\mathbf{Z} = (R + j\omega L)/(1 - \omega^2 LC + j\omega CR)$. At resonance, $\omega_R^2 LC = 1$ and $\omega_R L/R \gg 1$ so $Z_R \simeq L/CR$. Now the impedance near resonance at $\omega_R + \delta\omega$ is $\mathbf{Z}$ where

$$\mathbf{Z} \simeq jL(\omega_R + \delta\omega)/\{j(\omega_R + \delta\omega)CR - 2\omega_R\delta\omega LC\}$$

$$\text{i.e.} \quad \mathbf{Z} \simeq j\omega_R L(1 + \delta\omega/\omega_R)/j\omega_R CR(1 + \delta\omega/\omega_R - 2\delta\omega L/jR)$$

$$\simeq (L/CR)(1 + 2\delta\omega L/jR)$$

$$\simeq Z_R(1 - j2Q\delta\omega/\omega_R) \text{ where } Q = \omega_R L/R.$$

This is of exactly the same form as equation (15.39) so the Q factor of the resonant line may be written as $Q = \omega_R/2c\alpha = \pi f_R/\alpha c$ or $Q = 2\pi f_R Z_o/Rc$. Substituting $Z_o = \sqrt{L/C}$ and $c = 1/\sqrt{LC}$ in this expression gives $Q = \omega_R L/R$. Here R and L are the resistance and inductance respectively of both conductors *per unit length*, but the form of Q is familiar. Since R is normally small, Q is large.

Reactance developed by lines

Equation (15.20) can be put into the form

$$\mathbf{Z}_{is} = \mathbf{Z}_o(\sinh 2\alpha l + j \sin 2\beta l)/(\cosh 2\alpha l + \cos 2\beta l) \quad (15.40)$$

Since αl is small, $\mathbf{Z}_{is} \simeq \mathbf{Z}_o(\alpha l/\cos^2 \beta l + j \tan \beta l)$

Writing $\alpha = R/2\mathbf{Z}_o$

$$\mathbf{Z}_{is} \simeq \{Rc(l/\lambda)/2f \cos^2 2\pi(l/\lambda)\} + j\{\mathbf{Z}_o \tan(2\pi l/\lambda)\} \quad (15.41)$$

Similarly, for an open-circuited line, equation (15.25) leads to

$$\mathbf{Z}_{io} \simeq \{Rc(l/\lambda)/2f \sin^2 2\pi(l/\lambda)\} - j\{\mathbf{Z}_o/\tan(2\pi l/)\lambda\} \quad (15.42)$$

Hence, when a line is either open-circuited or short-circuited at the receiving end and is not an exact multiple of a quarter wavelength long, the input impedance is primarily reactive. The input impedance can be either inductive or capacitive depending on the line length. The ratio of the reactive to the resistive components of the input impedance can be called the selectivity factor of the reactance and for both cases considered equals $Z_o f \sin(4\pi l/\lambda)/Rc(l/\lambda)$.

For ordinary reactances the change of reactance δX produced by a fractional change of frequency $\delta f/f$ is simply $X\delta f/f$. In the case of transmission lines, however, this is no longer true. Thus, for a short-circuited line, $X = Z_o \tan(2\pi l/\lambda) = Z_o \tan(2\pi fl/c)$

$$\therefore \quad \delta X/\delta f = (2\pi l/\lambda)Z_o(\delta f/f)/\cos^2(2\pi l/\lambda)$$

$$\text{i.e.} \quad \delta X = (4\pi l/\lambda)X(\delta f/f)/\sin(4\pi l/\lambda).$$

The ratio of the selectivity factor of the line reactance to the selectivity factor of a lumped reactance is therefore $(4\pi l/\lambda)/\sin(4\pi l/\lambda)$. When l is very small this factor is approximately unity, but when l is large the factor becomes great.

Wave filters

A ***wave filter*** is a network whose function is to pass alternating currents in desired bands of frequencies freely while highly attenuating or suppressing neighbouring undesired bands. The band of frequencies in which the currents are passed freely is known as the ***pass-band***.

Filter circuits can be divided into four main types: 1, low-pass, 2, high-pass, 3, band-pass, and 4, band-stop (or band-elimination or band-rejection).

A ***low-pass filter*** transmits currents of all frequencies from zero to a certain cut-off frequency f_C without attenuation in the ideal case. Frequencies greater than f_C are attenuated.

A *high-pass filter* transmits when the frequencies of the currents lie between infinity and a certain cut-off frequency f_C. Frequencies less than f_C are attenuated.

A *band-pass filter* passes current whose frequencies lie between two limits f_{C1} and f_{C2} and attenuates currents of all other frequencies.

A *band-stop filter* transmits only when the currents have frequencies lying outside two limits f_{C1} and f_{C2} and those which have frequencies between f_{C1} and f_{C2} are attenuated.

The circuit of Fig. 15.7 may be used to represent a typical filter.

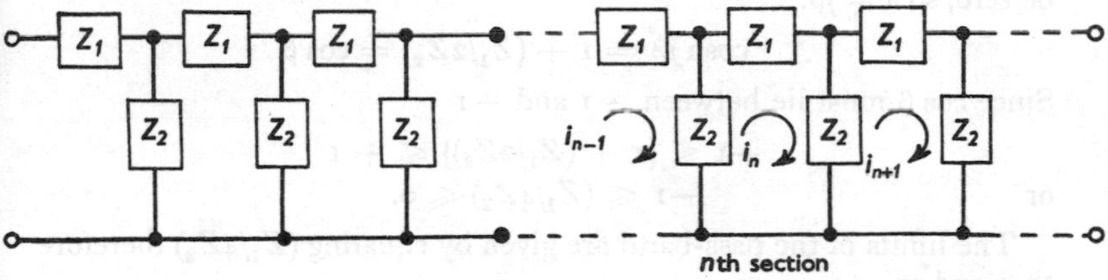

FIG. 15.7

Z_1 and Z_2 are normally taken as pure reactances in calculations and can be inductors, capacitors or combinations of these. The network can be built up by using T-sections as shown in Fig. 15.8 (*a*) or π-sections as in Fig. 15.8 (*b*).

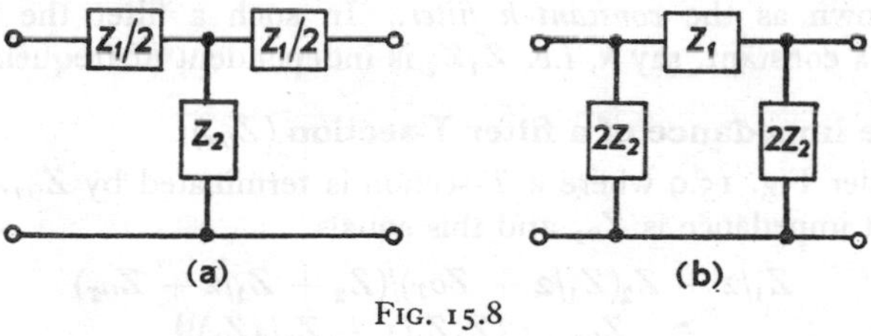

FIG. 15.8

Consider the nth section of the filter of Fig. 15.7 and apply Maxwell's Cyclic-Current Rule,

$$-Z_2(i_{n-1}) + (2Z_2 + Z_1)i_n - Z_2(i_{n+1}) = 0$$

This equation can be solved by letting $i_n = A\exp(n\theta) + B\exp(-n\theta)$. If i_n has this form, the difference equation gives

$$\exp(\theta) + \exp(-\theta) = (Z_1 + 2Z_2)/Z_2$$

or

$$\cosh\theta = 1 + (Z_1/2Z_2).$$

θ is the *propagation constant per section*; in general it will be complex so can be written as $\alpha + j\beta$ where α is the *attenuation constant* per section and β is the *phase constant* per section.

For a filter with an infinite number of sections $i_n = B \exp(-n\theta)$. Such a filter will have a certain input impedance which is known as the *iterative impedance* and corresponds to the characteristic impedance of a normal transmission line. It will therefore be denoted by Z_o. It will be evident that if a finite number of filter sections are joined together and the resulting network is terminated by Z_o the arrangement will act like an infinite filter. Since $i_n = B \exp(-n\theta)$ there will then be no reflected wave.

If a filter is to pass freely a certain band of frequencies then α must be zero, so $\theta = j\beta$.

$$\therefore \quad \cosh j\beta = 1 + (Z_1/2Z_2) = \cos \beta$$

Since $\cos \beta$ must lie between -1 and $+1$

$$-1 \leqslant \{1 + (Z_1/2Z_2)\} \leqslant +1$$

or

$$-1 \leqslant (Z_1/4Z_2) \leqslant 0.$$

The limits of the pass-band are given by equating $(Z_1/4Z_2)$ therefore to 0 and to -1.

Outside this pass-band currents are attenuated and

For $(Z_1/4Z_2) > 0$, $\alpha = \text{arc cosh}\,\{1 + (Z_1/2Z_2)\}$ and $\beta = 0$.

For $(Z_1/4Z_2) < -1$, $\alpha = \text{arc cosh}\,[(-1)\{1 + (Z_1/2Z_2)\}]$ and $\beta = \pm\pi$.

It will only be possible in this book to deal with a simple type of filter known as the *constant-k filter*. In such a filter the product $Z_1Z_2 =$ a constant, say k, *i.e.* Z_1Z_2 is independent of frequency.

Iterative impedance of a filter T-section (Z_{OT})

Consider Fig. 15.9 where a T-section is terminated by Z_{OT}. Then the input impedance is Z_{OT} and this equals

$$Z_1/2 + Z_2(Z_1/2 + Z_{OT})/(Z_2 + Z_1/2 + Z_{OT})$$

$$\therefore \quad Z_{OT} = \{Z_1Z_2(1 + Z_1/4Z_2)\}^{\frac{1}{2}}$$

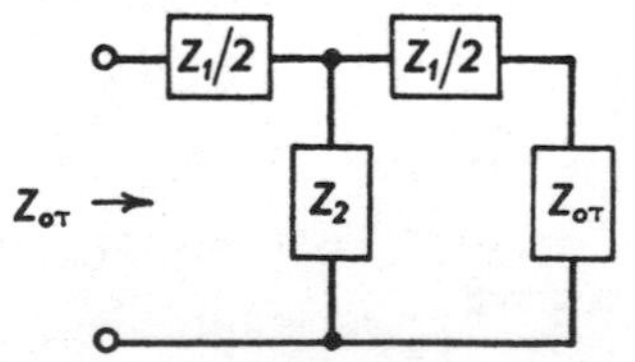

FIG. 15.9

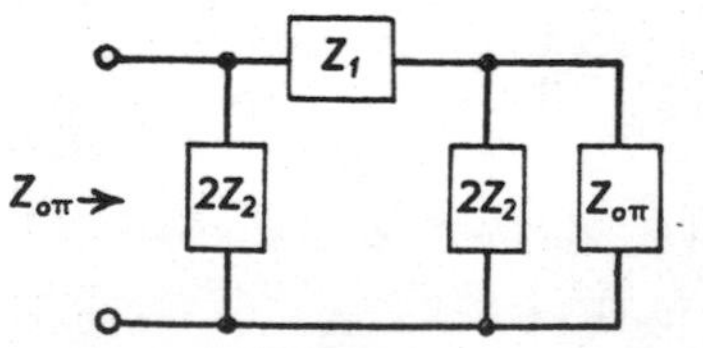

FIG. 15.10

Iterative impedance of a filter π-section ($Z_{O\pi}$)

Consider Fig. 15.10 where a π-section is terminated by $Z_{O\pi}$. It is easily shown that $Z_{O\pi} = 2Z_2\{Z_1/(Z_1 + 4Z_2)\}^{\frac{1}{2}}$ by a similar calculation to the one for the T-section.

Constant-*k* low-pass filter

In the constant-*k*, low-pass filter $Z_1 = j\omega L$ and $Z_2 = 1/j\omega C$. A section of such a filter is shown in Fig. 15.11.

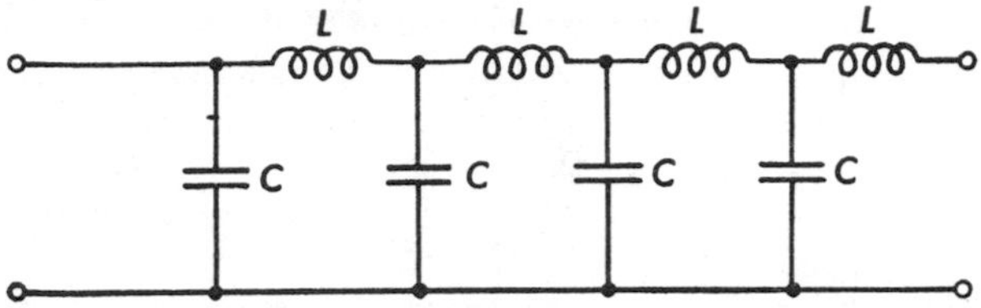

FIG. 15.11

The limits of the pass-band are given by equating $Z_1/4Z_2$ to 0 and -1 and the frequencies at these limits can be denoted by f_C (and $\omega_C = 2\pi f_C$).

Then $$j\omega_C L/(4/j\omega_C C) = 0 \text{ or } -1$$

$$\therefore \quad \omega_C = 0 \text{ or } 2/\sqrt{LC}$$

or $$f_C = 0 \text{ or } 1/\pi\sqrt{LC}$$

The iterative impedances of T and π sections are easily shown to be

$$Z_{OT} = \sqrt{L(1 - \omega^2/\omega_C^2)/C}$$

and $$Z_{O\pi} = \sqrt{L/(1 - \omega^2/\omega_C^2)C}$$

In the pass-band $\omega < \omega_C$ so Z_{OT} and $Z_{O\pi}$ arc pure resistances.

Constant-*k* high-pass filter

In the constant-*k*, high-pass filter $Z_1 = 1/j\omega C$ and $Z_2 = j\omega L$ (see Fig. 15.12). The cut-off frequencies are found to be ∞ and $1/4\pi\sqrt{LC}$ and the iterative impedances of T and π sections are given by

$$Z_{OT} = \sqrt{L(1 - \omega_C^2/\omega^2)/C}$$

and

$$Z_{O\pi} = \sqrt{L/C(1 - \omega_C^2/\omega^2)}.$$

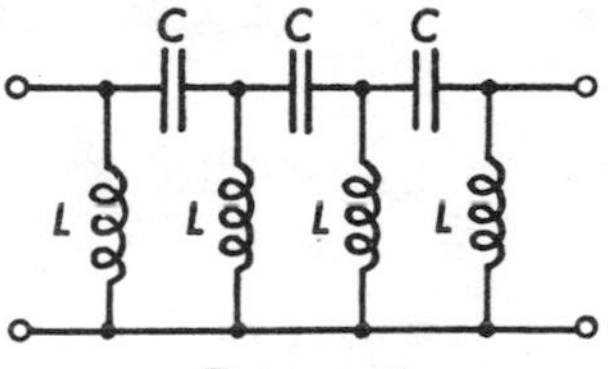

FIG. 15.12

In the pass-band $\omega > \omega_C$ so Z_{OT} and $Z_{O\pi}$ are pure resistances.

Constant-*k* band-pass filter

Consider the T-section of Fig. 15.13. There are several other possible alternatives to this general section. In fact, band-pass characteristics are obtained from such a section provided that *either* a series-resonant circuit is used for Z_1 *or* a parallel-resonant circuit for

Z_2; it is not necessary to have both present, L's and C's alone are sufficient for the remaining elements.

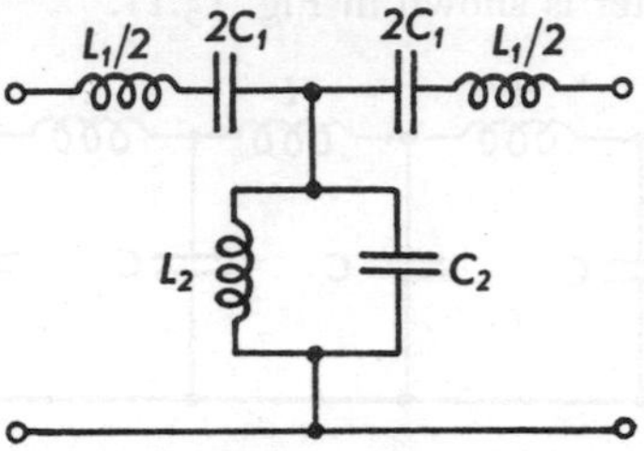

FIG. 15.13

For Fig. 15.13, $Z_1 = j(\omega L_1 - 1/\omega C_1)$ and $Z_2 = \omega L_2/j(\omega^2 L_2 C_2 - 1)$. The limits of the pass-band are then given by

$$Z_1/4Z_2 = 0 \text{ or } -1$$

i.e. $$(1 - \omega_C^2 L_1 C_1)(1 - \omega_C^2 L_2 C_2)/4(j\omega_C C_1)(j\omega_C L_2) = 0 \text{ or } -1.$$

The first of these conditions gives two cut-off angular frequencies ω_{C1} and ω_{C2} where

$$\omega_{C1} = 1/\sqrt{L_1 C_1} \text{ and } \omega_{C2} = 1/\sqrt{L_2 C_2}.$$

The second condition gives two more angular frequencies, ω_{C3} and ω_{C4}. In fact, two separate pass-bands are obtained as illustrated in Fig. 15.14.

It is usual to make $L_1 C_1 = L_2 C_2$ then $\omega_{C1} = \omega_{C2}$ and a constant-k filter results. A pass-band then exists from ω_{C3} to ω_{C4} (see Fig. 15.14).

FIG. 15.14

The condition that $Z_1/4Z_2 = -1$ now gives

$$(1 - \omega_C^2 L_1 C_1)^2 = 4\omega_C^2 L_2 C_1$$

i.e. $$(1 - \omega_C^2/\omega_{C1}^2)^2 = 4\omega_C^2 C_1/\omega_{C1}^2 C_2$$

$$\therefore \quad (1 - \omega_C^2/\omega_{C1}^2) = \pm 2(\omega_C/\omega_{C1})\sqrt{C_1/C_2}$$

or $$\omega_C^2/\omega_{C1}^2 \pm 2(\omega_C/\omega_{C1})\sqrt{C_1/C_2} - 1 = 0.$$

Taking the positive sign of this expression,

$$\omega_C = \omega_{C1}\{-\sqrt{C_1/C_2} \pm \sqrt{(C_1/C_2) + 1}\} \qquad (15.43)$$

Taking the negative sign of the expression,

$$\omega_C = \omega_{C1}\{\sqrt{C_1/C_2} \pm \sqrt{(C_1/C_2) + 1}\}. \qquad (15.44)$$

Equations (15.43) and (15.44) give ω_{C3} and ω_{C4}. Since these angular frequencies must be positive,

$$\omega_{C3} = \omega_{C1}\{\sqrt{(C_1/C_2) + 1} - \sqrt{C_1/C_2}\}$$

and

$$\omega_{C4} = \omega_{C1}\{\sqrt{(C_1/C_2) + 1} + \sqrt{C_1/C_2}\}$$

It should be noted that $\omega_{C3} \cdot \omega_{C4} = \omega_{C1}^2$.

Expressions for Z_{OT} and $Z_{O\pi}$ of such a filter can be found if required in the same way as for the low-pass and high-pass filters.

Constant-*k* band-stop filter

A constant-*k* band-stop filter can be obtained by simply interchanging the series and shunt elements of the band-pass filter of Fig. 15.13 to give the *T*-section illustrated in Fig. 15.15.

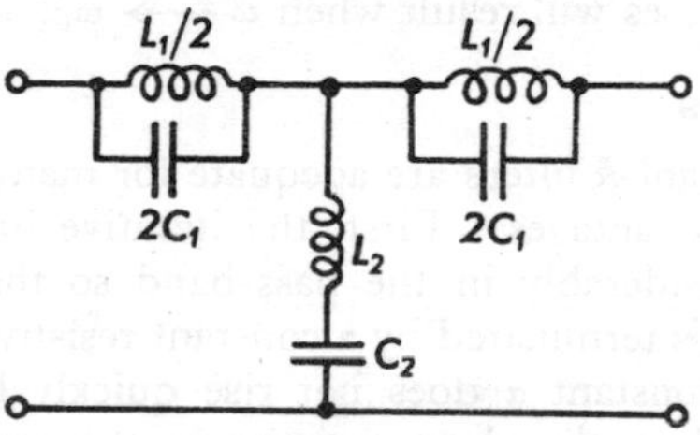

FIG. 15.15

The cut-off frequencies can be calculated in exactly the same way as for the other filters. Band-stop filters are not widely used.

Termination of constant-*k* filters

Consider a constant-*k* low-pass filter. It has been shown that for such a filter,

$$Z_{OT} = \sqrt{L(1 - \omega^2/\omega_C^2)/C}$$

and

$$Z_{O\pi} = \sqrt{L/(1 - \omega^2/\omega_C^2)C}$$

When $\omega = 0$, $Z_{OT} = Z_{O\pi} = \sqrt{L/C}$

When $\omega = \infty$, $Z_{OT} = 0$ and $Z_{O\pi} = \infty$.

Thus, Z_{OT} and $Z_{O\pi}$ vary considerably over the pass-band as the filter cannot be terminated correctly at all frequencies in the band (Fig. 15.16 (*a*)).

It will be seen that the constant-*k* high-pass filter also shows variations of Z_{OT} and $Z_{O\pi}$ in the pass-band. In this case as $\omega \longrightarrow \infty$, Z_{OT} and $Z_{O\pi}$ both $\longrightarrow \sqrt{L/C}$ (Fig. 15.16 (*b*)).

It is normal to terminate the filter by a load resistor $R_l = \sqrt{L/C}$ in both cases. Thus, a low-pass filter will be matched to its load when

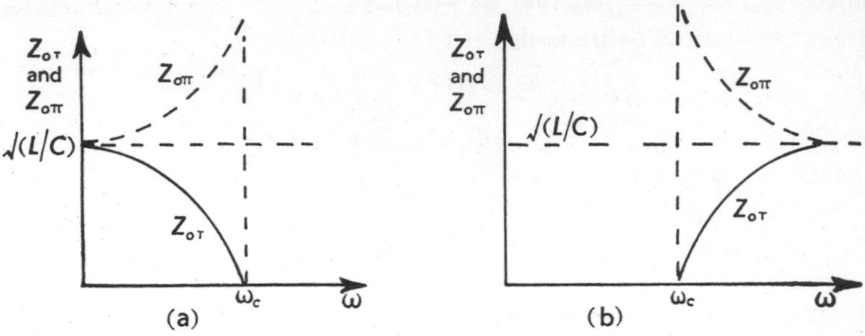

FIG. 15.16

$\omega \longrightarrow 0$ but will be mismatched when $\omega \longrightarrow \omega_C$ giving reflection. A high-pass filter will then be matched to its load when $\omega \longrightarrow \infty$ but again reflection losses will result when $\omega \longrightarrow \omega_C$.

m-derived filters

Although constant-*k* filters are adequate for many applications, they have certain disadvantages. First, the iterative impedance has been seen to vary considerably in the pass-band so that reflection losses occur if the filter is terminated by a constant resistive load. Secondly, the attenuation constant α does not rise quickly beyond the cut-off frequency. Further, the characteristics in the attenuation band are pre-determined when the cut-off frequency is chosen.

Other filters, known as *m-derived filters*, which were introduced by Zobel * to overcome these difficulties, give greatly improved performance.

Space does not permit of a discussion of these filters here, but for further information, the reader may consult the book by Jackson.†

EXAMPLE. A constant-*k*, low-pass filter is designed to have a cut-off frequency of 900 c/s and the resistance of the load circuit is 50 Ω. Determine the values of the components required, and the attenuation constant per section at a frequency of 1,350 c/s. [S.U.]

Solution.

$$f_C = 1/\pi\sqrt{LC} = 900 \text{ c/s}$$
$$R_l = \sqrt{L/C} = 50\ \Omega$$

where L is in henries and C in farads.

$$\therefore \quad \underline{C = 7{\cdot}07\ \mu\text{F}} \text{ and } \underline{L = 17{\cdot}68 \text{ mH.}}$$
$$\alpha = \text{arc cosh}\,[(-1)\{1 + (Z_1/2Z_2)\}]$$

* A. J. Zobel, "Theory and Design of Uniform and Composite Electric Wave Filters", *Bell System Tech. J.*, 2, p. 1 (1923); also, "Transmission Characteristics of Electrical Wave Filters", *ibid.*, 3, p. 567 (1924).

† L. C. Jackson, *Wave Filters*, 2nd Edition, Chapter 3 (Methuen, 1946).

Since $Z_1 = j\omega L$ and $Z_2 = 1/j\omega C$,

$$\alpha = \text{arc cosh}\,\{(-1)(1 - 2f^2/f_C^2)\}$$
$$= \text{arc cosh}\,\{(-1)(1 - 2 \times 1{,}350^2/900^2)\}$$
$$= \underline{1{\cdot}928.}$$

EXAMPLE. A constant-k, high-pass filter cuts off at a frequency of 2,300 c/s. The resistance of the load is 500 Ω. Calculate the values of the components used in the filter.

Solution.

$$f_C = 1/4\pi\sqrt{LC} = 2{,}300 \text{ c/s}$$
$$R_l = \sqrt{L/C} = 500\ \Omega$$

where L is in henries and C in farads.

$$\therefore\quad \underline{C = 0{\cdot}0692\ \mu\text{F}} \text{ and } \underline{L = 17{\cdot}3 \text{ mH.}}$$

EXAMPLE. In a constant-k, band-pass filter the ratio of the capacitances in the shunt and series arms is 90 : 1 and the resonant frequency of both arms is 900 c/s. Find the bandwidth of the filter.

Solution. The frequencies f_{C3} and f_{C4} at the ends of the pass-band are given by

$$f_{C3} = f_{C1}\{\sqrt{(C_1/C_2) + 1} - \sqrt{C_1/C_2}\}$$

and

$$f_{C4} = f_{C1}\{\sqrt{(C_1/C_2 + 1)} + \sqrt{C_1/C_2}\}$$

$\therefore$

$$\text{the bandwidth} = f_{C4} - f_{C3}$$
$$= f_{C1}(2\sqrt{C_1/C_2})$$
$$= \underline{190 \text{ c/s.}}$$

Rectifier Filters

Although not strictly within the scope of this chapter, rectifier filters will be dealt with briefly here.

Simple inductor filter

Fig. 15.17 (*a*) shows a full-wave rectifier circuit where an inductor L is connected in series with the load resistor R_l. The inductor will oppose any change of current through it and will therefore reduce the ripple on the output voltage, *i.e.* the output voltage will be *smoothed.*

It was shown in Chapter 10 that the Fourier expansion for the full-wave rectifier voltage waveform is:

$$V_m\left[\frac{2}{\pi} - \frac{4}{\pi}\sum_{n=2,4,6\ldots}^{n=\infty}\frac{\cos n\theta}{(n^2 - 1)}\right]$$

where V_m is the maximum value of the voltage from the transformer centre tap to either end of the secondary winding.

For the purpose of the present analysis it is reasonable to assume that only the second harmonic term and the steady term of the Fourier expansion are important so that the equivalent circuit of the arrangement is as shown in Fig. 15.17 (*b*). The magnitudes of other harmonic

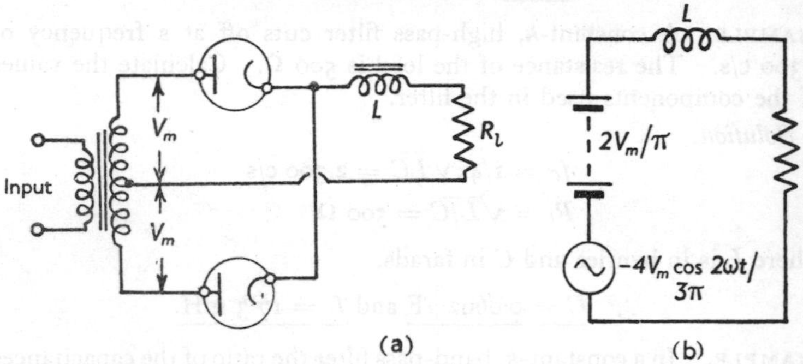

FIG. 15.17

terms are small compared with the magnitude of the second harmonic; even the fourth harmonic has a magnitude of only 20% that of the second harmonic. Further the reactance of L increases with frequency so better filtering will be obtained for higher harmonics than with the second. It will be assumed also that the transformer is perfect and that there is negligible voltage drop across each valve.

The load current

$$I_l = 2V_m/\pi R_l - 4V_m \cos(2\omega t - \phi)/3\pi(R_l^2 + 4\omega^2L^2)^{\frac{1}{2}}$$

where $\tan\phi = 2\omega L/R_l$

The ripple factor

$$r.f. = \{4V_m/3\pi\sqrt{2}(R_l^2 + 4\omega^2L^2)^{\frac{1}{2}}\}/(2V_m/\pi R_l)$$

$$i.e.\quad r.f. = \sqrt{2}/3(1 + 4\omega^2L^2/R_l^2)^{\frac{1}{2}}.$$

Thus, as R_l is reduced, *i.e.* as the load current increases, *r.f.* gets smaller. Also, large values of L give good smoothing. Therefore, large chokes of small resistance are desirable.

Only the full-wave rectifier circuit has been discussed above. Half-wave circuits employing simple inductor smoothing are rarely used.

Simple capacitor filter

Fig. 15.18 shows a half-wave rectifier circuit where a capacitor C shunts the load resistor R_l. If R_l was infinite C would charge up to approximately the maximum value of the voltage across the transformer secondary and would remain charged. When R_l is finite C can

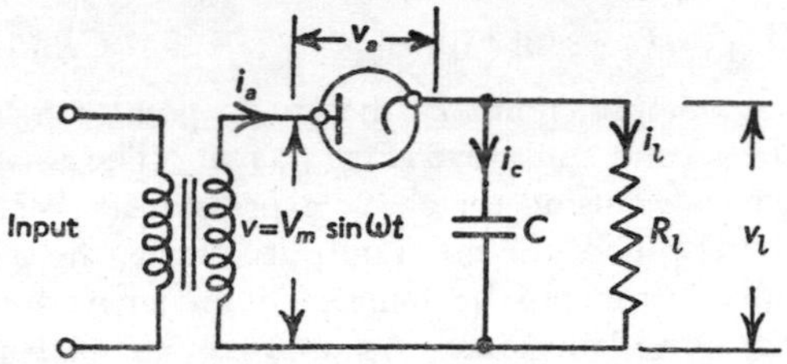

FIG. 15.18

discharge through R_l, so the filtering action depends on the time constant of the R_lC circuit.

From Fig. 15.18, during conduction,

$$i_a = i_c + i_l$$
$$= C\,dv_l/dt + v_l/R_l$$

Also, during conduction $v_l \simeq v = V_m \sin \omega t$ (neglecting v_a)

$$\therefore \quad i_a = \omega C V_m \cos \omega t + V_m \sin \omega t/R_l$$
$$\text{i.e.} \quad i_a = V_m(\omega^2C^2 + 1/R_l^2)^{\frac{1}{2}} \sin (\omega t + \theta)$$

where $\tan \theta = \omega CR_l$.

Thus, as C is increased to improve the smoothing, i_a increases. The current i_a has the form shown in Fig. 15.19, the actual shape depending on C and R_l.

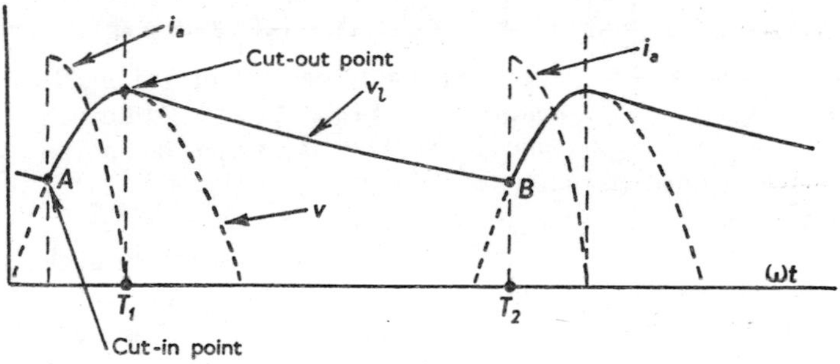

FIG. 15.19

During non-conduction of the valve, v_l decreases according to the law:

$$v_l = K \exp(-t/CR_l)$$

K can be found because at $t = T_1$, $v_l = V_m \sin \omega T_1$ so

$$K = (V_m \sin \omega T_1) \exp(T_1/CR_l)$$
$$\therefore \quad v_l = (V_m \sin \omega T_1) \exp\{-(t - T_1)/CR_l\}$$

At time T_1, however, $i_a = 0$, so $\sin(\omega T_1 + \theta) = 0$,

$$i.e. \quad \omega T_1 + \theta = \pi \text{ or } T_1 = (\pi - \theta)/\omega.$$

Thus, $$v_l = \{V_m \sin(\pi - \theta)\} \exp\{-(\omega t - \pi + \theta)/\omega C R_l\}.$$

If v_l is plotted against ωt, point B, the cut-in point can be found where v_l crosses the second sine wave (Fig. 15.19). The i_a curves can also be plotted against ωt using the above expressions. When the v_l and i_a curves are determined, the mean output voltage, the peak value of i_a and the ripple factor can be found. Such analysis has been undertaken * but is quite laborious. An approximate analysis of the filter can, however, be made by making a number of reasonable assumptions as shown by Seely †‡ and Millman.‡ They consider the v_l curve to be approximated by straight lines to give a triangular waveform for the ripple. For a full-wave circuit the ripple factor is then found to be

$$r.f. = 1/4\sqrt{3} f C R_l$$

Thus, as the load current increases the ripple factor gets larger. The ripple factor is also inversely proportional to C.

The regulation of this type of filter can also be shown to be poor.

Simple L-type filter

The simple L-type filter, which is shown in Fig. 15.20, is a combination of the two previous filters. The ripple factor can be calculated for a full-wave rectifier circuit using such a filter if it is assumed that the voltage at the imput terminals 1 and 2 may be represented by

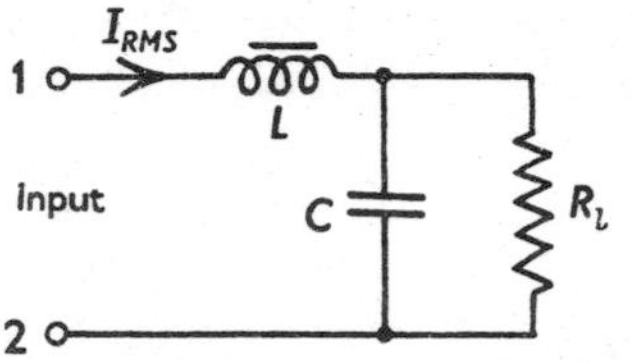

FIG. 15.20

$$v = V_m[(2/\pi) - (4/3\pi) \cos 2\,\omega t]$$

By making some further reasonable assumptions Seely †‡ and Millman ‡ have shown how the ripple factor can be very readily obtained, as illustrated below:

The r.m.s. value of the alternating component of $v = V_m(2\sqrt{2})/3\pi$.

Since the reactance $X_L\{= 2\pi(2f)L\}$ is large, the current through L, $I_{r.m.s.}$ is $2\sqrt{2}V_m/3\pi X_L$ approximately.

Further, since the reactance of C, X_C, which is $1/2\pi(2f)C$, is made much less that R_l, the alternating voltage across the load is

$$V_{r.m.s.} = I_{r.m.s.} X_C = 2\sqrt{2} V_m X_C / 3\pi X_L$$

* See O. H. Schade, " Analysis of Rectifier Operation ", *Proc. I.R.E.*, **31**, p. 341 (1943).

† S. Seely, *Radio Electronics*, pp. 71–3 (McGraw-Hill, 1956).

‡ J. Millman and S. Seely, *Electronics*, 2nd Edition, pp. 390–3 (McGraw-Hill, 1951).

$\therefore$ the ripple factor $r.f. = V_{\text{r.m.s.}}/(2V_m/\pi) = \sqrt{2}X_C/3X_L$
$= \sqrt{2}/48\pi^2 f^2 LC.$

When a filter is being designed, the maximum value of $r.f.$ and the equency f are specified and it is necessary to determine values of L ıd C. Thus, if $f = 50$ c/s,

$$LC = \sqrt{2}/120{,}000\pi^2\,(r.f.) \quad . \quad . \quad . \quad (15{\cdot}45)$$

[*Note.* L is in henrys and C in farads.]

The above theory only applies when current flows from the rectifier r the whole cycle. Cut-out points, similar to those discussed when ealing with the simple capacitor filter, must not occur if the analysis to hold. Thus, the maximum alternating current flowing into C ust be less than the direct load current.

$$\text{i.e.}\quad 2V_m/\pi R_l \geqslant 4V_m/3\pi X_L$$
$$X_L \geqslant 2R_l/3 \text{ or } L \geqslant R_l/6\pi f \quad . \quad . \quad . \quad (15{\cdot}46)$$

Equations (15·45) and (15·46) cannot be satisfied for all values of ad current, because when $R_l = \infty$, $L = \infty$. A 'bleeder' resistance ın, however, be placed in parallel with the load so as to draw current hen $R_l = \infty$. It is evident from equation (15·46) that L should ıcrease as the load current decreases. It is well known, however, that ıe inductance of an iron-cored choke varies with the direct current assing through the winding, the inductance being high at low currents ıd decreases with increasing current. Chokes which show a marked ıange of inductance with current and are called swinging chokes, are ıerefore advantageous when used in an L-type filter.

ultiple L-type filters

Smoothing may be improved by using two or more L-type filters in ıscade rather than a single one. Consider Fig. 15.21 which shows

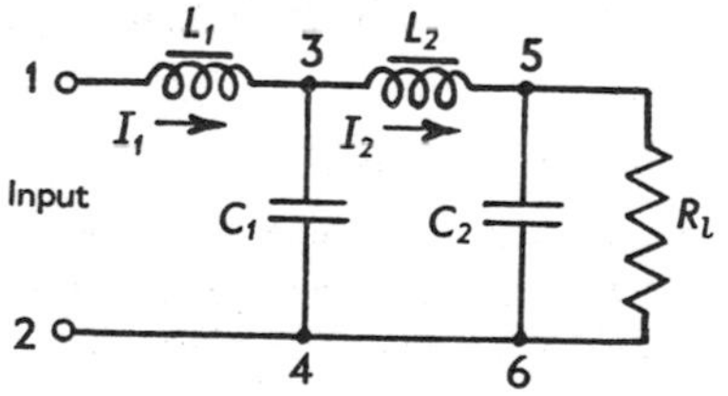

FIG. 15.21

wo filters in cascade and assume that the reactances X_{L1} and X_{L2} of L_1 and L_2 are large compared with the reactances X_{C1} and X_{C2} of the apacitors and the reactance of C_2 is small compared with R_l.

Impedance between points 5 and 6 is approximately X_{C_2}. Similarly, impedance between points 3 and 4 is approximately X_{C_1}, and impedance between points 1 and 2 is approximately X_{L_1}.

$\therefore$ the alternating current $I_1 \simeq 2\sqrt{2}V_m/3\pi X_{L1}$

and the alternating current $I_2 \simeq I_1 X_{C1}/X_{L2}$.

Alternating voltage across $R_l \simeq I_2 X_{C2}$

$$\simeq 2\sqrt{2}V_m X_{C1} X_{C2}/3\pi X_{L1} X_{L2}$$

The ripple factor $= \sqrt{2}X_{C1}X_{C2}/3X_{L1}X_{L2}$.

It is evident that for N *similar* sections the ripple factor $= \sqrt{2}(X_C)^N/3(X_L)^N$, where $X_C = X_{C1} = X_{C2} = \ldots X_{CN}$ and $X_L = X_{L1} = X_{L2} = \ldots X_{LN}$.

π-Type filter

A π-type filter is illustrated in Fig. 15.22.

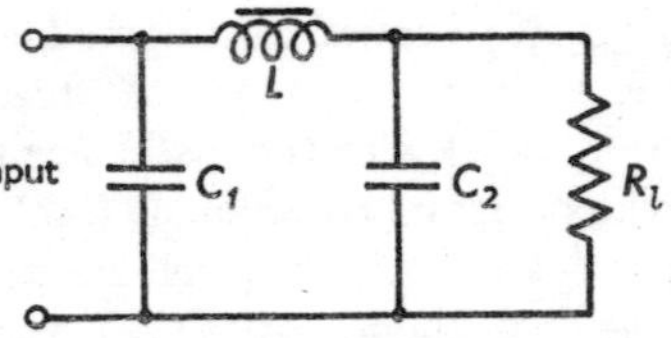

FIG. 15.22

Millman and Seely * have determined an upper limit for the ripple factor by assuming that cut-out takes place for the entire half cycle (of the full-wave rectifier). Thus, if the output voltage curve is approximated by straight lines the ripple waveform is triangular and the triangles have vertical sides. An alternative method which achieves the same result has been given by Arguimbau.†

The ripple factor *r.f.* is found to be $\sqrt{2}/R_l C_1 C_2 L(4\pi f)^3$. If C_1 and C_2 are expressed in microfarads, L still being in henrys and R_l in ohms and if $f = 50$ c/s,

$$r.f. = 5{,}700/C_1 C_2 L R_l.$$

In the case of low-current power supplies L is sometimes replaced by a resistor R. Such a filter would be analyzed in the same manner as above, the only difference being that R replaces X_L.

* J. Millman and S. Seely, *Electronics*, 2nd Edition, pp. 401–4 (McGraw Hill, 1951).

† L. Arguimbau, *Vacuum Tube Circuits*, Chapter 2 (John Wiley, 1948).

PROBLEMS

1. A series *LCR* circuit, with $R = 4\ \Omega$, $L = 100\ \mu$H and $C = 200\ \mu\mu$F, is connected to a constant-voltage generator of variable frequency. Evaluate the resonant frequency, the Q-factor and the frequencies at which half the maximum power is delivered.
[*Ans.* 1,126 kc/s, 177, 1,129 kc/s, 1,122 kc/s.]

2. A low-loss tuned circuit has a resonant frequency of 1·5 Mc/s. The capacitance of the circuit is 0·0002 μF. If the frequency of the voltage injected in series in the circuit differs from the resonant frequency by 7·5 kc/s the current falls to $1/\sqrt{2}$ of the maximum current. Determine the Q-factor and the parallel resonant impedance of the circuit.
[*Ans.* 100, 53·2 k Ω.]

3. A coil of inductance 88 μH is placed in series with a 4·8 Ω resistor. The combination is connected in parallel with a 375 μμF capacitor. Calculate the frequency of the circuit for which the effective impedance is a pure resistance. [*Ans.* 876·4 kc/s.]

4. An inductor has a Q-factor of 45 at a frequency of 600 kc/s. Calculate its Q-factor at a frequency of 1,000 kc/s assuming that its resistance is 50% greater at this frequency than at 600 kc/s. [*Ans.* 50.]

5. If a series *LCR* circuit of resonant frequency f_0 has induced in it a constant voltage of varying frequency there are two frequencies, f_1 and f_2 above and below f_0 at which the current in the circuit is one-half of the maximum value. Show that $f_1 f_2 = f_0^2$ and $f_1 - f_2 = \sqrt{3}R/2\pi L$.

6. A sinusoidal alternating voltage of constant amplitude and variable frequency f is connected across a series resonant circuit which contains inductance of L henrys, capacitance of C farads and resistance of R ohms. Show that the current in the circuit varies inversely as $\sqrt{(1 + y^2)}$, where $y = Q(f/f_0 - f_0/f)$, f_0 being the resonant frequency and $Q = 2\pi f_0 L/R$.
What is the corresponding expression for the phase angle between the applied voltage and the current? [*Ans.* − arc tan y.]

7. A pentode in a tuned-amplifier circuit has an anode-slope resistance of 500 kΩ and a mutual conductance of 5 mA/V. In its anode circuit is a 200 μH coil with a Q-factor of 50 and this is tuned to parallel resonance at 1,592 kc/s. The output voltage is fed to a second stage, of input resistance 500 kΩ, through a coupling capacitor of negligible reactance. What is the gain of this stage at resonance? [*Ans.* 48.]

8. A certain amplifier employs a valve with an amplification factor of 150 and an anode-slope resistance of 100 kΩ. In the anode circuit is an inductor of inductance 250 μH and resistance 12 Ω which is tuned by a parallel capacitor to resonate at a frequency of 1 Mc/s. Find the voltage gain at the resonant frequency and at a frequency 10 kc/s above the resonant frequency. [*Ans.* 101, 77.]

9. A loss-free transmission line of characteristic impedance 70 Ω is terminated by an impedance $R + jX$. The standing-wave ratio, expressed as a quantity greater than unity, is 2 and the position of the first voltage maximum is one-twelfth of a wavelength from the termination. Determine R and X. [S.U.] [*Ans.* $R = 80\ \Omega$, $X = 52\ \Omega$.]

10. The constants of a transmission line per loop mile are $R = 10\ \Omega$, $L = 0{\cdot}005$ H, $C = 0{\cdot}02\ \mu$F and $G = 0$. Determine the characteristic impedance, the attenuation constant and the wavelength constant if the frequency is 800 c/s. [*Ans.* $(510 - j93)\ \Omega$, 0·009 neper/mile, 0·05 (mile)$^{-1}$.]

11. A cable of length 20 miles has the following distributed constants all per loop mile, at a frequency of 1 kc/s: $R = 90\ \Omega$, $L = 0{\cdot}001$ H, $C = 0{\cdot}062\ \mu$F, $G = 1{\cdot}5$ micromhos. The cable is terminated in its characteristic impedance and is supplied at the input end with a power of 6 mW. Evaluate the characteristic impedances, the propagation constant, the magnitude of the current at the receiving end, the power received, the wavelength and the velocity of propagation.
[*Ans.* $536\lfloor\overline{-43^\circ}$, $0{\cdot}128 + j0{\cdot}137$, 0·31 mA, 0·037 mW, 46 miles, 46,000 miles/sec.]

12. The voltage on a uniformly loaded transmission line, which is terminated by its characteristic impedance, drops 10% in 2 miles. The phase change over this distance, measured at $(5{,}000/2\pi)$ c/s, is 20° Determine the attenuation factor for the line and the velocity of propagation. [*Ans.* 0·46 dB/mile, 28,600 miles/sec.]

13. At radio frequencies the resistance per unit length R of a concentric line of copper, with air dielectric, is given by $R = 41{\cdot}6\sqrt{f}[1/a + 1/b]10^{-7}$ Ω/m and the characteristic impedance is $Z_0 = 138 \log (b/a)\ \Omega$ where a is the outer radius of the inner conductor in cm, b is the inner radius of the outer conductor in cm and f is the frequency in c/s.

Calculate the input impedance of a quarter-wavelength, short-circuited line of this type at a frequency of 500 Mc/s, if $b = 1$ cm and $b/a = 9{\cdot}2$. What is the Q factor for the line? [S.U.] [*Ans.* 248,600 Ω, 1,468.]

14. Design a constant-k, low-pass filter to have a cut-off frequency of 796 c/s and a load impedance of 600 Ω using (*a*) a T-section, (*b*) a π-section.
[*Ans.* (*a*) Series inductances, 120 mH each,
Shunt capacitance, 0·666 μF,
(*b*) Series inductance, 240 mH,
Shunt capacitances, 0·333 μF each.]

15. A low-pass filter is constructed of π-sections having series arms of 63·6 mH inductors and shunt arms of 0·088 μF capacitors. Calculate the cut-off frequency and the attenuation per section at a frequency of 5,000 c/s. [*Ans.* 3,000 c/s, 19·1 dB.]

16. Calculate the values of the elements for a simple low-pass filter composed of π-sections to operate with a load of 600 Ω and to have a cut-off frequency of 1,500 c/s.
[*Ans.* Series inductance, 127 mH,
Shunt capacitances; 0·178 μF each.]

17. Calculate the values of the shunt and series elements of a high-pass T-type filter having a cut-off frequency of 10 kc/s which is suitable for insertion in a transmission line of characteristic impedance 600 Ω (resistive). Assume loss-free elements.
[*Ans.* Series capacitances, 0·0267 μF each,
Shunt inductance, 4·8 mH.]

18. A full-wave rectifier is used to supply power to a 2,000 Ω load. 'wo 20 H chokes and two 16 μF capacitors are available for filtering urposes. Calculate, approximately, the ripple factors for the following ases: (*a*) one choke only in series with the load, (*b*) two chokes in series 'ith the load, (*c*) one capacitor only in parallel with the load, (*d*) two apacitors in parallel with the load, (*e*) a single L-type filter using one hoke and one capacitor, (*f*) a single L-type filter using two chokes in eries and two capacitors in parallel, (*g*) a double L-type filter, each ection consisting of one choke and one capacitor. The supply frequency 50 c/s. [*Ans.* (*a*) 0·074, (*b*) 0·037, (*c*) 0·090, (*d*) 0·045, (*e*) 0·0037, (*f*) 0·0009, (*g*) $2{\cdot}95 \times 10^{-5}$.]

CHAPTER 16

ELECTRIC MACHINES

Electric machines

A detailed discussion of electric machines is of course impossible here, but it is appropriate to consider machines in connection with electric-circuit theory because they are in fact special types of electric circuit, and are also often represented by equivalent circuits. In all electric machines used in practice, the basic principle of action is the movement of conductors relative to magnetic fluxes, the latter being usually produced by currents flowing in other conductors (permanent magnets are also used to some extent for providing magnetic fields, particularly in small machines). In most cases, therefore, an electric machine can be considered to be an arrangement of mutual inductors whose coefficients of mutual inductance vary as the machine rotates.

The two machines which will be considered here are the synchronous machine-generator or motor, with balanced three-phase loading, and the three-phase induction motor. An important aspect of both these machines is the production of a *rotating* magnetic field of constant magnitude by the three-phase currents flowing in a three-phase winding.

Rotating field *

Consider a winding placed in slots on a laminated-iron stator, surrounding a laminated-iron circular rotor. When a current is passed through this winding a flux will traverse the air-gap between stator and rotor, the flux density at any point depending on the current in the coil and the position of the point relative to the axis of the winding. If the latter is properly distributed the flux density will vary approximately sinusoidally with position around the air-gap and, in any case, the space wave of flux produced will have a sinusoidal fundamental component, together with harmonics. The latter will be neglected here. Thus, in a three-phase machine with three sets of windings spaced at 120° (electrical), carrying three-phase balanced currents, the air-gap flux density due to coil A at a particular point in the air-gap is

$$B_A = B \sin \omega t \sin \theta$$

where θ is the angle (electrical) measured from the point where the flux density due to coil A is zero. The flux densities due to the other coils, assuming a linear flux density/ampere-turns relationship, are

* See also Chapter 4.

$$B_B = B \sin\left(\omega t - \frac{2\pi}{3}\right) \sin\left(\theta - \frac{2\pi}{3}\right)$$

and
$$B_C = B \sin\left(\omega t - \frac{4\pi}{3}\right) \sin\left(\theta - \frac{4\pi}{3}\right)$$

The total flux density is therefore

$$B_T = B_A + B_B + B_C = B\left\{\sin \omega t \sin \theta + \sin\left(\omega t - \frac{2\pi}{3}\right) \sin\left(\theta - \frac{2\pi}{3}\right) + \sin\left(\omega t - \frac{4\pi}{3}\right) \sin\left(\theta - \frac{4\pi}{3}\right)\right\}$$

i.e.
$$B_T = \tfrac{1}{2}B\left\{\cos(\omega t - \theta) - \cos(\omega t + \theta) + \cos(\omega t - \theta) - \cos\left(\omega t + \theta - \frac{4\pi}{3}\right) + \cos(\omega t - \theta) - \cos\left(\omega t + \theta - \frac{8\pi}{3}\right)\right\}$$

$$= \tfrac{1}{2}B\{\cos(\omega t - \theta) + \cos(\omega t - \theta) + \cos(\omega t - \theta)\}$$

[the other terms adding up to zero]

$$= 1\tfrac{1}{2}B \cos(\omega t - \theta)$$ as shown already in Chapter 4.

This represents a flux-density wave of maximum value $1\frac{1}{2}B$, sinusoidally distributed around the air-gap, and travelling at an angular speed of ω electrical radians/sec.

Similar rotating fields of constant magnitude are produced by *any* polyphase winding (two-phase, six-phase, etc.) carrying the appropriate alternating currents.

The direction of rotation of the field is reversed by changing the *phase-sequence* of the currents. In a three-phase machine this merely involves changing *two* connections so that coil B and coil C say are interchanged. (With a greater number of phases the reconnection is a little more complicated—*e.g.* for six-phase, the connections to A, B, C, D, E, F windings are taken in order to A, F, E, D, C, B windings to reverse the rotation.)

This rotating field is of considerable importance in both synchronous and induction machines. In a synchronous generator or motor, the angular frequency of the currents, ω is the same as the electrical speed of the machine, *i.e.* ω = (number of pairs of poles) $\times$ (actual speed in radians/sec). Thus the resultant field produced by the alternating currents in the three-phase windings, *rotates synchronously with the poles.*

In an induction motor, the rotating field produced by the primary (usually the stator) windings, cuts the conductors on the secondary (usually the rotor) and induces e.m.f.'s and currents in them. By invoking Lenz's Law, it is easy to see that the interaction of these induced currents and the magnetic field is such as to cause the secondary to try to follow the rotating fields, so as to reduce the rate at which the secondary conductors are cut by the flux.

It has been found that the simplest method of dealing with the complexities of the *dynamic* circuits comprising a machine, is to represent them in the form of equivalent *static* circuits, which are amenable to analysis by the ordinary circuit laws. This chapter is therefore concerned largely with deriving the equivalent circuits of the synchronous and induction machines, and showing how these are used.

The alternator

For a description of the construction and detailed operation of alternators, reference should be made to specialist books on electrical machines.* Here the alternator will be considered from the mutual inductance point of view, and it will be assumed that each coil produces sinusoidal space distribution of flux, and that the relation flux/m.m.f. is constant (no saturation). A three-phase cylindrical rotor machine will be considered, with a uniform air-gap. Let the d.c. excitation current be I_f, and the instantaneous values of the *balanced* three-phase armature currents be i_A, i_B, i_C. Let the mutual inductance between coil A and the field coil be $M_{Af} = M \sin \theta$ where $\theta = \omega t$, and the mutual inductances between B and C and the field coil be

$$M_{Bf} = M \sin\left(\theta - \frac{2\pi}{3}\right), \quad M_{Cf} = M \sin\left(\theta - \frac{4\pi}{3}\right)$$

Let the mutual inductance between one armature coil and another be $-M_P$ (the negative sign is used because of the normal current convention usual in three-phase circuits).

Open-circuit e.m.f.'s

The e.m.f. induced in coil A by the flux due to the field current,

$$e_A = -D\{M_{Af}I_f\} = -I_f D[M_{Af}]$$

since I_f is constant. *Note* here the difference between static circuits where the M's are constant and dynamic circuits where they are not. $M_{Af}I_f$ is of course the flux due to I_f linking with coil A, and the product (MI) must be differentiated as a whole.

$$e_A = -I_f D[M \sin \omega t] = -I_f \omega M \cos \omega t$$

Similarly
$$e_B = -I_f \omega M \cos\left(\omega t - \frac{2\pi}{3}\right)$$

$$e_C = -I_f \omega M \cos\left(\omega t - \frac{4\pi}{3}\right)$$

* See, for example, M. G. Say, *The Performance and Design of Alternating Current Machines* (Pitman, 1958).

ffect of armature currents

The total e.m.f. induced in the field winding by all three armature hases, carrying balanced currents which lag the e.m.f. by phase-angle is given by

$$= -D\{M_{fA}i_A + M_{fB}i_B + M_{fC}i_C\}$$

$$= -D\Big\{M \sin \omega t \cos (\omega t - \psi) + M \sin \left(\omega t - \frac{2\pi}{3}\right) \cos \left(\omega t - \frac{2\pi}{3} - \psi\right) + M \sin \left(\omega t - \frac{4\pi}{3}\right) \cos \left(\omega t - \frac{4\pi}{3} - \psi\right)\Big\}$$

$$= -\tfrac{1}{2}MD\Big\{\sin (2\omega t - \psi) + \sin \psi + \sin \left(2\omega t - \frac{4\pi}{3} - \psi\right) + \sin \psi + \sin \left(2\omega t - \frac{8\pi}{3} - \psi\right) + \sin \psi\Big\}$$

$$= -\tfrac{1}{2}MD[\sin \psi] = 0.$$

This means, of course, that the rotating field produced by the rmature current rotates synchronously with the field coil and thus nduces no e.m.f. in it.

The e.m.f. induced in coil A due to the currents in B and C is

$$e_A' = +M_P D[i_B + i_C] = -M_P D[i_A]$$

ince $i_A + i_B + i_C = 0$ in the balanced case.

In addition to e_A', the alternating current i_A itself will produce an .m.f. of self-induction in coil A, equal to $-L_A D(i_A)$ where L_A is the elf-inductance of coil A. It is convenient therefore to consider that oth e.m.f.'s are due to the *effective self-inductance* of coil A, which is alled the synchronous inductance L_S, the corresponding reactance eing the synchronous reactance $X_S = \omega L_S, = \omega(M_P + L_A)$.

Part of the flux corresponding to L_A also links with the rotor iron and he other armature coils, and part links coil A only. The latter is the eakage flux and may be designated l_A while the former L_A', is the rmature reaction flux due to i_A. Thus,

$$X_S = \omega(M_P + L_A') + \omega l_A.$$

In deriving e_A' no assumptions were made about the balance or nbalance of the currents, except that $i_A + i_B + i_C = 0$. However, f the currents are unbalanced, though summing to zero, the action is more complicated. It was shown previously that for balanced currents he resultant armature field rotates synchronously with the poles and field winding and induces no e.m.f. in the latter. When the currents are unbalanced there is a component field rotating *backwards*, that is at a speed of 2ω with respect to the poles. This induces e.m.f.'s and causes currents to flow in the field winding, in the iron of the pole structure (particularly if solid) and in the damper windings set in the pole faces if these are present. These currents will therefore induce another e.m.f. in coil A which will nearly cancel out the other e.m.f.'s of induction. (In symmetrical-component terms the negative-sequence reactance will be much less than the positive-sequence reactance, the synchronous reactance.)

For balanced conditions, the vector diagram and the equivalent circuit for one phase are as shown in Fig. 16.1 (*a*) and (*b*), E_1 being the

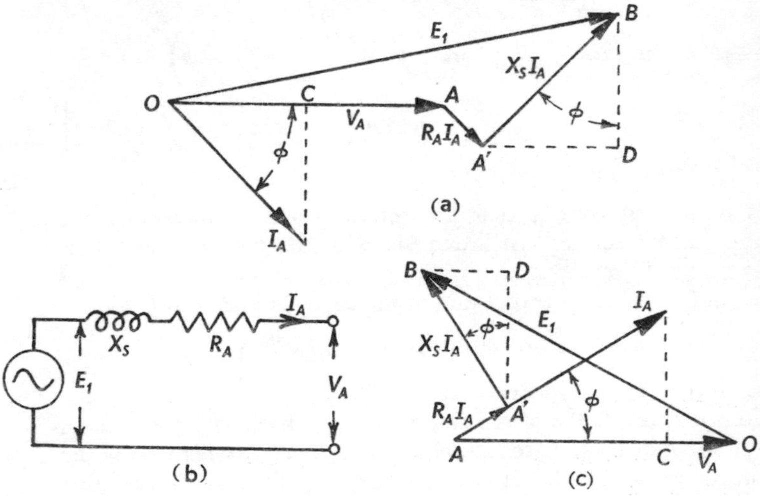

FIG. 16.1

rotational e.m.f. per phase due to the field excitation only and V_A the terminal voltage. R_A is the resistance per phase. In the case shown the load being supplied by the alternator has a lagging power-factor.

It is easy to combine this equivalent circuit with the circuits which are connected to the machine. In a synchronous motor the current flows into the machine against the e.m.f., and the vector diagram is as shown in Fig. 16.1 (*c*), the motor taking a leading current in this case.

In practice, saturation of the iron introduces complications, and for a machine with salient poles, with a non-uniform air-gap, special methods of analysis are required.*

However, the degree of saturation is usually fairly constant over the normal operating range, and the assumption that the synchronous

* M. G. Say, *The Performance and Design of Alternating Current Machines* (Pitman, 1958).

reactance is constant gives reasonable results. The armature resistance, R_A, is often so small that the voltage $R_A I_A$ is negligible, so that in the vector diagrams of Fig. 16.1, the points A and A' may often be taken to be coincident.

The leakage and synchronous reactances and the resistance are often expressed as per-unit or percentage values, in a similar manner to the reactances and resistances of transformers (Chapter 8). Thus, the percentage synchronous reactance, $(X_S)\%$, is given by

$$(X_S)\% = (\text{Actual } X_S \text{ per phase in ohms}) \times (\text{Full-load current per phase in amps}) \times 100 \div (\text{Normal voltage per phase})$$

In a large power network many alternators are connected in parallel to supply the total load, and adjustments to an individual machine have little effect on the system voltages. It is then convenient to consider such a system as an 'infinite bus bar', which accepts whatever power a generator produces without any change of voltage. Except possibly under fault conditions all the machines in a power-system run in synchronism.

The true power-output (kW) of an alternator is determined effectively by the output of the prime-mover driving it. Thus, in a thermal power-station the generator output is determined by the amount of steam supplied to the turbine. If the excitation is changed, so altering the e.m.f. E_1, without altering the prime-mover power, the true power output ($V_A I_A \cos\phi$ per phase) is hardly changed, but the values of I_A and of ϕ do change. Thus, considering Fig. 16.1 (*a*), if the excitation and E_1 are increased, I_A and ϕ will both increase, but $I_A \cos\phi$ will remain as before. Thus the machine under consideration will supply more of the *lagging* reactive kVA ($V_A I_A \sin\phi$ per phase). In the case of the synchronous motor, where the load is imposed on the motor, increasing the excitation (and therefore increasing E_1) will cause the leading phase-angle ϕ to increase so that the input to the motor will contain a larger *leading* reactive kVA component, but, again, the motor input will remain substantially as before so that $V_A I_A \cos\phi$ and therefore $I_A \cos\phi$ will be constant. (In both generator and motor, larger values of I_A will mean increased loss, but this effect is small and is often neglected.)

EXAMPLE. A 75,000 kVA turbo-alternator, with 45% synchronous reactance, and negligible resistance, is supplying 50,000 kVA at 0·9 power-factor lagging to a large supply network. If the machine is then made to supply its full-load current without the excitation being changed, determine the actual power it supplies and its power-factor. [S.U.]

Solution. The generator current is 2/3 of full-load current, so that the value of $X_S I_A$, as a percentage of the voltage, is $(2/3) \times 45\% = 30\%$.

A vector diagram similar to that of Fig. 16.1 (*a*) but with A and A' coincident, is constructed, OA being 100%, AB being 30% and the angle ϕ being $\cos^{-1}(0{\cdot}9) = 25° 50'$. The line OB is drawn, so giving E_1. When the machine is made to supply its full-load current (by increasing the steam supply to the turbine), $X_S I_A$ becomes 45%, and an arc of radius 45% (to the scale chosen) is described with A as centre. Another arc, of length $OB = E_1$ is described with O as centre, and the point of intersection of these arcs gives the new point B. The new value of ϕ may then be measured and the required result obtained. By measurement, the new value of ϕ is 9°, giving $\cos\phi = 0{\cdot}99$ and the actual power generated is therefore $75{,}000 \times 0{\cdot}99$

$$= 74{,}100 \text{ kW at } 0{\cdot}99 \text{ power-factor lagging.}$$

EXAMPLE. A 100 h.p, three-phase, 1,000 V, star-connected, synchronous motor requires a field current of 25 A when operating at half full-load, with an input power-factor of 0·8 leading and efficiency 80%. If the load is increased to full-load, determine the excitation required to give the same leading reactive kVA as before, if the efficiency is then 85%. The synchronous reactance per phase is 4 Ω and the armature resistance is negligible. The e.m.f. may be taken to be directly proportional to the excitation. [S.U.]

Solution.

The original input power per phase $= (50 \times 746)/(3 \times 0{\cdot}8) = 15{,}500$ W. The voltage per phase $= 1{,}000/\sqrt{3} = 577$ V.

The power component of current per phase $= 15{,}500/577 = 26{\cdot}9$ A, and the total current per phase $= 26{\cdot}9/0{\cdot}8 = 33{\cdot}5$ A.

Therefore,

$$X_S I_A = 4 \times 33{\cdot}5 = 134 \text{ V}$$

and

$$\phi = \cos^{-1}(0{\cdot}8) = 36° 54'.$$

A diagram similar to that of Fig. 16.1 (*c*) is constructed to scale, with $OA = 577$ V, $AA' = 0$, $A'B = 134$ V, $\phi = 36° 54'$. By measurement, $OB = E_1 = 677$ V. (Thus, 677 V corresponds to 25 A excitation.) Under the new conditions, AO will remain the same, but the point B will move to B_2 and D to D_2. Since the leading reactive kVA is to be the same, $I_A \sin\phi$ and $X_S I_A \sin\phi = D_2B_2$ will be of the same length as DB. Therefore B_2 must lie on a line through B perpendicular to AO.

The new power input per phase

$$= (100 \times 746)/(0{\cdot}85 \times 3) = 29{,}300 \text{ W.}$$

The *power* component of the input current per phase

$$= 29{,}300/577 = 50{\cdot}75 \text{ A.}$$

Therefore $X_S I_A \cos \phi = 4 \times 50{\cdot}75 = 203$ V. $A'D_2$ is therefore rawn to scale of length 203 V, and D_2B_2 drawn parallel to OA, so cating B_2. By measurement, $OB_2 = 690$ V, so that the new excitaon current required

$$= (25 \times 690)/677 = \underline{25{\cdot}9\ \text{A}}.$$

he three-phase induction motor

Although attention is confined here to three-phase machines, the ame principles are applicable to two-phase ones, or to any polyphase achine. The typical induction motor has a three-phase winding, the *rimary*, set in slots in the laminated *stator* iron, and a similar winding, r a squirrel-cage winding, which is the *secondary*, set in slots in the otor iron. The primary winding is connected to the three-phase upply, while the secondary is either short-circuited or connected to xternal resistors. ' Inverted ' motors are sometimes used, the primary inding being on the rotor and the secondary on the stator.

The three-phase currents flowing in the primary (stator) windings roduce a rotating magnetic field, which, cutting the secondary (rotor) onductors, induces e.m.f.'s therein, and so produces currents in the econdary windings. The forces produced by these currents and the ux producing them, cause the rotor to move in such a direction as to inimise the underlying cause (Lenz's Law). This means that the otor tends to *follow* the rotating field, so as to reduce the rate at which his cuts the rotor conductors. This is the simple qualitative explanaion of how the induction motor works. As was done with the synchroous motor, the performance may be elucidated from a consideration f the machine as an assembly of varying mutual inductances. However, this is rather complicated, due to there being six windings to conider, and a more straightforward approach is therefore given below.

he wound-rotor or slip-ring motor at standstill

When the stator or primary windings of a three-phase induction notor are connected to a three-phase supply, with the rotor openircuited, three-phase magnetizing currents flow which produce a otating field as shown above. This field cuts the stator windings, roducing a back e.m.f., E_1 per phase, which, as in the case of the ransformer, is nearly equal in magnitude and opposite in phase to the pplied voltage per phase V_1. This rotating field also cuts the secondary r rotor conductors at the same rate (the machine being stationary) roducing an e.m.f. E_2 per phase, where $E_1/E_2 = N_1/N_2$, where N_1 nd N_2 are the effective numbers of primary and secondary turns per hase. If now load impedances are connected across the slip-rings, he rotor being held stationary, rotor currents of supply frequency flow. These secondary currents produce their own rotating field cutting both stator and rotor conductors, and so upset the balance between E_1 and V_1. Consequently, just as in an ordinary transformer extra primary (stator) currents, I'_1 amps/phase, flow to balance the magnetic effect of the secondary currents (I_2 amps/phase), and $I'_1N_1 = -I_2N_2$ as in the transformer. In fact, when stationary, the slip-ring induction motor is a form of static transformer, and is so used, being termed an induction regulator. The same concepts which are found to be so helpful in the case of the transformer are also useful for the induction motor. Thus a practical machine is considered to consist of a 'perfect' machine in which all the flux links both windings, together with leakage inductances, resistances and a shunt magnetizing admittance. It is only necessary to consider one phase, since the arrangement is a balanced one. The equivalent circuit diagram per phase is therefore as shown in Fig. 16.2 for the stationary machine.

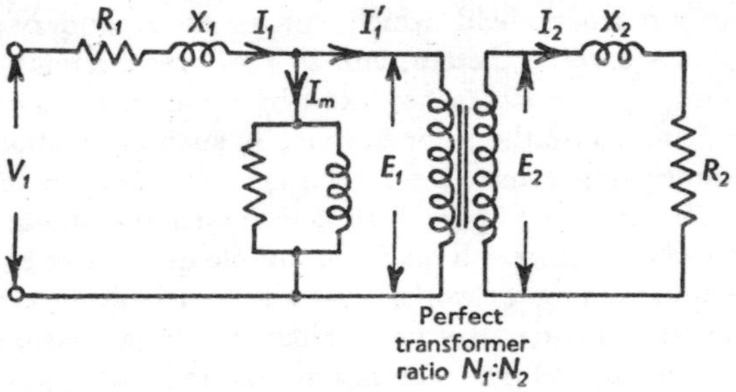

FIG. 16.2

R_2 consists of the winding resistance per phase, plus any external resistance, in the case of a slip-ring motor.

Again, just as for the ordinary transformer, the secondary impedances X_2 and R_2 may be referred to the primary winding to give

$$X_2' = X_2N_1^2/N_2^2 \text{ and } R_2' = R_2N_1^2/N_2^2,$$

the referred currents and voltages being,

$$I_1' = I_2N_2/N_1 \text{ and } E_2' = E_1 = E_2N_1/N_2'.$$

Induction motor rotating

When the rotor circuit is closed either by being short-circuited or connected to external resistors, and the machine is allowed to rotate naturally, it will attain a speed somewhat less than the speed of the rotating field produced by the stator currents. This latter speed, N_s r.p.m. or ω_s electrical radians/sec is termed the synchronous speed, and the difference between this and the actual rotor speed N r.p.m. or ω radians/sec is termed the 'slip-speed'.. The slip, symbol s, is defined as the ratio $(N_s - N)/N_s$ or $(\omega_s - \omega)/\omega_s$ so that $N = N_s(1 - s)$ or $\omega = \omega_s(1 - s)$.

The speed at which the rotor conductors are cut by the rotating field is now $(N_s - N)$ r.p.m. or $(\omega_s - \omega)$ electrical radians/sec, *i.e.* sN_s r.p.m. or $s\omega_s$ electrical radians/sec, so that the angular frequency of the rotor e.m.f.'s is now $s\omega_s$, and the frequency itself is (sf) c/s where f is the supply frequency. The e.m.f. per phase is now sE_2, where E_2 is the standstill ($s = 1$) e.m.f. per phase for the same air-gap flux. The leakage reactance of the secondary is now sX_2, where X_2 is the standstill reactance, corresponding to full supply frequency f.

Since the rotor frequency has been reduced to (sf) c/s, the rotating field produced by the rotor currents now has an angular velocity, *relative to the rotor*, of $s\omega_s$ or sN_s. The speed of this field *relative to the stator* is thus $\omega + s\omega_s$ or $N + sN_s$, since the rotor itself is rotating.

But, $\qquad \omega + s\omega_s = \omega_s(1 - s) + s\omega_s = \omega_s$

or $\qquad N + sN_s = N_s(1 - s) + sN_s = N_s$

so that the rotor field rotates synchronously with the stator field, whatever the actual rotor speed, *and the ratio between I_1 and I_2 is independent*

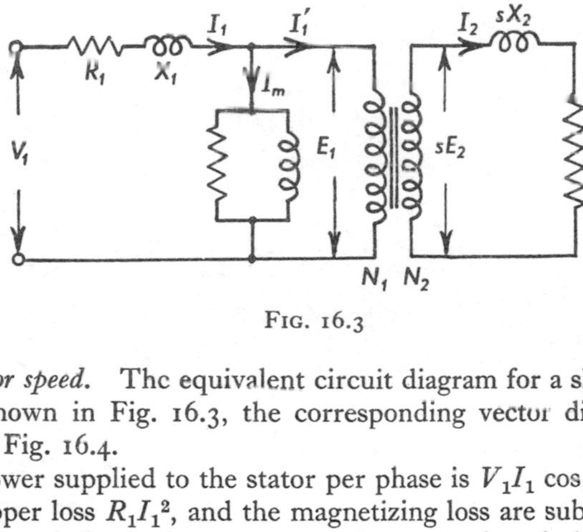

FIG. 16.3

of the rotor speed. The equivalent circuit diagram for a slip s is therefore as shown in Fig. 16.3, the corresponding vector diagram being shown in Fig. 16.4.

The power supplied to the stator per phase is $V_1I_1 \cos \phi$, but if the stator copper loss $R_1I_1^2$, and the magnetizing loss are subtracted from this, the remainder is the power per phase transferred via the mutual flux to the rotor, and this is $E_1I_1 \cos \psi_2 = E_2I_2 \cos \psi_2$.

However, the total *electrical* power per phase appearing in the equivalent circuit and shown on the vector diagram is $sE_2I_2 \cos \psi_2$. Since under motoring conditions s is <1, there would appear to be some loss of power. In fact, the difference constitutes the mechanical power required to turn the rotor against the imposed torque, which does not appear in the electrical circuit or in the vector diagram. Thus, the total mechanical power per phase, including the friction, windage and some iron loss, is given by $P = (1 - s)E_2I_2 \cos \psi_2$ watts. If T is the torque

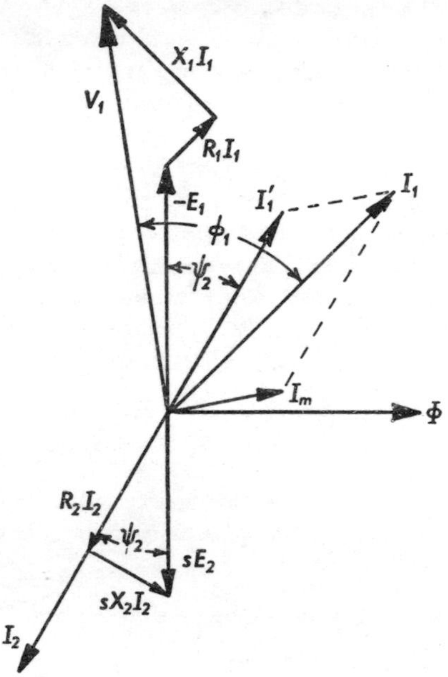

FIG. 16.4

per phase in lb-ft and $2p$ the number of poles, the actual rotor speed therefore being ω/p radians/sec,

$$\frac{T \times \omega/p \times 746}{550} = (1 - s)E_2I_2 \cos \psi_2$$

or $$T = [0{\cdot}737p(1 - s)E_2I_2 \cos \psi_2/\omega]\text{lb-ft.}$$

and since $$\omega = (1 - s)\omega_s$$

$$T = 0{\cdot}737pE_2I_2 \cos \psi_2/\omega_s$$
$$= 0{\cdot}737E_2I_2 \cos \psi_2/\omega'_s = 0{\cdot}737T'/\omega'_s$$

where $\omega'_s = \omega_s/p$, is the physical synchronous speed in radians/sec.

Since for a given machine, supplied at a constant frequency, ω'_s is constant, the torque per phase is proportional to $E_2I_2 \cos \psi_2$, the rotor *input* power per phase. From this arises the common definition of the torque T' in terms of this rotor power, as *synchronous* watts, that is as $T' = E_2I_2 \cos \psi_2 = I_2^2R_2/s$ watts per phase.

Equivalent static circuit

As shown above, the equivalent circuit for the machine under dynamic conditions is incomplete because the mechanical power is not shown.

However, it is easy to devise an equivalent *static* circuit, in which all the powers are electrical, the mechanical power of the actual machine being represented by the loss in an extra rotor resistance. As far as observations on the primary are concerned this equivalent static device, which is of course only a transformer, must be identical with the actual machine, and must have the same effective impedance. The secondary e.m.f. per phase of the static circuit is $E_2 = E_1N_2/N_1$, the secondary frequency being the same as the primary, so that the leakage reactance is now X_2 per phase. I_2 must be the same in both dynamic and equivalent static circuits, both in magnitude and phase. In the dynamic circuit

$$I_2 = sE_2/\sqrt{\{R_2^2 + (sX_2)^2\}}, \ \tan \psi_2 = sX_2/R_2,$$

whereas in the static circuit, if the equivalent resistance per phase is now r,

$$I_2 = E_2/\sqrt{\{r^2 + X_2^2\}}, \ \tan \psi_2 = X_2/r$$

This is obviously satisfied if $r = R_2/s$.

Therefore by adding an *additional* resistance of $(R_2/s - R_2) = R_2(1/s - 1)$ to the rotor circuit, the stationary machine has the same equivalent impedance as the actual machine working at slip s. The input power to the rotor is the same, but is now absorbed entirely in resistance loss, the *extra* component of which $R_2\left(\frac{1}{s} - 1\right)I_2^2$, represents the mechanical power per phase of the actual machine, the copper loss in the rotor still being $R_2I_2^2$ watts per phase.

The equivalent static circuit per phase thus appears as shown in Fig. 16.5.

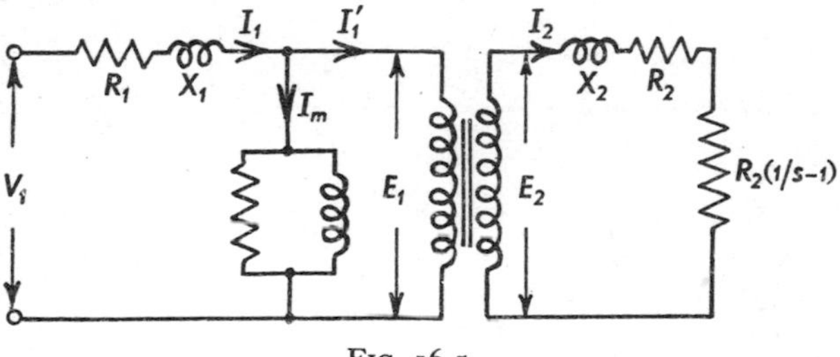

FIG. 16.5

This circuit is not susceptible of very easy analysis and therefore the same approximation as used for transformers is usually adopted. It is assumed that the voltage drops due to the current I_m in R_1 and X_1 are small, so that the shunt magnetizing admittance may be transferred to the input terminals.*

* See Chapter 8 for a fuller discussion on this, and also D. Harrison, " The Equivalent Circuit of the Transformer and Induction Motor ", *Electrical Energy*, 1, 7, pp. 208–11 (March 1957).

The secondary voltages, currents and impedances may also be referred to the primary side as in the transformer. (Alternatively, of course, all quantities may be referred to the secondary.) The approximate static equivalent circuit for one phase then appears as in Fig. 16.6 where

$$X_2' = X_2N_1^2/N_2^2 \text{ and } R_2' = R_2N_1^2/N_2^2$$
$$I_2' = I_1' = I_2N_2/N_1,\ E_2' = E_1 = E_2N_1/N_2$$

The torque in synchronous watts per phase is now given by $(I_1')^2R_2'/s$ and the output power per phase by $(I_1')^2R_2'\left(\frac{1}{s} - 1\right)$ watts.

Torque and output power

The equivalent circuit shown Fig. 16.6, is sufficient for a complete determination of the performance of the motor, provided that the impedances are known for the conditions of operation under consideration. Over the normal working range the resistances and reactances are reasonably constant, but when the current is much in excess of the full-load current, such as occurs when starting a squirrel-cage motor, the reactances may be reduced considerably due to saturation effects. During normal operation the rotor frequency is quite low and the rotor

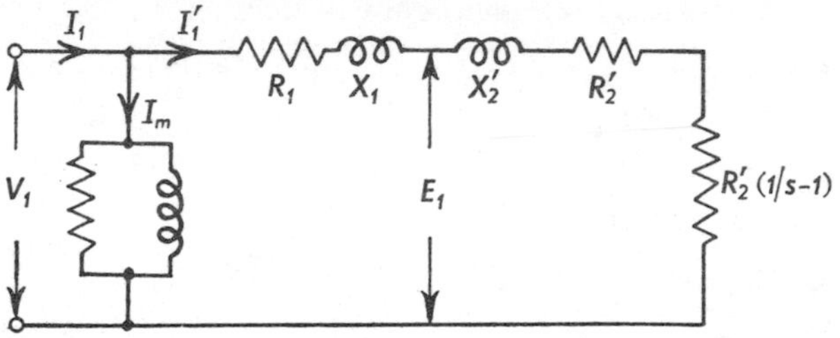

FIG. 16.6

resistance is effectively the d.c. value, but again during the starting period when the rotor frequency is higher the effective resistance may be much greater. This is actually an advantage for starting and special machines are designed to make use of this effect to give better starting performance.*

From the circuit shown in Fig. 16.6,

$$I_1' = V_1/\sqrt{\{X^2 + (R_1 + r)^2\}}$$

where $X = (X_1 + X_2'),\ r = R_2'/s.$

The torque $T' = r(I_1')^2$

$= rV_1^2/\{X^2 + (R_1 + r)^2\}$ synchronous watts per phase.

* M. G. Say, *The Performance and Design of Alternating Current Machines* (Pitman, 1958).

The maximum value of torque occurs when

$dT'/dr = 0$, that is when,

$$\{X^2 + (R_1 + r)^2\} - 2r(R_1 + r) = 0$$

or
$$r^2 = X^2 + R_1^2$$

or
$$r = R_2'/s = \sqrt{\{X^2 + R_1^2\}}$$

In practice, R_1 is usually fairly small compared with X, so that the approximate condition for maximum torque is

$$r \simeq X$$

The maximum torque itself is

$$T_{max} = \frac{V_1^2\sqrt{(X^2 + R_1^2)}}{X^2 + R_1^2 + 2R_1\sqrt{(X^2 + R_1^2)} + (X^2 + R_1^2)}$$
$$= V_1^2/2\{\sqrt{(X^2 + R_1^2)} + R_1\} \simeq V_2^2/2X \text{ Syn. watts per phase.}$$

The output power per phase is given by

$$P = R_2'(1/s - 1)(I_1')^2 = V_1^2R_2'(1/s - 1)/\{X^2 + (R_1 + R_2'/s)^2\} \text{ watts.}$$

For a given machine, supplied at fixed voltage and frequency, and taking X and R_1 as constant, the maximum torque is also constant, as shown by the expression above. It is seen from the equations above that the value of slip s at which maximum torque occurs will depend on the value of rotor resistance R_2. In fact, since $r = R_2'/s$ is the only variable quantity in the expressions for current and torque, the latter are uniquely determined by the value of r. If the actual rotor resistance R_2 is increased, the slip s for a given current and torque will increase in direct proportion.

With a squirrel-cage motor the rotor resistance is unalterable (though possibly varying with rotor frequency), but with a slip-ring motor external variable resistors may be connected to the slip-rings to give speed control and to improve starting performance. To illustrate the use of the equivalent static circuit diagram consider the following example.

EXAMPLE. A 30 h.p, 400 V, three-phase, 50 c/s, six-pole induction motor has a delta-connected stator (primary) winding, and the following impedances, all referred to the primary, per phase.

$R_1 = 0{\cdot}5\ \Omega$; $R_2' = 0{\cdot}39\ \Omega$; The total leakage reactance $X = (X_1 + X_2') = 4{\cdot}92\ \Omega$. The no-load (magnetizing) current (line) = 10 A at 0·2 power-factor.

Determine the full-load line current, power-factor, speed and torque, the maximum torque and the starting torque and current. The friction and windage may be neglected. [S.U.]

Solution. The magnetizing current per phase, has components co-phasal and in quadrature with the voltage of 1·155 A and 5·65 A respectively. The equivalent circuit for one phase is as shown in Fig. 16.7.

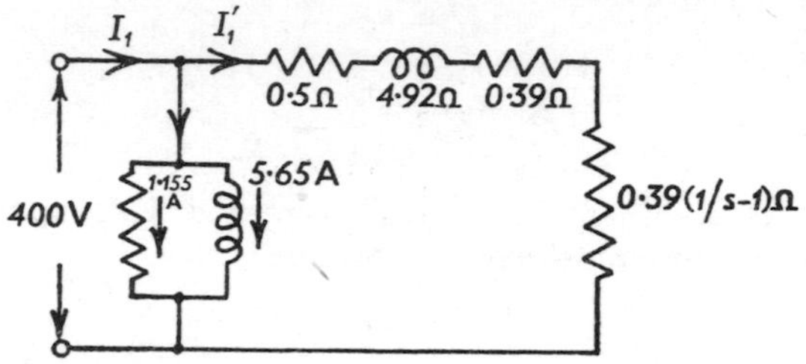

FIG. 16.7

$$(I_1')^2 = 400^2/\{4\cdot92^2 + (0\cdot5 + 0\cdot39/s)^2\}$$

and letting $x = 1/s$, the output per phase in watts is

$$P = 0\cdot39(1/s - 1)(I_1')^2 = \frac{400^2 \times 0\cdot39(x-1)}{4\cdot92^2 + (0\cdot5 + 0\cdot39x)^2}$$

But the full-load output per phase is 10 h.p or 7,460 W, so that

$$7{,}460 = \frac{400^2 \times 0\cdot39(x-1)}{4\cdot92^2 + (0\cdot5 + 0\cdot39x)^2}$$

whence, $x^2 - 52\cdot5x + 213 = 0$

Thus $x = 48\cdot05$ or $4\cdot45$

and $s = 1/x = 0\cdot0208$ or $0\cdot2250$.

The *smaller* value of s is the correct one, so that $s = 0\cdot0208$,

$$r = 0\cdot39/s = 18\cdot75\ \Omega$$

$$\text{Full-load speed} = 1000(1 - 0\cdot021) = 979 \text{ r.p.m.}$$

$$I_1' \text{ (full-load)} = 400/\sqrt{\{24\cdot2 + (0\cdot5 + 18\cdot75)^2\}}$$

$$= 400/19\cdot85 = 20\cdot1 \text{ A}$$

This current lags by arc cos $(19\cdot23/19\cdot85)$ on the voltage, so that its in-phase and quadrature components are, 19·5 A and 4·98 A respectively. Therefore the components of the total current are

$$I_1 \cos\phi_1 = 19\cdot5 + 1\cdot155 = 20\cdot655 \text{ A}$$

$$I_1 \sin\phi_1 = 4\cdot98 + 5\cdot65 = 10\cdot63 \text{ A}$$

and $I_1 = \sqrt{541\cdot5} = 23\cdot25$ A

whence $\cos\phi_1 = \underline{0\cdot888}$

and the full-load line current

$$= \sqrt{3} \times 23\cdot25 = \underline{40\cdot3 \text{ A}}.$$

The full-load torque $= (I_1')^2\, 0{\cdot}39/s$

$= 20{\cdot}1^2 \times 18{\cdot}75 = 7{,}600$ synchronous watts/phase

or total full-load torque $= 3 \times 7{,}600$ synchronous watts/phase

$= 0{\cdot}735 \times 3 \times 7{,}600/(2\pi \times 50/3)$

$= \underline{160{\cdot}5 \text{ lb ft.}}$

(Check—h.p. $= 160{\cdot}5 \times 2\pi \times 979/33{,}000 = 30$ h.p.)

Maximum torque occurs when

$0{\cdot}39/s = \sqrt{(4{\cdot}92^2 + 0{\cdot}5^2)} = 4{\cdot}93$

and $s = 0{\cdot}0792$ so, speed $= 920{\cdot}8$ r.p.m.

$T'_{max} = 400^2/2(4{\cdot}93 + 0{\cdot}5) = 14{,}750$ synchronous watts/phase

$T_{max} = \underline{311{\cdot}5 \text{ lb ft. total.}}$

When starting, $s = 1$

$$I_1' = 400/\sqrt{\{4{\cdot}92^2 + 0{\cdot}89^2\}} = 80 \text{ A}$$
$$\cos\phi_1' = 0{\cdot}178, \ \sin\phi_1' = 0{\cdot}985$$
$$I_1'\cos\phi_1' = 14{\cdot}25 \text{ A}, \ I_1'\sin\phi_1' = 78{\cdot}8 \text{ A}$$
$$I_1\cos\phi_1 = 15{\cdot}405 \text{ A/phase}$$
$$I_1\sin\phi_1 = 84{\cdot}45 \text{ A/phase}$$
$$I_1 = \sqrt{\{15{\cdot}405^2 + 84{\cdot}45^2\}} = 85{\cdot}8 \text{ A/phase}$$

Therefore the line current $= 85{\cdot}8 \times \sqrt{3} = \underline{148{\cdot}6 \text{ A.}}$

The starting torque

$$T' = (I_1')^2 R_2' = 6{,}400 \times 0{\cdot}39$$
$$= 2{,}495 \text{ synchronous watts/phase}$$

and the total starting torque

$$= \underline{52{\cdot}7 \text{ lb ft.}}$$

These values of starting current and torque should be regarded as very approximate only because it is likely that the heavy currents will cause saturation in the stator and rotor teeth, so reducing the leakage reactance considerably.

EXAMPLE. If the above machine is a slip-ring motor with a star-connected rotor winding, the open-circuit voltage across a pair of slip rings being 200 V when the stator voltage is 400 V, determine the external rotor resistance per phase (star-connected) to give (*a*) a starting torque equal to full-load torque, (*b*) a starting torque of $1{\cdot}5 \times$ full-load torque, and the corresponding current.

Solution. (*a*) To give a starting torque equal to full-load torque, the rotor resistance at starting must be equal to R_2/s at full-load. Thus if r_2' is the total rotor resistance referred to the stator, $r_2' = 18{\cdot}75\ \Omega$. The phase/phase voltage ratio, rotor to stator $= (200/\sqrt{3})/400$.

Therefore the actual rotor winding resistance/phase

$$= R_2' \times 200^2/(3 \times 400^2) = 0{\cdot}39/12$$
$$= 0{\cdot}0325\ \Omega.$$

The total resistance/phase for starting

$$= 18{\cdot}75/12 = 1{\cdot}5625\ \Omega$$

and the external resistance/phase

$$= (1{\cdot}5625 - 0{\cdot}0325) = \underline{1{\cdot}53\ \Omega}.$$

(*b*) Let the total rotor resistance/phase referred to the stator be r ohms.

$$I_1' = 400/\sqrt{\{24{\cdot}2 + (0{\cdot}5 + r)^2\}}$$

and the torque

$$T' = 400^2 r/\{24{\cdot}2 + (0{\cdot}5 + r)^2\} \text{ synchronous watts/phase}$$
$$= 1{\cdot}5 \times 7{,}600.$$

Whence $$r^2 - 13{\cdot}05r + 24{\cdot}45 = 0$$
$$\textit{i.e.}\quad r = 2{\cdot}27 \text{ or } 10{\cdot}78.$$

The larger value is the correct one, giving the smaller current for the required torque. The actual required rotor circuit resistance/phase is therefore $10{\cdot}78/12 = 0{\cdot}898\ \Omega$, and the external resistance/phase is $(0{\cdot}898 - 0{\cdot}0325) = \underline{0{\cdot}8655\ \Omega}$.

The corresponding value of I_1' at $s = 1$ is given by

$$I_1' = 400/\sqrt{\{24{\cdot}2 + 11{\cdot}28^2\}}$$
$$= 32{\cdot}5 \text{ A}$$
$$I_1' \cos \phi_1' = 29{\cdot}8 \text{ A},\ I_1' \sin \phi_1' = 13{\cdot}0 \text{ A},$$
$$I_1 \cos \phi_1 = 30{\cdot}955 \text{ A},\ I_1 \sin \phi_1 = 18{\cdot}65 \text{ A},$$
$$I_1 = 36{\cdot}2 \text{ A/phase}$$

Line current $$= 36{\cdot}2 \times \sqrt{3} = \underline{62{\cdot}7 \text{ A}}.$$

Measurement of induction-motor impedances

The effective resistances and reactances of the induction motor are measured by no-load and locked-rotor (standstill) tests which correspond to the open-circuit and short-circuit tests used for transformers. When a motor runs light on normal voltage, the slip is very small so that the effective rotor impedance is very high and the input impedances calculated from readings of voltage, current and power are essentially those of the magnetizing impedance of the equivalent circuit of Fig. 16.6.

For greater precision the motor may be driven at exactly synchronous speed, when $s = 0$, or in the case of a slip-ring motor, the rotor circuit may be opened with the machine running at full-speed.

The locked-rotor test is carried out with the machine stationary, a low polyphase voltage of normal frequency being applied to the primary, so that the current is not excessive. From the readings of voltage, current and power, the effective total resistance $(R_1 + R_2')$ and the total leakage reactance $(X_1 + X_2')$ referred to the primary may be calculated. A correction may be made for the shunting magnetizing impedance if necessary. The separate values of R_1 and R_2' are required, and these are usually determined by suitable d.c. measurement of the winding resistances. For a slip-ring motor the voltage ratio may be measured by applying a polyphase voltage to the stator, with the machine stationary, and measuring the voltage between the open circuited slip-rings. If R_2, the actual rotor resistance per phase, is then measured, $R_2' = R_2 \times$ (voltage ratio per phase stator to rotor)^2. The rotor resistance of a squirrel-cage machine cannot be measured directly, so that the measured stator resistance per phase, R_1, is subtracted from the total resistance per phase $(R_1 + R_2')$ as measured by the locked-rotor test, to give R_2'.

Circle diagram of the induction motor

In the equivalent static circuit shown in Fig. 16.6, the only variable parameter is the effective rotor resistance R_2'/s. Thus, as s varies the end P of the current vector $\mathbf{I}_1'$ (O_1P) follows a semicircular locus (see Chapter 9), as shown in Fig. 16.8. The diameter of the circle is

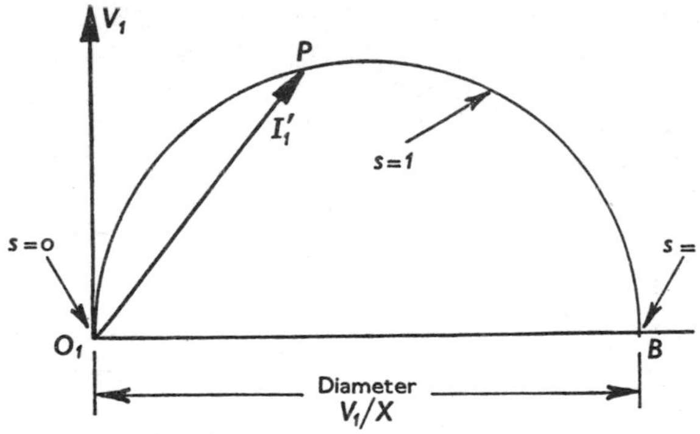

FIG. 16.8

V_1/X, where $X = (X_1 + X_2')$. The total stator current per phase, $\mathbf{I}_1$, is represented by the vector OP in Fig. 16.9, since $\mathbf{I}_1 = \mathbf{I}_m + \mathbf{I}_1'$

(vector sum). The circular locus for a particular motor supplied at constant voltage can be drawn to scale, provided the magnetizing current I_m is known in magnitude and phase as well as the total leakage reactance, X. These quantities may be determined by the tests described above. However, the circle may also be constructed direct from the test

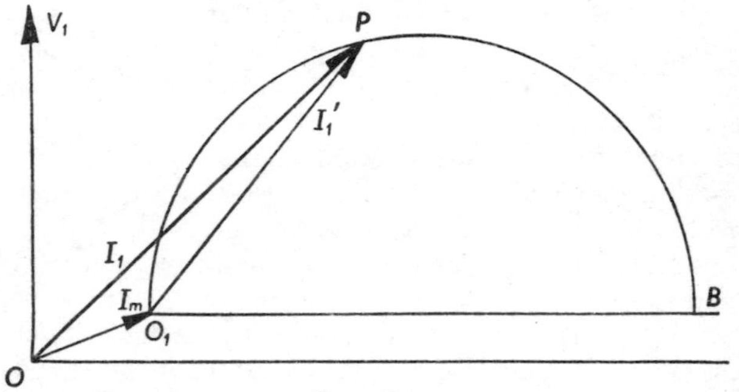

FIG. 16.9

readings without calculating the actual value of X. The point O_1 is determined by plotting the magnetizing current vector OO_1 to scale (Fig. 16.10). One other point on the circle is then required and the most convenient is that for standstill, $s = 1$, corresponding to the locked-rotor test. If the applied voltage for this test is v_1 per phase, the

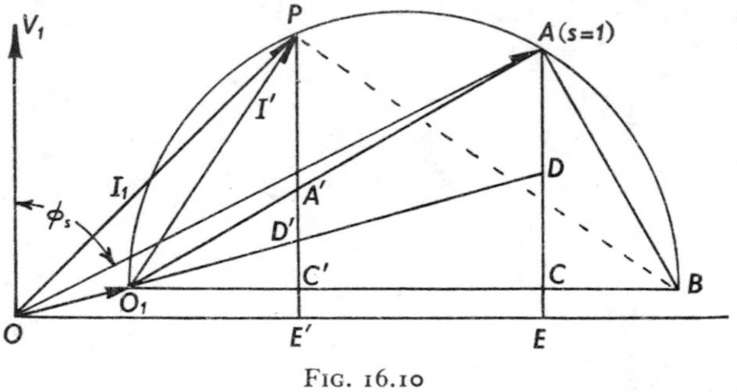

FIG. 16.10

measured current i_1 per phase, and the power-factor $\cos \phi_s$, while the normal voltage per phase is V_1, the current vector required is $I_1 = V_1 i_1 / v_1$, and its phase-angle is ϕ_s. This vector is plotted as OA in Fig. 16.10. A semi-circle is then drawn on a diameter O_1B where O_1B is perpendicular to OV_1, to pass through O_1 and A. This is the required locus, the point P moving on this locus as s is varied. $OP = I_1$ and $O_1P = I_1'$.

Determination of performance from the circle diagram

If ACE is drawn parallel to the voltage vector OV_1, then EA is the *power* component of the current at standstill, so that the total loss per phase in watts at standstill, which is the power input per phase, $= EA$ (amps) $\times V_1$ (volts). If $CD/DA = R_1/R_2'$, $CD \times V_1$ and $DA \times V_1$ represent respectively the stator and rotor copper loss at standstill (there is no output power) and $EC \times V_1$ gives the magnetizing loss which is considered constant (see the equivalent circuit of Fig. 16.6). When the machine rotates so that $s < 1$, and the stator and referred rotor currents are OP and O_1P respectively, the power input per phase is given by $E'P \times V_1$.

The straight lines O_1A and O_1D, are drawn to meet $E'P$ at A' and D'. Then $C'A'/CA = C'D'/CD = D'A'/DA = O_1C'/O_1C$.

Triangles $O_1C'P$, O_1PB are similar, so that

$$O_1C'/O_1P = O_1P/O_1B \text{ or } O_1C' = O_1P^2/O_1B.$$

Similarly $$O_1C = O_1A^2/O_1B$$

so, $$O_1C'/O_1C = O_1P^2/O_1A^2.$$

Therefore $$CA'/CA = CD'/CD = D'A'/DA = O_1P^2/O_1A^2$$

which is the square of the ratio of the currents corresponding to points P and A.

Thus, for point P,

$C'D' \times V_1 =$ stator copper loss
$D'A' \times V_1 =$ rotor copper loss
$D'P \times V_1 =$ rotor input power which is proportional to the torque
$A'P \times V_1 =$ power output/phase
$D'A'/D'P =$ slip, s
$A'P/E'P =$ efficiency (neglecting friction losses).

EXAMPLE. Tests on a 12 h.p, 415 V, three-phase, squirrel-cage motor gave the following results:

(*a*) Running light with normal supply voltage: line current = 6 A, total power input = 540 W.
(*b*) Locked rotor: line voltage = 100 V, line current = 16 A, total power input = 900 W.
(*c*) The resistance measured between a pair of stator terminals = 1·0 Ω.

Draw the circle diagram to scale and determine the full-load current, power-factor, efficiency and speed, and the ratio of starting torque to full-load torque. The friction and windage losses may be neglected. The synchronous speed is 1,000 r.p.m. [S.U.]

Solution. In the calculation below, the motor is assumed to have a star-connected stator, though the same results are obtained if a delta connection is assumed.

No-load: Power-factor $= 540/(\sqrt{3} \times 415 \times 6) = 0{\cdot}125$

Therefore, angle V_1OO_1 in Fig. 16.10 * is

$$\cos^{-1}(0{\cdot}125) = 82^\circ\ 49$$

OO_1 is drawn, of length 6 A at this angle to the voltage vector.

Locked rotor: Current for normal voltage $= 16 \times 415/100 = 66{\cdot}5$ A. Power-factor $= 900/(\sqrt{3} \times 100 \times 16) = 0{\cdot}325 = \cos\phi_s$, and $\phi_s = 71^\circ\ 3'$.

OA is therefore drawn of length 66·5 A at this angle.

A line is then drawn through O_1 and perpendicular to OV_1, and a circle with its centre on this line is constructed to pass through O_1 and A.

From the locked-rotor test, the total effective resistance per phase, referred to the stator, $= 900/(3 \times 16^2) = 1{\cdot}17\ \Omega$.

At the voltage used in this test, the iron loss will be quite small, say about 10 W or less, so that it may be ignored, and the total resistance considered to be due to the winding resistances only.

The stator resistance per phase $= 0{\cdot}5\ \Omega$, so that the rotor resistance, referred to the stator, per phase, $= 1{\cdot}17 - 0{\cdot}5 = 0{\cdot}67\ \Omega$.

The line CA (Fig. 16.10), is therefore divided at D so that $CD/DA = 0{\cdot}5/0{\cdot}67$, so giving the torque line O_1D.

At full-load, the total output $= 12 \times 746$ W, and the corresponding component of stator current per phase $= (12 \times 746)/(3 \times 415/\sqrt{3}) = 12{\cdot}5$ A. A point P on the circle is found, such that $A'P = 12{\cdot}5$ A, P then being the full-load point.

The full-load current per phase is given by $OP =$ 16·8 A, and the power-factor is given by cos (angle V_1OP) = 0·846.

The starting (standstill) torque is represented by DA and the full-load torque by $D'P$, and the measured ratio $DA/D'P =$ 0·89.

The full-load efficiency is given by the ratio $A'P/E'P =$ 0·86.

The full-load slip may be obtained as the ratio of $D'A$ to $D'P$, but is difficult to estimate from the diagram because $D'A'$ is of such a small length. A more accurate calculation is made as follows:

From the diagram, $D'P = 13$ A, so that the rotor input per phase $= 13 \times 415/\sqrt{3} = 3{,}120$ W. The rotor current per phase referred

* Fig. 16.10 is not drawn to scale—it is left to the reader to do this.

to the stator $= O_1P = 14$ A (measured), and the rotor loss per phase is therefore $0{\cdot}67 \times 14^2 = 132$ W.

The slip is therefore $s = 132/3{,}120 = 0{\cdot}0425$

The full-load speed $= 1{,}000(1 - 0{\cdot}0425)$

$= \underline{957 \text{ r.p.m.}}$

PROBLEMS

1. A 6,600 V, three-phase, star-connected turbo-alternator, of synchronous reactance 0·5 Ω per phase is supplying 40,000 kVA at 0·8 power-factor lagging to a large power system. If the steam supply is cut off, explain what takes place, and determine the current the alternator will then carry, assuming negligible losses. [S.U.]

[*Ans.* The machine will run as a synchronous motor; 2,510 A.]

2. An isolated alternator with 40% synchronous reactance and negligible resistance is supplying 3/4 full-load current at 0·7 power-factor lagging at normal terminal voltage. If the current rises to the full-load value at 0·6 power-factor lagging, determine the percentage change in the terminal voltage if the excitation is unchanged. [S.U.]

[*Ans.* Voltage falls by 12·4%.]

3. A 5 kVA, 400 V, three-phase, star-connected alternator running at normal speed requires a field current of 1·0 A to give 400 V (line) on no-load, and 1·3 A to give 400 V with full-load current at 0·7 power-factor lagging. If the armature resistance is 1·5 Ω per phase, determine the synchronous reactance per phase, assuming a linear relationship between the excitation and e.m.f. [*Ans.* 11·2 Ω.]

4. The machine described in problem 3 is run as a synchronous motor, supplied at 400 V at the normal frequency, the input current being 5 A and the power-factor 0·5 leading. Determine the field current.

[*Ans.* 1·21 A.]

5. A 3,300 V, three-phase, star-connected synchronous motor, whose synchronous reactance is 12 Ω per phase and whose resistance is negligible, takes 100 kW input power at 0·6 power-factor leading. If the load on the motor is increased, without any change in excitation, until the input power-factor is unity, determine the input power. [S.U.]

[*Ans.* 515 kW.]

6. A three-phase, 1,100 V, star-connected synchronous motor drives a compressor and is also used for power-factor correction. The operating range is such that the motor input power may vary between 20 kW and 100 kW. With the latter loading at unity power-factor the excitation required is 20 A. The synchronous reactance is 4 Ω per phase and the resistance is negligible. Determine the maximum and minimum excitation required if the leading reactive kVA taken by the motor is to be capable of adjustment between zero and 100 kVA for any compressor load. The e.m.f. is directly proportional to the excitation. [S.U.]

[*Ans.* 26 A, 19 A.]

7. A 10 h.p, 400 V, three-phase, four-pole 50 c/s, slip-ring induction motor takes a no-load current of 6 A at 0·2 power-factor. The motor

has delta-connected stator and star-connected rotor windings, and with the rotor open-circuited, and full voltage applied to the stator, the voltage between slip-rings is 150 V. The stator and rotor leakage reactances are 8Ω and 0·3 Ω per phase respectively and the resistances are 2 Ω and 0·2 Ω per phase. Determine the full-load speed, torque, current and power-factor, neglecting friction losses. [S.U.]

[*Ans.* 1,375 r.p.m., 38 lb-ft, 16·4 A, 0·825.]

8. The speed of the motor referred to in the previous question is reduced to 50% of the full-load speed by connecting external rotor resistances. If the torque at this speed is exactly 50% of the full-load torque, determine the extra rotor resistance per phase required, and the input line current and power-factor under these conditions.

[*Ans.* 2·8 Ω, 9·22 A, 0·753.]

9. The following test results were obtained on a 5 h.p, 220 V, three-phase, squirrel-cage motor: (*a*) running light with rated applied voltage, line current = 5 A, input power = 490 W, (*b*) with locked rotor, line voltage = 60 V, line current = 15 A, input power = 570 W.

Draw the circle diagram to scale and determine therefrom the efficiency and power-factor for full-load, and the maximum horse-power. [S.U.]

[*Ans.* 83·5%, 0·857, 9·4 h.p.]

10. The following test results were obtained on a 20 h.p, three-phase, 400 V, 50 c/s, four-pole slip-ring induction motor: (*a*) running light with normal supply voltage; line current = 10 A, power-factor = 0·2 lagging, (*b*) with locked rotor; line voltage = 120 V, line current = 30 A, power-factor = 0·3 lagging.

The phase-voltage ratio, stator: rotor, is 2 : 1 and the phase-resistance ratio, stator : rotor, is 3·6 : 1. Determine the external rotor resistance required to give a starting current of 1·25 times the full-load current and the ratio of the starting to the full-load torque. [S.U.]

[*Ans.* 1·5 Ω per phase, 1·2 : 1.]

APPENDIX I

CRAMER'S RULE

Cramer's Rule for the rapid solution of simultaneous equations

Consider the following linear equations with n unknowns:

$$\left.\begin{array}{l} a_{11}x_1 + a_{12}x_2 + a_{13}x_3 + \ldots + a_{1n}x_n = K_1 \\ a_{21}x_1 + a_{22}x_2 + a_{23}x_3 + \ldots + a_{2n}x_n = K_2 \\ a_{31}x_1 + a_{32}x_2 + a_{33}x_3 + \ldots + a_{3n}x_n = K_3 \\ \ldots\ldots\ldots\ldots\ldots\ldots\ldots\ldots \\ a_{n1}x_1 + a_{n2}x_2 + a_{n3}x_3 + \ldots + a_{nn}x_n = K_n \end{array}\right\} \quad . \quad \text{(A.1)}$$

where x_1, x_2, x_3 . . . x_n are the unknowns. and a_{11}, a_{12} . . . a_{nn}, K_1, K_2 . . . K_n are constants.

Let

$$D = \begin{vmatrix} a_{11} & a_{12} & a_{13} & \ldots & a_{1n} \\ a_{21} & a_{22} & a_{23} & \ldots & a_{2n} \\ a_{31} & a_{32} & a_{33} & \ldots & a_{3n} \\ \vdots & \vdots & \vdots & & \vdots \\ a_{n1} & \ldots & \ldots & \ldots & a_{nn} \end{vmatrix} \quad . \quad . \quad . \quad . \quad . \quad \text{(A.2)}$$

$$D_1 = \begin{vmatrix} K_1 & a_{12} & a_{13} & \ldots & a_{1n} \\ K_2 & a_{22} & a_{23} & \ldots & a_{2n} \\ K_3 & a_{32} & a_{33} & \ldots & a_{3n} \\ \vdots & \vdots & \vdots & & \vdots \\ K_n & a_{n2} & a_{n3} & \ldots & a_{nn} \end{vmatrix} \quad . \quad . \quad . \quad . \quad . \quad \text{(A.3)}$$

$$D_2 = \begin{vmatrix} a_{11} & K_1 & a_{13} & \ldots & a_{1n} \\ a_{21} & K_2 & a_{23} & \ldots & a_{2n} \\ a_{31} & K_3 & a_{33} & \ldots & a_{3n} \\ \vdots & \vdots & \vdots & & \vdots \\ a_{n1} & K_n & a_{n3} & \ldots & a_{nn} \end{vmatrix} \quad . \quad . \quad . \quad . \quad . \quad \text{(A.4)}$$

etc.

Then Cramer's Rule states that for a set of equations such as (A.1), if $D \neq 0$,

$$x_1 = D_1/D,\ x_2 = D_2/D,\ x_3 = D_3/D\ \ldots\ x_n = D_n/D.$$

APPENDIX 2

MINORS OF A DETERMINANT

Minors of a determinant

When the row and column containing a particular element are removed from a determinant, the remaining determinant is called the *minor* of the element.

The value of a determinant can be found by taking the elements in, say, the first column, multiplying each by its corresponding minor and, beginning with the product of the first element and its minor, prefixing alternate positive and negative signs. The determinant can be evaluated in this way using any row or column for *cofactors.*

For example, consider the determinant

$$D = \begin{vmatrix} a_{11} & a_{12} & a_{13} \\ a_{21} & a_{22} & a_{23} \\ a_{31} & a_{32} & a_{33} \end{vmatrix}$$

By the method of minors and using the first column for cofactors

$$D = +a_{11} \begin{vmatrix} a_{22} & a_{23} \\ a_{32} & a_{33} \end{vmatrix} - a_{21} \begin{vmatrix} a_{12} & a_{13} \\ a_{32} & a_{33} \end{vmatrix} + a_{31} \begin{vmatrix} a_{12} & a_{13} \\ a_{22} & a_{23} \end{vmatrix}$$

APPENDIX 3

CONVERSION OF BELS, DECIBELS AND NEPERS

Bels and decibels

If the common logarithm of the ratio of two powers P_1 and P_2 is taken there results a number which is expressed in *bels*. A more common unit is the *decibel* which is one-tenth of a bel and is abbreviated *dB*. *i.e.* the difference in level between two powers P_1 and P_2 watts is n *dB* where $n = 10 \log_{10} (P_2/P_1)$.

In the case of d.c. circuits, $P_2/P_1 = R_1V_2^2/V_1^2R_2$ *i.e.* provided the resistance is the same for P_2 and P_1 ($R_1 = R_2$),* $P_2/P_1 = V_2^2/V_1^2$.

$\therefore$ if the resistance is constant $n = 20 \log_{10} (V_2/V_1)$.

For a.c. circuits,†

$$\begin{aligned} n &= 10 \log_{10} (V_2I_2 \cos \phi_2/V_1I_1 \cos \phi_1) \\ &= 10 \log_{10} (V_2^2Z_1 \cos \phi_2/V_1^2Z_2 \cos \phi_1) \\ \therefore\quad n &= 20 \log_{10} (V_2/V_1) + 10 \log_{10} (Z_1/Z_2) \\ &\qquad + 10 \log_{10} (\cos \phi_2/\cos \phi_1) \\ &= 20 \log_{10}(I_2/I_1) + 10 \log_{10}(Z_2/Z_1) + 10 \log_{10} (\cos \phi_2/\cos \phi_1). \end{aligned}$$

Nepers

Two powers P_1 and P_2 differ by N *nepers* when

$$N = \{\log_e (P_2/P_1)\}/2$$

Thus,

$$\begin{aligned} N/n &= \{\log_e (P_2/P_1)\}/20 \log_{10} (P_2/P_1) \\ &= 1/8{\cdot}686 \end{aligned}$$

So, to convert nepers to decibels multiply by 8·686 *and to convert decibels to nepers multiply by* 0·1151.

* R_1 and V_1 are the resistance and voltage respectively corresponding to power P_1. Similarly R_2 and V_2 correspond to P_2.

† V_1, I_1, Z_1 and $\cos \phi_1$ are the voltage, current, impedance and power-factor respectively corresponding to P_1. Similarly V_2, I_2, Z_2 and $\cos \phi_2$ correspond to P_2.

INDEX